NORTHAMPTON COLLEGE
LIBRARY

NORTHAMPTON COLLEGE

R23219F 0098

NORTHAMPTON COLLEGE
LIBRARY

The Collector's Guide to

MASKS

The Collector's Guide to

MASKS

TIMOTHY TEUTEN

BRACKEN BOOKS

The Collector's Guide to Masks

This edition first published in 1995 by Bracken Books,
an imprint of Random House UK Ltd,
Random House, 20 Vauxhall Bridge Road,
London SW1V 2SA

Reprinted 1996

Copyright © Random House UK Ltd 1996

All rights reserved. No part of this publication may be reproduced, stored in a
retrieval system, or transmitted, in any form or by any means, electronic,
mechanical, photocopying, recording or otherwise, without the prior
permission of the copyright holder.

The chapter on European Masks was written by Mike Hitchcock at the
University of Hull.

ISBN 1 85891 201 6

Printed and bound in Singapore

PUBLISHER'S NOTE

Prices for masks sold at specific auctions are given in the local
currency with the date of sale; where there is more than one
mask in a single image the reader should read the dimensions
and prices from left to right. All other prices mentioned are given
in £ sterling followed by US$ in brackets; the exchange rate has
been calculated at £1 to US$1.65.

CONTENTS

INTRODUCTION

asks as a serious subject for the collector are a relatively recent phenomenon. It is only in the past thirty years that auction houses have begun to devote sales exclusively to tribal art. Prior to that, collecting masks and tribal art was the preserve of relatively few collectors, who were doubtless regarded as eccentric by their contemporaries, and who were consequently able to buy masks and other tribal artefacts for sums that seem extraordinary today.

Even many museums failed to appreciate the importance of their collections and before the Second World War were happy to exchange their masks and other artefacts for pieces of local farm machinery and the like considered far more worthy of preservation. In the 1930s, for instance, James Hooper went to the West Country to visit a museum that was disposing of its surplus stock and noticed a girl wearing a pair of sealskin boots washing down a car. When he enquired where she had obtained them, he was told that they had been rescued from a cartload of similar items sent to the local incinerator the previous day. Many such horror stories have been recorded. The catalogues of dealers in 'ethnographical specimens' such as Oldman and Webster in the early years of this century make very interesting reading. The prices of masks and figures are similar to those of clubs and other weapons, the aesthetic quality of a piece having little bearing on the price and all such items being regarded as 'curios' rather than works of art.

Today most of the early collections brought back from European colonies have been dispersed and the supply of fine, early specimens is therefore very limited. Prices are consequently high, and masks can sell at auction today for in excess of £200,000 (US $330,000). In fact, in 1989 the world record price for a piece of African art topped the million-pound mark. Many of the masking traditions described in this book, however, are still alive today and are a vital component of the society in which they are still found. In some areas, where the tradition has died or been weakened, masquerading has been or is being revived. Tourism, too, has played its part: in Bali, for instance, increasing numbers of visitors have enjoyed the per-

Olmec, Mexico, wood
*Masks in this style (**above left**) but carved from stone date back to the origins of the masquerading tradition in Central America. Sometimes the mask was embellished with semi-precious stones.*

Kwele, Gabon, wood
*This striking, stylized mask (**right**) represents an antelope. There is a wide range of masks carved by the various tribes of equatorial Africa; more information about such masks starts on page 32.*

formances of the *wayang topeng*, and in Africa since the 1940's some masquerades have been choreographed so that they may be performed in hotels. However, there is an increasing awareness of the need for preserving traditions throughout the world, and this has led to further, more serious revivals, as is the case in Vanuatu, where customs are seen as essential to the health and well-being of the community. For the new collector there is therefore a steady supply of new masks coming onto the market, not all

of which are made exclusively to satisfy the demand of tourists and dealers, and many of these can be obtained by collectors at modest prices.

The wooden face mask springs to most people's minds when the word mask is used, but in fact the variety of mask materials varies as much as the forms they take. Stone, gold, silver, bronze, hide, paper, cloth, palm spathe, woven or plaited fibre and lacquer are or have in the past been used. It must be remembered, however, that a mask is only a small, albeit important, part of the masquerader's costume, which would often consist of elaborate and colourful garments covering the wearer from head to foot. Divorced from its context it is often impossible to identify the character represented, or perhaps even the tribal group that made it.

Basically, a mask is a disguise. Its function may be to personify spirits, gods or ancestors, to assume social control, to educate or to elude responsibility for one's actions. The use of masks is almost exclusively re-stricted to men—even when, as is often the case, the characters represented are female. There are notable exceptions, however, such as the Sande society of Sierra Leone, in which the females wear the blackened helmet masks called *sowei*, the role of the male being relegated to the joker, or *gongoli*. Masking traditions are found in all continents with the notable exception of Australia, where the Aborigines have instead developed a system of body painting. The use of masks is generally restricted to forested areas, though again there are exceptions, notably the Inuit tradition (which may not date back beyond the first European contact).

Only a very small selection of the masking traditions from around the world can be mentioned in this book. But the illustrations will, I hope, indicate the variety that is to be found, and tempt you to investigate the subject further. A vast number of scholarly books exist on masks, and a selection of them is listed at the end of the book.

Alaska, wood
*This mask (**below**) would have been carved by a shaman to represent a spirit he had seen. The distorted features would inspire amazement in the spectators at the shaman's power to communicate with the spirit world.*
Height: 6¼in (16cm)

*Lower Sepik River New Guinea, wood (**right**)*
Height: 9½in (28cm)

Tolai, Gazelle peninsula, east New Britain, Papua New Guinea
These dukduk *masks (**left**) are up to 53⅜in (210cm) high.*

AFRICAN MASKS

African masks and headdresses reflect ceremonial traditions established many centuries ago. However, the perishable materials from which most of these masks are made mean that, despite the antiquity of many of the styles and cultures, only a few extant examples, such as bronze Benin masks, date from before the nineteenth century.

African masks first began to receive widespread attention from artists, critics and collectors in the early years of the twentieth century. At this time, a series of revolutionary art movements—Cubism, Fauvism and so on—overturned the conventions that had governed Western art since the Renaissance, and painters and sculptors such as Picasso, Braque and Epstein were enormously stimulated by the energy and freedom of 'primitive' art. These three great artists and several of their contemporaries had fine collections of African tribal art, including masks, and many examples of direct influence from the objects they owned have been traced in their work. Their love of African masks was genuine and deep, but it was also severely limited, for they responded to them purely as aesthetic objects and had little or no knowledge of their place in the cultures that produced them. To the makers and users of the masks, they are not simply beautiful ceremonial or ornamental objects, but rather an essential part of their spiritual lives. It is only when something is known of this context that the imaginative richness of African masks can be appreciated, and such knowledge can add greatly to the enjoyment that collectors derive from them.

Africa is an enormous continent and its size and diversity are reflected in the huge variety of masks made there. Nevertheless, in discussing masks, the continent can be divided into various broad areas. Two of these areas are by far the most important: west Africa; and the Zaire basin and equatorial Africa. In other areas, masking traditions have either ceased to exist or have never been of comparable importance. Africa north of the Sahara, for example, no longer has a living masking tradition and has tended to gravitate so strongly towards Mediterranean and Islamic culture that it is usually excluded from discussions of African traditional art.

Dogon, Mali, wood
*The rectangular forms of this mask (**above left**) are typical of the Dogon. The mask, called* walu, *represents an antelope and is one of the most popular Dogon masks.*

Bena-Biombo, Zaire, wood, raffia
*The bands of triangular decoration in reddish brown, black and white (**right**) are typical of the Bena-Biomba and neighbouring Pende.*
Height: 15in (38cm)

WEST AFRICA

Of the many groups in west Africa that have been well studied and documented, the one whose art is perhaps most popular with collectors is the Dogon of central Mali. The Dogon live on the Bandiagara escarpment, a long stretch of cliffs east of the River Niger. Dogon villages are an extraordinary sight, the simple mud-brick buildings with thatched roofs clinging like limpets to the stark rockface behind. The Dogon are farmers, their principal crop being millet, which they produce from a land of poor soil and low rainfall. Islam has penetrated to this region, but it has modified rather than eliminated the masking tradition, for example in encouraging the use of simple geometric designs, not only for masks but also for delineating farmland.

Religious ceremonies among the Dogon are principally concerned with the spirits of ancestors. All Dogon men become members of the masked dancing society—*Ava*—and perform at funerals and at the *Dama* rituals that take place several years after the funeral of an important man of the community (preparations require considerable time and money). Several hundred masks may be required, and large quantities of food and millet beer are distributed to add prestige to the deceased and his family. The masked dancers escort the soul of the deceased from the village and throw it into the bush.

Several types of masks are used on these occasions (more than 70 were listed in the 1930s). Those made of wood usually represent animals or birds and are generally of rectangular shape, with two square or oblong eyeholes, a form that is thought to reflect the appearance of the mosques of the area. Perhaps the most distinctive and familiar to collectors are the *kanaga* masks. These are surmounted by a superstructure consisting of a vertical bar crossed by two horizontal bars with vertical projections at each end. This has been said to represent God, and at the same time the upper bar may represent the sky and the lower one the earth. During the performance the masquerader bends down, bringing the top of the superstructure in contact with the ground. The masks are painted in white and black and are worn with a plaited fibre headcovering and an elaborate costume. It consists of a vest worn with cloth strips sewn with cowrie shells, a pair of indigo leg coverings over which the dancer wears skirts of red, yellow and black dyed fibres, and dyed fibre armbands. Several of these masks are danced together and there seems to be no objection if the dancers are witnessed by outside observers.

Rarer, but similar in style to the *kanaga* masks, are the *sim* masks. These have a similar superstructure, but of more fragile and slender form, which sways as the masquerader dances and is said to represent a human spirit. The mask that covers the face represents an antelope, with 'ears' at the sides and two deep grooved channels for the eyeholes. Mask and super-

structure are joined by a pierced lozenge and the whole is painted with chevrons (V-shapes) and zigzags. More commonly, antelope masks are found without this superstructure, but with horns and more naturalistic ears. Other animals represented in Dogon masks include monkeys, crocodiles and rhinoceroses.

Humans are also represented in the *Dama* ceremonies, although the masks representing them are usually of cloth, fibre and cowrie shells rather than wood. They may represent neighbouring tribes, such as the Bambara, Fulani and Tuareg, or sometimes Europeans and Arabs of particular groups from within their own community, such as blacksmiths and other craftsmen. The *samana* mask is a rare exception in that it is wooden and represents a foreign warrior.

Gurunsi, Burkina Faso, wood, early twentieth century
Many of the masks of Burkina Faso represent animals,
although it is often difficult to identify the species. This
*mask (**above**) appears to be an antelope.*
Height: 14in (35.5cm)   Christie's London 1989, £990

Bambara, Mali, wood
The horizontal form of the chi wara *headdress (**left**) is*
one of the most popular and widely available of West
African masks. The dancer wearing this male example
would have been accompanied by a female.

Although it has similar angular features to the animal masks, it is usually distinguished by three vertical striations on each cheek. The dancer holds a sword and lance and performs a mock battle with an invisible enemy. He also jokes rudely with the dancers wearing female masks (who don carved representations of breasts) and interacts with the audience.

An important ceremony, known as *Sigi,* is held once every 60 years to commemorate the mythical first death of an ancestor among the Dogon. A tall mask, sometimes measuring as much as 15ft (4.5m) in height, is carved in each community on this occasion and is said to represent a snake. These masks, called *imina na* or 'mother of masks', were not intended to be worn, but were carried or simply viewed in a stationary position. Some ancient examples survive in museums and private collections and may be as much as 200 years or more old.

To the south-west of the Dogon, the Bambara (also called Bamana) produce several types of mask associated with ancestors and funerals. However, they are best known among collectors of African art for what must be among the most familiar of all African carvings—the antelope headdresses called *chi wara.* These are danced in rituals associated with the planting and harvesting of millet. According to Bambara mythology, it was the water spirit Faro, in the form of an antelope, who first taught man to work the fields. The masks are danced in pairs, a male and a female, during the planting and harvest seasons to ensure crop fertility.

13

Although all masks should be seen when danced, this is particularly true of the *chi wara,* which make a marvellously stirring sight when moving across a skyline. The headdresses are attached to fibre caps from which fibre strands descend to cover the dancers' bodies, which are bent over for the entire performance, leaning on two short sticks. The male is more athletic in his movements and sometimes screeches, while the female, more gentle, remains silent.

There are three distinct styles of headdress. Tall, vertical examples are said to come from the area of Segu. The male is often represented with a large, curved neck and mane pierced with bands of triangles, with tall, almost vertical horns and a diminutive stylized body. The female also has tall vertical horns and a slender neck and can be clearly distinguished by the young antelope standing on her back. This is probably the type most frequently encountered today and large numbers are now made to supply the tourist trade in Bamako and elsewhere. The carvers are also becoming skilled at reproducing dark, glossy patinas and signs of wear that, under normal circumstances, are a sign of considerable age. Other *chi wara* can be divided into two main categories, low horizontal ones, which are said to come from Beledugu, and ones in which the antelope is highly stylized, from Oussulu.

Among the other mask types of the Bambara asociated with the male initiation societies is the *n'tomo,* which has a stylized humanoid face surmounted by a row of vertical projections inset with cowrie shells and red abrus seeds. The number of projections varies between four and ten and indicates the gender of the masks; three, six and nine indicate masculinity, four and eight femininity, and two, five and seven androgyny. The hyena mask, with a long, oval face, slender nose, pricked ears and pierced square eyes, is much sought after by collectors. Nearly all Bambara masks have a dark patina, which can be glossy or crusty with age and use.

Across the border from Mali, several mask-producing tribes are found in Burkina Faso. The principal groups of the area are the Kurumba, Mossi, Gurunsi, Bwa, Bobo, Lobi and Tusyan. The Lobi are famous for figurative sculpture, but do not have a masking tradition. The Mossi produce an enormous variety of masks, mostly representing totemic animals, spirits and occasionally humans, through which they commune with ancestors. They are usually made from the wood of the cotton tree, which is easy to carve and light to wear, although also prone to insect damage. Consequently, each year after the harvest but before the masquerade season commences (usually in February), the masks are taken from the village to a swamp or river and immersed with heavy stones for several weeks to kill any infestations. This removes all the pigment from the surface with the exception of black, which is not water soluble. The masks are then re-painted by the young initiates; the thickness of the

black pigment can therefore help to indicate the age of a mask. Among the Mossi, some of the most frequently encountered totems are the hawk, ram, small antelope, large antelope, hornbill and human albino. The sizes vary enormously, from small crests worn on the top of the head or at an angle on the forehead to large masks covering the whole face. The degree of naturalism also varies; some totems are clearly identifiable, while others are abstracted, although there is usually one particular feature that stands out and helps with problems of identification.

A particularly distinct type of mask is found among the Mossi of Yatenga province. Known as *karanga,* it consists of a whitened oval face with a vertical, raised, notched ridge down the middle between the two triangular eyeholes. Above the face is a small antelope head with long horns and this is surmounted by a tall slender plank pierced with geometric shapes and carved and painted with geometric ornament. Another type of mask from the same area of Burkino Faso, known as *karanwemba,* has a similar face but is surmounted by a female figure.

The adjacent Gurunsi and Bwa use animal masks similar to those of the Mossi, and in addition they make a plank mask, with a circular face surmounted by a large rectangular plank. This has a crescent finial carved and painted with typical geometric ornament. The Bwa are also known for broad horizontal masks, more than 4ft (1.2m) in width, representing hawks, with hooked projections from the top of the head, and for even broader masks, sometimes more than 8ft (2.4m) in width, representing butterflies.

Despite the enormous variety of mask forms from the area, there is a unifying feature that distinguishes most of the masks from Burkina Faso—surface decoration. Most of them are extensively carved and painted with geometric ornament (bands of triangles, zigzags and lozenges, for example) in white, black and reddish brown. Usually traditional pigments are used, but recently commercially produced paints have been available, and this has broadened the range of colours. Such splendid painted decoration is a characteristic feature of a type of headdress carved by the Kurumba, who live to the north of the Mossi. It represents an antelope, the totemic emblem of most of the Kurumba clans. These headdresses are relatively naturalistic in form, having a long neck and slender head with tall horns above. The surface is painted with a vibrant pattern of zigzags and spots. Although many fine old specimens have found their way into museums and private collections, the majority available to the collector today are made expressly for the art market.

The tribes living in the forested areas along the Guinea Coast, from Guinea-Bissau in the west to Cameroon in the east, are among the most prolific in Africa for wood carving and for mask production. In the far west, off the coast of Guinea-Bissau, are the Bissagos Islands, home of the Bijugo, who produce a

Ekoi, Nigeria, wood, skin, rattan, early twentieth century
The large spiralling horns of this headdress (**left**) represent the ceremonial coiffure worn by Ekoi women. Although very varied in their forms, Ekoi masks are distinguished by the covering of antelope skin that is frequently used.

Nafana, Ivory Coast or Ghana, wood
This style of large mask (**above**) would seem to derive from an early type of which only two examples are known to exist. The style disappeared, and re-emerged in about 1915. Many examples appeared on the market around 1950, apparently made for expatriates.
Height: 51³/₁₆in (130cm)

*Bijugo, Bissagos Islands,
wood, horns, fibre,
twentieth century
Bovine masks, the most
familiar of a number of
naturalistic masks
representing animals, were
danced by members of age-
grade societies. Other
masks represented sharks
and sawfish.*

variety of masks principally for use in 'age-grade' initiation ceremonies. The masks are carved by trained artists, sometimes in large numbers, and are then stored in granaries in preparation for use in the major festivals. First-grade initiates, aged between 12 and 17, wear small headdresses representing fish or domesticated animals, while older grades wear larger headdresses representing more dangerous animals. These include sharks and rays, but most familiar are the bull helmet masks. They cover the entire head of a dancer and are carved and painted in a naturalistic style, with real horns and often with green bottle-glass eyes. They sometimes also have dilated nostrils and a protruding tongue. During the masquerade, the dancer scrapes the ground with his foot and charges at the crowd. Although physically mature, an adult is not considered socially responsible until he has passed through the age grades, after which he abandons his mask and no longer takes part in masquerades.

One of the most massive of all types of African masks is found among the Baga, who live along the coast of neighbouring Guinea. These are the masks popularly known as *nimba,* although more correctly called *damba. Damba* is not a sacred spirit, but rather

Dan, Ivory Coast, wood, twentieth century
Female masks, representing the ideal of Dan beauty, are among the most popular of west African masks. This small example was formerly in the collection of Mrs Webster Plass.
Height: 6⁷/8in (17.3cm)

represents the idea of women who have borne children. Their veneration is considered essential to ensure both human and crop fertility. The mask consists of a large bust, with cantilevered head on four pronged supports. Two holes for the eyes are carved between the breasts, and a long fibre fringe covers the dancer's body. Early masks of this type are rare and they have not been danced in Guinea since the 1950s, when the last 'genuine' examples were exported by the French. Large examples have, in recent years, appeared on the market although the artists who made them have often, apparently, been unable to resist the temptation of exaggerating the features. On several occasions I have attempted to 'test' the authenticity of such heavy masks by lying the mask on the ground and trying to crawl inside on my back between the prongs to see if it is possible for a dancer to put his head inside and see through the eyeholes. This has made me aware of the immense weight of the masks and has made me appreciate the considerable strength that was required to support them in a masquerade. Smaller masks worn in a similar manner to the *damba* are known as *damba-pa-fet*. These are carved as a small head above a stylized plank-like torso, with the breasts in relief.

Mama, northern Nigeria, wood, twentieth century
Masks from northern Nigeria rarely appear on the
market. This stylized buffalo mask (above) is one of the
more familiar types.
Height: 17³/₄in (45cm)

Mende, Sierra Leone, wood, fibre, twentieth century
These masks (left), danced by the women's secret society
among the Mende and neighbouring tribes, are still made
and used today.
Height: 46¹/₂in (118cm)

Closely related to the Baga are the Nalu, a much smaller tribe to the north and west. They make a type of large mask known as *banda*, which is worn horizontally on the head. Measuring 5ft (1.5m) or more in length, it combines features both of humans and of several types of animal, having long jaws with carved teeth, a slender nose, long ears and intertwined snake-like elements at the top of the head. The entire surface is carved in low relief, often with florets and motifs reflecting Portuguese influence, and is painted in various colours including unusual pinks, greens and mauves.

The only masking tradition in Africa reserved exclusively for women is found among the tribes spanning the border of Sierra Leone and Liberia, such as the Mende, Temne and Sherbro. Here the women have a secret society called *Sande*, counterpart to the men's society, *Poro*. Both these societies are concerned with the initiation of youths, boys and girls being confined to separate camps. Boys are taught agricultural skills and crafts such as basketry and the making of nets and traps, as well as learning how to play the drum and sing the songs of the *Poro* society. The skills taught to the girls include homecrafts, childcare, sexual matters, singing and dancing. In this they are assisted by masked spiritual helpers who also escort the initiates to and from the camp. The masked spirits do not speak, but communicate in a graceful language of gesture and dance. At the end of this period (which traditionally lasts about three years) the girls emerge as women ready for marriage.

The helmet masks worn by these spirit helpers are called *sowei* and are said to represent the ideal of Mende beauty. The facial features are small, with a high forehead and usually an elaborate coiffure, sometimes surmounted by an animal or bird. The rings about the neck denote the plumpness of a wealthy women—a sign of beauty and affluence among these tribes. The blackened surface is rubbed with palm oil to achieve a dark glossy patina. Although worn by women, these masks are carved by men. They are still made and used today, and a large number appear on the market. It is sometimes difficult to differentiate between those made for tribal use and those made for tourists, but the ones that are too small to be worn comfortably must have been made for the art market. *Sowei* move slowly and gracefully and, to lighten the atmosphere created by these stately females, a joker called *gongoli* is introduced. Formerly he wore a large rough mask with domed forehead, long nose and projecting ears, but old re-used *sowei* are often danced today.

There are several mask-producing tribes in the Ivory Coast, among them the Dan, whose masks are highly prized among collectors of African tribal art. The majority of Dan masks represent spirits who are believed to dwell in the mountains. In fact, 'represent' is not really the right word to use in this context, since for the Dan the mask *is* the spirit and it is said that when a mask is lying on the ground one can sometimes hear it 'grinding its teeth'. When a mask is damaged and no longer usable it must not simply be discarded, but must be treated with respect. The capturing of masks was one of the prime aims of war campaigns, although a new owner could not immediately wear a captured mask—he had to wait until the mask spirit acknowledged him. Sometimes several generations might pass before the mask accepted its new ownership. The masked spirits speak in a language unintelligible to the audience; it has to be translated for them by means of an interpreter.

The Dan today recognize 11 different categories of mask, but identification for the collector is often by no means easy. For the spectator at a masquerade this would be made clear, partly by the actions of the dancer, but also by the type of headdress attached to the mask. There were various types of cloth headdress and others of feathers and leaves, which are usually absent in specimens in collections and museums. Most Dan masks are approximately life-size and all are worn vertically over the face of the masquerader. They are either male or female; masks with oval faces, narrow eyes and fairly naturalistically carved mouths and noses are usually female and represent the Dan ideal of female beauty, while male masks are more varied and include all the types of animal mask.

Of the 11 categories, some are easily identifiable. The masks of the bird masquerade, *Gegon* (the most popular masquerade among the northern Dan), usually have slender eyes surrounded by applied metal bands, and a long beak-like nose with articulated lower jaw with attached fur from the colobus monkey. Masks of the hooked-stick masquerade, in which the dancer beats spectators with a hooked stick, are of animal form, often representing a cow, bird or monkey. The eyes are either deep-set triangular apertures or cylindrical projections, and cheeks are usually conceived as bulging pyramids. The masks have large projecting mouths and beaks, occasionally with large teeth. Masks used in the war masquerade, *Bugle,* are roughly carved, with bulging cylindrical eyes and a large mouth inset with large teeth. They are often covered in a crusty patina resulting from the application of sacrificial blood and chewed kola nuts.

The fire-prevention masquerade was at one time widespread among the northern Dan, particularly those tribes living in the Dent du Man mountain range. Here, on the high savannas, strong winds build up towards midday, posing a fire risk among the houses with thatched roofs. The function of the masquerader was to ensure that all cooking fires were extinguished before this time, and any woman failing to put her fire out before the masquerader came on his rounds had her cooking pots overturned and was beaten. The masks are distinguished by the application of red cloth or red pigment, clay, camwood powder or paint. The other categories of masquerade were the masquerade of the circumcision camp, the entertainment masquerade, the racing masquerade, the stilt-dancing masquerade, the dancing and miming masquerade, the symptom of illness masquerade and the judgement masquerade.

In addition to the life-size masks used in such masquerades, the Dan and other nearby tribes also carved miniature masks, measuring up to about 6in (15cm).

Guro, Ivory Coast, wood
A unique and lively interpretation of an antelope, the zamle *is believed to have been created at the turn of the century.*

A miniature copy of a full-size mask might be carved by the owner of a mask to carry with him if he travelled away from home. In this way he could continue to communicate with the spirit and make any sacrifices that might be necessary. It might also serve the purpose of a 'passport' to identify to other groups his right to wear a particular type of mask. Unlike the use of full-size masks, the ownership of miniature masks was not a male preserve, and before she left home to marry, a girl might choose to commission a miniature copy of an important full-size mask belonging to her family. In such cases the small mask would be laid overnight with the larger prototype, after which sacrifices would be made. Miniature masks also served the purpose of witnesses to the proceedings in the circumcision camps.

To the south east of the Dan, the Ngere (or We) speak a different language but their culture resembles that of the Dan in many ways. Their masks have similarities to those of the Dan, but are more grotesque, with bulging cylindrical or slit eyes. A wide variety of materials are applied to the faces: horns, teeth, fur, bells, and even objects such as used rifle cartridge cases, which have been used to make beards. The masks of the Bete to the east are similar, but the tradition is believed to have been adopted from the Ngere only in the first quarter of the twentieth century.

The tribes of central Ivory Coast, such as the Baule, Guro and Yaure, produce masks in a style that is especially attractive to Western eyes and this no doubt explains the large quantity made today for the international art market. Human masks are the most notable in this respect, and among the Baule some are in

*Guro, Ivory Coast, wood
This mask (**above**)
exemplifies the typical
features of Guro human
masks, such as the slender
nose and small mouth.
However, the horn is an
unusual addition.
Height: 25in (63.5cm)*

*Baule, Ivory Coast, wood
The delicate features of the
Baule masks have an
obvious appeal to western
tastes and many copies of
masks of this type (**left**)
find their way onto the
market.
Height: 12¼in (31cm)
Christie's London 1988,
£4620*

Yaure, Ivory Coast, wood The zigzag border is a common feature of Yaure masks. As in this fine example, the masks are often more dramatic and the expressions less sweet than those masks of the neighbouring Guro and Baule tribes. Height: 9in (23cm)

fact portraits. For these, the carver would have to obtain permission from the subject, who would also have to be present when the mask was danced. Others represent general types such as 'prostitutes' or 'slaves'. Human masks are usually life-size, with small features, a slender nose, narrow slits to the eyes and a small mouth. It is often difficult to distinguish human masks of the Baule from those of the Yaure and Guro, but scarification and coiffure styles are helpful indicators.

Masks representing animals are also widely used. Some are carved in a naturalistic manner, clearly identifiable as buffalo, antelope or some other animal, but others are given human features and are distinguishable only by the addition of attributes such as horns. The masqueraders would appear one at a time in a series of entertaining sketches mimicking village life, starting with the least important characters, perhaps domestic animals, and finishing with important village personages. In the *Goli* masquerade, four pairs of masks were danced in order of importance, the least important being the distinctive *kple kple* mask. These are of simple design, the flat, circular face having a small, rectangular mouth with carved teeth. The eyes are carved as small projecting cones within a

painted lenticular- or drop-shape. The curved horns above almost join at the top to form a circle and are sometimes spirally carved. The face is blackened, with eyes and mouth embellished with white and red paint. They are usually no more than 18in (45cm) high, although some examples, perhaps made for the art market at a fairly early date, are much larger.

In the north of the Ivory Coast, in an area spanning the border of Mali and Burkina Faso, are the Senufo, who are closely related to the Dogon of Mali. They produce three main types of mask that the collector is likely to encounter. The most common of these is the *kpelie* mask, a female mask used principally as part of the ceremonies associated with the initiation of members into the *Poro* society. The face is of slender form, with narrow pierced eyes and a small mouth. Scarification marks are carved in relief. Almost invariably two curved 'legs' are carved from the bottom of the cheeks and represent hornbills—symbolic birds for the Senufo. The masks are surmounted by the horns of a ram or buffalo.

The most striking of Senufo masks is popularly known as the 'fire-spitter' and is again associated with

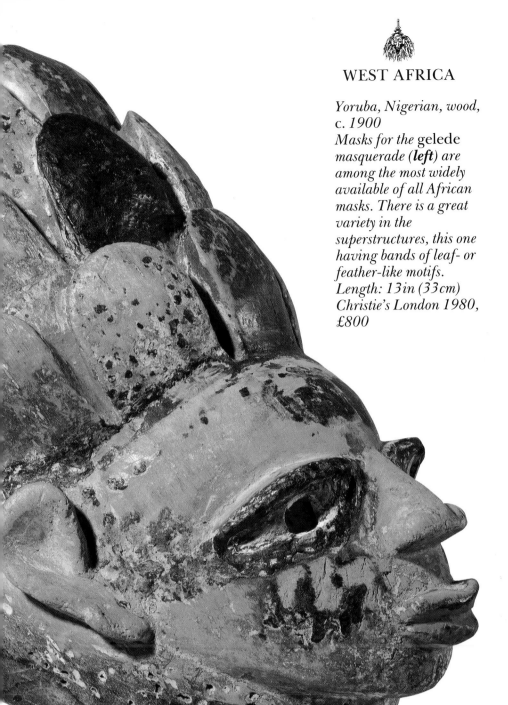

Yoruba, Nigerian, wood, c. 1900
Masks for the gelede *masquerade (**left**) are among the most widely available of all African masks. There is a great variety in the superstructures, this one having bands of leaf- or feather-like motifs.*
Length: 13in (33cm)
Christie's London 1980, £800

Senufo, Ivory Coast, wood
Kpelie *masks are characterized by horns projecting from the chin. They are frequently surmounted by a hornbill. This example (**above**) is unusual in having a panel of pointed projections.*

the *Poro* society. In fact, only a few of the Senufo groups use fire as part of the ritual associated with the masks, whether it be walking through fire or 'spitting' fire (by putting a few embers in the jaws), and masks rarely show any signs of scorching. The masks are of helmet form and combine features from various animals of symbolic value to the Senufo, such as horns of the bush cow, tusks of the wild boar, jaws of the crocodile, and a hornbill bird between the horns. Less common are masks of the type called *degele*. These consist of a simple unadorned helmet with a rectangular slit or two holes for the eyes. They are surmounted by a standing figure, sometimes carved in the typical manner of their figure sculpture, with tall crested coiffure, sometimes more stylized, and long

ringed neck or body, often without arms or legs.

On the border with Ghana are some groups that are influenced by Islam. Those known as the Ligbi produce masks somewhat resembling the Senufo *kpelie*, but with graceful rounded forms, the eyes pierced with curves. A group further north (on the border of Ghana and the Ivory Coast) produces masks up to 9ft (2.7m) tall, with the triangular face pierced with eyeholes surmounted by circular discs, supported by connecting struts and topped by horns. The earlier masks were smaller.

The Yoruba of south-west Nigeria are not only the largest tribe in Africa, but also probably the most prolific wood carvers. Masks are made for a number of societies and festivals, most notably the *Gelede* and *Egungun* societies and the *Epa* festival. The function of the *Gelede* secret society is to maintain the health

Yoruba, Nigeria, wood Two masks for the Epa masquerade. The one on the left was acquired from the Church Missionary Society in 1935 and the one on the right was acquired from the Rev. Mr Lupton, to whom it was given by a missionary. Heights: 49¼in (125cm) and 51½in (131cm) Christie's London 1976, £2600 and £1300

NORTHAMPTON COLLEGE
LIBRARY

and prosperity of the community through plays and dances handed down from ancestors. The masqueraders always appear in pairs, one pair after another, and as many as 50 pairs, all different and each with its own name, might appear in quick succession at a single performance. Any male can carve the mask and dance in the *Gelede* masquerade, which is also said to placate the witchcraft in women.

The faces are naturalistically carved, normally having Yoruba facial characteristics; many show scarification marks on the cheeks, indicating the particular group to which they belong. Others may represent foreign characters; one popular character, 'the Brazilian', with white face, dark beard and hat, occurs around Lagos, which has long had a trading link with Brazil. Often in stark contrast to the serene faces of these masks, the coiffures, headdresses or superstructures show an immense variety of forms. Some have elaborate coiffures, others are carved with themes taken from all aspects of Yoruba life—groups of figures at work, domesticated animals, scenes from proverbs and so on. The eyes are usually pierced. This is not to enable the dancer to see (since the mask is worn on the top of the head), but rather is intended to add realism. The *Gelede* masquerade is held on the death of a member of the society and also in many towns in an annual festival.

The *Gelede* masquerade is practised only by the south-west Yoruba, in Nigeria and across the border in neighbouring Benin, but the *Egungun* masquerade is found throughout Yorubaland. The name *Egungun* means masquerade, though it is now used only to describe those ceremonies held to honour the ancestors. The cloth costume is of greater importance in *Egungun* ceremonies than is usual in most other African contexts; indeed it is sometimes danced with no mask, and it has been suggested that in these instances the characters may be of greater importance than those danced with a mask or headdress. The face masks are carved in a wide variety of styles and can often be confused with those from other areas. One which is easily recognizable, however, has a crest carved as a wooden head, with the hair carved as a long plait to one side of, and free of, the face. It is worn by a subgroup known as *Egungun layewu*, and is the privilege of the chief of hunters.

The most spectacular of Yoruba masks are found in north-east Yorubaland. These are the large helmet masks for the *Epa* festivals, held every two years in March and lasting for three days. The masks, measuring up to 5ft (1.5m) in height, are intended to be as large, unwieldy and elaborate as possible. The boys and young men who wear these masks have not only to dance, but also to jump onto a mound 3ft (1m) high, and for this the masqueraders must practise for months beforehand.

Yoruba, Nigeria, wood, metal
Similar to the gelede *masks, these are worn in the* Magbo *masquerade, a much rarer cult introduced from the neighbouring Ijo.*

Heights: 25¼in (64cm) and 18½in (47cm)
Christie's London 1986, £12,100 and £13,200

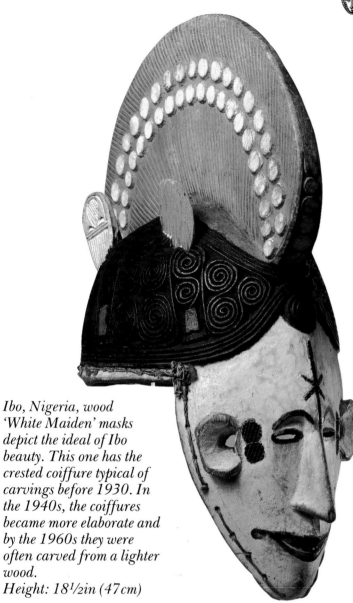

*Ibo, Nigeria, wood
'White Maiden' masks
depict the ideal of Ibo
beauty. This one has the
crested coiffure typical of
carvings before 1930. In
the 1940s, the coiffures
became more elaborate and
by the 1960s they were
often carved from a lighter
wood.
Height: 18½in (47cm)*

The masks consist of a helmet carved as a grotesque face, with a large slit for the mouth, through which the dancer can see, surmounted by a disc (the entire mask is, however, carved from a single piece of wood). The large superstructure often consists of a chiefly figure, male or female, standing alone or sometimes surrounded by several attendants, all carved in the round, occasionally in several tiers. The principal mask of the *Epa* masquerade, however, depicts animals rather than humans. Known as *oloko,* it shows a leopard jumping onto the back of an antelope, surmounted by a cockerel. The ethnologist William Fagg, who was permitted to photograph several *Epa* masks at Ilofa, was told that the *oloko* could be brought out only if a dog were sacrificed.

To the east of the Yoruba, the Ibo are similarly large in number, but they live in much smaller communities—autonomous villages rather than large towns. The variety of masks produced by the Ibo and their neighbours is immense and only a few of the most popular and familiar can be mentioned here. Perhaps the type most likely to be encountered by collectors is the *mmwo* mask, danced in the annual 'fame of maidens' festival by the Ibo of the north

central region. The masqueraders are men belonging to the second of three age grades (that is, between the ages of about 30 and 50). They represent adolescent girls and embody the Ibo ideal of feminine beauty: pale complexion, straight slender nose and small mouth. The coiffures are moulded with clay, charcoal and oil into solid crests or other constructions decorated with bells, combs and similar ornaments. These highly elaborate styles were worn on masquerades celebrating special occasions, for example a marriage or the birth of a first child.

Mmwo masks would be worn with one of the most splendid of African masquerade costumes—a tight-fitting cloth outfit with appliqué geometric and floral patterns in red, green and other bright colours. The 'maidens' would be accompanied in their graceful dances by their sisters and mother, and occasionally an amusing contrast would be provided by an amorous, perhaps bawdy male masquerader.

To the south of the Ibo, the Ibibio (including the sub-groups Eket and Ogoni), though a much smaller tribe, are prolific carvers. Their principal society *(Ekpo)* is concerned with ancestor worship. Some masks have refined, naturalistic features with flowing curves, while others are more stylized and fierce, even grotesque. In the latter style, masks depicting faces ravaged and disfigured by tropical disease range in concept from a stark realism to more exaggerated representations of deformity, for example with the nose and mouth twisted in opposite directions. Keloids (raised scarification marks) are often prominent and the surface of the mask is usually blackened. A characteristic feature of Ogoni masks, by no means common elsewhere in Africa, is the articulated lower jaw, often inset with wooden teeth. This feature also occurs in Ibibio wooden puppets.

Masks carved by the tribes of the Benue Plateau and Upper Benue River have been collected only relatively recently, and much research has still to be published, but one can make the generalization that the masks from this area are among the most highly stylized of all Africa. The Mama carve headdresses of simplified form representing bush cows, with triangular snouts and stylized curved horns joined at the tips to form a circle. The most abstract of all African masks must be those of the Jukun. The Jukun were ruled by a divine king, the Aku of Wukari, who on accession was required to eat the brain, kidneys and heart of his predecessor, and was himself in turn strangled after seven years on the throne. One type of mask, known as *aku-onu,* consists of a concave oval, pierced with geometric shapes, said to represent a human head, with a conical projection at the back standing for the topknot worn by men on their otherwise shaven heads.

A highly distinctive group of masks and headdresses is found in the Cross River region of eastern Nigeria, spanning the border with Cameroon. Here the Ekoi (or Ejagham) carve headdresses and helmet masks of

Ibo, Nigeria, wood
This highly abstract mask
(**above**) *is a very rare type*
of which few other
examples are known.
Height: 18⁷/8in (48cm)
Christie's London 1980,
£2300

Ibibio, Nigeria, wood
This highly dramatic
mask (**right**) *is a fine*
example of the type
representing sufferers
from diseases or deformity.
This appears to represent a
sufferer with yaws, a
tropical skin disease most
notably affecting the nose.

*Bangwa, Cameroon, wood
This type of mask (**right**) is used by members of the 'night' society. Its use is restricted to an elite and it is seen only on rare occasions. Some later examples, on a much larger scale, were collected in about 1970.*

*Benin, Nigeria, bronze, copper, iron
There is no masking tradition at the court of Benin, the greatest kingdom in Nigeria. However, the oba or king of Benin wore bronze hip masks to secure his skirt-like drapery. The simple treatment of this ram's head (**left**) might indicate that it was cast in Owo, or in Benin by an Owo caster.
Height: 7⅞in (20cm)
Christie's London 1977, £3800*

*Cameroon grasslands, wood
The exotic headdresses of the chiefs or fons in the Cameroons grasslands are reflected in the superstructures of this mask (**right**). The headdresses would have been made of beaded fibre or cloth.
Christie's New York 1985, $17,600*

remarkable naturalism. The headdresses usually depict a head and neck, some larger than life-size, others smaller; examples carved as a whole figure are also known. The most notable feature of this group of masks is the antelope skin covering. Realism is enhanced by the addition of painted designs resembling tattoos and by the insertion of metal or wooden teeth, or occasionally by the addition of hair. Some examples represent young girls, their hair dressed in an extraordinary local ceremonial style of long spiral horns. It is said that originally these headdresses represented heads of enemies killed in local wars, and it has often been said by historians that early examples were covered in human skin; there does not seem to be any evidence to corroborate this, however, and intensive tests are needed to establish the identity of the skin once it has been treated and placed on the mask. Helmet masks are similarly covered in skin; some are carved in Janus form, with a pale-coloured female face and a dark male face, while others, more rarely, have as many as four faces. Skin-covered masks in the form of animal heads are said to represent animals killed during hunting expeditions.

The Cameroon grasslands are inhabited by numerous chieftaincies, some very small, ruled by a chief or

fon. Social control is maintained by a regulatory society that, in each chieftaincy, owns a number of masks. Masks can also be owned by other groups, such as the society of princes, who were debarred from joining the regulatory society. The majority are human in character and larger than life-size. They may consist of just a face or be of helmet form. Despite the large number of chieftaincies, there is a unity of style evident in these masks. Usually they are carved with distinctive large eyes, which, as the mask is worn on top of the head, are not pierced; cheeks often bulge and ears stick out at the sides. The mouths are usually open and pierced with carved teeth, and white pigment is applied to teeth and eyes. The sex of the mask is generally not clear, but may be indicated by the type of coiffure. These can be very elaborate in themselves and may be carved with various animals associated with royalty, such as spiders and buffalo, often in a highly abstracted form.

Animal masks are also carved in a more naturalistic form, elephant masks having long straight trunks that project forward when the mask is worn on top of the head. More stylized elephant masks occur principally among the Bamileke and are worn by members of the *Kuosi* society, whose membership was limited to men

Kwele, Gabon, wood, early twentieth century
*This mask (**above**) has a whitened concave face typical of*
Kwele masks. Some examples are known with curving
horns framing the face and meeting below the chin.
Height: 24⅝in (62.5cm)

Mahongwe, Congo, wood, early twentieth century
*Only a few examples of this sort of mask (**above**) exist. A*
mask of this type was thought to have influenced Picasso's
painting Les Demoiselles d'Avignon.
Height: 14in (35.5cm)

of high rank who were able to pay the expensive entrance fees. These masks are made of cloth, sewn extensively with geometric designs in coloured glass beads, and have circular ears and a rectangular trunk that hangs loosely down the front of the wearer, who dresses in a voluminous indigo cloth outfit. They were worn at biannual festivals of the society and at funerals of both royalty and society members.

One of the finest of all African masks is the extremely rare type made by the Bangwa. No more than one such mask has been found in any single chieftaincy, which would seem to indicate their importance and their connection with royalty; their exact function, however, remains a mystery. Only 15 genuinely old examples are known to exist. The extraordinary conception, with the angled planes of cheeks and mouth and the tall, vertical structure above the eyes finely carved with parallel grooves, is highly individual. Some masks of this type, but larger than usual, were collected during the 1970s, and may have been made with an eye on the art market.

To the south, the Cameroon grasslands give way to dense, humid rain forest. Inhabitants of the area live in small villages of extended family units. The most famous tribe of the area is the Fang, best known for their reliquary figures—carved wood statues that are fixed to bark boxes or baskets containing the preserved bones of ancestors. They also produce several types of mask, although the original ceremonial purpose of many of these has been lost. Data of this kind is similarly lacking for many of the masks of the area, making precise attribution difficult. Helmet masks with up to six faces are used in ceremonies known as *Ngontang* (head of a young, white girl). The small whitened faces have small eyes and mouth, the wide brows curving towards the edge of the face to form a heart shape. Eyeholes for the wearer are carved below one of the faces. Single-face masks were made for the same ceremony and seem to pre-date the helmet variety. One such type is known through only a few examples, all of which are thought to date from about 1900. The whitened face has a slender nose, small eyes carved close together, and a small mouth, slightly open with carved teeth. The distinctive hairstyle is represented by a band of scorched triangles. At least one of these masks is carved with a moustache, which, together with the facial features, seems to indicate that they are intended to be representations of Europeans, who were becoming increasingly numerous in the area at the end of the nineteenth century.

The Fang society called *Ngil* is well known for the ritual executions that its members had to commit, a practice which, like the society itself, disappeared early in the country's colonial period. A type of mask, highly prized by collectors, is reputedly associated with *Ngil*, although there seems to be little evidence to support the connection. The masks are large, sometimes more than 3ft (1m) long, and are whitened with kaolin. The

*Fang, Gabon, wood
The Fang invariably
whiten their masks with
kaolin: this example
(**above**) may have been
intended to represent a
European.
Height: 15½in (39.5cm)
Christie's New York 1984,
$24,200*

*Fang, Gabon, wood
Mission stations
commissioned masks from
traditional carvers in
Gabon for sale to
Europeans. These were
usually single-faced
masks, and helmet masks
such as this (**left**) are more
likely to have been carved
for traditional purposes.
This example was formerly
in the collection of André
Breton.
Height: 13⅜in (34cm)*

narrow heart-shaped face has a long, slender nose and the small eyes and mouth are scorched. The function of the execution rituals within *Ngil* society was to punish social deviants.

To the east of the Fang, and related to them, are the Kwele. Few artefacts by them are known, but the majority are masks. Little is known about their use; some show no evidence of having been worn and may simply have been displayed on ceremonial occasions. Those of human form generally have small heart-shaped faces and small mouths (although the mouth is sometimes omitted altogether). The eyes are raised, with narrow slits that are not always pierced—one of the reasons for thinking that not all were intended to be worn. Faceted horns on some masks curve about

the face; they sometimes meet below and frame the face, and they may be carved with small faces or eyes. The Kwele also make animal masks, representing gorillas, antelopes and elephants. Antelopes are of simplified geometric form, with lozenge-shaped faces echoed in the lozenge shape formed by the horns above. Elephant masks have faces resembling those of the human masks, but are carved with a faceted trunk curving down from the top of the head.

To the south of the Kwele, the Kota and Mahongwe are famous for their brass-covered reliquary figures. The Mahongwe also made a style of mask now very rare (there may be no more than four old examples in existence today), with a concave face tapering to a point at the chin. The forehead is prominent and the

eyes are raised, with pierced slits. The nose is triangular and the mouth small and conical.

A number of related tribes along the Ngunie River in southern Gabon produce a type of mask that is without doubt the most famous of all Gabonese masks. This is the white-faced mask made by the Punu and related tribes such as the Lumbo. The earliest known example was collected in 1867 and is now in the Pitt-Rivers Museum in Oxford. They gained popularity in the 1920s and 1930s, when many arrived in Europe, sadly with no collection data. As a result, precise attribution has been made difficult, if not impossible. They have been said to represent female ancestors and were worn in the *Okuni* masquerade, in which the dancer performed acrobatic feats on tall stilts. The masks, with serene expressions, are whitened with kaolin and have reddened lips. The eyes have curved narrow slits and the overall effect is remarkably reminiscent of Japanese female faces or masks. On most examples the blackened coiffure has a tall central lobe flanked by two lower lobes, and keloids are frequently carved in relief on the centre of the forehead, usually a group of nine forming a lozenge.

To the south of Gabon, across the border and into the People's Republic of the Congo, are the Teke. Only the eastern Teke, known as the Tsaye, produce masks, called *kidumu*. Their masking tradition is believed to have commenced only in the nineteenth century, and few of the surviving masks are thought to date from before the start of the twentieth century. The masks are circular (some of the late examples are oval) and flat, divided horizontally by a ridge at the level of the top of the nose. All of them, not surprisingly, are vertically symmetrical, but two of the oldest examples are also horizontally symmetrical. The masks are incised with geometric designs and painted in colours, usually black, white and red or orange. Two symbolic traditions are said to exist—one of them political, featuring crocodiles, crossroads, moons, pythons and rainbows, the other more generalized, with moons, sun, stars and rainbow. Sometimes these motifs suggest a resemblance to a face, but this is said to be a trick designed to mislead the uninitiated. The masks are pierced about the border for the attachment of feathers and raffia fibres. It is thought that production of these masks ceased in about 1920 and was revived only in the past 20 years or so, some of the modern artists relying for their inspiration on western books on African art.

EQUATORIAL AFRICA

The Portuguese explorer Diego Cao first reached the mouth of the Zaire (or Congo) River in the 1480s and found here the flourishing Kongo kingdom, with complex political institutions and social life. The Kongo kingdom maintained close contact with Portugal from the fifteenth century, notably for the trade in ivory and slaves. Many upper-class Kongo were

Kongo, Zaire, wood
*Masks from the area of the mouth of the Congo River such as this one (**right**) are among the most naturalistic of all African interpretations of the human face, but are scarce.*

Teke-Tsaye, Zaire, wood
*Few old examples of this type of mask (**above**) are known to exist. Many were collected in the 1950s, or later, when the tradition was revived.*
Christie's London 1980, £6600

Punu, Gabon, wood
*The tribes along the Ogowe River all carved masks with a somewhat oriental appearance (**right**); the scarification and the coiffure vary from one example to the next.*
Christie's London 1987, £7700

Pende, Zaire, wood and raffia
*The masquerades of the Pende include a large number of characters who wear similar types of mask (**right**) and examples are readily available on the market.*
Length: 23⁵/₈in (60cm)
Christie's London 1978, £3600

Lega, Zaire, wood and fibre
*Lega masks are made in various sizes and, like this one (**above**), are usually carved in wood, although they can also be ivory or elephant hide. The Bwami society still exists, and it is often difficult to tell the age of a mask.*
Height: approx. 6in (15cm)

converted to Christianity, and Portuguese members were among the group of governors who elected the king, or *ntotela*, to office. Not surprisingly, European influence, particularly Christian themes, are evident in the art of the area from an early date. The most famous carvings from the area are large nail fetish figures and small wooden maternity figures.

Various tribes were dominated by the Kongo or came within their sphere of influence. Of these, the Woyo and the Yombe produce masks. The Woyo, who live on the west coast, north of the estuary of the Zaire River, use masks known as *ndunga*, which are still made and danced today in ceremonies associated with initiation. The masks are larger than life-size, with projecting foreheads, swelling cheeks and narrow pierced eyes. The mouths are open, with carved teeth. The surface is painted either white or in colours, often in an asymmetrical design of broad areas of colour speckled with spots. The masks of the Yombe, to the north, are much rarer and little is known about their use. They display a much greater degree of realism than those of the Woyo and are life-size.

To the south-west, both in Zaire and across the border in Angola, are the Yaka and Suki, who live in an area of sparsely populated savanna. They share institutions concerning leadership and divination, and their art, which is relatively well documented, has many similarities. Both tribes have initiation schools (like the *Poro* of west Africa) in which the youths are circumcised and taught various skills, songs and dances. Various masks are used in connection with the accompanying ceremonies. Helmet masks, known as *hemba*, are predominantly used by the Suku. These usually have a whitened face with blackened incised coiffure, which is often surmounted by a bird, animal or figure. Examples carved since 1930 also have a handle carved below the chin.

Among the northern Yaka is made a series of masks said to represent departed elders, the most elaborate of which is called *kholuka*. These have a small face with bulging eyes and an open mouth with carved teeth. One of the most distinctive features of the masks is the nose, which is always prominent and often turns sharply upwards, a characteristic often seen in the figure sculpture from the same area. The headgear is made of raffia cloth and is frequently conceived as a cone, with one or more horizontal flanges or upward curved projections. The flanges and prongs denote the grade and are specified by the society, while the wooden mask can be carved to the whim of the man who commissions it. This headgear is sometimes surmounted by a figure or figures, frequently featuring sexuality and procreation in both humans and animals. On others, items associated with domestic activity are shown, or they may be topped by mammals, birds, fish or reptiles. Among both the Suku and the Yaka a type of very large mask is made averaging almost 3ft (1m) in height. Known as *kakuungu*, they were supported by a vertical handle from the chin, hidden in performance behind the raffia fringe. They have bulging cheeks and chin and a projecting, pouting mouth. The face is painted with red and white pigment.

The Western Pende, to the east of the Suku on the upper Kwilu River in Zaire, live in numerous chiefdoms of varying size. Ancestors, who are at the root of all Pende religion, are worshipped in shrines and make themselves visible at masquerades. There are two types of masks: *minganji*, which are the more powerful, represent ancestors, while *mbuya* are village masks representing various character types, such as chief, executioner, fool, flirt and prostitute. There are as many as 20 types, although only a few appear in any one ceremony. The performances are entertaining and amusing, but also a means of effecting social control. The *mbuya* masks usually have a triangular-shaped face, with half-closed, bulging eyes and eyebrows carved in relief meeting at the centre above the nose; mouths are often open with carved teeth. Some characters have a long, rectangular beard curving out below the chin and carved with grooves. The masks are painted in various colours, usually black, white and red; the epileptic, *mbangu*, has a face painted half black and half white.

The more forceful *minganji* masks, representing ancestors, are of simpler form. They are circular and made from plaited raffia, with tubular eyes and no other facial features. All mask manufacture is a sacred process that must not be seen by women and children, who are permitted to view them only in the masquerade; consequently masks are carved away from the village. *Mbuya* dancers in *Makenda* circumcision ceremonies emerge from the bush one at a time and dance in the village square from afternoon until dusk, at which time the *minganji* masqueraders appear, but only at a distance. They rush around on the outskirts of the village but never enter it, and they make themselves only partly visible to the spectators, thus adding to the sense of awe and fear they are intended to create. At the conclusion of the ceremony, the masqueraders remove their masks in the presence of the newly initiated youths at the circumcision camps, who are then allowed to touch and handle the masks and are thus acknowledged as equals.

Small versions of these masks, measuring approximately 2–2½in (5–6cm) in height, are carved in ivory or wood and are worn as amulets. Ivory examples often acquire a fine smooth surface and golden colour much admired by collectors. European fakers are becoming increasingly skilled at reproducing these characteristics and giving them just the right amount of 'wear' around the suspension holes. Small wooden masks, measuring about 2½–4in (6–10cm), are carved as oracles and are fixed to the end of a concertina of wooden sticks, like a jack-in-the-box. They are pierced about the top of the head for the attachment of a feather coiffure.

The eastern Pende produce a number of regional mask styles. One of these, the *giphogo*, forms part of the chief's treasury. It is a cylindrical helmet mask, with almond-shaped slit eyes and a projecting cylindrical nose. Below the chin is a wide flange carved and painted with bands of triangles. The name *giphogo* is also applied to another type of mask surmounted by two sword-like projections.

The Kuba kingdom incorporates almost 20 different tribes, the Bushoong and Kete being the largest. The Kuba live in Zaire in the fork of the Kasai and Sankuru rivers. Art and masks play an important role in court ritual, initiation and funerals. A number of related masks, used in dances re-enacting the origins of the Kuba kingdom, are made from a combination of several materials. The most important of these masks among the Bushoong is called *moshambwooy*, which has the following legendary origin. A water spirit once haunted the country, inflicting blindness and fatal illnesses on the inhabitants. In the time of the king Bo Kyeen, a man called Bokomboke met the spirit in the forest. Frightened, he returned to the village and recounted to the king what he had seen, but was unable to describe the being in words. The king ordered him to build a hut on the edge of the village, and with some barkcloth, the skin of a bat and feathers he made a strange costume, which he painted in yellow, black and white. The king saw the costume and had an idea. He disappeared for so long that people wondered what had happened to him. One night, a strange being appeared in the capital. Wearing a costume imitating the spirit *moshambwooy*, it was the king frightening the inhabitants. Then the king hid the costume in the bush. Next day the king re-appeared and expressed great astonishment at the story of the visit of the strange being, but claimed to know the reason for the stranger's visit. It was *moshambwooy* come to see if there were any querulous women or disobedient youths to be punished.

The face of the mask is usually of leopard or antelope skin, to which a wooden mouth and nose are attached. Cowrie shell eyes are surrounded by glass beads, and a panel of beads with chevron or zigzag designs runs down the centre of the face. A chevron at the bottom of the face represents a beard and is sewn with rows of cowrie shells. The mask is supported and strengthened by a rigid crown of rattan sewn all over with beads, which also serves to hold in place the raffia cloth head covering. This is also sewn extensively, with coloured beads forming interlocking geometric designs; such designs are typical of the Kuba and are seen also in wood carving and scarification patterns. The mask is worn with a highly elaborate costume made from similar materials and is surmounted by a crown of feathers. A number of masks are similar in appearance to the *moshambwooy* and are sometimes confused with it. *Mukyeem* may have served a similar function and differs from the *moshambwooy*

Kuba, Zaire, wood, raffia, cloth, cowries and metal
A number of tribes within the Kuba kingdom made elaborate masks from a wide variety of materials;
Moshambwooy *masks (**above**) are the most elaborate. Height: 17¾in (45cm) Christie's London 1989, £462*

Salampasu, Zaire, wood, feathers, fibre and rattan
*The form of the Salampasu mask (**right**) is very distinctive with rounded forehead, small rectangular mouth and triangular face. Height: 30⅜in (77cm)*

in having a trunk-like projection from the top of the head, a feature which is derived from the trunk of an elephant, a symbol of power.

Various explanations have been given for the origin of the mask known as *bwoom*, which sometimes appears alongside *moshambwooy*. One is that it represents a pygmy, another that it represents the hydrocephalous head of the son of a fourteenth-century king. The wooden mask is of helmet form and has a prominent forehead and large nose. The forehead, cheeks and mouth are usually covered with sheets of copper and again the surface is extensively embellished with beads and cowrie shells.

The female mask, *ngady amwaash*, also appears

Chokwe, Zaire, wood, fibre, glass beads and metal
This impersonation of female beauty, called mwana pwo, *is worn by a masquerader on stilts. Shown in profile (**right**) and face-on (**far right**), this is a very fine example of the most widely available of all Chokwe masks; however, the quality can vary considerably. Large quantities were made at the Dundo Museum in Angola.*

alongside *moshambwooy* and *bwoom*. It is a face mask of wood and, compared with other Kuba masks, is of fairly naturalistic form. A vertical panel of beads runs down the length of the nose and mouth and the eyebrows are also beaded, but the remainder of the face is painted with bold geometric designs in black and white. The attached raffia headgear is sewn with cowries and painted with geometric designs.

To the south of the Kuba the Bena Biombo produce helmet masks showing the clear influence of the Pende to the west and Kuba to the north. The face is reddened and the cheeks and chin are carved and painted with bands of triangles in black and white.

Slightly further south, the Salampasu make masks in both wood and fibre. The wooden masks have prominent bulging foreheads and pointed chins, large apertures for the eyes and rectangular pierced mouths with carved and whitened pointed teeth. On some masks copper panels are attached to the surface. Frequently the coiffure is represented by balls of woven cane, and similar balls may be suspended from the chin on lengths of plaited fibre to represent a beard. Masks were also made from woven fibre, resembling the wooden masks in having bulging forehead and similar eye apertures. These masks also sometimes have the cane ball coiffures, or alternatively, are topped with woven fibre or feathers. Although the Salampasu are said to have destroyed their masks in

the early 1960s, partly in an effort to move into con-temporary life, it was reported in 1975 that mask pro-duction had increased to meet a growing demand, no doubt from the art market.

The Lwalwa are related to the Salampasu and at one time were under their domination. They produce four types of similar mask; they have concave, almost lozenge-shaped faces, with reddened patina, some-times embellished with white. Three are male and one female. Eyes are rectangular slits and mouths are small and project forward. The male *nkaki* mask has a long, prominent and slender nose extending to the top of the forehead, and *shifola* masks, also male, have shorter, rounded noses. The female mask, *mushika*, is

distinguished by a lateral crest to the coiffure, and noses are generally less pronounced. The fourth type, *mvondo*, also male, has a nose similar to the female mask, but does not have the crested coiffure.

There are three categories of mask used by the Chokwe, who live on the border of Angola and Zaire. The most important are sacred masks called *cikungu*, worn by chiefs at their enthronement and while mak-ing certain sacrifices. Made of black resin on a wooden frame, they have large circular discs for ears, a stylized chin and a large elaborate headgear. They are painted with geometric designs in red and white. There are various types of circumcision masks, also with resin faces, though with less pronounced features. *Cikungu*,

Mbunda, Zambia, wood
*Influenced by their Chokwe neighbours, Mbunda masks (**above**) have clear affinities with Chokwe masks although they are larger and rarer.*
Height: 13³⁄₄in (35cm) Christie's London 1989, £4620

the most important of these, has a tall conical super-structure, sometimes over 3ft (1m) high, representing the horns of the roan antelope and with a series of rings representing the rings of growth. These masks are usually destroyed after the initiation ceremonies have taken place, and they are therefore unlikely to be encountered by the collector.

The most familiar Chokwe masks are the dance masks, which are kept by professional dancers, who destroy them only if they are damaged. Dancing is a hereditary occupation handed down from uncle to nephew. There are two principal types of masks: the *cihongo*, which is male, and the more common *pwo*, which is female. Both types are made in resin and wood. The *cihongo* is approximately life-size, with slit almond-shaped eyes within concave sockets. The pierced mouth is broad, with carved whitened teeth; the chin is stylized, represented by a projecting disc. The forehead is usually incised with a scarification mark called *cingelyengelye*, shaped like a Maltese cross. The mask represents the male ancestor and symbolizes power and wealth, the virile dance contrasting to the elegance of the female (though the two were rarely, if ever, performed together).

The female mask, *pwo* or *mwana pwo* (young woman),

Songye, Zaire, wood
Height: 20⁷⁄₈in (53cm)
Christie's London 1989, £3850

*Songye, Zaire, wood, fibre and
feathers
Height: 18¹/₈in (46cm)
Christie's New York 1984, $33,000*

represents the female ancestor and imparts fertility to the spectators. These masks are more naturalistic than the *cihongo* masks, and although they represent the female ancestral spirit, some have the appearance of portraits. The faces are reddened and usually have a serene expression. The artist is said to be inspired by the looks of a particularly beautiful woman, and since he has to work far away from women, he studies his model at length, often for several days, to imprint her features on his mind. Eyes are frequently represented in a similar way to those on *cihongo* masks, but the mouth, which may be open or closed, is smaller. The dancer is dressed as a woman, with false breasts. The solemn bearing and elegant gestures of the *pwo* masks are said to teach the Chokwe women to act in a graceful manner. The Chokwe also carve masks representing animals such as pigs, monkeys and guinea fowl.

To the south of the Chokwe, on the borders of Angola and Zambia, are the Mbunda. They are related to the Chokwe and make large wooden masks, over life-size, which have a distinctive large rectangular mouth, often with carved teeth. The forehead is very prominent and is sometimes carved with curved parallel grooves. Some masks have bulging cheeks reminiscent of masks from the Cameroon grasslands.

Probably the most striking masks from Zaire are the *kifwebe* masks of the Songye and Luba, highly distinctive because of their cubistic forms and vibrant painted decoration. Writers disagree as to which tribe adopted the style from the other. There is considerable stylistic variation, but the masks usually have a square jaw and rectangular mouth projecting to the same distance as the nose. A median crest of varying height runs from the top of the head, often linking up with the nose (though this is absent or very shallow on female masks). The eyes frequently have large projecting hoods. Most of the masks are incised and painted with bands of alternating colours, the most common being black, white and red. Generally speaking, those masks with very exaggerated features are later in date. Among the Luba, whose kingdom dominated and influenced a wide area of south-west Zaire, *kifwebe* masks of similar style are carved in the east. This region is also associated with masks of hemispherical form, with similar surface decoration of parallel grooves, in this case usually painted white on a black ground, and with large helmet masks of rounded form. The features are more naturalistic than on the *kifwebe* masks and the surface is blackened. Some of these, though of human form, have curved horns.

To the east of the Luba, and closely related to them, are the Hemba. Although best known for their figure sculpture, the Hemba also make small masks representing chimpanzees, with wide grinning, crescent-shaped mouths and narrow eyes. These masks usually have a dark crusty patina. Called *soko mutu*, or *soko muntu*, they were probably not intended to be worn over the face as dance masks. Their exact function is unclear; some writers describe them as masks to be worn hung on a belt, and they have also been described as charms to be hung in the home to impart both protection and fertility.

All forms of art among the Lega of eastern Zaire are connected with the *Bwami* association. This association through which all Lega, both male and female, aim to progress, has five grades for men and three for women, and masks are used particularly in the highest grades. They are used in a great variety of ways, not simply as face coverings. For example, they may be worn on the back of the head or on the knee, attached to a pole or fence, or swung or dragged by their beards. The way in which the masks are handled is part of an elaborate language of meaning. Masks of ivory and bone, which are associated with death and sorcery, are not worn on the body.

Lega masks are usually of simple form, with a heart-shaped face within an oval, and the eyes and mouth simply indicated, often as raised almond shapes. Because many of the masks are not intended to be worn on the face, the eyes are not always pierced. Kaolin is frequently applied to the surface of the wooden masks and most of these also have a pierced lower border for the attachment of a long fibre beard. The masks are still made and used by the Lega today and it is often difficult to judge their age and to tell if they were made for the art market or for tribal use.

EAST AFRICA

Outside the two great areas of west and equatorial Africa, masking traditions are much less important. A few tribes in east Africa produce masks, however, and of these the best known are the Makonde, who live in the area along the border of Tanzania and Mozambique. They use both helmet masks and face masks in rites associated with circumcision and initiation. Helmet masks are used only by the southern Makonde groups in Mozambique. They are worn either on the top of the head, with a cloth attached at the base to cover the face, or else over the head, with the wearer looking through the mouth. Most of them show a considerable degree of realism, sometimes with an element of caricature. The typical scarification patterns on the face were originally reproduced in black beeswax; later they were carved in relief, and later still engraved. On some examples, probably also of late date, scarification is reproduced in pokerwork. Human hair is often attached to the top of the head with beeswax. Women are frequently represented in masks with a large lip-plug in the upper lip. Dancers representing women also held a large plank mask over the body, carved with breasts and adorned with beeswax scarification.

The main dance of the masqueraders was performed in pairs, a male and a female, their arms and legs remaining motionless with only the lower part of

Lula, Zaire, wood
*Lula masks are rare and have a distinctive shallow, oval form (**above**). They are usually painted blue and white*
Height: 15³⁄₄in (40cm) Christie's London 1989, £5500

Luba, Zaire, wood
*Early Luba masks such as this (**right**) are extremely rare, and the most famous example is in the Tervuren Museum outside Brussels. Height: 18⁷⁄₈in (48cm)*

their bodies moving in simulation of sexual intercourse. Other performances portrayed various aspects of life among the Makonde, with masks representing particular characters: old man, young girl, doctor, even foreign characters such as Arabs. The face masks are often more stylized than the helmet masks, but beeswax scarification and human hair sometimes add realistic details. Animal masks are used in certain dances, including monkey masks similar to Balinese examples. Masks combining both animal and human features also occur; those with horns and bears portray the devil.

PACIFIC MASKS

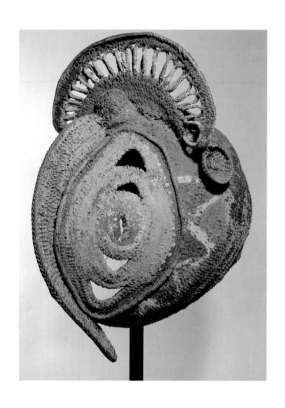

Like the masks of many African cultures, those of Melanesia reflect a strong tradition of ceremonial masquerades and religious rituals. Probably the strongest thematic link between the various cults is the importance accorded to tribal ancestors, whose benevolent spirits are frequently invoked.

The islands of the South Pacific, collectively known as Oceania, are divided into three major groups: Melanesia, Micronesia and Polynesia. In Micronesia and Polynesia masks are virtually unknown, but in the larger islands of Melanesia the situation is completely different, for these islands are a treasure house of masks, comparable to Africa for variety and artistic quality. Much of the old tradition is as strong as ever, and many of the masquerades are still being danced today.

MELANESIA

Although many of the peoples of Melanesia are confessed Christians of one denomination or another, they practise many of the old rites, and most of the churches recognize the value of leaving those bonds of society intact, provided they are denuded of any destructive elements. Masks play a vital and prominent part in these peoples' lives. They do not view the supernatural from the same standpoint as a European, but as an extension of the everyday world. The most powerful and influential spirits are generally held to be those of important ancestors, and particular atten-

tion is paid to the proper performance of mortuary and funerary rites at the passing of men of high status. Spirits are potentially either malevolent or benevolent and human actions can placate or aggravate them. Societies were created to control, direct and modify their power, and the feasts given to appease them and to venerate the ancestors were linked with initiation rites of boys and young men.

The masks used at such ceremonies are sometimes abandoned afterwards, but others are kept for years;

Maprik, New Guinea, basketry, twentieth century
*Used in dances connected with the yam cult, masks such as this (**above left**) come in a variety of forms and sizes. They are abandoned after the ceremony, and are widely available on the market today.*

Unea Island, barkcloth, various fibres, cane and feathers
*These rare large conical fibre masks (**right**) are painted in striking, bright colours.*
Height: 27½in (70cm)

MELANESIA

scattered with small islands, on most of which are constructed tortoiseshell masks of great complexity. Panels of shell from the local turtles are pared down and cut into the necessary shapes and sewn together with plaited coconut fibre to make long masks, worn at an angle on the heads of the masqueraders. A smaller mask, the size of a human head, is often applied on the forehead of the larger mask, which can incorporate monstrous features. Cassowary feathers are inserted about the fretted borders, large conus and other shells are suspended about the rim, and long wooden prongs with inserted white feathers form a crest. Occasionally the crest is of fish form. The initiates were taken for several weeks to a secret camp in the bush, where they were taught the myths and legends, dances and rites relating to the culture heroes. The dances were performed at night before a screen hung with shells, skulls and effigies. The masqueraders, representing the mythic ancestors, wore long grass costumes beneath the masks, and were seen by the initiates alone. Later the initiates, having passed all the tests, were bathed, painted and dressed, then taken back to the main camp, where they were greeted as though returned from the dead, re-united with their families and made ready for marriage. Few of these splendid masks have survived intact; but in the small masks that are attached to the larger ones the particular process of creative thinking is still evident, and even stripped to the minimum of just the oval face with the attached looped nose, some of the mystic element is retained. On Saibai Island, just off the coast of New Guinea, are carved long wooden masks, with an eye form similar to the others of the Torres Straits, with inset hair and beard, and incised, painted borders.

About 100 miles (160km) to the east of New Guinea, across the Siassi Sea, is the island of New Britain. Some masks there are similar to those made on New Guinea, but in the far east of the island—in the Gazelle Peninsula—masks of a dramatically different kind are produced. They are used in mourning ceremonies, to commemorate those who had died during the previous year, and to celebrate the ripening of the taro harvest; this represented a ritual continuation or activation of a pattern of cyclical change of birth, growth and death of all living things. One type of mask, called *hareiga*, is truly gigantic, being some 30-40ft (9-12m) high, and is carried to the dance area by a large group of men. It is constructed of barkcloth over a cane frame, with a round or ovoid head, the features painted in black, on a long, thin neck, a small body below. Such huge objects naturally tend to find their way into museums rather than private collections. The best examples are in German museums, especially that at Bremen, where clustered in a corner, they are awe-inspiring.

There are several types of smaller headdress masks, similarly constructed and painted, but none is still made today. Large composite helmet masks known as *oggeroggeruk* are, however, produced today; indeed,

the former are usually available on the market, but when the latter appear for sale they may have been acquired illegally. This fact accounts in part for the importance that many collectors attach to provenance. The acquisition of a mask or other work of art is usually channelled through the headman of a village. Some collectors have had the galling experience of paying for an artefact, only to have it wrested from them when the indignant, real owner suddenly and unexpectedly appears.

Some parts of Melanesia have been accessible for well over a century, but others, because of the difficult terrain or inhospitable climate are little explored even today. New Guinea is the largest and best-known island in Melanesia and it also has the richest artistic traditions. The most prolific area for masks is probably the vast valley of the Sepik River, especially along the middle and lower reaches, where the waters flow from west to east in great lazy loops. Ceremonies are centred on the men's meeting houses, called *Tambaran*—huge thatched buildings with upturned eaves to each end, and a tall decorated front. Inside, the most sacred masks and figures are stored from ceremony to ceremony (the dancing takes place on the dance floor nearby). The masks of the middle Sepik are usually made of wood or woven split cane, rattan, or a mixture of both. Some large conical masks extend to below the waist of the wearer, so that he puts his arms through two holes at the sides. Often a further mask of wood or clay is attached both before the face and at the summit of the cone; the clay masks are embellished with cowrie shell eyes and bands of small nassa shells are usually inset about the rim. Other rattan masks can be woven as animals, chiefly crocodiles.

All the ceremonies need the beneficial presence of the ancestors, and celebrate the emergence of the initiates from their seclusion, fortified by their trials and grown from boys into men. Among the Maprik, who live in a mountainous area to the north of the middle Sepik, the ceremonies are centred about the cultivation of yams, and the rattan masks are painted in bright colours—bands of red, yellow, black and white, sometimes also green. They vary in size from huge hemispherical constructions that engulf the torso of the masquerader to small ones, less than 12in (30cm) high, which are used to decorate the enormous yams grown especially for the feasts. After the ceremonies most of the masks are abandoned in the forest, so this type of mask is readily available on the market. Woven rattan masks are made by other groups in this area, and are painted in earth colours of reddish-brown, black and white, with sometimes a little green. The colours fade and some masks are repainted for each performance.

Further downstream, near Anggoram, the people use large, oval, dish-like masks attached to rattan. This type of mask has proved popular with collectors and many are made today for the art market. Similar masks

Sepik River, wood, shell and fibre
*The slender oval face and hooked nose (**above**) is typical of masks from the lower Sepik River area. Christie's London 1979, £2200*

*Papuan Gulf, cane and barkcloth (**right**)*

MELANESIA

*Witu Island, wood
This wooden helmet mask
(**above**) is of a type rarely
available on the market.
Height: 20in (51cm)
Christie's London 1980,
£6000*

*Tami Island, Papua New
Guinea, barkcloth,
feathers, fibre and shells
This particular type of
barkcloth mask (**left**) is
known as* tago

are carved in the Sepik Delta area and up the Ramu river, some of the masks having long, thin noses in a rather long oval face.

The wooden masks of the Yuat river, a tributary of the Sepik, are of rather bulbous form, usually the size of a human face. They are painted in colours, predominantly white, red and yellow, over areas indicated in relief, and have rather aggressive features. Masks from the Ramu, Murik Lakes and the Sepik Delta are usually covered in a reddish mud paste and sometimes have an animal carved in high relief on the forehead and a long, looped nose. A 'classic' type of Sepik mask, the oval about the size of a human face, and with typical scrolls carved at intervals about the border and features, is carved on Manam Island, just off the north coast of New Guinea, and is traded to neighbouring islands as well as to other villages along the coast. Such masks are still carved today with great precision, and it takes a well-trained eye to pick out the old ones from the new.

Wooden masks from Irian Jaya, the north-western promontory of New Guinea, are rare and show the influence of neighbouring Indonesian islands. The Asmat to the south have knotted fibre masquerading costumes that cover the whole body. Their masks are roughly conical, painted reddish-brown and white, with applied round eyes of wood and a woven nose with a wooden nose ornament attached. At the top of the head is inserted a stick with pendants of white feathers and seed pods from the plant called Job's tears. Even further south are the people of Marind Anim, who wear very elaborate constructions of sago palm trunk, with applied abrus seeds, shell ornaments and feathers; many similarly decorated panels are worn about the whole figure, making a vast and colourful assemblage.

Some of the finest New Guinea masks come from the Gulf of Papua on the south coast, an area of river deltas and mud flats. They are made of bark cloth stretched over a cane frame, the black and white designs outlined by further applications of split cane and surmounted by tall oval panels decorated with stylized faces and figures. All masks from this area have a conical base to enclose the head, with the eyes embellished with a forked motif. Above this cone are attached large oval panels (typical of the western part of the Gulf) or bird and fish forms (found further east along the Gulf).

The final main masking area of New Guinea is in the north-east, from Astrolabe Bay to the Huon Gulf. In this area are carved rather heavy wooden masks, painted with designs in red, black and white; apart from their rectangular form, they are recognizable by the forked decoration about the eyes and the large, often looped, ear lobes. A round mask, called *tago*, of palm spathe topped by a bunch of cassowary feathers, is also made in this area and painted similar colours.

The Torres Straits, to the south of New Guinea, are

scattered with small islands, on most of which are constructed tortoiseshell masks of great complexity. Panels of shell from the local turtles are pared down and cut into the necessary shapes and sewn together with plaited coconut fibre to make long masks, worn at an angle on the heads of the masqueraders. A smaller mask, the size of a human head, is often applied on the forehead of the larger mask, which can incorporate monstrous features. Cassowary feathers are inserted about the fretted borders, large conus and other shells are suspended about the rim, and long wooden prongs with inserted white feathers form a crest. Occasionally the crest is of fish form. The initiates were taken for several weeks to a secret camp in the bush, where they were taught the myths and legends, dances and rites relating to the culture heroes. The dances were performed at night before a screen hung with shells, skulls and effigies. The masqueraders, representing the mythic ancestors, wore long grass costumes beneath the masks, and were seen by the initiates alone. Later the initiates, having passed all the tests, were bathed, painted and dressed, then taken back to the main camp, where they were greeted as though returned from the dead, re-united with their families and made ready for marriage. Few of these splendid masks have survived intact; but in the small masks that are attached to the larger ones the particular process of creative thinking is still evident, and even stripped to the minimum of just the oval face with the attached looped nose, some of the mystic element is retained. On Saibai Island, just off the coast of New Guinea, are carved long wooden masks, with an eye form similar to the others of the Torres Straits, with inset hair and beard, and incised, painted borders.

About 100 miles (160km) to the east of New Guinea, across the Siassi Sea, is the island of New Britain. Some masks there are similar to those made on New Guinea, but in the far east of the island—in the Gazelle Peninsula—masks of a dramatically different kind are produced. They are used in mourning ceremonies, to commemorate those who had died during the previous year, and to celebrate the ripening of the taro harvest; this represented a ritual continuation or activation of a pattern of cyclical change of birth, growth and death of all living things. One type of mask, called *hareiga*, is truly gigantic, being some 30-40ft (9-12m) high, and is carried to the dance area by a large group of men. It is constructed of barkcloth over a cane frame, with a round or ovoid head, the features painted in black, on a long, thin neck, a small body below. Such huge objects naturally tend to find their way into museums rather than private collections. The best examples are in German museums, especially that at Bremen, where clustered in a corner, they are awe-inspiring.

There are several types of smaller headdress masks, similarly constructed and painted, but none is still made today. Large composite helmet masks known as *oggeroggeruk* are, however, produced today; indeed,

Torres Straits, Papua New Guinea, turtleshell, shells, fibre, feathers
Turtleshell was rarely used for masks outside the Torres Straits (between the south of New Guinea and the northern tip of Australia). Masks from this region command high prices at auction. They are more usually of human form, and this fish mask **(left)** is particularly rare.

Baining, Gazelle Peninsula, New Britain, cane and barkcloth
Several different types of barkcloth masks are used in the area of the Gazelle Peninsula in the east of New Britain. Some are of immense size and are consequently rarely seen on the market. The pig mask **(above)** is one of several animals represented in barkcloth masks danced at night.

PACIFIC MASKS

Sulka, New Britain, wood, various fibres
Masks from central New Britain are among the most dramatic of Melanesian masks. Delicacy and fragility no doubt partly account for their relative scarcity on the market today. Several examples were collected at the beginning of the century, the majority of which are to be found in German museums.

the tradition they serve seems to have originated in its present form only in the twentieth century. These masks, said to symbolize the slow growth of trees, have a long, slightly-tapered, cylinder with a curious face at the end, just above the dancer's head. They are sometimes found on the market today, as are examples of a type of mask danced at night. Again, these are made of barkcloth over a rattan or cane frame, and painted with black designs. They fit over the dancer's head and resemble to a greater or lesser degree the creatures they are said to represent—the owl, hornbill, flying fox, pig, cow and fish.

Similar masks from the central Baining area of the island are made for another night dance, known as the Baining snake dance. Two types, called *kavat* and *vungvung*, are still made today in the area. The *kavat* masks have a distinctive iconography, depicting various flora, birds, mammals, insects, reptiles, natural phenomena and human processes and products. Typical features include *slabam* ('vertebrae of a pig'), *saulki* ('support post of a house'), *rengit* ('leaf used for wrapping food for cooking') and *surraga* ('wise old man'). Older masks have fine negative designs painted in black on the natural barkcloth, but later types are more simply decorated, concentrating on huge eyes painted in red and black with concentric circles.

Sulka, New Britain, wood, fibres
There is a great variety in the Sulka masks. This one clearly represents a human figure. Others are made as huge discs worn on top of the head and resembling umbrellas. The painted decoration is usually in the favoured colours of pink and green.

The mask made today in the largest quantities has huge round eyes within a lobed structure, which tapers above the rounded jaws; a lip or tongue-like protrusion hangs below the jaw and the structure extends at the back to fit on the head of the dancer. The whole creation can be about 3ft (1m) high, but smaller ones are made, probably with a view to export. As they come leaping out of the forest at night, they make a stirring impression, even if they do have a certain resemblance to Mickey Mouse and Donald Duck.

The Tolai people in the Tolai mountains, also in the north-east of New Britain, have two types or families of mask. The first is the *dukduk*, a high composite cone with a long waving topknot. *Dukduks* are thought of as the 'sons' of conical palm spathe masks with large circular painted eyes. (Some authorities believe they are rather the male and female types of the same masking tradition.) The latter are made today in a number of different materials—cotton cloth, mosquito netting, printed cloth or anything similar that is available. These cones are perched above an enveloping tiered leaf robe. The 'mother' of both these masks is said to dwell in the Duke of York Islands, to the east, but she does not accompany the *dukduks* and their 'mothers' when they arrive on the beach in their

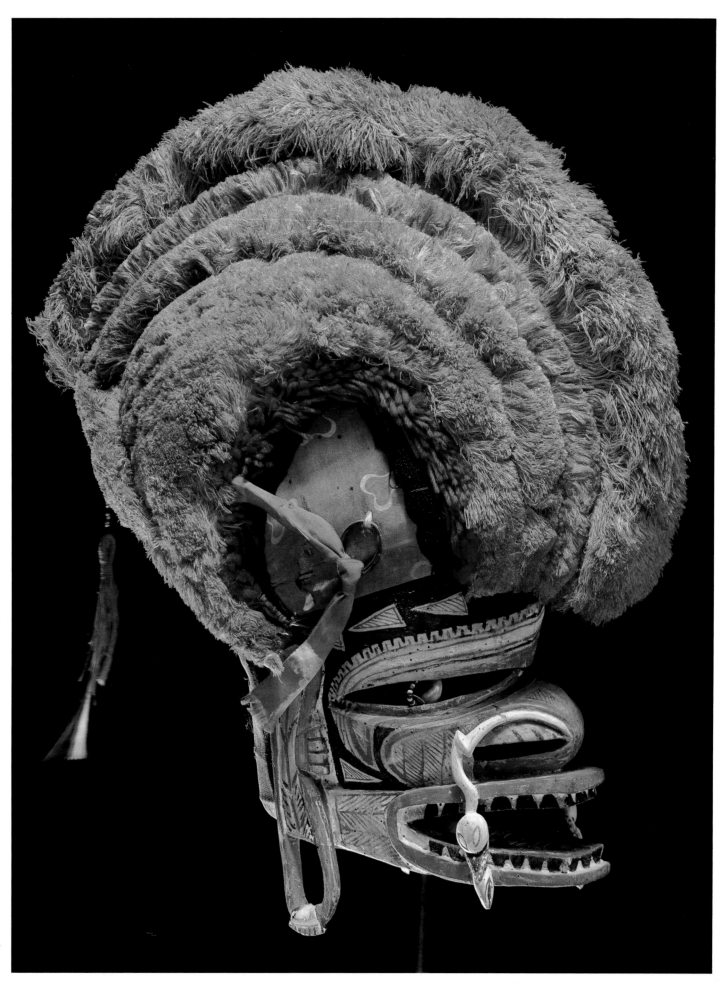

canoes. Having arrived by sea, the *dukduks* and their mothers dance on the beach and enter the village only to take food. Although they are in fact men from that village, when masquerading they have the absolute right to take whatever they wish—fruit, yams, even a small pig—to be eaten by the elders and the young initiates. The masks are highly sacred and it is forbidden for the people to sell them. They are also extremely frail, and consequently are seldom found on the market, or even in museums.

The same is true of the other type of mask made by the Tolai. This consists of a hemisphere of rattan, covered in ferns or other fibres, with a triangular wooden face attached to one side; this in turn often has a fibre beard, feathers about the neck, pierced nose ornaments and bright painted decoration (all the colours used are made from natural materials, except the blue, which is a bleach bought at the trade stores). On the top of this structure can be attached a wooden figure, usually about 18in (45cm) high, finely-carved and with animated stance. This also is brightly coloured, and often embellished with thorns, intricately-applied eyes and inset fibre hair; it stands within three or four finely-serrated wooden cascades curving from a pole above the head to the circular platform at the base. These two elements, the figure and the mask, are stored in separate huts, and must never be seen by women, especially when joined together for the dance, when their potency is comparable to lightning or an electric charge. It is probably because of this method of storage that the mask is seldom collected whole, and even in museums the figures have often been separated from the faces.

Along the coast of the Gazelle Peninsula is found a mask made from a human skull, minus the jaw, with a mud and gum encrustation, inset hair, and a small stick at the back with which to hold it in the dancer's teeth. Then to the south of the peninsula is found another group of highly dramatic masks, among the most spectacular made anywhere in the world—fantastical structures made of rattan, covered in pith, and then painted a variety of pinks, bright greens, black and white. Although the basic mask is of conical or truncated cylindrical form, the superstructures can resemble vast umbrellas, with the eyes separated on stalks and other features stylized or exaggerated. In addition to traditional materials, the makers of the masks use wire, cotton cloth, paper, cardboard, netting or whatever else may be to hand. Inset feathers are used, as everywhere in Melanesia, and the masqueraders show great imagination with their inventions. The celebrations continue all day and all night for several days, after which the masks are abandoned in the forest. It is not always easy to tell what characters the dancers impersonate, because something that may look like a fish to an outsider is a man to the villagers. The masks are seldom seen in collections outside the area because the villagers are vague as to their whereabouts, and they are both large and fragile, making transport and display difficult. The Hamburg Museum in Germany, however, has a superb display.

The Kilenge people of western New Britain carve wooden masks similar to those of the Huon Gulf of New Guinea. These are danced at circumcision ceremonies. Much more spectacular are those called *bukumo*, which are danced at a later rite, when the boys have their ears pierced and their hair cut. The base is a carved and painted oval wooden mask, which is surrounded by cut leaves of palm and long canes, each of the latter with a feather inserted at the tip. This creates a disc some 12ft (3.6m) across, which ripples and sways to striking effect when danced.

About 20 miles (30km) east of New Britain is New Ireland. In the north-western part of this island considerable quantities of the mask known as *tatanua* are made for performances related to the *Malanggan*, a second burial ceremony that not only commemorates the deceased but also introduces new initiates. It is a major event, involving a complex marshalling of resources. After the death of a chief the clan have to

New Ireland, wood and fibre
Larger and more elaborate than the tatanua *masks,* kepong *masks such as this (**above**) were used in* Malanggan *ceremonies to mark the second burial of a deceased. They are rarer than the* tatanua.

New Ireland, wood, fibre, cloth, shell and metal
Tatanua *masks from New Ireland (**left**) are distinguished by the tall fibre median crest, often whitened with chalk. Occasionally the mask may have a small dance ornament inserted in the mouth.*

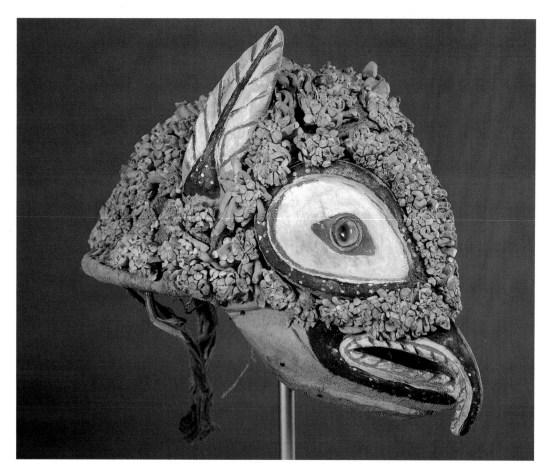

New Ireland, wood, shell, fibre, sponge, late nineteenth century
*This mask (**left**) representing an owl is a particularly naturalistic example. The opercula of the* turbo petholatus *shell with its green spot on a white ground adds a particularly realistic touch.*

Pentecost Island, Vanuatu, wood
*This mask (**right**) is without doubt one of the finest to have survived from Melanesia.*
Height: 13½in (34.5cm)
Sotheby's London 1978, £180,000

have the time to gather the necessary number of pigs and grow the yams for a series of feasts marking the building of the *Malanggan* house. The celebrations range from minor feasts marking the cutting of the trees for the carvings, to the final festival when the house is completed and the initiates are ready to emerge from their seclusion. The *tatanua* represent deceased persons and each in fact is given the name of a dead man. They are not abandoned in the *Malanggan* house after the performance, but are instead saved for the next. The masks have wooden faces, carved with square jaws and coloured red, black and white on the natural wooden ground—a decorative scheme used also for the house. To this wooden face is attached a high curved headdress of cane, covered in fibres, bark or trade cloth, encrusted with white chalk, and inset with sticks, seeds or twisted fibres; any or all of these are used in a variety of ways as panels, with cursive borders each side of a high median crest of brown fibres, resembling the helmet crest of a Roman centurion. The eyes are made from snail shells, which can give the masks a ferocious expression.

Other masks have broader faces than the *tatanua*, are carved in wood, and also have inset shell eyes, but the headdress is usually of tufted fibres; large wooden ears are inserted on each side and a wooden carving is thrust into the mouth, sometimes a stuffed hornbill head. Some masks can have exotic crests made from wooden insertions, and others, rarely, are carved as

pig heads. The exact function of these masks varies and it is usually impossible to discover them once they are removed from their context.

About 1,000 miles (1,600km) south-east of New Guinea lies the group of islands called Vanuatu (formerly New Hebrides). Society on the islands is carefully graded, and on one of the largest islands—Malekula—the rituals, regalia and titles associated with the levels of social prestige have been studied in detail. The different croton leaves each grade is allowed to wear, for example, are carefully specified. The masks in southern Malekula are linked to the death of chiefs and the circumcision of youths. Structures are erected in a compound *(longhor)* and feasts are given at intervals to mark the progress. The masks and headdresses are known as *temes mbalmbal (temes* being spirit) and are made of perishable materials that are abandoned after the ceremony. The mask is usually of conical form—typically a section of bamboo, split into strips, splayed and joined at the top; the free ends are fastened into a ring of mangrove wood, and over this a mulch of vegetable material is laid. This is then painted in coloured pigments with motifs resembling a human face. Others are covered with spiders' web and are worn by men of high rank. The masks are made by the older men—it seems to be considered presumptious for a young man to make one. The lower grades wear headdresses without masks. Some masks are like tall tapered hats that sit on the dancer's shoulders, so he has to be led by

NORTHAMPTON COLLEGE
LIBRARY

another dancer who walks before him wearing a trail of croton leaves. On the nearby island of Ambryn are made gaily painted headdresses resembling plumed cocked hats and also rare wooden masks with trailing fibre surrounds.

Another island in the Vanuatu group is Pentecost, where a wooden mask is worn, carved with a rather long, oval, face, domed forehead and strongly curved nose, the whole blackened with soot and oil. These masks are only rarely found in collections today and some fakes have been made in the 1980s. They bear a resemblance to the only carved masks found further south, on the island of New Caledonia. These masks do not represent the horde of ancestors, however, but a specific mythical being, Pijeva, who leads the dance of the dead in the country underwater. He wears a wooden face mask above a costume of net and black feathers. New Caledonian masks are often collected with the costume of attached black feathers, which vary greatly in length; sometimes they come to just below the shoulders and sometimes they cover the whole torso of the masquerader. The masks of Pentecost, however, never seem to be collected with the costume attached.

Vanuatu, fibre
*Vegetable fibre is the material most often used for masks from the various islands of Vanuatu, and they are usually painted in bright colours; in this example (**left**) the colours may have worn off.*

New Ireland, wood, fibre, late nineteenth century
*A fine and unusual mask from New Ireland (**right**), this was collected at the end of the last century.*
Height: 10¼in (26cm)

ASIAN MASKS

The diversity of Asian cultures, religions and geography is borne out by the startling variety of masks illustrated in this chapter. These range from the fantastical intricacies of multi-coloured **Gurula** *bird masks from Sri Lanka to the stylized simplicity of white Noh masks from Japan.*

Asia is by far the largest and most populous continent in the world, so it is not surprising that it has a great variety and abundance of masks. Few societies have been entirely without them. However, as this book concentrates on masks that are available to collectors, it discusses only the following areas of production, mainly in south-east and east Asia: Indonesia; Sri Lanka; India and neighbouring countries; and finally Japan.

INDONESIA: SUMATRA AND BORNEO

The Republic of Indonesia consists of more than 13,000 islands (about half of which are inhabited) lying between the Indian and Pacific oceans. The islands stretch for more than 3,000 miles (4,800km) from the northern tip of Sumatra to Irian Jaya in the east, encompassing considerable climatic, geographical and cultural differences. Irian Jaya (the western part of New Guinea) is politically part of Indonesia, but culturally it belongs with Melanesia, and so is discussed in the Oceanic section of this book. Sumatra, Borneo and Java are the largest islands of Indonesia, and Bali—although small—is one of the most famous and beautiful.

Sumatra, the easternmost island of Indonesia, stretches some 1,200 miles (1,900km) from north to south across the equator. In the north of the island the Batak live in the area around Lake Toba, which gives its name to what is probably the oldest of the main groups who make up the Batak: the Toba, Karo, Pakpak, Simalungun, Angkola and Mandailing. The Toba live on Samosir island in the middle of the lake and on the shores to the west and south. The Batak were well known among their neighbours for their ferocity. Members of the community who violated religious laws might be eaten, and drinking the blood of a sacrificed prisoner of war was thought to be a way of strengthening one's *tondi* or soul.

The village is the principal political unit and is headed by a chief who is responsible for the most important religious ceremonies and for offerings to the ancestor spirits. Witchcraft was practised by the *datu*, or sorcerer, though in some instances this role might also be performed by the chief. The *datu* kept recipes for various powerful concoctions in a book of

Sri Lanka, wood
*Sanni masks were used to exorcise the spirits which cause disease. Each mask represents an ailment or deformity; this one (**above left**) may be deafness.*
Height: 7¾in (18.5cm)

Thailand, papier mâché
This mask would have been used in Khon *plays, which*
feature characters taken from the great Indian epics such
as the Ramayana.
Height: 22¼in (56.5cm)

folded bark, called *pustaka*. One such medicine, *puk-puk*, was used to activate the long staffs carved with figures used by the *datu*. It was made from a human heart or brain, usually that of a child kidnapped from an enemy village and forced to drink molten lead.

The most familiar mask of the Batak is that of the *sina*, a mythical beast whose head, carved with a tall crest and usually incised with scrolls, adorns houses, sarcophagi and the majority of small ritual objects. These masks were not carved to be worn, but masks were worn in ceremonies connected with the death of important men of a village. Masked dancers, accompanied by music, followed the coffin to the tomb. One such mask consists of a hornbill head attached to the top of a rattan frame, the dancer's head and body being covered with cloth. Costumes known as *hoda-hoda* were also worn and represent horses with naturalistically carved wooden heads. This tradition almost certainly derives from India, as must the similar dance with a two-dimensional horse popular today in Java. In former times the wearers of these masks were said to be sacrificed when they reached the place of burial, so that their spirits might accompany the deceased on his voyage to the next world. One or more slaves might also be sacrificed at the same time.

Among the Karo Batak, large masks of human form were worn by sorcerers at funerals. These are of helmet form, with pierced eyes and mouths and darkened faces. The mouths often have a broad grin, with carved teeth. On some fine and early examples, copper is applied to the forehead and nose and about the eyes and mouth, and horsehair is attached to the top of the head. The masked dancer would also hold a pair of wooden hands. Among the Simalungun Batak, the masks worn in funerary ceremonies are smaller and painted white, with embellishments in red and black. Goat- or horsehair is sometimes attached about the border and may also form a moustache or beard. Among the Toba Batak the human masks were placed in miniature houses built on the tomb, whereas among the Karo they were retained by the *datu* for use at ceremonies in the future.

Borneo is the third largest island in the world (after Greenland and New Guinea), but is thinly populated. Only the southern two thirds are under the political jurisdiction of Indonesia, the northern parts being made up of Sabah and Sarawak (both part of Malaysia) and the Sultanate of Brunei. The Dayaks are the longest-established inhabitants of the island and live inland in the rain forests, while more recent immigrants have settled along the coasts. The name Dayak actually means 'inlander' or 'uplander' and is generally used by writers today, and indeed by the Dayak themselves, to cover many different groups. Despite differences such as language and art, they have many similarities in their economic and religious life. For most Dayak groups, rice is the staple crop and many of their ceremonies are connected with the rice-growing season.

For the mask collector the Kayan and Kenyah related groups are perhaps the most notable. Highly distinctive masks, called *hudo*, are used during a dance feast held shortly after sowing time, to protect the young rice plants from evil influences (such as rodents) and to propitiate the rice spirits. These masks may represent humans or animals, including wild boar, birds, monkeys and crocodiles. The masks have bulging eyes and large ears resembling the wings of a butterfly. Ear ornaments are often suspended and horns inserted at the tip. Noses or beaks are usually long and pointed and the prominent mouth or snout is carved with teeth, sometimes large fangs. On some examples the lower jaw is articulated to be opened and closed by the wearer. When danced, the mask is surmounted by a woven rattan dome into which hornbill feathers are inserted, but this is usually missing in specimens brought back to the west. Painted bands, spots, and scrolls in red, white and black cover the entire surface. The scroll is a motif that occurs on

Dayak, Borneo, wood and rattan, late nineteenth century
*Used in dances to ensure crop fertility, this Dayak mask (**above**) is a typical example, with the painted scrolling ornament and the attached butterfly-like ears.*
Height: 14in (35.5cm)

almost all Kenyah and Kayan Dayak artefacts and is associated with the *aso*, usually described by writers as a mythical dog or dragon. Three other types of mask are typical among the Dayak of Long Segar in East Kalimantan. *Kitaq* are large painted masks of human form, with long elegant scrolls to each side; *hudoq taing* is a large wild boar mask; and *hudoq kibah* are hood masks, the faces being made of a panel of coloured beadwork with typical scrolling designs and with three copper caps in place of the eyes and mouth. They are worn by women, who sway their heads from side to side and move slowly.

Masks are used by the Dayak tribes of Sarawak in northern Borneo on various occasions. Those used in ceremonies connected with the harvest are less frightening and grotesque than those intended to represent demons. The masks from this area have smaller features than the *hudo* masks, nose and ears being of more naturalistic size. The surface is coloured with lime and soot, and hair, beards and moustaches

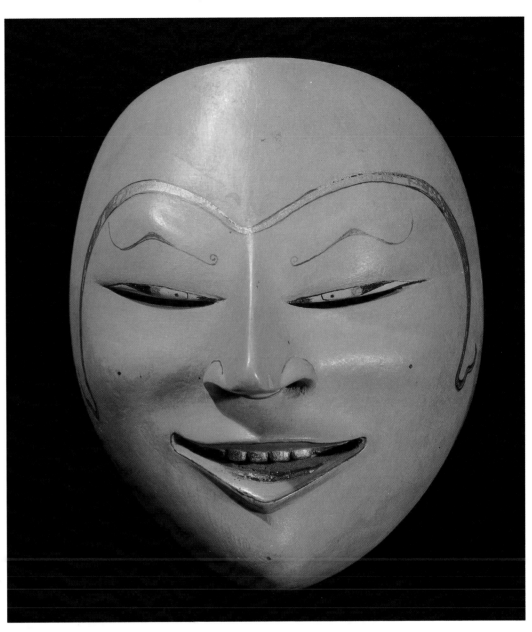

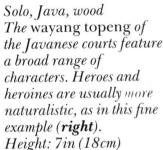

Solo, Java, wood
The wayang topeng *of the Javanese courts feature a broad range of characters. Heroes and heroines are usually more naturalistic, as in this fine example (**right**). Height: 7in (18cm)*

are sometimes applied with monkey- or horsehair or strands of sugar palm.

In southern Borneo, grotesque masks are worn by clowns in funeral ceremonies, called *tiwah*. Behind the masks the clowns have licence to perform various pranks. The masks have bulging eyes, long noses and large ears and the open mouths are carved with teeth and long fangs. They are painted white with embellishments in black and red.

BALI AND JAVA

The appearance and function of masks from Bali and Java are quite different from those of tribal peoples of Sumatra and Borneo and show strong influences from India. In Java, troups of professional actors attached to the court performed masked dance dramas, the stories being most frequently based on the great Indian epics the *Ramayana* and the *Mahabharata*. This form of dance theatre, called *wayang topeng*, almost certainly developed from the

puppet theatre, which is known to have existed as early as the eleventh century. The earliest type, *wayang kulit*, were shadow puppets made of perforated leather (*wayang* literally means 'shadow', and *kulit* 'leather'). Later forms were *wayang klitik*, flat wooden puppets, and *wayang golek*, three-dimensional puppets manipulated with rods. In the *wayang topeng*, dancers imitate the movements and speech of the puppets. A performance might contain 30 or even more masks representing different characters. The masks are small and light and are painted in various colours, which help to identify the character represented. Noble characters are refined in appearance, and vulgar ones are grotesque, with exaggerated features. Minor characters speak in the performance, but major ones do not, their lines being spoken by the *dalang* or producer. As long ago as the sixteenth century, however, the *wayang topeng* declined in popularity and was superseded by the *wayang orang*, in which the dancers are unmasked.

Tibet
This is one of several types of demonic masks worn in mystery plays called tsham *which were performed in Buddhist monasteries. The plays sometimes involved large numbers of characters and were therefore very costly to produce.*

One of the most popular masked dances in Bali features a battle between Barong and Rangda, symbolizing the struggle between good and evil. Barong personifies good, but is also a mischievous creature. In one of the most dramatic moments in the dance, Rangda, the evil witch, puts the supporters of Barong into a trance in which they try to stab themselves with their swords. Barong, with equally effective magic, prevents the weapons from harming them and they rush around madly attempting to stab themselves. Finally, good triumphs over evil. Both masks are fantastic and brightly painted with bulging eyes. Barong usually takes the form of a dragon, tiger, cow or boar, and Rangda usually has large fangs and a long, lolling tongue. Both have elaborate costumes to complement the masks; Rangda also has long nails with which she claws the air.

The Balinese *topeng* are chronicle plays of a more secular nature, dealing with amorous adventures, heroic deeds and court intrigues, in the lives of kings, noblemen and warriors. Actors wear small masks similar in style to the *wayang topeng* masks of Java.

SRI LANKA

The importance of the masking traditions of Sri Lanka (formerly Ceylon) is clearly indicated by the large number of fine examples to be found in western collections and museums today. Apart from masks used in processions and festivals, Sri Lanka is notable for two distinct groups of masks: those used in curative rituals called *tovil*; and those used in dance-dramas, such as the *kolam*. All are made of a light wood, usually kadura, which has to be seasoned for several weeks before it is carved.

The *sanni yakuma* is a night-long ceremony in which dancers wear *sanni* masks representing demon spirits responsible for causing disease. The ceremony is intended to exorcise the evil spirit responsible for a particular disease and thus restore the sufferer to health. Probably the most striking and certainly one of the largest of all south-east Asian masks is the *maha-kola-sanni-yaka*, the lord of the *sanni* masks. The large figure stands on a mask, holding the bodies of one or more victims in his hands and sometimes with another in the fangs of his large mouth. On each side is a panel of nine smaller masks, his assistants, each responsible for a particular disease or deformity, such as blindness, hallucinations, dumbness, rheumatism and boils. The group is flanked by cobras and further cobras issue from the top of the main mask's head. The quality of the carving and painting on old examples is extremely fine.

Kolam masks are of a more secular nature and are worn in ceremonial dance-dramas, especially in the southern and western coastal areas. There are more than 100 different characters, many having counterparts in the Indian folk masking tradition, from which they must have derived. These include *Gurula*, the local equivalent of Garuda, the mythical bird on which the Hindu god Vishnu rode. Among the various animal masks is the tiger (although the animal itself is not found in Sri Lanka). One of the most frequently encountered of *kolam* masks is the snake demon, *naga rassa*. This has large bulging eyes and wide-open mouth with painted teeth. The headdress is a large cobra and the separately carved ears are coiled cobras.

Kolam natima is said to have originated in the craving of a pregnant Indian queen to see a new kind of masked dance. While her despairing husband slept, Sara or Sakka (the local equivalent of the Hindu god Indra) arranged for masks to be carved. They were placed in the royal gardens, together with the book of the play, and the following morning they were discovered by a terrified gardener. The queen was delighted with the performance that followed.

Although there have been many changes in performance practice over the years, the play generally opens with a herald recounting the story of the pregnant queen. The herald introduces a pair of warriors (or sometimes a warrior and his wife), who enact a rumbustious scene. This always seems to have been a highly popular part of the performance, for warrior masks are among the most common and are found in many collections. The warriors are followed by a variety of human characters (government official, village headman, money-lender and so on), each wearing a small but distinctive face mask that reveals his identity. The king and queen wear the largest and tallest masks of all; they are so top-heavy that they have to move slowly to their seats, where they take no active part in the performance. There are also various animals and demons.

INDIA, THAILAND, TIBET AND NEPAL

The art of India has been an inspiration to Sri Lanka and many other neighbouring countries, but masks have played a comparatively small role in Indian culture and examples are fairly uncommon in western collections and museums. They are found mainly in folk traditions, rather than directly in the service of the great religions. The *Chau* dance festival of Bihar in northern India, for example, has close similarities to the *kolam* dramas of Sri Lanka. It is held in the spring in honour of Nata Bhairaba, an aspect of Shiva (or Siva), the Hindu god who was Lord of the Dance. The themes may be secular, religious or mythical, but all symbolize the victory of good over evil. The masks used were originally made of wood but today they are usually of papier mâché.

Masks produced by tribal groups in India are usually simple and dramatic, having more in common with the masks of Africa than those of the rest of India. Those made by the Bhuiyas of Orissa in north-east India, for example, are intended for divination before the annual hunt, while those made by the Khonds (or Konds), who live in the same state, are connected with their former practice of human sacrifice. The masks of the Muria of the Madhya Pradesh region of central India are worn by young boys acting out short themes from daily life, while the Gonds, who also live in Madhya Pradesh and neighbouring provinces, wear masks for dancing during weddings.

Indian influence on the art of far-eastern countries spread with Buddhism and Hinduism. In Thailand, theatrical performances include themes from the great Indian epics such as the *Ramayana*. The masks often have tall elaborate gilt headdresses. In Tibet, Lamaism (a form of Buddhism) uses masks in mystery plays, *tsham*, held in the monasteries. These may have developed from ancient fertility exorcism rites, and themes include the Dance of a Hundred Gods (performed only in the largest monasteries in view of the cost of the masks and costumes), which recounts the birth of the Buddha and the introduction of Buddhism into Tibet. Out of context, and stripped of the attributes worn or held by the characters, these masks are often difficult to identify.

The mask of death is a type frequently encountered in the Buddhist temples of Tibet; it is not a result of a morbid fascination with death, but rather a celebration of the victory of religious teaching over death. The masks, carved as a human skull, often have a crown of smaller skulls at the top. Masks representing deities frequently have ferocious expressions and wide-open mouths with long teeth. Crowns of small skulls are common as is the 'third eye' at the centre of the forehead. A wide variety of material is used, including papier mâché, wood and hide.

In Nepal a number of tribal groups such as the Magar and Gurung used masks that have a thick black crusty patina; this results from the accumulation of

years of smoke from storage in the rafters of houses. Many are of simple and striking form, with rough, vigorous carving. Eyes and mouths are often simple circles or rectangles. Fur is frequently applied as hair, beard or moustache. Many tribal masking traditions have been gradually replaced by the spread of Hinduism and Buddhism.

JAPAN

Japan has a rich tradition of theatrical masks. They belong to three groups, the Gigaku, Bugaku and Noh (or No), which developed in that chronological order. They are made from lacquer and wood and are always painted, as much time being spent on decoration as on modelling. The *men-uchi* (carvers) were limited in the way they carved a particular mask type by *honmen* (the traditional prototype of a mask), and any deviation from this was considered an artistic failure. The use of colour also followed strict rules and was significant in identifying a character. More freedom could, however, be exercised when making masks representing demons and mythical creatures.

The earliest type of theatrical mask known in Japan is Gigaku ('skilled music'), said to have been introduced from China by a Korean migrant named Mimashi. Artists from Iran, Tibet, Manchuria, Korea, Indochina and Indonesia performed at the court of the T'ang dynasty (AD 618–906), and these diverse racial types were represented by Gigaku masks carved in a naturalistic style usually depicting a fixed emotion or state such as anger or drunkenness. Gigaku performances were comic or coarse skits, played among crowds near Buddhist temples or in open squares and accompanied by an orchestra of three main instruments: flute, drum and gong. Only 15 or so characters featured in Gigaku performances, including *Baramon*, an Indian Brahmin, *Kongo Rikishi*, protector of Buddhism (*rikishi* meaning 'mighty one' and *kongo* 'thunderbolt' or 'diamond'), *Suiko-o* and *Suiko-ju*, drunken revellers (either Central Asian or Iranian), *Taikofu*, a feeble tottering old man, and *Shishi*, the lion.

Gigaku waned in popularity in the ninth century and was superseded by Bugaku. Bugaku also featured a variety of racial types, but the masks have more stylized features and often ferocious expressions, though the dances were more subtle than those of Gigaku and used a more elaborate orchestra accompanied by singers. Performances were reserved for festivals, commemorations and religious ceremonies and were patronized by the Imperial court. Older masks covered all of the face and the back of the head, while later styles covered only the face. A characteristic of the Bugaku mask is the use of free-moving parts, which emphasize the rhythmn of the dance. The most elaborate of these articulated masks was *Genjoraku*, with movable eyes, nose, chin and cheeks.

Noh drama was an entirely Japanese invention, originating in about the fourteenth century, and it is still considered one of the purest and most distinctive expressions of the nation's culture. The masks are more subtle than earlier types, hiding only the face rather than the entire front of the head. Performances were originally mainly for the samurai class, with occasional benefit and gala shows for ordinary people. Noh drama is poetic, stylized, musical and extremely slow, its solemnity recalling a religious ceremony.

The principal actors wore magnificent heavily brocaded robes; masks therefore had to be bold to be in keeping with them, yet suble enough to convey the sensitive emotions required of the performers. They were made of light kiriri wood and painted with distemper, with a thin layer of lacquer on the inside. Human characters gradually developed into standard types, such as 'young woman' or 'old man'. Certain characteristics, such as a small variation in the arrangement of hair, enabled these to be divided into particular types favoured for individual roles. Ghosts, demons, spirits and gods also feature. All parts were played by men or boys. Those representing females, gods and demons were necessarily masked, but some male roles were performed without masks.

The finest Noh masks are among the most beautiful produced anywhere in the world, combining subtle stylization with delicate naturalism. Among the most popular and familiar is the 'young woman', representing the traditional Japanese ideal of beauty. She is depicted with long straight black hair parted in the centre, with carefully arranged strands framing the forehead. The face is whitened, with the eyebrows painted in black high on the forehead. Lips are reddened and teeth painted black. Masks representing old men have carefully painted or carved wrinkles; hair is often attached through holes carved at the top of the head and also for beard and moustache. Certain masks were used to represent one specific character who occurs in just one particular play. One such character is *Shojo* ('the Dancing Orang-utan'), a drunken youth, characterized by his red face, a result of too much sake. His lips are parted in a half-smile, the upper and lower teeth exposed, and he has a tousled fringe and dimples. The mask is small and earless and always worn with a long red wig.

Kyogen plays were performed as comic interludes during a Noh drama and were in stark contrast to the elegance of the main work. Colloquial language was used and fewer characters wore masks, which were much less subtle than Noh masks.

Unlike maskmakers from most parts of the world, some of the Japanese carvers signed their work and won renown for their skill. The Deme or Demme family, who flourished particularly in the seventeenth century, were perhaps the best known. Like other mask carvers, they supplemented their income by carving miniature masks as *netsuke*—small toggles used to attach various small pouches and containers to the belt of the traditional Japanese costume.

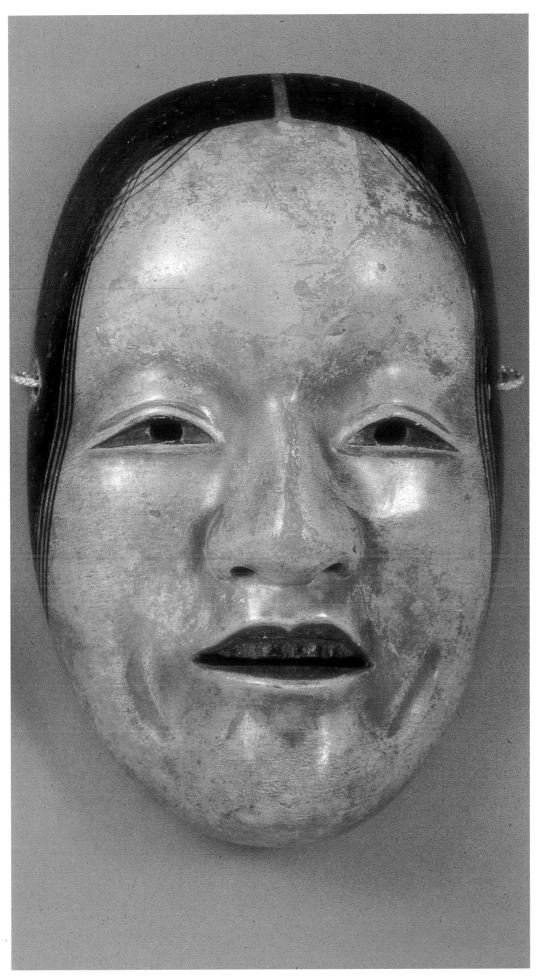

Japan, wood, nineteenth century
*This mask (**left**), used in the Noh plays, represents the ideal of a beautiful woman, Ko-Omote.*
Height: 8¹/₂in (21.6cm)

Japan, wood, eighteenth century
*Kyogen plays were performed as comic interludes to the Noh plays, and this mask (**above**) is in stark contrast to the one on the left. It represents a woman, Oto (also known as Okame), the most popular of Kyogen characters.*
Height: 7⁵/₈in (19.5cm)
Christie's London 1988, £1500

NEW WORLD MASKS

Masks from the Americas comprise an enormous range of styles. They are no less linked to ritual and superstition than are masks from Africa or Asia, and some, such as the famous transformation masks of the Kwakiutl, are among the most dazzling and sophisticated examples of tribal art from anywhere in the world.

The masking tradition in the Americas dates back very many centuries. Archaeological finds among the ruins of the ancient civilizations of South and Central America give some indication of the significance of masks in these societies. In North America, too, the tradition can be traced back to long before the first European contact in the sixteenth century.

NORTH AMERICA

Wooden masks from as early as AD 800 were found at the end of the nineteenth century on the west coast of Florida, and stone and clay funerary masks have been found in ancient sites in the southern Great Lakes area. Since the sixteenth century, four areas have been notable for mask production: the north-west coast, the east, the south-west and the Arctic.

THE NORTH-WEST

The masks of the north-west coast are carved in a large variety of shapes and forms and painted in startling colours. The principal tribes in the area, the Tlingit, Tsimshian, Haida, Bella Bella, Bella Coola, Kwakiutl and Nootka, live along the 1,000-mile (1,600km) stretch of coastline from the Columbia

River in Washington State to Yakutat Bay in Alaska. This is a rocky coastline of endless bays and inlets with a multitude of small islands; wooded slopes come down to stony shores, appearing and disappearing through the mists that usually shroud the coast. A skein of larger islands lies parallel to the coast. The rainfall in the area is the highest in the world, but warm currents mean an ice-free zone far further north and for a much longer time than for the same latitude on the east coast. Although they speak different languages, the tribes of the region share a common culture and masks made in widely separated communities may share distinctive characteristics, such as

Tlingit, wood, mid-nineteenth century
*This shaman's mask (**above left**) is essentially human; it has bear-like ears, however, and a pierced mouth.*
Height: 10⅝in (27cm)

Tlingit, wood, fibre and feathers
*This mask (**right**) has a headband inset with feathers and hair; others might have been decorated with inset seal whiskers or plaited cedar bark.*
Height: 11in (28cm) Christie's London 1976, £16,000

asymmetrical painted designs representing the stylized features of spirits. However, as a generalization, the masks from the northern groups tend to be smaller and more naturalistic, while those of the southern tribes tend to be larger, very fantastical and brightly coloured, with a predominance of red, white and blue.

Among the naturalistic masks from the north, most notably those of the Haida, many seem to be portraits and are carved with such features as moustaches, wrinkles and pierced ears. Some are shown wearing oval lip-plugs, to represent women of high rank; others, notably from the third quarter of the nineteenth century, are clearly intended to represent Europeans, with the fashionable hairstyles and beards of the time. Many of the masks have elaborate contraptions to open and close the eyes and mouth, and among the southern tribes such sophistication was taken to extremes in the transformation masks of the Kwakiutl. In these a mask opens to reveal yet another mask inside, transforming the dancer into another spirit.

Many North American Indians lead a nomadic existence, following herds of buffalo across the plains, but the tribes of the north-west coast spend most of their time fishing. They preserve their abundant catch by smoking, drying and processing for oil, providing food for the long winter days. As a result, there is little subsistence work to be done during the winter months, which can therefore be devoted to leisure activities. This has led to the development of a sophisticated ceremonial tradition centred around the famous potlach feasts. These occasions were used by the host to assert his social status and involved lavish hospitality and festivities, including dancing.

Tribes were divided into clans and moieties (literally 'halves') named after a real or mythological ancestor. Tlingit society, for example, was divided into two moieties, the Raven and the Eagle (or further south the Wolf). Each clan owned a number of animal crests, personal names, songs and dances. A great variety of animals, fish and birds were adopted as crests. Those not playing an important part in the economy were more common; among the Tlingit they included the raven, hawk, brown bear, killer whale, otter, mouse, frog, and even wood-worm. The right to wear such crests, and ancestral rights to dances, territories and other privileges, were witnessed when a chief held a potlach and distributed these valuables to his heirs and friends.

Among the Kwakiutl in the south, the winter season of ceremonies was known as *Tsetseka,* and the principal dance, the *Hamatsa,* formed part of a ritual that lasted for at least four days. Initiates possessed by the spirit Bakbakwalanooksiwae (Cannibal-at-the-North-End-of-the-World) were inspired with the desire to eat human flesh. They were abducted and taken into the woods, where they were taught the ways of the group and were later returned to the village as fully-fledged members of the society. In their absence, dancers rep-

Kwakiutl, wood and feathers
Kwakiutl masks are the most dramatic and largest of the Northwest coast masks. In this transformation mask the mythical raven opens to reveal one of its descendents of human form.

resenting mythical creatures associated with this spirit appeared from behind painted screens and danced about an open fire. When Dzoonokwa, the terrifying giant of Kwakiutl mythology, leapt from behind the screen making a fearsome sound, a chill would go through the audience.

Other masks are the Thunderbird, who caused thunder by the beat of his wings, and bird monsters who lived on human flesh. The spectacular bird monster masks measured up to 8ft (2.4m) in length and it would have required considerable strength and skill to operate the pulleys that caused the beaks to snap shut in time to the songs accompanying the dances. Other dancers included the fool dancer, Noolmhal, whose tasks included keeping the spec-

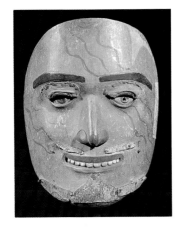

Tongass, Southern Tlingit, wood
*The eyelids on this mask (**above**) could be articulated by the wearer pulling a short stick.*
Length: 9in (23cm)
Christie's London 1976, £36,000

Tongass, Southern Tlingit, wood and hide
*This mask (**below**) has an articulated jaw. Along with the example above it was collected by W. E. Gordon, R.N., in 1851–4.*
Height: 10in (25.5cm)
Christie's London 1976, £20,000

tators under control and possibly supplying human flesh for the bird monsters. It is not known whether actual cannibalism at one time formed part of these rituals; certainly by the end of the nineteenth century it was no longer practised.

The Rockies to the east of the coastal region are too snow-bound in winter to support permanent settlement and the tribes of the Great Plains do not wear masks, although some have elaborate headdresses. It is on the other side of the Great Lakes that masquerading communities are once more encountered.

THE EAST

The masks of the False Face Society were first recorded in 1687, when the first Europeans visited the lower Great Lakes area, but there is no evidence to indicate how long the society had existed before then. The society was at that time, and still is, found among the five main tribes of the Iroquois nation: the Mohawk, Oneida, Onandaga, Cayuga and Seneca. Its main purpose was the prevention and cure of diseases, achieved through both public and private ceremonies. An Iro-

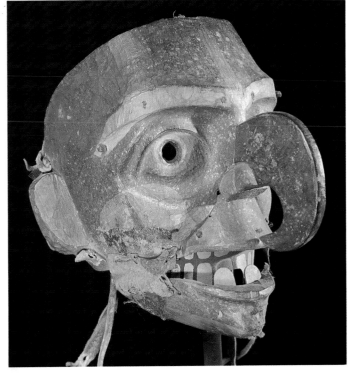

quois legend tells of the contest between the Creator of the World and the first False Face spirit to decide who should rule the world. The Creator agreed to acknowledge the superiority of the False Face if he could command a mountain to come to them. The False Face shook his rattle and commanded the mountain, but it came only part of the way. The Creator then summoned the mountain; it approached from behind False Face, who turned around impatiently just as the mountain came near, striking him in the face. It broke his nose and caused him to twist his mouth in pain. In consequence of losing the contest, False Face was charged by the Creator with the task of driving out disease from the earth. The first False Face, also known as the Great Doctor, then gave the power of healing the sick to humans if they agreed to carve masks ('false faces') in his image and make offerings to him of tobacco and corn mush.

Masks representing the Great Doctor are fairly easy to distinguish and occur among all five main tribes of the Iroquois nation. There are several other lesser spirits, that are more difficult to identify, notably the Common Faces. These are beings thought to live in the forests; they are sometimes described as being deformed, with crippled legs or hunched backs, or even as having no bodies or limbs but only faces.

A person might decide to join the False Face Society to find a cure for an illness or after a dream of impending sickness. The candidate would then be expected to give a feast (and would thereafter be required to do so annually) and would need to acquire a mask. He could inherit one, could carve it himself, commission someone to carve it for him or borrow one, and his dream might indicate which of these options he was to adopt. The mask might then be carved to represent the image in his dream or it might be interpreted for him by a seer and then carved. Such a system led to a considerable diversity in appearance and makes the identification and interpretation of some masks very difficult.

To carve a mask, a tree (usually basswood) was selected in the forest and offerings of tobacco were lit at the base. The mask was roughed out while still on the tree and the block would then be removed and taken home by the carver to be finished at leisure. Today, masks might be simply carved from an available block of wood, but in earlier times it was considered important to remove the block of wood from the tree without causing the tree to die; it was no doubt thought that the continued existence of the tree added to the potency of the mask. The mask was painted red if work on the carving began in the morning and black if carving began in the afternoon. This symbolism refers to the belief that the Great Doctor lives on the rim of the world and follows the path of the sun. Horsehair was attached and metal rings have frequently been applied about the eyes, perhaps to enhance the effect of the mask when danced around a fire. The initiate and his mask would then take part in the ceremony, in which prayers were recited and offerings of tobacco were burned. Tiny bags of tobacco were also hung from the mask and the mask was then invested with the power to cure.

Public ceremonies were held in the spring and autumn to wipe out disease in the community. Members of the society, wearing masks and carrying turtle-shell rattles, would visit each house in turn, shouting and chasing out disease. After this they would proceed to the longhouse, where they banged their rattles on the door and crawled in towards a fire in the centre. After speeches honouring the spirits and offerings of tobacco, the sick came forward and were treated with ashes blown onto their heads and rubbed into their hair. Payment was made in the form of tobacco and corn mush. For a similar payment a private treatment could be made at a patient's house. Only certain ailments could be cured, however: those of the head, shoulders and joints. False Faces are particularly concerned with nosebleed, earache, toothache, sore eyes, facial paralysis and facial swelling. They were sometimes assisted in these rituals by an associated society known as the Husk Faces, believed to be a more recent development. Members wore masks, slightly smaller than those of the False Face Society, made of coils of braided or twined husks. They were made by women but worn only by men. Miniature False Face masks were also made as charms for protection against sickness or witchcraft.

The False Face mask itself is considered an object of remarkable power and has to be treated with great care. Offerings of tobacco must be made regularly and the mask must be stored face down, with the rattle placed in the hollow at the back, together with a package of tobacco. According to the Seneca, an upward facing mask is a sign of disrespect and is associated with death. If hung on a wall for storage, a mask must either face the wall or remain covered. On the death of the owner, a mask might be buried with the owner, given to another member of the society, or sold. If sold, an offering of tobacco is made and the mask is told it is leaving and is instructed not to cause harm either to the new owner or to the old one. There are tales of masks coming back to haunt their former owners, and Iroquois believe that a fire in the New York State Museum in 1911 was the result of the museum's failure to give tobacco to the masks while they were in their care.

THE SOUTH-WEST

The third principal area of mask production in North America is in the south-west, in the states of Arizona and New Mexico. The Indians of the Rio Grande area are known as Pueblos, a name also given to the permanent villages of mud buildings in which they live. They are farmers, dependent on crops of corn, beans and squash. For communities of farmers living in such an

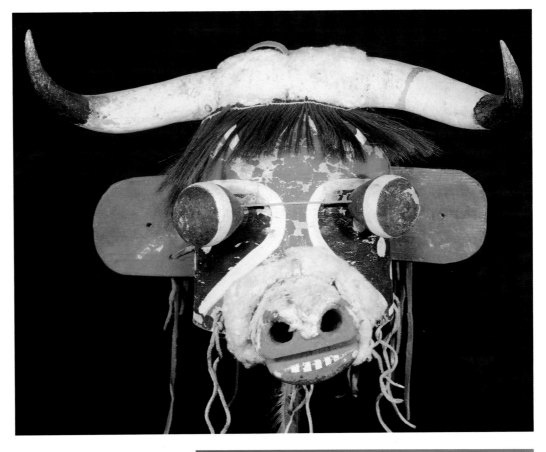

Iroquois, wood, metal and hair
The masks of the False Face Society are usually realistic: the extensive wrinkles on this example (**above**) are typical. The metal about the eyes would add to the dramatic effect when danced about a fire.

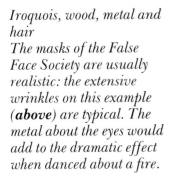

Pueblo, wood, hair, hide and horns
An unusual type of Pueblo mask, this bull (**above right**) is made of wood and is particularly naturalistic. Kachina masks were worn in ceremonies to mark various stages of the agricultural year.

Kwakiutl, wood, nineteenth century
Hamatsa *masks such as this (**right**) were used by the Kwakiutl during the winter season of ceremonies. Cords enable the wearer to move the eyes and beak.*
Length: 11½in (29cm)

arid climate, the main rituals are associated with water and crop fertility.

The Pueblo Indians believe that the natural phenomena of this world have a spiritual counterpart, or *kachina,* and the cult associated with these spirits encompasses the whole Pueblo community. The most familiar representation of *kachinas* are the wooden dolls that were traditionally carved by the men and given as gifts to children and women, particularly to girls of marriageable age. Dances form an important part of the rituals associated with the *kachina* cult; the masked dancers do not simply impersonate the *kachinas,* but embody them. Among the Hopi there are five major ceremonies during the *kachina* season, beginning with the winter solstice ceremony in December. The bean ceremony follows in February to mark the start of the growing season, which is also the time for initiation of children into the cult. At the end of February or the beginning of March is the Water

Serpent ceremony, and the cycle is completed at the close of the season by the Home Dance ceremony in July. It is so named because it is the last occasion on which the *kachinas* make their appearance before they return to what the Hopi believe to be their homes on the San Francisco peaks. Other ceremonies are held after July, but *kachina* dances do not form a part of the proceedings. Some ceremonies are held in secret in *kivas* or underground chambers, while others, including a number of one-day ceremonies, are held wholly or partly in public, in the plazas or village squares.

The masks worn by the dancers are constructed of hide. The most common type is composed of a cylinder made from two pieces of hide with a circular top. Ears, noses, snouts, horns and feather headdresses can then be attached to this base. Although the basic shape is simple, the vibrant painted decoration makes the Pueblo masks extremely striking. A simple painted motif, such as a hand or claw, may indicate

Inuit, Alaska, wood, cane
The masking tradition of
the Inuit may not date back
before the first European
contact. This mask (right)
is typical of examples from
Alaska, which are usually
small and often highly
elaborate with various
limbs and other items
about the border.
Height: 10¼in (26cm)

Iroquois, fibre, twentieth
century
Corn husk masks such as
this (above) were worn by
dancers who assisted the
False Faces. They were
probably a later
development.
Height: 13¾in (35cm)

the *kachina* represented, and the bold colours in which it is painted are symbolic. They are said to indicate the direction from which a *kachina* comes: yellow indicates north or north-west; blue or green, west or south-west; red, south or south-east; white, east or north-east; black indicates a downward direction. Because the basic construction of the masks was the same, a mask could be adapted for use on a subsequent occasion by adjustment of the appendages and by applying a further coat of paint. In addition to this most common type of mask, there are also half-masks, covering the upper part of the head with feathers and hair below, and circular masks.

THE ARCTIC

Sophisticated masking traditions exist among the Eskimos of the Arctic region, which stretches from the Bering Sea in the west to Greenland in the east, through Alaska and the islands of northern Canada. The climate in the north of this region is certainly inhospitable, but the Eskimos (or Inuit as they call themselves, preferring their term, meaning 'real people', to the derogatory 'Eskimo', meaning 'meat eaters') have adapted well to the environment. It provides an abundance of food, including seals, whales, walrus and various inland mammals (principally caribou), as well as fish. As on the north-west coast, the practice of preserving food in the summer for the winter months has provided much leisure time in winter for the development of an artistic tradition. This finds its greatest expression in the extraordinary masks of the area. Ivory burial masks were made by the Eskimos perhaps as long as 2,000 years ago (some superb examples have been excavated), but their tradition of masks for dancing does not seem to be of great antiquity. Excavations at many pre-historic sites have yielded great numbers of wooden artefacts but have failed to unearth more than a few masks or fragments of masks. This may be in part because of the practice of destroying masks after a ritual, but as almost all the masks now in existence date from the nineteenth and twentieth centuries, it seems likely that the tradition developed, or expanded, after contact with Europeans.

Eskimo dancing masks were usually made by, or for, shamans, the men who provide the community's link with the spirit world. They were danced in winter ceremonies such as the Messenger Feast and Bladder Festival, intended to appease the spirits of the animals hunted for food and ensure continued success in the hunt. The masks represent spirits of the animals that play such an important role in the life of the Eskimo, and sometimes spirits associated with natural phenomena, such as the sun and the moon, or even spirits of places or ancient objects. They are not based on naturalistic physical appearance, but on images seen by the shaman on his visits to the spirit world. The mask would therefore inspire awe and wonder in the spectator at the ability of the shaman to communicate with another world, to which only he has access.

The most remarkable and fantastic of these masks are from the Bering Sea area. They are basically two-dimensional in form and almost all are painted, the most common colours being white, black, red and blue. Many are surrounded by willow bands that support a variety of appendages and pendants of wood, feathers and caribou fur. Composite masks also exist (though they are less elaborate than those of the northwest coast), an outer mask opening to reveal the soul of the animal spirit inside, or a human mask inside that of an animal, thus emphasizing the close link between the animal and human worlds. The dance was accompanied by singing and the beat of a drum and the lively movements of the masked male dancers contrasted with the graceful swaying of the women, who sometimes formed a chorus. The women also wore small finger masks—discs of wood with two holes to one side for the insertion of fingers, adorned with feathers and painted decoration.

SOUTH AMERICA

The dense rain forests of the Amazon are populated by a large number of different tribes. Travel in the area is difficult and dangerous, either overland or by boat, along the vast network of rivers and tributaries. Communications are consequently limited between the

Upper Xingu River, Brazil, wood, fibre, feathers, late nineteenth century
Masks from the area of the upper Xingu River are characterized by their rectangular form and the painted geometric decoration. Height: 25¼in (64cm)

various tribes, many of which, as a result, retain a highly distinctive artistic style. There is a vast array of different mask types, only a few of which can be mentioned here. The recent concern in the West about the plight of many of these peoples—in the wake of the destruction of their environment for cattle ranching and the search for minerals—has come too late to save many of them from extinction and one can only hazard an educated guess at the function of some of the masks they have left.

Among the Indians of the area of north-west Brazil and eastern Columbia—those of the Arawak and Tucano groups—large masks of barkcloth are made for use in mourning rites. After a death, all the deceased kinsmen are instructed by the headman to make a mask, and the elaborate preparations for the rites can take up to six months to complete. The masks are of conical form, coming down to the chest, with cylindrical projections for the arms and with a fibre fringe below. Eyeholes are not required, as the beaten fibrous material is sufficiently thin to allow the dancer to see through. The masks are painted with a variety of bold geometric designs in black and shades of brown; lozenges and triangles are particularly favoured, and facial features are sometimes painted. Tucano mourning ceremonies are said to have a threefold function. First, they provide the occasion for the expression of grief by kinsmen of the departed; second, they allow grief to be assuaged by the consoling presence of ancestors and other beings, including forest monsters, fish, insects, animals and birds; and third, they drive the ghost of the deceased from the house.

Several different types of mask are made by the tribes of the Upper Xingu River in central Brazil. Among them are flat oval straw masks and flat rectangular wooden masks carved with a simple nose and projecting forehead, often with a fibre beard below. As with the Tucano fibre masks, geometric ornament is popular and similar designs of triangles and lozenges are employed. To the north of these tribes, the Caraja make tall cylindrical headdresses for use in cults connected with the head and with supernaturals. The masks are worn with long fibre fringes to cover the head and body and are decorated with designs in variously coloured feathers. They are cults for men only, and any woman intruding upon their secrets is said to be subjected to gang rape. For the Tapirape, further north, agriculture is important and various ceremonies are held to ensure fertility of the crops. In the Banana Festival, however, large semi-circular wooden masks covered with designs in brightly coloured feathers are worn in pairs and represent the souls of enemies killed in battle.

CENTRAL AMERICA

Several Mexican masks survive from before the time of European contact, but as the majority are made of stone, it seems unlikely that they were intended for use in masquerades. This does not, however, indicate that masks were not worn in ancient Central America; in fact the only object of perishable material to have survived from the Olmec culture of central Mexico is a wooden mask (now in the Museum of Natural History, New York). The mask was found in a cave south of Taxco in Guerrero state, where it may have lain for more than 2,000 years. Its size, and the fact that there are pierced holes on the border, indicate that it was almost certainly intended to be worn. As with Olmec masks in stone, it displays a typical blend of jaguar and human features, the mouth and eyes turning down at the corners. The remains of a jade mosaic about the mouth may be a later addition. Stone masks also survive from later cultures, such as that of Teotihuacan, though their function remains obscure. Like Olmec stone masks, many are pierced, possibly for suspension as pendants, or for use in burials, perhaps for attachment to mummy bundles.

The Aztecs encountered by the Spanish *conquistadores* in the early sixteenth century also produced stone masks, which are said to have been placed over the faces of the dead. Perhaps the most striking are those depicting the creator god, Xipe Totec, god of spring and fertility. Priests of his cult would dress themselves

Teotihuacan, Mexico, stone, 100BC–AD600
*Many stone masks such as this one (**above**) survive from Mexico's ancient past. However, there are no accurate tests for dating and experts often disagree over the authenticity of particular examples.*

Cubeo, Brazil, barkcloth, cane, twentieth century
*Large conical masks such as this (**right**) are made by various groups of Indians of north-western Brazil and eastern Columbia for use during mourning rites. The mask covers the head and upper part of the body, with the fibre fringe extending below.*

in the skins of flayed sacrificial victims, and the god is depicted dressed in this way, with eyes closed and mouth hanging open. For the collector, such stone masks present considerable problems of authenticity. There are no scientific tests to establish even the approximate period when a mask was carved, and many of those that appear on the market today are of relatively recent origin. Experts frequently disagree about the authenticity of a mask, as there is often no more than stylistic evidence on which to make a judgement about the possible date.

The most remarkable of Aztec masks, and perhaps the most familiar, are made of mosaic. Turquoise is the most common material, although other stones, such as jade, obsidian, quartz and malachite, are also used. The mosaic technique was used on various Aztec ceremonial objects, but few survive today because of the fragile nature of their construction, the small tesserae usually being fixed with vegetable glue to a wooden base. Most of them were broght back to Europe at the time of, or shortly after, the conquest and are now in museums.

Mexico, wood, twentieth century
*There are a large number of festivals in Mexico today in which masks such as these two (**above**) are worn. Most coincide with dates in the Christian calendar, although their religious nature is far from obvious.*

EUROPEAN MASKS

Europe possesses a number of fascinating masquerade traditions performed in a variety of contexts. Some of them are influenced by cultures from other areas of the world, and many of the masquerades are pagan in origin; over the centuries, however, they have been accommodated within a broadly Christian framework.

Europe possesses a rich and varied mask-making heritage. Since Ancient Greece, professional actors have made use of masks, and in one of the continent's most famous theatrical traditions, the Italian *Commedia dell' arte*, masked performers played a central role. Masks are also found among peasant communities and are still worn to celebrate a wide range of festivals, many of which have ancient origins. The rural and urban masquerades did not invariably develop in isolation from one another and influences and counter-influences are readily detectable.

The earliest evidence of the use of masks in Europe comes from the cave of Trois Frères, in southern France, which is decorated with painted and 'engraved' images dating from about 15,000-8,000 BC. The cave walls are filled with overlapping depictions of bison, stags, reindeer, horses and ibex, in the midst of which are scattered human figures. These are thought to be ritual dancers, performing perhaps a sacred rite associated with hunting, and some are shown masked with animal heads. The most striking feature of the cave, however, is a painting, with engraved outlines, which shows a man wearing the head and antlers of a stag. Although the significance of this image remains unknown, archaeologists have speculated that it may

represent a kind of powerful shaman or perhaps a supreme deity.

A direct link cannot be drawn between the rituals of Stone Age hunters in France and the customs of contemporary rural populations, but it is interesting that animal, or half-animal, characters still play an important part in numerous masquerades.

Horns and fur are worn by masked dancers in many European regions, and 'hairiness' has long been popularly associated with the non-human worlds of animals and spirits. Many of these folk festivals have pagan origins, although they have adopted Christian elements and have been incorporated into the Church's calendar.

Bavaria, Germany, wood, fibre, late eighteenth century
*Hairy characters are included in many European masquerades. This mask (**above left**) has long hair, bushy eyebrows and a flowing beard and moustache.*

Tyrol, Austria, painted wood, c. 1900
Noisy parades of masked characters are traditionally found in many Alpine regions. This Hutler *mask (**right**) has much in common with the masks worn during the* Schemenlaufen *festivals.*

BRITAIN

Some of the finest examples of animal masquerades are found in Britain. One of the best known of these is the 'horn dance' of Abbots Bromley in Stafford-shire, which traditionally takes place on the first or second Monday in September. Six dancers take part in the celebration, each one carrying a pair of antlers attached to a wooden deer's head mounted on a pole. They are accompanied by several other characters, including a simple hobby-horse with a small head and snapping jaws.

Although the British 'horn dance' is rare, the hobby-horse, of which there are several varieties, is quite widely distributed. Hobby-horses may be accompanied by other performers, such as Morris dancers or, as used to be the case in Land's End in Cornwall, by 'guisers' masked and draped with bullock hides. The horse's head is often made from

Bavaria, Germany, painted wood
A pair of masks representing a man and a woman. The idealized couple have a sense of perfection lent to them by the wholly painted features. Such masks were also used in boisterous Schemenlaufen *festivals.*

inexpensive and readily available materials, and the carrier is usually concealed by a hanging cloth. In Bwca Lwyd in Wales the hobby-horse used to comprise a painted canvas head stuffed with straw and mounted on a hay fork. Leather fastened to the prongs served as ears. A horse's skull set on top of a pole was used in some places, whereas in Thanet in Kent the head is traditionally carved from a single block of wood and is painted. By tugging on a leather lace, the carrier of the Kentish *hoden* horse can bang open and shut the hinged jaws.

Switzerland, painted wood, various materials, c. 1900
This festival mask was probably made in Basel. It is
distinguished by its elaborate headdress decorated with
ostrich feathers and artificial flowers.

Switzerland, painted wood, cloth, c. 1900
In Alpine regions, festivals are held in midwinter to
celebrate the victory of 'young' spring over 'old' winter.
This mask represents an old woman.

The Minehead hobby-horse in Somerset custom-arily appears between 30 April and 3 May. It has a fearsome tin mask, partly covered with a ribbon bonnet, which is hung from a boat-shaped frame. A hoop 6ft (1.8m) in diameter is used on the Padstow (Cornwall) hobby-horse to support a long and fringed black tarpaulin. This May Day *Oss* has a small wooden head with snapping jaws and a fringe of hair. The letters O.B. appear on the conical hat worn by the horse and these are thought to represent either the initials of a long-dead resident of Padstow or an abbreviation of 'hobby-horse'.

The ghost-like *Mari Lwyd* of Glamorganshire and Carmarthenshire in Wales, a well-known Christmas visitor, contrasts markedly with other brightly colour-ed hobby-horses. Folklorists have likened the Welsh hobby-horse (*Y Mari Lwyd* probably means 'the grey mare') to the Irish horse of the feast of Samain. In parts of County Cork this ancient Celtic festival is traditionally marked by processions led by a white-robed man bearing the semblance of a horse's head. Samain, which is celebrated around 1 November, marks the end of the summer.

Aside from the hobby-horse, a variety of masked characters features in British folk festivals, especially those associated with the agricultural cycle. The Scot-tish *Bury Man* of West Lothian, who appears in August, wears a hat planted with 70 red roses and one red dahlia. His face is concealed by a back-to-front bala-clava hat, furnished with eyeholes, and is covered with sticky burrs from the burdock plant. A man cov-ered from head to foot in twisted straw braids tradi-tionally walks through the streets of Whitby (Yorkshire) on the Saturday before Plough Monday (the first Monday after the Christmas holidays). Straw charac-ters are also known in the Irish countryside, where young men, dressed in women's garments, used to wear cone-shaped festival masks made of straw.

AUSTRIA

Many other European peoples mark seasonal changes with celebrations involving masked performers. One of the best known of these masquerades takes place every three years, before the beginning of Lent, in the town of Imst in the Austrian Alps. Known as *Schemenlaufen* (*scheme* is an archaic word for 'mask' and *laufen* means 'to run'), this festival symbolizes the struggle between winter and spring for the domi-nation of nature. Only men may take part in this masquerade, which is held to frighten away the accumulated spirits and to ensure prosperity and a bountiful harvest in the coming year. The fearsome

masks and jangling bells worn by the participants, who follow a winding course through the town, are thought to put the evil demons to flight. The masks are carved in wood and the male ones can be distinguished by their beards, the female ones having smooth pink faces. Huge headdresses, decorated with braids and baubles, are also worn by the good characters. The runners are accompanied by witches, whose masks have goggle eyes and fang-like teeth. Their facial hair is made with either pigs' bristles or feathers. There is also a sorcerer, who wears a mask with a goatee beard and carries a magic sceptre, as well as a *Sackner* who throws handfuls of corn from his sack at the feet of the spectators. The onlookers may also be squirted with water from a syringe carried by a masked figure known as a *Spritzer*. The *Schemenlaufen* festival was once more widely distributed than it is today. For example, similar masked figures used to accompany the Nuremberg butchers' guild, a practice that was discontinued in 1539.

Rowdy processions are also held on Twelfth Night, which is associated with the pre-Christian deity Perchta, the custodian of the dead. According to German mythology, Perchta and her followers rush through the night, sometimes perpetrating good deeds, and sometimes bad. Their impersonators wear exotic horned and hairy masks, which are intended to frighten naughty children and to ensure the fertility of the crops. In Salzburg these masqueraders used to enact a ritual battle between the good characters, distinguished by their beautiful visages and ornate headdresses, and the evil ones, dressed in unkempt masks. Similar shaggy figures are known throughout the Bavarian, Swiss and Austrian Alps, but without the element of combat.

EASTERN EUROPE AND THE BALKANS

Lively festivals, involving parades of hideously masked characters blowing on horns, are encountered in Hungary. In Fejér, for example, cloth masks with straggling beards and eyebrows are worn under battered felt hats decorated with ribbons. Carved and painted female masks, which have much in common with those of neighbouring Austria, are also worn.

The tradition of holding noisy mid-winter festivals continues in Romania, especially in the northern county of Maramureş. Shaggy devil headdresses with horns are worn by the participants, as well as disguises incorporating other features such as Second World War gas masks. Masks representing 'old men' are known on both the Transylvanian and Moldavian sides of the Carpathian mountains. Made of hessian, these masks are furnished with seed teeth and hemp fibre beards. The Romanian hobby-horse, *caluşar*, which is associated with All Souls' Night, also performs during the mid-winter festivals. Characters representing a fool and a 'man-woman' accompany the hobby-horse, as does a troupe of dancers who

engage in a ritual battle.

Turon, another festival which includes a hobby-horse, is observed by Polish peasants. It takes place in the period following Christmas and is thought to have its origins in the veneration of the Slavic winter god, Radegast. The festival is named after *Turon*, a fabulous creature from Polish mythology. *Turon*'s head is usually carved from a single block of wood, to which a hinged jaw is attached. The head may be painted with bright colours and the ears are sometimes studded with nails. As is the case with other hobby-horses, the mask is supported on a pole and the carrier is shrouded with a cloth. *Turon* is the most popular of the animal disguises assumed by the revellers as they go from house to house singing carols and receiving refreshments. Other masks worn by villagers include representations of bears, wolves and goats.

In common with other Slavic peoples, the Bulgarians make masks resembling animals such as bears, foxes, wolves, birds and other fantastic creatures. These masks are worn during New Year festivities, especially in the west of the country. Of particular significance in Bulgaria are the agrarian rituals, which are thought to have roots in ancient Thrace. Held on the first Sunday before Lent (that is, at the beginning of the new agricultural year), these celebrations involve large groups of

Hungary, gourd, early twentieth century
*Parades of devils are traditionally held in rural regions of Hungary. This painted mask (**left**) was probably made for a child.*

Romania, dried calabash
*Inexpensive materials are often used to make masks in rural areas. This mask (**above**) has large teeth made from beans. The expression is both comic and sinister and the mask has much in common with clown-devil masks from other areas of Europe.*

Northern Transylvania, Romania, wool, cloth, beans
*This pair of typical Maramureş masks (**right**) represent grotesque devils. The masks are thought to frighten away the evil spirits of winter.*

Switzerland, painted wood, c. 1900
*Masks representing animals are worn in the high Alpine regions of Switzerland. This pig mask (**above**) comes from the mountainous canton of Graubündan.*

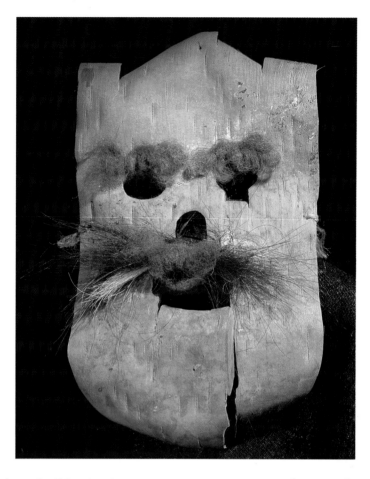

Sweden, painted wood, fibre
*Although European masqueraders often perform plays that have Christian elements, the masking tradition dates back to pagan festivals. This mask (**left**) represents Judas Iscariot.*

Bern, Switzerland, c. 1960
*This large mask (**right**) belongs to the comic European masquerade tradition. It has a helmet which is too small, and a foolish grin. In mock-heroic fashion, a knife is held between the oversized teeth.*

men dressed as both domestic and wild animals. During the festival the men jump, so that the wheat will grow tall and make a great deal of noise, to scare away the old year and its evil forces. Many of the cloth masks have moustaches and beards made from scraps of fur, feathers and hemp fibres. They may also be embellished with swirling lines of small metal discs. Some of the performers, wearing horned sheepskin masks representing oxen, are harnessed to wooden ploughs.

The Greeks traditionally mark the beginning of the new agricultural year with rituals that resemble those of Bulgaria and other Balkan neighbours. A *kalogheroi* dancer of Thrace, for example, wears a bonnet made of fox or wolf fur. Goatskins, equipped with eyeholes, are hung from the headgear, covering the performer's shoulders and chest. Numerous bells are slung from the waist and in Skyros phallic-shaped rods are carried. Masquerades are also found in the northern provinces, where masks are worn representing characters such as the devil, the Vlach (Romanian shepherd), the Moor and the female doctor.

ITALY AND SPAIN

A wide variety of masquerades are known in Italy, including many that are associated with rural rites. An interesting example of the latter, which symbolizes dying vegetation, is traditionally performed in Perugia. It involves an 'old woman' wearing a tree-bark mask, who encounters some wood-cutters. Mistaking the 'old woman' for an oak tree, the wood-

cutters proceed to cut her up, despite the intervention of various other characters. The mistake is eventually realized and several attempts are made to revive the woman, but without success, and finally the doctor is called in. He wears a wooden mask and wooden shoes and has a false tail.

Although Italy's rural masquerades are fascinating, what the country is best known for, in terms of masks, is the *Commedia dell' arte*, a theatrical genre that flourished from the sixteenth century to the eighteenth century. Its constellation of characters, many of whom wore masks, remained the same, whatever the changes in the plot. Harlequin, who is thought to be related to the clown-devils of traditional masquerades, usually wore a demoniacal half-mask made of leather or waxed cardboard. He can be distinguished by his bushy eyebrows and moustache, snub nose and the large carbuncle on his forehead. Brighella, the cunning servant, wore an animal-like mask with slit eyes and a crooked nose. Pulcinella, the buffoon, wore a bony mask with a hooked nose and prominent eyebrows. The doctor, who wore academic dress, usually had a half mask with a bulbous nose and flaccid cheeks.

In addition to the *Commedia dell' arte*, Italy is also well known for the Venetian carnival of the seventeenth and eighteenth centuries. The carnival began just after Christmas and finished towards the end of June, and during this period black or white masks could be worn by both rich and poor alike. The wearers of masks were entitled to certain privileges, such

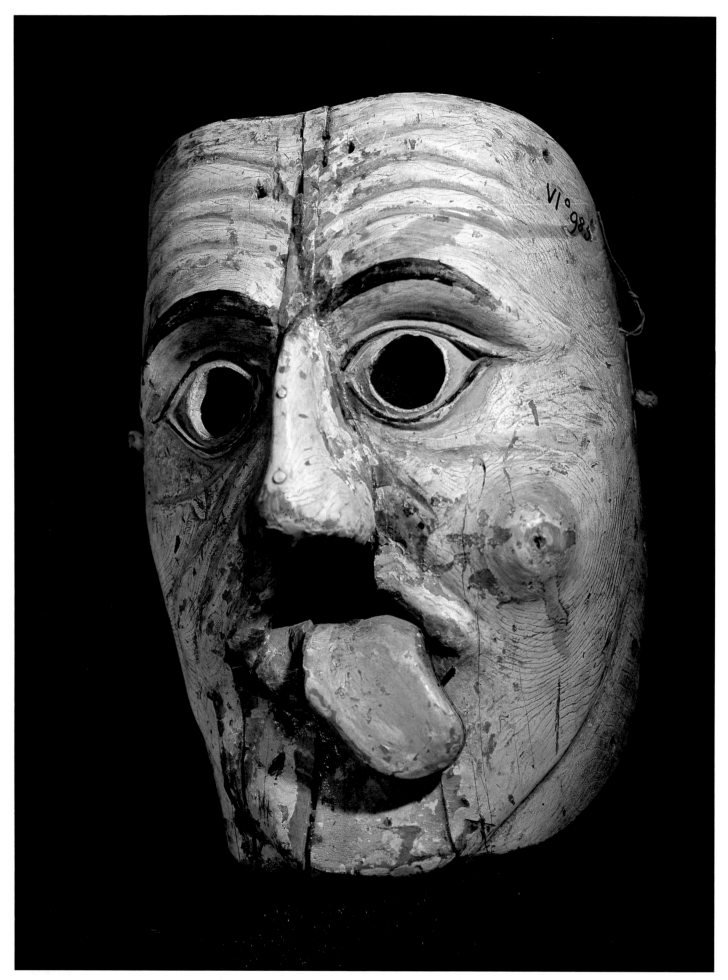

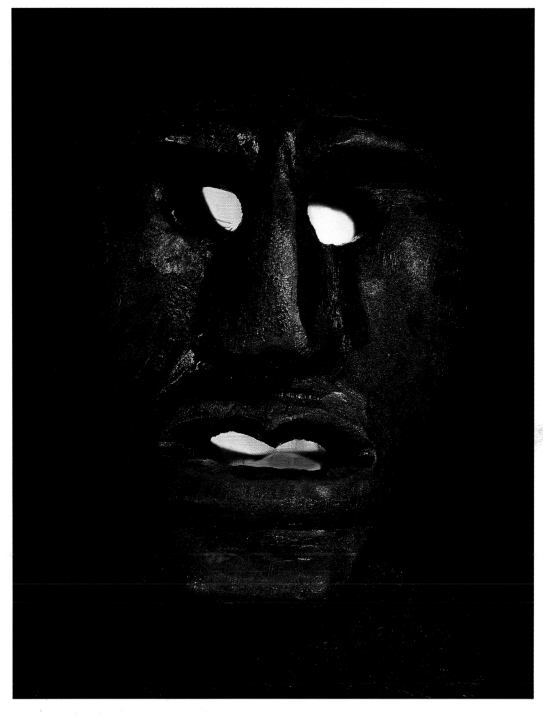

Italy, painted wood, mid-twentieth century
This grotesque mask (**left**) has a large lolling tongue and an unsightly carbuncle on one cheek. The masks of the famous Commedia dell'Arte had their origins in traditional masks like this one.

Sardinia, Italy, carved wood
This folk festival mask (**right**), which may represent a character from the spirit world, has been blackened with smoke.

as the right to engage in gambling from eight- or nine-o-clock in the morning, providing their faces remained covered.

Like the Italians, the Spaniards have a distinguished tradition in masking, especially during religious festivals. In Holy Week, for example, penitents wear tall pointed hoods equipped with eyeholes. Made in silk, these hoods mask the face and cover the shoulders. Each religious fraternity has its place in the Holy Week processions, and members of the different brotherhoods can be distinguished by their badges and the colour of their hoods.

The Spanish also wear masks to perform the *Morisca* (Moorish dance), an important masquerade that has been known on the Iberian peninsula for at least 400

years. It represents the battle between the Moors and the Christians and is enacted during Catholic festivals, notably at carnival time, during San Juan's Day and Corpus Christi. A variety of painted faces are worn, though some performers use make-up or hide their faces with bandannas.

What is interesting about the *Morisca*, in a wider European context, is the way in which Spanish elements appear to have been borrowed by other European peoples and adapted to local circumstances. The *Morisca* is closely related to other masquerades, especially those involving stick or sword dances, such as the Portuguese *Mouriscada* and the Basque *Mascarades*. Many other European masquerade traditions are also thought to have their roots in Spain.

BUYER'S GUIDE

Masks as a category in the collecting field are very different from such categories as dolls or cameras, in that there are no dealers (to my knowledge) who specialize in masks alone and it is not as yet a subject to which auction houses devote sales exclusively (although this may occur if they are called upon to disperse a particular collection). The main auction houses in Europe have sales devoted to tribal art covering the arts of Africa, the Americas, the Pacific, Indonesia and parts of mainland Asia and these will invariably include several masks. In New York similar sales are held, with separate sales often devoted to North American Indian art. A Japanese mask might appear in a sale devoted to Japanese or Oriental art, a Sri Lankan mask in a sale of Indian or Oriental art and so on.

One of the best ways to find out about the forthcoming sales at an auction house is to subscribe to the catalogues, although this could be an expensive exercise. Japanese masks, for instance, do not appear very frequently at auction and to buy and scan the pages of all the Japanese catalogues would be a waste of time and money. A more sensible alternative is to notify the auction house of your interests and ask them to let you know when an example of a particular type of mask you are interested in is coming up for sale.

It is also a good idea to find a dealer you can trust, although these also tend to specialize in specific areas such as African or Oriental art. Through a network of contacts, however, they may well be able to help with masks from areas outside their sphere.

Before starting a collection the novice must decide on the scope he wishes his collection to cover. This will be dictated by the availability of the various types of mask on the market and, of course, on the collector's budget. Masks from Africa are relatively numerous and it would be possible to form a collection covering a wide geographical area without spending more than £100 (US $165) on any one example, although of course the quality would not be particularly good. Prices for African masks run upwards not only to four- or five- but even to six-figure sums. Sri Lankan masks are relatively undervalued at auction and some very fine and old specimens occasionally appear on the market, often for no more than £200–£300 (US$330–$495). North American Indian masks are less affordable for the collector with a modest budget. The number of collectors in North America and the relatively small number of masks that appear on the market means that prices are usually in excess of £1000 (US $1650).

Punu, Gabon, wood
*This dance mask (**above**) from the Ogowe River region is less oriental in appearance than most examples.*
Height: 9¹/₂in (24cm)

Sri Lanka, wood
*This fine mask (**right**) may represent Garuda, the mythical bird of Indian legend. Its size suggests that it was paraded, rather than worn, at ceremonies.*
Height: 54¹/₂in (138.5cm)
Sotheby's London 1983, £1000

*Sepik River, Papua New
Guinea, wood
This carved, mask-like
piece (**above**) would have
been worn as a charm.
Height: 2³/₄in (7cm)*

For the new collector it would be wise to familiarize himself with as many examples of a particular type of mask as possible before actually buying. There are many excellent books and exhibition catalogues to refer to, some of which are very specific in scope and in the recent past their number has increased dramatically. Of course, it would be dangerous to base your judgement on what you have seen in a book or catalogue alone. Visiting museum collections is also helpful and here you will have the opportunity of seeing types of masks even the collector with unlimited funds is unlikely ever to have the opportunity of owning. Often the museum will quote collection data very useful for comparative purposes. The new collector will thus be able to learn to recognize features and signs that indicate the age of a particular mask, information often absent when a mask is offered for sale.

Many small provincial museums have particularly fine collections of masks that have come to them through a local benefactor, and it is often a great surprise to come across them in unlikely places. However, bear in mind that the curators of such museums often have responsibility for a far greater variety of materials than the auction-house expert or dealer and there is consequently just as much scope for errors in identification and attribution as there is in the commercial world.

Visiting museums is all very well, but seeing a mask behind glass is a poor substitute for being able to handle it. Therefore, previewing and attending a

Dan, Ivory Coast, wood,
*fibre (**left**)*
Height: 5in (12.5cm)

Black Forest, Germany,
carved and painted wood,
early nineteenth century
Masks representing
beautiful people are also
traditionally worn in the
rowdy midwinter
Schemenlaufen
festivals. This high-quality
*mask (**right**) is attributed*
to Dominikus Ackerman.

public auction provide an invaluable opportunity for the collector to 'get the feel' of a good mask. In a relatively small field such as tribal art, auctions are also something of a social event, providing a good opportunity to meet dealers and collectors both from home and abroad. It is always interesting to hear other people's views on a particular piece, but if you are eavesdropping in the hope of learning something to your advantage, treat such opinions with caution: people often play their cards close to their chests at auction and it is common to hear someone speak scathingly about a piece at a preview only to see them bidding for it at the sale, or similarly to wax lyrical about a mask and then fail to raise their hand even when it appears to be selling cheaply (after all, it

might be theirs!).

As a rule sales are held on week days, which is an inconvenience for many private collectors. Increasingly, however, auction houses are providing an opportunity for viewing in the evenings or at weekends in order to encourage more private buyers. If you cannot attend a sale personally it is possible to leave a bid with the auction house, although it is very difficult to decide the price you are prepared to pay a day or two before the sale. Collectors often ask how much they should leave on a particular lot. It is a good idea to imagine yourself telephoning after the sale to find out the results. If you leave a bid for a certain amount and then find out that the mask was sold for a higher price that you would still have been

prepared to pay, then you should have left at least that much. This may sound obvious, but it is extraordinary how many people leave a bid to cover a lot in case it sells cheaply and then are disappointed when it goes for more than they left but less than they really feel it was worth to them.

Of course, it is much more exciting to attend the sale yourself and, contrary to popular belief, there is really little danger of an auctioneer interpreting a scratch of the nose as a bid. Should you make an error, however, and you find you have bought the wrong lot, make it known to the auctioneer straight away and do not wait until after the sale when it is too late to be remedied.

Most auction catalogues now include estimated prices for each lot. The buyer must bear in mind that these are only a guide and are perhaps the opinion of only one individual. Various factors play a part in arriving at these estimates. If an owner simply wants to get rid of a single lot or of a collection and wants to avoid the risk of a lot being unsold, the estimates may be conservative to encourage bidding. On the other hand, an owner may consign a particular lot for sale with a price in mind that may be a little optimistic. So it would be wrong to think you should pay no more than the top estimate or that it would necessarily be worth buying a lot because it is selling below the estimate. Experts make mistakes, too, and one of the excitements at a sale is to see a 'sleeper' with a modest estimate suddenly take off, leaving the audience gasping and the expert looking a little embarrassed. This may in any case not be entirely the fault of the auction house. It only takes two determined bidders to push the price far beyond what most buyers might consider reasonable.

Before you decide what, if anything, you wish to bid for, ask the expert in charge of the sale what his or her opinion is as to the value of a lot (and preferably consult any other person whose judgement you have come to trust). By the time of the preview the expert may be able to give you a more up-to-date estimate based on people's reactions at the time and, if you know beforehand that the lot in which you are most interested is going to be way beyond your reach, you may prefer to concentrate on another. Decide before the sale what you are going to bid for and how much you are prepared to pay for it—and then stick to your decision. With perhaps up to 400 lots to get through in a single session the auctioneer has to keep up a fairly rapid pace and if you have not decided an upper limit on a particular lot it is easy to find your-

self paying considerably more than you intended to. Bear in mind also that you will have to pay the auctioneer's commission on the hammer price and possibly a sales tax.

It would be nice to think that, having bought your mask, you can then expect it to appreciate in value to keep pace with inflation. I have often been asked the likes of 'If I buy this mask and bring it back in five years time how much do you think it will fetch?' My answer to such questions has always been that if that is your concern you would be better off keeping your money in a bank. Buy your mask because it gives you pleasure to own it; the purchase of your mask should not be disappointing if the market collapsed in a year or two. It is very difficult to predict which categories are on the increase and which are likely to drop in popularity. In recent years masks have followed the trend of other fields: the very best command very high prices that often outpace inflation, while more pedestrian examples from Africa, of which there is a steady supply, have fared less well, their prices often remaining fairly static.

One of the factors in assessing the value of a mask is its provenance, and in recent years this has become increasingly important, due no doubt to the increasing competence of fakers. Many buyers are reassured by a good early provenance, which reduces the onerous task of having to rely on one's own judgement. If it is known where a mask was collected, when and by whom it can affect the price considerably. A valuable provenance does not simply mean that the name of the person who collected the mask in the field is known. It may simply have belonged to a particular collector or even have passed through the hands of a well-known dealer. Masks that had once belonged to the artist, Maurice de Vlaminck, have recently been sold at auction in Paris for sums far in excess of their intrinsic value. Similarly, masks that have passed through the hands of the English dealers, Webster and Oldman, at the beginning of this century might today fetch two or three times the sums of similar masks without this significant connection.

A word of warning is needed here, however. You should take care when confronted with old labels, since it is not unknown for unscrupulous dealers to remove old collection labels from items of relatively small value and affix them to more valuable objects. This has happened in the case of items from the Beasley Collection. Fortunately, Beasley kept ledgers in which he recorded against his inventory number such information as an item's description and where and when he purchased it. The ledgers are now in the British Museum and it is possible to check the label against his entry. Of course, exactly what constitutes an early provenance will depend on the area from which the mask comes. The vast majority of African, south-east Asian or Pacific masks seen on the market or even in museum collections will have been collect-

Bavaria, Germany, carved and painted wood, early twentieth century
The noise of jangling bells, according to tradition, is thought to frighten away the evil spirits of winter. This mask (left) was worn during Schemenlaufen festivals.

Alpine, painted wood
The midwinter festivals
that are held in the Alps to
frighten off the
accumulated spirits of
winter are usually noisy.
This mask has a hole in the
mouth so that the wearer
could blow on a pipe.

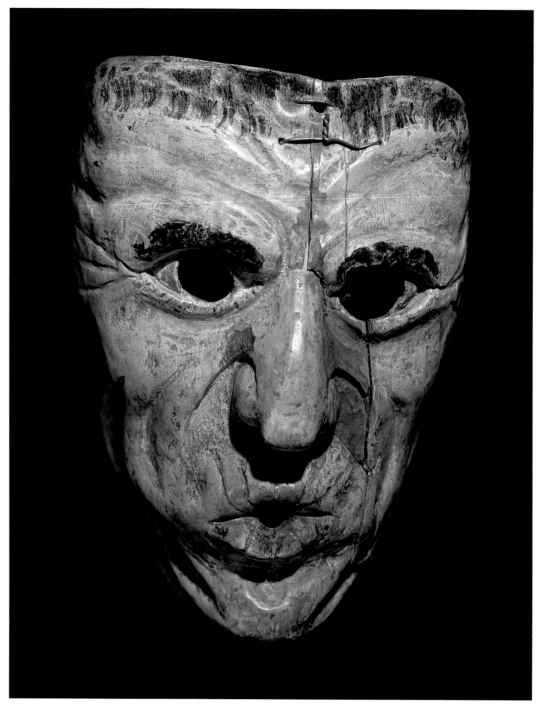

ed this century and an early twentieth-century prove-nance therefore should not be considered too late to be of significance but can make a considerable differ-ence to the price. The use of masks for traditional purposes declined in many cultures after European contact and was revived only in relatively recent times, sometimes due to a renewed pride in a people's cultural heritage (though often commercial considerations have played a part).

It was in the 1950's and 1960s that production of many types of African masks for the art market was at its height and consequently a pre-1940 date should not be regarded as too late to be of significance. On the island of Pentecost in Vanuatu, the carving of masks has been revived only in the past twenty years,

while some fairly good fakes may have originated in Europe even more recently. Consequently you would not have to trace the history of a mask back too far to be reasonably sure it was an old example.

Unfortunately, there are a great many fake masks on the market from many continents. 'Fake' is a term to be used with caution. A 'fake' is something in-tended to deceive and is not synonymous with 'modern'. It must be remembered that many of the masking traditions of Africa, Europe and Central and South America are still thriving today.

There are no hard and fast rules to guide the novice collector in spotting a fake. You can learn to recognize certain signs from experience in handling masks, but even experienced collectors and dealers will often

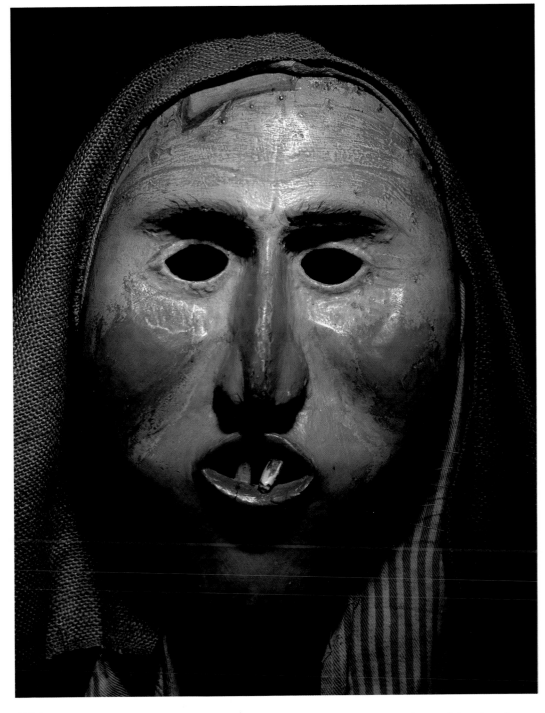

Alpine, carved and painted wood, cloth, early twentieth century
This mask represents a poor, old woman. According to popular tradition, Alpine mask makers sometimes designed caricatures based on real people.

disagree over authenticity. The most telling signs of the authenticity of a mask are not on the front but on the back, a view one is denied in the museum, and the collector should take full use here of the opportunity to handle tribal art presented at auction previews. It may be a little dangerous to generalize, but as a rule there is no need for the carver of a mask to pay much attention to the reverse; this will not be seen by the spectator in the masquerade or play and, as very little of the surface of the mask comes into contact with the face of the wearer, there is no need to smooth the surface for comfort. Consequently, in many good old masks the adzing is clearly visible on the reverse, whether neatly or roughly executed. Fake masks are often given an overall smoothing of the back and also

of the edges to give the impression of having been worn over a long period of time. On a genuine old mask, however, the wear will not be uniform over the whole surface, and the lower edges that might come in contact with the face may appear darker and glossier than the rest of the back surface. It should be remembered, however, that a mask may have been collected before it had had much use, so signs of wear are by no means an essential requirement for an old or genuine mask. In the case of many fakes from Zaire the back is also scorched or blackened with soot. It is a good idea to smell the surface. Does it smell as though it has really been in an old colonial family for generations or does it smell as though it came out of Africa last week?

CARE AND MAINTENANCE

amage is perhaps less important when buying masks than other objects. Tropical climates are unsuitable for the conservation of the soft, light woods usually employed by carvers in parts of Africa and a certain amount of damage is almost inevitable. Termite damage is also common and is positively encouraged by carvers of fakes in West Africa as a sign of 'authenticity'. Light woods are also attractive to other insects and masks should be checked for signs of activity. Two years ago I set up a shield from the highlands of New Guinea in our photographic studio to be photographed and was surprised to see a fat bug crawling out from the wood, presumably brought to life by the heat from the spotlights. The woods are also prone to damage by woodworm and any evidence of infestation should be checked to ensure it is not live. Damage sustained during a masquerade can positively add to the value of a mask where a neat mend by a native craftsman is evident.

Restoration should always be left to a professional and should only be undertaken if the damage is so severe as to detract considerably from the mask's appearance. Evidence of restoration will make many collectors suspicious and therefore may not add to the resale value of a mask. The cost may also be prohibitive and it will often be difficult, if not impossible, to match exactly the materials used. Always photograph the mask, preferably from more than one angle, before any restoration is undertaken.

Many of the masks described in this book were made for use in a single performance and durability ws therefore not a consideration of the carver. Many masks are very fragile and, in many cases, even cleaning with a duster may not be possible. A solid wood surface can be dusted but not if the mask has a crusty patina, which may flake. Great care should be taken if the mask is painted; many types of paints such as those used on the north-west coast of America are not as permanent as modern synthetic paints. If the mask has an old label attached, giving details of its provenance or of a collection through which it has passed, take great care of it since to lose it would reduce the mask's value. Bronze masks should not be cleaned with metal polish, as removal of the original patination will reduce their value; this fate has befallen many of the bronze hip masks brought back to England from Benin at the end of the last century.

Masks of bark cloth or fibre, such as those from South America or parts of New Guinea, are often too delicate for any sort of cleaning by anyone other than a professional. A reputable dealer, auction house or museum may be able to suggest a specialist to tackle the job, though it is likely to be costly. If you are going away for any length of time and such a mask is on display uncovered, it is worthwhile to cover it loosely with a thin sheet of plastic to reduce the accumulation of dust but to allow the circulation of air as, should moisture be trapped inside, this will cause damage. Avoid storing or displaying masks where they will be subject to fluctuations in temperature or humidity, since this is likely to cause splits in wooden masks and will cause natural fibres to become brittle and eventually decompose. The application of a layer of varnish to some wooden masks brought back to Europe earlier this century was not uncommon and can be removed by a professional restorer without harm to the original patina underneath.

CATALOGUING AND DISPLAY

Although masks may not be as obvious a target for a thief as silver or jewellery, they have nevertheless been stolen in the past from museums, private collectors and auction houses. Without a photographic record of your collection it is very difficult to describe a mask sufficiently well, either in writing or verbally, to enable it to be identified. I face a similar problem every week with people trying to describe a mask or figure over the telephone in the hope that I will be able to visualize it and give them some idea of its value. Take photographs of every mask in your collection, preferably from more than one angle, so that these can be circulated to auction houses and dealers in the event that they are stolen. Keep the photographs together with a record of when and where you bought the mask, how much you paid for it and any other information you may have concerning its history, such as when and where it was collected and by whom. Since today this type of data can often affect an object's price, an auction house or dealer will usually try to obtain this information when they first obtain the mask (but if they have not, ask them if they can supply any more information beyond what they have already quoted). If the mask came from a private source it may be possible to make contact with the previous owner. Although auction houses will not release the names of vendors they will often have no objection to forwarding a letter to a vendor on your behalf and will probably be able to tell you whether or not this effort is worthwhile.

Not all masks can be categorized definitely as belonging to one particular tribal group. For many geographical areas much work is still to be done by scholars. Some masks may in fact combine features of various tribal styles. It is therefore worthwhile keeping a record of any similar masks you come across in museums or published in books or catalogues.

The obvious way to display a mask is simply to hang it on the wall. The wall would have to be of a uniform colour if the mask is to be clearly visible and it should not be prone to damp or condensation. It would also be unwise to hang a mask above a radiator, where the constant change in temperature is likely to cause damage. A small and delicate mask may look lost on a vast expanse of wall and it could not be seen to its best advantage in such a position. Many masks are not designed to be worn on the front of the face in a vertical position and these would therefore also be unsuitable for a wall display. A Yoruba *gelede* mask, for example, would be facing towards the floor if hung on a wall, and would be seen to much better advantage if simply lain on a shelf.

Many buyers of masks prefer to mount masks on stands rather than hang them on the wall; this is particularly suitable for small masks, which can then be rotated and seen from all angles. Most stands consist of a simple metal loop that curves around inside the border of the mask with the ends slotting into holes found in the borders of most masks. This loop is joined to a vertical support inserted into a rectangular or wooden block. Dealers and auction houses have frequent cause to use the services of a stand maker and should be able to recommend one to you. Many are very skilled and Inagaki, a Japanese stand maker who died shortly after the Second World War and who specialized in stands for works of tribal art, is now so highly regarded that his stands can add considerably to the price of a work of art.

MUSEUMS

Many museums in Europe and North America, both small and large, have fine collections of masks, some broad in scope and others quite limited, often reflecting the colonial past of the countries in which they are to be found. Just a sample is listed here.

UNITED KINGDOM

Museum of Mankind, London
Horniman Museum, London
Pitt Rivers Museum, Oxford
Cambridge University Museum of Archaeology and Anthropology, Cambridge
Liverpool Museum, Liverpool
Hunterian Museum, Glasgow
Royal Museum of Scotland, Edinburgh
Brighton Art Gallery and Museum, Brighton
Ipswich Museum, Ipswich
Manchester Museum, Manchester
Powell-Cotton Museum, Birchington
Royal Albert Memorial Museum and Art Gallery, Exeter
Ulster Museum, Belfast

NORTH AMERICA

American Museum of Natural History, New York
Brooklyn Museum, New York
Metropolitan Museum of Art, New York
Buffalo Museum of Science, New York
Cleveland Museum of Art, Cleveland
Dallas Museum of Fine Arts, Dallas
Detroit Institute of Arts, Detroit
The Denver Art Museum, Denver
Field Museum of Natural History, Chicago
Indiana University Art Museum, Bloomington
Museum of Cultural History, Los Angeles
Seattle Art Museum, Seattle
Peabody Museum of Archaeology and Ethnology, Cambridge
Lowie Museum of Anthropology, Berkeley
National Museum of African Art, Washington D.C.
Royal Ontario Museum, Toronto

EUROPE

Musée de l'Homme, Paris
Musée National des Arts africains at océaniens, Paris
Musée Royal de l'Afrique Centrale, Tervuren, Belgium
Rautenstrauch-Joest-Museum für Völkerkunde, Cologne
Museum für Völkerkunde, Berlin
Museum für Völkerkunde, Frankfurt
Staatliches Museum für Völkerkunde, Munich
Linden Museum für Lander und Völkerkunde, Stuttgart
Museum für Völkerkunde, Freiburg im Breisgau
Hamburgisches Museum für Völkerkunde, Hamburg
Museum Rietberg, Zurich
Museum für Völkerkunde, Basel
Museum für Völkerkunde, Vienna
Rijksmuseum voor Volkenkunde, Leiden
Koninklijk Instituut voor den Tropen Museum, Amsterdam
Museum voor Volkenkunde, Rotterdam
Volkenkundig Museum Nusantara, Delft
Museo Nazionale Preistorico Etnografico "L. Pigorini", Rome
Museo Nazionale di Antropologia e di Etnologia, Florence
National Museum of Denmark, Copenhagen
Museu de Etnologia, Lisbon
National Museum of Ireland, Dublin
Musée International du Carnaval et due Masque, Binche

BIBLIOGRAPHY

Ali, A.K., The Hidden Power of Shaman Masks from Sarawak, *Connaissance des Arts Tribaux* no.19, Geneva

Barbier, J.P. and Newton, D. (editors), *Islands and Ancestors*, New York, 1988

Bastin, M–L., *La Sculpture Tschokwe*, Meudon, 1982

Biebuyck, D., *Lega Culture*, Los Angeles, 1973

Bleakley, R., *African Masks*, London, 1978

Bourgeois, A.P., *Art of the Yaka and Suku*, Meudon, 1984

Cameron, E.L., Sala Mpasu Masks, *African Arts* Vol. XXII no.1, Los Angeles, 1988

Cole, H.M. and Aniakor, C.C., *Ibo Arts Community and Cosmos*, Los Angeles, 1984

Cole, H.M., *I am not myself: the Art of African Masquerade*, Los Angeles, 1985

Cornet, J., *Art Royal Kuba*, Milan, 1982

Cordry, D.B., *Mexican Masks*, Austin, 1980

Dark, P.J., *Kilenge, Life and Art*, London, 1974

Deacon, A.B., *Malekula, A Vanishing Peoples in The New Hebrides*, London, 1934

Dockstader, F.J., *South American Indian Art*, London, 1967

Donne, J.B., Ceylon Masks in the British Museum, *The Connoisseur*, April, 1978

Eckholm, G.F., *Ancient Mexico and Central America*, New York, 1970

Ezra, K., *Art of the Dogon*, New York, 1988

Fagg, W.B., *Tribes and Forms in African Art*, Paris, 1965

Fagg, W.B., *Masques d'Afrique dans les collections du Musée Barbier-Müller*, Geneva, 1980

Fagg, W.B., Pemberton, J., and Holcombe, B., *Yoruba Sculpture of West Africa*, New York, 1982

Fischer, E. and Himmelheber, H., *The Arts of the Dan in West Africa*, Zurich, 1984

Goonatilleka, M.H., *Masks and Mask Systems of Sri Lanka*, Colombo, 1978

Guiart, J., *Arts of the South Pacific*, London, 1963

Hasibuan, J., *Art et Culture Batak*, Jakarta, 1985

Hersak, D., *Songye Masks and Figure Sculpture*, London, 1985

Heurley, E., *Pearls and Savages*, New York, 1924

Himmelheber, H., *Art et Artists Batshiok*, Brousse, 1939

Holm, Bill, *Spirits and Ancestors*, Seattle, 1987

Holy, L., *Masks and Figures from Eastern and Southern Africa*, London, 1967

Kecskési, M., *African Masterpieces and Selected Works from Munich: The Staatliches Museum für Völkerkunde*, New York, 1987

King, J.C.H., *Portrait Masks from the Northwest Coast of America*, London, 1979

Lamp, F., The Art of the Baga: A Preliminary Enquiry, *African Arts*, Vol. XIX, no.2, Los Angeles, 1986

Levi-Strauss, C,. *The Way of the Masks*, London, 1983

Lewis, P., The Social Context of Art in Northern New Ireland, *Fieldiana: Anthropology*, Vol. 58, Chicago, 1969

Lucas, H., *Ceylon Masken*, Kassel, 1958

Lucas, H., *Lamaïstische Masken*, Kassel, 1962

Mead, S.M., ed., *Exploring the Visual Art of Oceania*, Honolulu, 1979

Moore, D.R., *The Torres Straits Collection of A.C. Haddon*, London, 1984

Newton, D., *Crocodile and Cassowary*, New York, 1971

Northern, T., *The Art of the Cameroon*, Washington, 1984

Pannier, F. and Mangin, S., *Masques de l'Himalaya du Primitif au Classique*, 1989

Perrois, L., *La Statuaire Fan*, Paris, 1972

Perrois, L., *Ancestral Art of Gabon from the Collections of the Barbier-Müller Museum*, Geneva, 1985

Phelps, S.J., *Art and Artefacts of the Pacific, Africa and the Americas, The James Hooper Collection*, London, 1976

Redinha, J., *Campanha Etnografica ao Tchiboco*, Lisbon, 1953/5

Roy, C., *Art of the Upper Volta Rivers*, Meudon, 1987

Schmalenbach, W. (editor), *African Art: The Barbier-Müller Collection*, Geneva, 1988

Schmitz, C.A., *Oceanic Art*, New York, 1971

Stöhr, W., *Art of the Archaic Indonesians*, Geneva, 1982

Timmermans, P., *Les Lwalwa*, Tervuren, 1967

Vogel, S. (editor), *For Spirits and Kings, African Art from the Paul and Ruth Tishman Collection*, New York, 1981

Wardwels, A., *The Art of the Sepik River*, Chicago, 1971

NORTHAMPTON COLLEGE
LIBRARY

INDEX

ACKNOWLEDGEMENTS

The author and publishers would like to thank the private individuals, museums and other establishments for granting permission to reproduce photographs in this book on the following pages:

6 – American Museum of Natural History; 7 – P A Ferrazzini/Musee Barbier-Müller; 8 – Studio Lemaire/ van Bussel Archive; 9 – (left) van Bussel Archive, (right) van Bussel Archive; 10 – Private Collection; 11 – van Bussel Archive; 12 – Private Collection; 13 – Christie's London; 15–(left) British Museum, (right) Christie's London; 16 – British Museum; 17 – British Museum; 18 – British Museum; 19 – British Museum; 20 – Sotheby's London; 21 – (left) Christie's London, (right) Christie's London; 22 – Archive Leloup; 23 – (left) Christie's London, (right) Private Collection; 24 – Christie's London; 25 – Christie's London; 26 – A C Cooper Ltd; 27 – (left) Christie's London, (right) courtesy Entwistle, London; 28 – Christie's London; 29 – (left) Museum Rietberg, Zurich, (right) Christie's New York; 30 – (above) Asselberghs/Musee Barbier-Müller, (below) P A Ferrazzini/Musee Barbier-Müller; 31 – (left) Sotheby's London, (right) Christie's New York; 32 – (above) courtesy Entwistle, London, (below) Christie's London; 33 – Christie's London; 34 – (left) Christopher Taylor, (right) Christie's London; 36 – Christie's London; 37 – van Bussel Archive; 38 – courtesy Entwistle, London; 39 – courtesy Entwistle/Photo Werner Forman, London; 40 – (left) Christie's London, (right) Christie's London; 41 – Christie's New York; 42 – Christie's London; 43 – Seattle Art Museum/Katherine White Collection; 44 – Peter Adler; 45 – Studio Lemaire/van Bussel Archive; 46 – (above) Christie's London, (below) Peter Adler; 47 – (above) Christie's London, (below) van Bussel Collection; 48-9 – British Museum; 49 – Studio Lemaire/van Bussel Archive; 52 – van Bussel Collection; 53 – van Bussel Collection; 54 – University of East Anglia/ Sainsbury Centre; 55 – (left) Sotheby's London, (above right) Studio Lemaire/van Bussel Collection, (below right) University of East Anglia/Sainsbury Centre: 56 – British Museum; 57 – British Museum; 58 – A C Cooper Ltd; 59 – van Bussel Collection; 60 – British Museum; 63 – (left) Christie's London, (right) Christie's London; 64 – Christie's London; 65 – Christie's London; 66-7 – American Museum of Natural History; 67 – (above) Christie's London, (below) Christie's London; 69 – (left) American Museum of Natural History, (above right) Private Collection, (below right) British Museum; 70 – (left) British Museum, (right) British Museum; 71 – Museum für Völkerkunde, Berlin; 72 – British Museum; 73 – (left) British Museum, (above right) Christie's London, (below right) Christie's London; 74-83 inclusive – Claus Hansmann Archive; 84 – van Bussel Archive; 85 – Sotheby's London; 87 – Claus Hansmann Archive; 88 – Claus Hansmann Archive; 90 – Claus Hansmann Archive; 91 – Claus Hansmann Archive.

UNBORED

For Sam and Max; Peter, Henrik, and Luisa; Luciano and Luna

INDOORS / OUTDOORS / ONLINE / OFFLINE

UNBORED

THE ESSENTIAL FIELD GUIDE TO
SERIOUS FUN

JOSHUA GLENN & ELIZABETH FOY LARSEN

DESIGN BY TONY LEONE

ILLUSTRATIONS BY MISTER REUSCH & HEATHER KASUNICK

CHAPTER LETTERING BY CHRIS PIASCIK

BLOOMSBURY

LONDON · NEW DELHI · NEW YORK · SYDNEY

Our thanks to: Anton Mueller at Bloomsbury for his vision and support; Richard Atkinson and Xa Shaw Stewart at Bloomsbury UK; dauntless fact-checker Chloe Puton; talented design assistant and colour queen Colleen Venable; and idea maven Helen Cordes. Matthew De Abaitua's assistance on the British edition of the book was indispensable. We are particularly grateful to Susan Roe, Walter Schleisman and Amanda Leone for their steadfast love, inspiration and patience.

Josh thanks Jon Pinchera and all the other J[osh]-Scouts, including: Charlie Mitchell, Adam Banks and Harry Parker; Jack and Lucas Mueller; Peter and Simon Klee; Haley, Liza and Ella Roe; Cole and Josie Johnson; Finnuala and Caimin Cradock; Taylor, Callie and Tiger Wright; Tyler and DeVonté Austin; and Lila, Garet and Emmett Glenn. Peter Parker and Emma Tourtelot, for their suggestions of British media; and Helen Skelton, and Beth and Edie Deakin. Many thanks to Patrick Glenn, for being the greatest uncle (and brother) ever.

Elizabeth thanks Bridget Bradley for her thoughtful research; Oscar and Louie Cleveland, and Annie Gillette Cleveland; Stephanie Sorenson for her beautiful photos; the Larsen-Schleisman-Morgan-Stout family, especially Charlie, Michael, Patrick and Catherine Hooley and Maggie Fields; and Madeline McCormick. Special thanks to Lake Country School, Kenwood School and St Paul Academy; Camp du Nord; Ginia Bellafante; Kara Corridan; *Parents* Magazine; and to all the mums and dads who helped shape this book in ways big and small.

Tony thanks Mark Reusch and Heather Kasunick for their generosity of talent and ideas; Chris Cannon, Scott Dasse, Tammy Dayton, Bill Stewart, Vanessa Dina, Neyah Bennett and Dirk Ahlgrim for their expertise and enthusiasm; Patti Ratchford at Bloomsbury for the direction and translations; and his niece, Thea Nickolas, for her insightful advice.

Copyright © 2012 by Joshua Glenn and Elizabeth Foy Larsen
Photographs © 2012 by Joshua Glenn and Elizabeth Foy Larsen, unless otherwise noted
Illustrations © 2012 by Mister Reusch, as noted
Illustrations © 2012 by Heather Kasunick, as noted
Chapter divider and contents page illustrations © 2012 by Chris Piascik

The moral right of the authors has been asserted.

Bloomsbury Publishing, London, New Delhi, New York and Sydney

50 Bedford Square, London WC1B 3DP

Bloomsbury.com

A CIP catalogue record for this book is available from the British Library

ISBN 978 1 4088 3025 3
10 9 8 7 6 5 4 3 2 1

Design and Art Direction by Tony Leone, Leone Design
Design assistance by Colleen Venable
Illustration illumination by Tony Leone and Colleen Venable

Cover design by Tony Leone
Cover illustration by Mister Reusch

Printed in China by South China Printing Company, Dongguan, Guangdong

All papers used by Bloomsbury Publishing are natural, recyclable products made from wood grown in well-managed forests. The manufacturing processes conform to the environmental regulations of the country of origin.

For more activities and info, visit our website: Unbored.net

DISCLAIMER

———

The information contained in this book is for informational and entertainment purposes only. We have done our best to be as factual and accurate as possible but we do not guarantee that any of the information contained in this book is correct or workable. Be responsible, exercise good sense, and take every safety precaution — not limited to the precautions that we suggest. Also, we do not advocate the breaking of any law.

Note that when following our instructions, switching materials, assembling improperly, mishandling and misusing can cause harm; also, results may vary.

It is important that you understand that the authors, the publisher, and the bookseller cannot and will not guarantee your safety. Physical or mental harm is not intended so be cautious and use at your own risk. The authors and publishers expressly disclaim liability for any injury or damages resulting from the use (proper or otherwise) of any information in this book.

RECIPES, FORMULAS, ACTIVITIES AND INSTRUCTIONS IN THIS BOOK SHOULD BE FOLLOWED EXACTLY AND SHOULD NOT BE ATTEMPTED WITHOUT ADULT SUPERVISION.

Most major websites are restricted to users aged 13 and older. We do not advocate lying about your age in order to access websites, games, apps, social media services and anything else online mentioned or not mentioned in this book. Parents should not help their children lie about their age online; if underage children make use of email, instant messaging, Facebook, YouTube, Twitter, or any other website, game, app or social media service, including web searches, they should only do so via a parent's account and with close parental supervision and collaboration.

While the authors have made every effort to provide accurate internet addresses at the time of publication, neither the publisher nor the authors assume any responsibility for errors, or for changes that occur after publication. Further, the publisher does not have any control over and does not assume any responsibility for author or third-party websites or their content.

CHAPTER 1
YOU

chapter 2
HOME

CHAPTER 3

SOCIETY

Chapter 4
ADVENTURE

The joy of making stuff often surpasses the joy of consuming mass-produced stuff.

INTRODUCTION
USE THE WORLD, OR THE WORLD WILL USE YOU

By Mark Frauenfelder

When I was much younger, I became friends with Roger Price, who was then in his sixties. His creations included the popular game Mad Libs and Droodles (cryptic line drawings with punchlines). I wanted to be a writer and illustrator like him, so Roger gave me some advice: 'Use the world, or let the world use you.'

Because he had a streak of dark curmudgeonly humour, I assumed that Roger was just being cynical. Today, though, I realise he was warning me that if I didn't take responsibility for how I lived my life, I would be swept up by the blind forces of society. I would lose the power to call my own shots.

Roger would have loved *Unbored* as much as I do, because it's the first kids' book to truly encourage a hands-on approach to creating a personally meaningful life. To live any other way is to swallow whatever pap the world doles out to you 'on the end of that long newspaper spoon', in the words of William S. Burroughs. This book is a powerful antidote to those forces that constantly try to shape us into passive consumers of pre-made reality.

The hidden cost of convenience

Reading *Unbored*, I'm reminded of an incident from a few years ago. My daughter brought some friends over to our house, and they watched me pulling up carrots from the garden. One of these kids remarked, 'They're upside down!' I asked her what she meant and she explained that the orange part of the carrot should be sticking up, not buried in the ground. A couple of weeks later, I told this story to a primary school art teacher; she told me that her students sometimes drew gardens with carrots growing orange-side-up out of the soil.

If you're lucky enough to live where food is inexpensive, you don't have to grow your own carrots. Similarly, thanks to mass production, you can buy clothes, toys, tools and other goods for very little money compared to what our ancestors paid for the things they needed. I can't argue that it's not wonderful to be able to buy quality, inexpensive products, or hire experts to solve problems like a leaky roof or a broken dishwasher. But this cheap bounty means you don't have to invent your own solutions. Which can lead to a loss of connection to the world around you, a lack of caring about how it works. You might stop being observant, creative, resourceful; you might grow up not knowing that carrots grow with their roots sticking down.

Illustrations by Heather Kasunick

A question you can ask yourself to make everything you do more interesting

A few years ago I came across a Second World War-era poster that showed a woman sewing a man's torn trousers while he repaired a lawn mower. The poster encourages people to be thrifty; its slogan is 'USE IT UP – WEAR IT OUT – MAKE IT DO!' This message made sense during wartime shortages and, despite the best efforts of corporations to convince you that yesterday's shiny thing is no longer any good (and that today's shiny thing is essential), it still makes sense. Ever since I saw that poster, whenever I get the urge to pull out my wallet, or enter my credit card number on a website, I've asked myself, 'Instead of buying something, can I make something – or modify, repair, or reuse what I already have?' Often, the answer is: 'Yes.'

Not only does asking yourself this question help you save money, it helps you have fun. Actively contributing to the human-made world is an incredible consciousness expander – it will make you more observant, creative, and resourceful.

Say, for instance, that you want to buy a new computer game. Instead of heading to your computer to order one, ask yourself, 'Can I make something – or modify, repair, or reuse what I already have?' Like thousands of other kids have, you might download the free educational programming language Scratch (scratch.mit.edu), and program your own games. You might discover that creating games is at least as fun, and maybe more fun than playing commercial computer games; at any rate, you will gain inside knowledge about how computer games work. Even if programming doesn't turn out to be your thing, you'll learn that about yourself – and you'll appreciate commercial computer games in an entirely new way.

Why create instead of consume?

The things we create ourselves might not be as 'good' as slick manufactured versions. But it doesn't matter: the joy of creating stuff often surpasses the joy of consuming mass-produced stuff. The things I make – skateboards, cigar box guitars, whittled wooden spoons – don't look as polished and perfect as their shop-bought counterparts, but making them has several rewards:

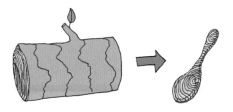

Every time I use my wooden spoon to stir pancake batter, and every time I play my cigar box guitar, I'm aware that I created that thing. I have a deeper connection to these unique creations than I do to any purchased item I own. My personal connection to the things I make is more valuable to me than the meaningless quality you get when you buy a mass-produced item.

Making things causes me to become more aware of the world around me, which is a wonderful way to go about my day. Let's say I build a simple piece of furniture – a stool, perhaps. Doing so will lead me to become curious about how all furniture is made. So I will begin to look at the way chairs are built to be stable, how the pieces are fastened, and the wide variety of solutions people have come up with over the years to make their own chairs. It's impossible to be bored!

As my skills develop, the human-made world around me becomes less confounding, and more like the ultimate 'hackable platform' (as DIYers call any technology which can be modified to one's own unique specifications), inviting me to participate in it. Instead of feeling helpless and buying a solution to every problem that comes my way, I feel confident that I can at least attempt to solve the problem myself. Sure, in the long run, I might save some money by calling a plumber or electrician to take care of problems around the house – but to me the time I spend trying to fix things myself, thus boosting my sense of self-efficacy, is time well spent.

Get started by getting started

As you embark on the journey of doing and making things yourself, here are three travel tips:

1. Don't fear mistakes

If most people grow up thinking that mistakes are something you should avoid, it's probably because at school mistakes result in bad marks. I wish schools wouldn't give marks, because teaching us that mistakes are bad makes us afraid to try new things. The greatest makers I know agree that their secret skill is not how knowledgeable they are about tools or materials or fabrication methods – it's their willingness to make mistakes and learn from them. So don't be afraid to make mistakes. Don't make them intentionally, of course! You should always do your best. But when the inevitable mishap occurs, welcome it.

Brain researchers have found that making mistakes is a very effective way to learn new skills – and besides, a mistake can take you in a new direction that you wouldn't have been able to imagine otherwise. For instance, one time I was sawing fret grooves in the neck of a cigar box guitar and I misplaced a groove. I thought the neck was ruined. But then I thought of something: I filled the groove with a putty made from wood glue and sawdust, and when it dried I painted the entire fretboard with lime-green coloured paint to cover the scar. Now, whenever I make a new cigar box guitar, I always paint the neck a bright colour. It's become my trademark.

2. Choose meaningful projects

Do projects that will have the biggest impact on the way you live. For me, making a wooden spoon is more fulfilling than making a robot, because I use my spoons every single day; if I made a robot, I wouldn't do much with it after it had been built. For many people, making robots is a very fulfilling pursuit – but almost every day I eat yogurt and sauerkraut, drink Kombucha (it's made from tea), play guitar and cook. So keeping bees, making cigar box guitars and fermented foods, and whittling spoons has turned me into a producer instead of a consumer of things that are important to me.

Do projects that will improve the way you live.

3. Ignorance is no excuse

We live in a culture of experts who like to say 'Don't try this at home.' That's rubbish. I'm not saying you should go out and play with high voltages (if you don't understand electricity) or scale a cliff (if you've never had experience with technical climbing). But don't let your ignorance be an impediment; instead of worrying that you don't know how to do something, just try doing it! Use the internet to connect to communities of practice. Seek out a hacker space in your community. You'll find that enthusiasts are happy to help anyone who is sincerely interested in learning how to do something. And once you pick up skills of your own, you too will discover how enjoyable it is to help others out.

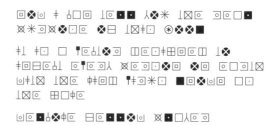

PLAY THE GAME

By Josh

My sons' friend DeVonté taught us The Game; I wish he hadn't! Once you learn how to play it, your life is altered, forever. And now I'm about to alter your life, too. Sorry about that.

I've heard that The Game was invented by members of a science-fiction club at Cambridge University in 1977. This may or may not be true, but what is incontrovertible fact is that The Game is a diabolically clever (and annoying) pastime.

There are three rules:

1. You're *always* playing the game. So is everyone else in the world, *even if they don't realise it yet*.
2. If you think about The Game, you lose The Game.
3. Whenever you lose The Game, you must say the following phrase aloud, to whoever happens to be nearby: 'I lost The Game.' Doing so, of course, causes everybody who hears you to lose the Game. They may groan and throw things at you.

How do you win The Game?

You can't! The best you can hope for is to avoid losing – for a few days, weeks, months. Someone or something will eventually make you lose.

Most players suggest that after you lose The Game, you can't lose it again for a certain period of time – perhaps an hour. This makes sense, because

otherwise once one person in a room loses The Game and says so, everyone else in the room will lose The Game and say so, which will cause everyone in the room to lose The Game and say so… on and on without end. Some schools have banned The Game precisely because it can sometimes cause an ongoing disruption – particularly when a student loses The Game during a test, and says so.

How do you make others lose The Game?

You can make others lose The Game via text or email, or by passing a note – or by wearing a T-shirt that says 'You Just Lost The Game'. The only problem is that whenever you make someone lose The Game in this fashion, they'll say 'I lost The Game' and then you'll lose too.

An even sneakier strategy is making other players lose The Game *while you're not around*. Write the phrase 'The Game' or 'You just lost The Game' on a piece of paper and sneak it into a friend's schoolbook, or their desk, for example. Some players write 'The Game' or 'You just lost The Game' on five-pound notes, on stickers, on webpages, and other places that people might stumble upon. You might get into trouble for trying some of these strategies – so avoid vandalism and graffiti.

We've scattered the phrases 'The Game' and 'You just lost The Game' throughout this book. Now you know why.

Illustration by Chris Piascik

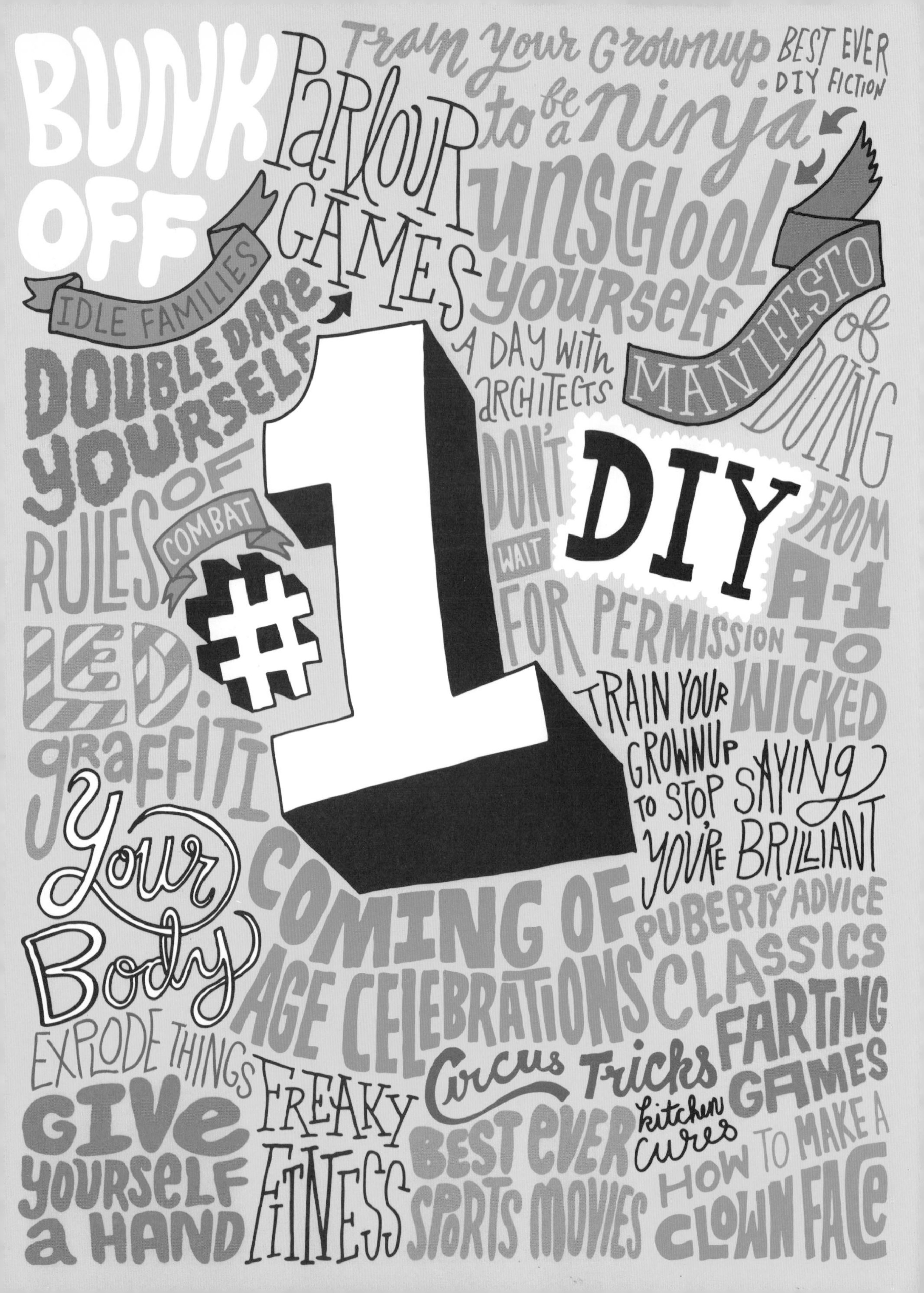

BUNK OFF

IDLE FAMILIES

TRAIN YOUR GROWNUP to be a ninja

BEST EVER DIY FICTION

PARLOUR GAMES

UNSCHOOL YOURSELF

MANIFESTO of DOING

DOUBLE DARE YOURSELF

A DAY WITH ARCHITECTS

RULES OF COMBAT

DON'T WAIT FOR PERMISSION

 # 1

DIY

FROM A-1 TO WICKED

L.E.D. graffiti

TRAIN YOUR GROWNUP TO STOP SAYING YOU'RE BRILLIANT

Your Body

COMING OF AGE CELEBRATIONS

PUBERTY ADVICE CLASSICS

EXPLODE THINGS

GIVE YOURSELF a HAND

FREAKY FITNESS

Circus Tricks

kitchen cures

FARTING GAMES

BEST EVER SPORTS MOVIES

HOW TO MAKE A CLOWN FACE

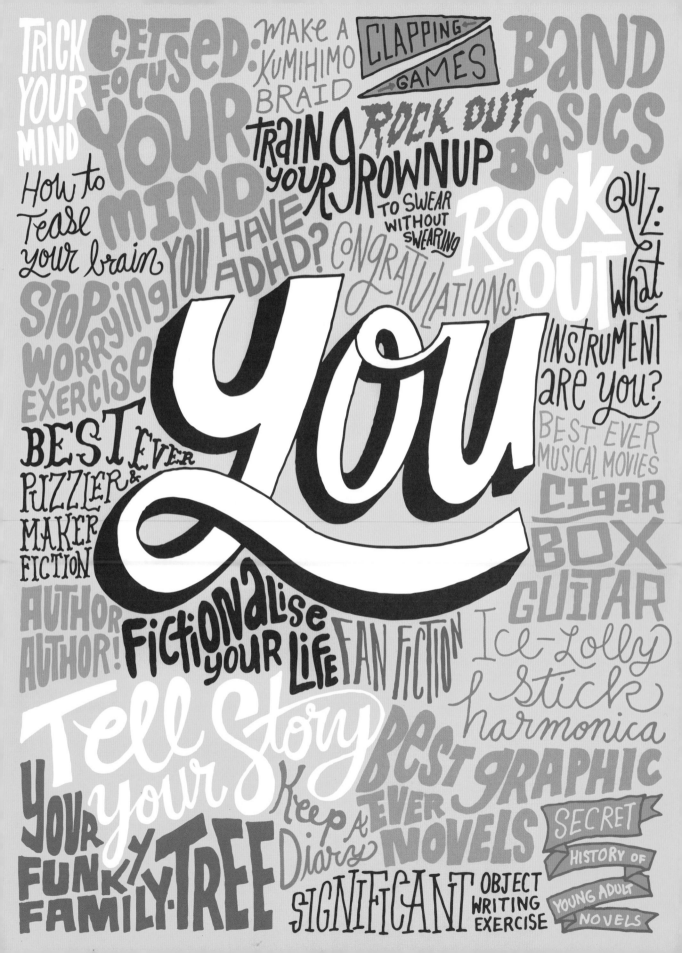

IDLE
FAMILIES

Q&A WITH TOM HODGKINSON

Kids spend too much time staring at TV and computer screens, videogames, MP3 players, and mobile phones. Meanwhile, busy grownups over-schedule their kids with after-school sports, chess, violin, gymnastics and karate lessons, not to mention homework and tutoring.

Tom Hodgkinson, who edits a magazine called *The Idler*, claims that kids and grownups alike would be happier if they'd spend less time doing these things, and more time idling – chilling out, that is.

Tom lives on a farm in Devon with his wife, Victoria Hull, and their children Arthur, Delilah, and Henry. We asked him for pointers on idling for the whole family.

PARLOUR GAMES

By Josh

Before the invention of boardgames, not to mention radio, movies and TV, parlour games were popular in England and the United States. Parlour games involve sophisticated wordplay, dramatic skill, cultural knowledge, and sometimes a little bit of good-humoured play fighting.

You may already be familiar with parlour games like Charades, Twenty Questions, and Dictionary; here are a few fun ones my mother taught me. (Thanks Mum!)

Coffeepot

One player leaves the room; the others choose an activity that she commonly performs. For example: 'take the bus to school', 'watch football on TV'. The player who left the room is then called back in. She tries to discover what the mystery activity is by asking yes/no questions, substituting the word 'coffeepot' for the verb. For example: 'Do I coffeepot outdoors?' 'Do I coffeepot with friends?' She continues until she's figured it out; or you can give her a certain number of tries.

A Coffeepot variation

Here's another version. One player leaves the room; the others choose a common noun or verb.

The first player returns and tries to discover the mystery word by asking each player a different question. The answers don't need to be truthful, but they must include the mystery word – however, instead of actually saying that word, the player says 'coffeepot'.

So, if the mystery word is 'campervan', and the first question is 'What does your family do for fun?' the answer might be: 'We take our coffeepot to the park and go rollerblading.' If the second question is 'Who is your favourite movie monster?' the answer might be: 'King Kong, because he squashes coffeepots as he stomps down the street.'

Illustrations by Heather Kasunick

UNBORED: What's an idler?

HODGKINSON: An idler is not just somebody who is lazy. An idler is someone who wants to enjoy their life and enjoy lots of freedom in their life.

UNBORED: One of the books you've written is called *The Idle Parent: Why Less Means More When Raising Kids*. How would you describe an idler family?

HODGKINSON: It's a family where the grownups have plenty of time to be at home. Idler families are not rich in money, but they are rich in time. My family spends a lot of time playing games. We take time to sit around the table and eat properly. We eat home-cooked food. We have animals everywhere. And we have lots of books.

UNBORED: Do idler grownups raise irresponsible children?

HODGKINSON: No – idlers raise children who are more independent and do more for themselves. Children should be useful in the household, not just a burden. If kids need their sports equipment, for example, they are responsible for finding it – not their grownups.

UNBORED: Is an idler kid the same thing as a lazy kid?

HODGKINSON: Kids aren't lazy, even if they do like to flop out in front of the television sometimes. They're really busy little creatures. My oldest son, Arthur, is good with computers and started working at our London shop, The Idler Academy, when he was 11. Delilah is good at taking care of animals – so she cleans the ferret cage, feeds the chickens and looks after her cat. It's great to harness kids' energy.

UNBORED: How late should kids allow their grownups to sleep on weekends?

HODGKINSON: Until at least 9.30 or 10 a.m! Most kids can make their own breakfast, whether it's a bowl of cereal or toast. Also, grownups aren't supposed to be entertainment centres.

First Sentence

Also known as The Book Game, the only equipment required for First Sentence is a pile of paperback books, some identical slips of paper and some pencils.

One player picks a book; she is that round's designated Reader. The Reader shows the others the book's cover, reads the description from its back cover, then copies the book's first sentence onto a slip of paper.

Each of the other players takes a few minutes to dream up a possible first sentence for that book: if it's a romance, the first sentence might be something like, 'Laura had been watching Harold for days.' Each player writes his or her made-up sentence onto a slip of paper, signs his or her initials underneath it, and hands the slip to the Reader.

The Reader reads each slip silently to herself, shuffles all the slips up, then reads them aloud. Each player then votes on which sentence he or she suspects is the real one, from the actual book.

If you correctly deduce the actual first sentence, you are awarded two points; if someone votes for your invented sentence, you are awarded one point. Keep track of your points – after each player has had a chance to be the Reader, whoever has earned the highest score is the winner.

UNBORED: What do idler families do on holidays?

HODGKINSON: A camping holiday with a large group is the best. There's lots of company, both for the adults and the children. You cook outdoors together. There are lots of laughs. And camping is really cheap. Also, in Britain, we have huge summer festivals that are dedicated to music or literature or drama. We recently went to a festival with 10,000 people.

many Hands make light work.

UNBORED: Do idler grownups allow their kids to have friends over, or would that make the household too un-peaceful?

HODGKINSON: Friends are an important part of being an idler. There's a saying that 'Many hands make light work', and I think it's true that when you have a lot of friends over, life is easier.

Go camping on your next holiday!

Wink Murder

This game requires at least six players. In each round of Wink Murder, one player is assigned the role of Murderer, and one the role of Detective; the other players are Victims.

Write 'Murderer' and 'Detective' on slips of paper, mix them up with other slips that read 'Victim', and get everyone to pick a slip out of a bowl.

The players sit in a circle; everyone must be able to see everyone else's face. The Detective reveals her identity to the group, then the round begins. One by one, the Murderer makes eye contact with a Victim and 'murders' him – by winking at him. (If you are winked at, you must 'die' dramatically.) The objective of the Murderer is to wink-murder as many players as possible before the Detective identifies him. The objective of the Detective is to identify and accuse the Murderer. She may only make one accusation; if she guesses incorrectly, the Murderer wins.

Wink Murder variations

There are several variants of Wink Murder. In one, the Detective must sit in the centre of the circle of players. In another, the Detective is allowed to make one or two wrong accusations. In another variant,

an Accomplice may kill one Victim; if she is accused, the Murderer wins.

In the game Vampire Murder, the Murderer is a Vampire; she kills not by winking but by baring her teeth.

Botticelli

Though it began as a parlour game, Botticelli is fun on car trips, too.

The Chooser thinks of a famous person, announces the first letter of their name (last name, usually; but if that makes the game too difficult, it can be either a first or last name), then answers questions asked by the other players (the Guessers). The mystery figure might be a prime minister, athlete, musician, or actor,

UNBORED: What sorts of skills should grownups teach kids?

HODGKINSON: Making a fire, sewing, learning languages, and other useful skills. But imaginary play should be up to kids, not grownups – because kids are better at making things up.

UNBORED: Idlers like to have fun, and videogames are fun. Do idler parents approve of them?

HODGKINSON: Computer and videogames in moderation are fun, but the games and the equipment they are played on are very expensive. Grownups have to work harder to afford them, which means they have less time to spend having fun with their kids. Parlour games – old-fashioned games that require only a paper and pencil, and maybe a pack of cards – are less expensive, and best of all, instead of staring at a screen alone you're sitting around the table looking at each other. There is a lot more laughter in those games.

UNBORED: Is there anything about the internet and social media that idler parents consider OK?

HODGKINSON: My son is on a social gaming and networking site called The Casual Collective. It's quite good. He's meeting kids who are home-schooled. They correct each other's spelling and grammar… and build their own web browsers.

UNBORED: What can kids do to fight back against a society that disapproves of idlers?

HODGKINSON: The best way to fight back is to create your own fun. Don't rely on the computer and television to entertain you, or else you will never learn how not to be bored. Ride a bicycle – a fantastic invention that gives you tons of independence at a low cost. Learn about animals. Experiment with electricity. Learn how to be a good cook. Discover carpentry. Be interested in books and reading. Learn how to grow food, create a zine, play an instrument. The more you can do for yourself, the more independent you are.

for example; or perhaps a fictional character from a novel, cartoon show, or comic book.

No fair picking someone obscure! The figure has to be very famous – like Wayne Rooney, Scooby-Doo, Taylor Swift, Hermione Granger, or Spider-Man.

A Guesser must think of a famous person or character whose name begins with the same first letter as the mystery figure's name; for example, if the mystery figure is *X Factor* host Dermot O'Leary, and the initial announced is 'D', perhaps a Guesser will think of Dame Judi Dench. Using some detail about Dame Judi Dench, the Guesser would then ask the Chooser an indirect question; in this case, the question might be: 'Are you a famous actor?'

If the Chooser replies, 'No, I am not Dame Judi Dench' (or another famous actor whose name begins with 'D'), then it becomes another Guesser's turn.

The Yes/No round

If the Chooser replies, 'I give up,' because she can't think of anyone who fits the criteria, then the Guesser reveals who they were thinking of, and asks the Chooser direct yes/no questions about the mystery figure – continuing to do so until the Chooser answers with a 'No'. ('Are you a real person?'

'Yes.' 'Are you a man?' 'Yes.' 'Are you on TV?' 'Yes.' 'Are you an actor?' 'No.')

How to win (or lose) Botticelli

If a Guesser deduces the mystery figure's identity ('You're Dermot O'Leary!'), then he becomes the next Chooser; however, if the Guesser is mistaken in his guess, then he's out of the game. If every Guesser guesses incorrectly, or if they're all stumped, then the Chooser wins.

DOUBLE DARE
YOURSELF

AN EXCERPT FROM

ANNE OF GREEN GABLES

by Lucy Maud Montgomery

Anne of Green Gables (**1908**) was written by Canadian author Lucy Maud Montgomery. An elderly brother and sister try to adopt an orphan boy to help with chores at Green Gables, their farm on Prince Edward Island. By mistake, the orphanage sends a mischief-making, talkative, 11-year-old girl named Anne Shirley. In this scene, Anne demonstrates her impressive commitment to bunking off – no matter what the consequences.

Josie Pye dared Jane Andrews to hop on her left leg around the garden without stopping once or putting her right foot to the ground; which Jane Andrews gamely tried to do, but gave out at the third corner and had to confess herself defeated.

Josie's triumph being rather more pronounced than good taste permitted, Anne Shirley dared her to walk along the top of the board fence which bounded the garden to the east. Now, to 'walk' board fences requires more skill and steadiness of head and heel than one might suppose who has never tried it. But Josie Pye, if deficient in some qualities that make for popularity, had at least a natural and inborn gift, duly cultivated, for walking board fences. Josie walked the Barry fence with an airy unconcern which seemed to imply that a little thing like that wasn't worth a 'dare'. Reluctant admiration greeted her exploit, for most of the other girls could appreciate it, having suffered many things themselves in their efforts to walk fences. Josie descended from her perch, flushed with victory, and darted a defiant glance at Anne.

Anne tossed her red braids.

'I don't think it's such a very wonderful thing to walk a little, low, board fence,' she said. 'I knew a girl in Marysville who could walk the ridgepole of a roof.'

'I don't believe it,' said Josie flatly. 'I don't believe anybody could walk a ridgepole. *You* couldn't, anyhow.'

'Couldn't I?' cried Anne rashly.

'Then I dare you to do it,' said Josie defiantly.

'I dare you to climb up there and walk the ridgepole of Mr Barry's kitchen roof.'

Anne turned pale, but there was clearly only one thing to be done. She walked toward the house, where a ladder was leaning against the kitchen roof. All the fifth-class girls said, 'Oh!' partly in excitement, partly in dismay.

'Don't you do it, Anne,' entreated Diana. 'You'll fall off and be killed. Never mind Josie Pye. It isn't fair to dare anybody to do anything so dangerous.'

'I must do it. My honour is at stake,' said Anne solemnly. 'I shall walk that ridgepole, Diana, or perish in the attempt. If I am killed you are to have my pearl bead ring.'

Anne climbed the ladder amid breathless silence, gained the ridgepole, balanced herself uprightly on that precarious footing, and started to walk along it, dizzily conscious that she was uncomfortably high up in the world and that walking ridgepoles was not a thing in which your imagination helped you out much. Nevertheless, she managed to take several steps before the catastrophe came. Then she swayed, lost her balance, stumbled, staggered, and fell, sliding down over the sun-baked roof and crashing off it through the tangle of Virginia creeper beneath – all before the dismayed circle below could give a simultaneous, terrified shriek. […]

'Anne, are you killed?' shrieked Diana, throwing herself on her knees beside her friend. 'Oh, Anne, dear Anne, speak just one word to me and tell me if you're killed.'

To the immense relief of all the girls, and especially of Josie Pye, who, in spite of lack of imagination, had been seized with horrible visions of a future branded as the girl who was the cause of Anne Shirley's early and tragic death, Anne sat dizzily up and answered uncertainly:

'No, Diana, I am not killed, but I think I am rendered unconscious.'

RULES OF
COMBAT

By Josh

Though some grownups' first reaction to rowdy physical interaction – from pillow fights to wrestling – is to say 'Cut it out!' play fighting is good for kids.

Sure, you might get a few scrapes and bruises, but it's a great way to let off steam. Besides, studies of rough-and-tumble play have found that kids who do it more at home get better marks (and make better friends) than those who don't!

Play fighting teaches you where you end and the world begins, and it helps you bond with friends and family – as long as no one is injured. In order to prevent bruises and hurt feelings, my family has agreed on the following Rules of Combat.

DO

1. Remove your shoes.
2. Play fight on a soft surface.
3. Shove, grab, leg-sweep.
4. If you're going to punch your opponent, do so lightly on the arms, legs, back, chest. Never punch the stomach, neck, face or head, or private parts.
5. Use only safe wrestling holds. For example, the Body Scissors, where you squeeze your opponent (lightly) between your legs, is OK.

DON'T

1. Choke, strangle, or smother. This means no choke-holds or headlocks, and no covering your opponent's mouth or nose.
2. Kick. You can use your feet to block an attack, but don't use them as a weapon.
3. Bite, scratch, pinch, head-butt, or pull hair.
4. Use weapons or throw stuff. Except a pillow.
5. Bend necks, elbows, knees, ankles, wrists, fingers, or toes in the wrong direction.
6. Yell or scream in your opponent's ear.
7. Drop your opponent on their head or neck.

ALSO

If somebody says 'Stop!' then you must stop wrestling immediately.

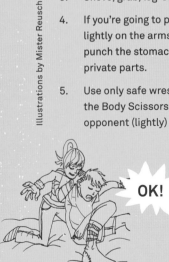

Illustrations by Mister Reusch

MAKE LED GRAFFITI

Because they are so efficient, LEDs (light-emitting diodes) are used in digital clocks, Christmas lights, torches, traffic signals, and all sorts of electronic devices. With the help of a cheap lithium battery and some tape, LEDs can also be used to build tiny 'glowies' that shine colourfully in the dark. Add a powerful magnet, and, like some guerrilla artists do, you can make temporary 'graffiti'.

You'll need:

- At least twenty 10mm diffused superbright LEDs. Try to get a mix of different colours. These are available at electronics shops, and also many websites – including Amazon.
- Twenty 3V lithium batteries, size CR2032
- 20 'rare earth' magnets: nickel-plated, disc-shaped, 12mm diameter x 3mm thick. One example of a rare earth element is neodymium (which has the chemical symbol Nd). So when shopping for these magnets, one description you might see is: 12mm-diameter x 3mm-thick NdFeB Disc Magnet, Ni-Cu-Ni plated. Another description for the same magnet might be: Neodymium magnets, 12mm x 3mm disc.
- Strong 25mm-wide tape. Use gaffer tape or electrical tape.

Try this:

1. Study your LEDs. Each one has a longer leg (known as the anode) and a shorter leg (known as the cathode).

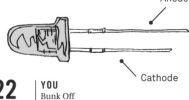

Anode

Cathode

2. Study your batteries. A disc-shaped lithium battery's positive (+) terminal extends around the sides of the battery; its negative (-) terminal is smaller.

3. Study your magnets. They are very powerful, so don't place one near a card with a magnetic strip – you might ruin the card. Same thing goes for computer hard drives.

    Touch the LED's anode to the battery's positive terminal, and its cathode to the battery's negative terminal. (Careful! If you touch the cathode to the battery's positive terminal, you might ruin the LED.) If the LED doesn't light up, try another LED. Experiment with adding more than one LED to a single battery.

4. Keeping the LED's legs in place, wrap a small strip of tape tightly around the battery. You've just made an LED glowie.

Illustrations by Mister Reusch

CODE RED! Some grownups are paranoid about devices made of LED lights, batteries and tape; they're worried they might be explosive devices. So don't use these devices in airports or attempt to carry them onto aeroplanes. And you might not want to bring them to school, unless you have permission from your teacher to do so.

5. Place a magnet on the battery's positive terminal (over the tape). Wrap some more tape around the magnet. Now you've converted your LED glowie into an LED throwie.

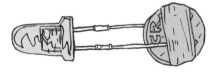

Lightly throw – that's why they're called 'throwies' – your LED device onto the refrigerator door, or other ferromagnetic surfaces. (Why won't magnets stick to some metals? Look it up!)

Walk around your neighbourhood tossing throwies onto appropriate metal objects (not cars, you might scratch the paint). Try to form patterns and designs. When you're finished enjoying your throwies, take them down again, otherwise your neighbours might object.

Take your glowies apart when you're not using them, so the batteries will last longer.

RECYCLING
BATTERIES

When the lithium batteries in your glowies or throwies stop working, don't throw them out with the rubbish. Batteries contain a number of heavy metals and toxic chemicals; when they are thrown out, they can contaminate the soil and pollute groundwater. Instead, drop them off at a household hazardous waste facility, or participate in one of the many battery recycling programmes that are available.

Many shops that sell electronics have recycling receptacles that will accept most types of batteries; if the battery is not recyclable, the shop will get rid of it safely. One of the recycling processes available for lithium-containing batteries involves recovering the lithium and selling it back to battery manufacturers.

EXPLODE
THINGS

By Elizabeth

While these experiments are pretty safe, you never know what's going to happen so always use caution. Goggles are necessary, and a grownup should supervise. Things can get messy, so only do these activities outside in a wide-open space.

BASIC GEYSER

This chemical reaction became famous when viral YouTube videos showed choreographed plumes of Diet Coke shooting into the air.

You'll need:

- 2 litre plastic bottle of Diet Coke
- 6 Mentos sweets
- Piece of paper rolled into a tube
- Small piece of cardboard
- An open area at least 20 sq metres big
- Grownup supervision

Try this:

1. Set the bottle on the ground and remove the cap, then put the cardboard on top.

2. Put the Mentos into the rolled tube of paper. Then hold the tube upside down on top of the piece of cardboard so that the bottom Mento is resting on the cardboard.

3. Pull the cardboard out from under the tube so that the Mentos drop into the bottle.

4. Run! The reaction happens the instant that the Mentos land in the Diet Coke. PS: The Guinness World Record for the largest number of simultaneous Mentos and fizzy drink geysers is 2,865. It was achieved in Manila (Philippines) in 2010.

Illustrations by Mister Reusch

GEYSER ROCKET

When properly executed, these rockets can really take off – and could easily break a window! So it's best to do this activity in an open field or empty car park.

You'll need:

- 500ml plastic bottle of Diet Coke
- 2 Mentos sweets
- A cement surface in an open area at least 95 sq metres big
- Grownup supervision

Try this:

1. Remove the cap from the Diet Coke bottle.
2. Chew the Mentos until they become pliable. Take them out of your mouth and cram them into the bottlecap. This is your rocket's fuel.
3. Screw the bottlecap onto the bottle.
4. Shake the bottle once. Quickly turn it upside down and throw it onto the cement – the idea is to smack the bottlecap on the ground so forcefully that it cracks or breaks.
5. Duck! This baby really flies – when my kids and I tried this activity, the rocket flew 15 metres.

Try turning a larger fizzy drink bottle into a rocket. Just make sure you do it where you can't damage anyone or anything – like someone's car or house.

DELUXE GEYSER

You'll need:

- 2 litre bottle of Diet Coke
- 4 Mentos sweets
- Needle and thread
- Drill (or hammer and nails)
- A cement surface in an open area at least 50 sq metres big
- Grownup supervision

Try this:

1. Thread your needle. Double your thread and tie a knot when both lengths of thread are 30cm long.
2. Thread four Mentos and push them down the double strand of thread until they rest on the knot. Getting the needle through the Mentos can be tough. Try putting a Mentos on a table, pushing the needle halfway through, then picking it up to shove the needle the rest of the way through. (Be careful!) When you're done, leave the needle on the thread.
3. Take off the bottle's top. Using a power drill or a hammer and nail, make a hole in the middle of the bottletop. If you want to make your geyser look more like a fancy fountain, drill three holes. (PS: Do a web search for 'mentos geyser tube' and you'll see that some companies now sell special tubes that screw onto plastic bottles.)
4. Push the needle upward through the bottom of one of the bottlecap's holes. Pull the thread through the hole until the Mentos are flush against the underside of the bottlecap.
5. While holding the thread tightly, so the Mentos stay flush against the bottlecap, cut the needle off the thread. (You will probably need a helper.)
6. Screw the bottlecap onto the full bottle of diet cola, still holding the thread tightly. Then let go of the thread so the Mentos drop into the cola.
7. Run! The cola has to force itself through small holes, so this version of the geyser shoots higher – and lasts longer – than the basic geyser.

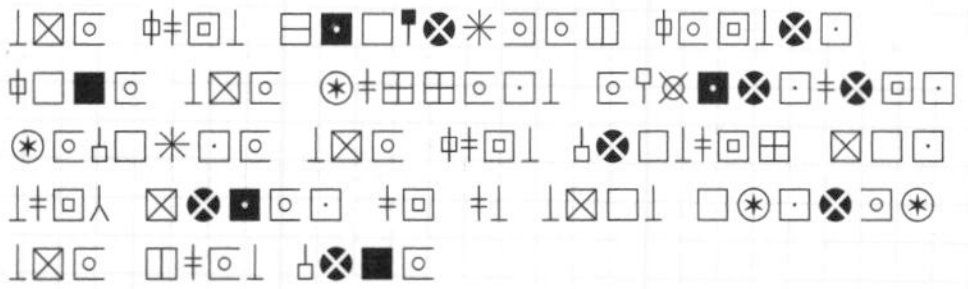

BAGGIE BOMB

I read about this in a book and found a few variations online. This is the version my kids and I like best.

You'll need:

- Sealable sandwich bags
- Paper towels or tissue
- Bicarbonate of soda
- Vinegar
- Warm water
- Grownup supervision

Try this:

1. Make sure your bag has no holes by filling it halfway with water. Then zip it shut and turn it upside down. If nothing leaks out, empty out the water.

2. Tear a sheet of paper towel into a square that's approximately 15cm x 15cm. Or just grab a piece of tissue.

3. Put the bicarbonate of soda into the towel or tissue and fold it so that the powder is inside. This is your 'charge' (a measured quantity of explosive material).

4. Pour 120ml vinegar and 60ml warm water into the bag. Seal the bag halfway.

5. Quickly put the charge into the bag. Seal the bag entirely, put it on the ground, and stand back at least a metre, or duck behind shelter.

6. Explosion time!

⬚¶⬚⬚⬚‡⬚⬚⬚ ⬚‡⬚ ⬚⬚⬚✳⬚⬚⬚ ⬚⬚⬚
⬚⬚⬚⬚⬚ ⬚⬚⬚⬚⬚⬚⬚✳⬚⬚ ⬚⬚ ⬚⬚⬚
⬚⬚‡⬚⬚ ⬚⬚⬚‡⬚⬚⬚‡⬚⬚ ⬚⬚⬚⬚⬚⬚ ⬚⬚⬚
⬚⬚⬚ ⬚⬚⬚⊞

TRAIN YOUR GROWNUP
TO BE A NINJA

By Josh

When I was 13 and my brother was 12, we watched *A Shot in the Dark*, the second movie of the Pink Panther series.

The bumbling Inspector Clouseau (Peter Sellers) shares his home with a manservant named Cato (Burt Kwouk). The character of Cato was a spoof on Kato, a character from *The Green Hornet*, a popular 1930s–40s radio show about a crime fighter and his karate-chopping sidekick.

In order to keep Clouseau's combat skills keen and his alertness sharp, Cato leaps screaming out of various hiding places – including the refrigerator. After we saw this movie, my brother Patrick and I started doing the same thing to each other – hiding behind doors and under tables, then POW!

Turns out this is an exciting game for a kid to play with his grownup. In my house, you never know when someone will leap out from behind a door, screaming like a maniac and throwing karate chops. You've got to be prepared to defend yourself at every moment.

Try this:

1. Always be ready for an attack. Particularly when you're waking up in the morning, or stepping into the hallway from your bedroom – or even from the bathroom. Peek around corners.

2. Martial arts star Bruce Lee played a brilliant Kato in the American TV show *Green Hornet*, which came out at the same time as *A Shot in the Dark*. Try practising what Bruce Lee called the 'Way of the Intercepting Fist' – which means that instead of first blocking an attack and then counter-attacking (like you see in kung fu movies), you attack your opponent *while he is about to attack you*. It's very effective, if you're speedy enough.

3. My son Max offers this advice: If you're smaller than your opponent, you've got to get inside his or her 'reach'. This means getting as close to your opponent as possible. Also, if you want to knock down someone who is bigger than you, tackle them at the knees or ankles.

4. Never give up, even if you're pinned down.

5. If your opponent says 'Stop', then you must stop fighting immediately!

Illustration by Mister Reusch

UNSCHOOL YOURSELF

By Zoe Cordes Selbin

I never really went to school until I started university. My older sister, Jesse, and I were homeschooled.

When I was five years old, my parents decided homeschooling was a better choice for Jesse than the school she was to enter that autumn.

It wasn't that the schools in my Texas town near Austin were bad, or that Jesse was having any problems academically or socially. But Jesse was different from many other kids her age – rather than shop at the mall and watch Britney Spears videos, she was more interested in making her own clothes, reading Shakespeare, and listening to rock and roll. My mum and dad thought she'd get a more meaningful education, and have more fun, if she was allowed to learn by exploring her own interests – instead of being required to stick to the national curriculum.

My mum is a freelance writer whose office is in our house, so she was our main teacher. My dad is a political science professor, and he did his part, too. For subjects that my parents weren't as knowledgeable about, such as more advanced maths and sciences, I took classes at a local community college. I loved it!

Homeschooling enabled me to pursue my passions, including my love of music. I began writing music criticism when I was in primary school; by the time I hit Year 7, I was submitting my record reviews to local and national magazines – and getting published. I also joined a student radio show on a community station in Austin and began interviewing bands.

Through my journalism, I eventually met and interviewed not only bands, but authors, filmmakers, and politicians. My work on the radio show helped me get internships (on-the-job

apprenticeships) at public relations firms, advertising firms, booking agencies and record labels. I've also gone on tour with bands. If I'd been tied down to a normal school schedule, I never would have had these opportunities.

Throughout it all, I kept up my schoolwork, took the exams, got into university and got my qualifications at the same time as my friends attending traditional schools.

I know that homeschooling is not for everyone. Even so, you can make learning so much more interesting and joyful by 'unschooling' yourself – which is to say, taking control of your own education. You will need to work closely with your grownups to accomplish your goals, but at the end of the day it's up to you to make it happen.

Get involved in activities that aren't connected to your school

School-related extracurriculars are great, but they aren't the only thing out there. Being part of a teen radio show changed my life! If you are interested in the media, you can explore local community radio stations, TV stations, smaller newspapers and websites. If you're interested in music and arts, get involved in community choirs and orchestras, or volunteer at an art gallery. If you like sports, look into joining community and citywide teams or helping with sports programmes – like refereeing games for younger kids.

Illustrations by Mister Reusch

Apprentice yourself

If you know grownups who have cool jobs – whether it's a football coach, a hairstylist or an architect – ask if you can help out around their work, even if it's just for a day or two. In Austin, homeschoolers as young as 11 have apprenticed with videogame makers. The videogame companies get free help. The students get invaluable experience in a line of work that's almost never taught at school. Homeschoolers have also apprenticed with chefs, working alongside them in the kitchen.

Because you're young, some grownups will assume you can't handle a lot of responsibility – so they won't want to take you on as an intern or apprentice. It's wise to gain real-world experience by doing your first internship with your grownup, or a relative, or a family friend, who already knows you. This grownup can then reassure others that you're trustworthy. Also, make a good impression! Before you ask for an opportunity, rehearse your request until you sound responsible and mature. And if you write to or email someone – even if it's your uncle – proofread your writing to make sure it's mistake-free.

Don't limit yourself to one school

Homeschooling allowed me to learn wherever I could. As I entered my teens, I sat in on university classes and took community college classes, where I got to discuss issues with older people who had more experiences and different worldviews. Even if you go to a traditional school, universities, technical colleges, and even community centres offer classes on anything from computer programming to knitting or stop-motion animation.

A DAY WITH ARCHITECTS
By Peter Schleisman

The summer before going into Year 8, I spent a day at an architecture firm in my city. I know Paul and Mark, the architects, because they are friends of my parents and they designed an addition to our house. They knew I was interested in architecture so they invited me to see what they do.

I did a lot of things that day, including practising AutoCAD, a computer program that architects use to create floor plans and layouts. By using this program, I found out that architects have to get measurements *exactly* right. It's also really hard to figure out how thick the walls are of the building you are designing.

My favourite part of the visit was seeing all the projects Mark and Paul have designed, including a resort in Morocco that fits perfectly into the landscape of North Africa.

My dad works in a school and my mum's office is at home, so this was the first time I'd ever been in a real office. I didn't expect it to be so casual – everyone there works together and knows each other so well. I was also surprised that architects don't have to use a lot of complicated maths. Paul and Mark told me that's just a rumour. That was a relief to me because I'm not the best at maths and I hope that one day I can design skyscrapers.

I wrote my thank-you note on Google SketchUp, a free program that lets you design pretty much anything. I saw someone in the office using it and now it's my favourite computer program. Plus, I knew my parents wanted me to write one and would not say no to this idea – and then they'd have to give me more computer time.

Love skateboarding and making movies? Do both at once – for a school project.

Make your passions part of your schoolwork

So you love videogames? Ask your history teacher if you can write an essay on the history of videogames. Or ask your music teacher if you can do a project on videogame soundtracks. If you love films, ask your science teacher if – instead of writing an essay – you can make a film for a class assignment. If you love art, ask your maths teacher if you can write about the place of maths in art – for example, 'the golden ratio'. Or ask your English teacher if you can read a book about art history.

Seek out groups of like-minded people

Volunteer with political campaigns or other groups that focus on issues you care about, from environmental causes to animal rights to literacy issues. Just dive in and ask questions about what you want to know – most people love to talk about their passions and share information. They'll help you meet others with the same interests.

Make the most of wherever you live

As soon as we could demonstrate to our grownups that we could handle the responsibilities of venturing away from home on our own, my homeschooled friends and I took advantage of all that Austin had to offer – including arts programmes, public pools, museums, and just walking around the city and exploring! Even if you're stuck in class during the school day, you can still explore the city or countryside on your own after school.

Enjoy yourself – and believe in yourself!

The most important thing to do with your education is to *have as much fun as possible and never doubt your ability to push yourself.* If you are required to read over the summer, don't waste time on a book you don't love. If you have any leeway on an assignment, tailor it to your interests. Take harder classes, whenever possible – because they are often more interesting. Get to know your teachers, who are often great people with cool ideas on how to make your education work best for you.

MANIFESTO
OF DOING

By Bre Pettis & Kio Stark

We once published a 'Manifesto of Done', which told people not to worry about doing things perfectly.

Instead, we urged them to get stuff done, learn from their mistakes, then get more stuff done! Our manifesto was very popular, so here's some advice for kids who want to grow up happy and creative… while getting lots of stuff done.

Do what you love
This above all else. You have to give yourself to things to find out if you love them. When you grow up, if you can find a career that lets you do some of the things you love now, you'll be both lucky and happy. So figure out what gives you satisfaction and do as much of it as possible.

Develop expertise
Pick a subject and become an expert on it. It could be beekeeping, explosives, football stats or the Angel of the North. Whatever it is, figure out everything you can about it. If your subject is something that can be done, find a way to do it.

Express yourself without words
Practise 'blind contour drawing', which is both simple and hard, and very satisfying. Look at an object and choose one of its edges. As you move your eye along the object's edge, imagine that your pencil is touching the object. Let your pencil move the same way that your eye moves along the contours of the object. Don't look down at the paper until you reach the end of a line; then, place the pencil in a new position, look back at the object and repeat.

Interrogate grownups
Ask them why they chose their jobs, what cross-roads they have reached in their life, and what their hopes and dreams are. Bonus points for recording these interviews in some way – documenting is a useful skill for when you become a secret agent.

Get mobile
A bicycle isn't just transportation, it's a vehicle of independence. With a bike and the skills to repair it, you don't have to count on anybody else to go (almost) wherever you want. So learn how to fix flat tyres, and maintain your bike.

Fix stuff
When things break or become too old, take them apart and see how they work. Keep any parts that might be useful for fixing other things. Ask for tools. Learn to sew buttons back onto your clothes. Become a person who can solve problems in unexpected ways. Enjoy the satisfaction of making something work that was broken.

Make money
Understand how money works and how it's earned. If you open a cake stall, work out how much a piece of cake costs you and charge your customers more than that. Experiment with price, location, and time of day. Keep notes.

Share what you know
Sharing knowledge and skills will make you friends and build your community – and it's an important way to learn. If you can teach it to someone else, then you truly know what you're doing.

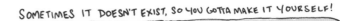

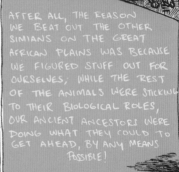

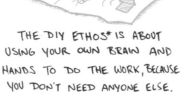

Comic by Joe Alterio

TRAIN YOUR GROWNUP
TO STOP SAYING
YOU'RE BRILLIANT

By Elizabeth

If you're like my kids, you're probably used to hearing your grownups tell you that you're *fantastic* at anything you try.

If you so much as walk on the football pitch, you're *brilliant*. Ditto taking a tiny bite of salmon or spinach or anything that doesn't involve tomato sauce and cheese. Make your bed every morning? *You rock!* Complete your homework on time? *Cool!*

The problem with this constant encouragement is simple: kids are smart. You know when you've worked hard and when you haven't. According to some experts who figure out how to help kids live happy lives, getting a pat on the back for ordinary tasks doesn't make you feel better about yourself. In fact, it might make you less happy.

Why? Being told that you are *utterly smashing* even when you aren't can make you feel like your grownups expect you to be *fantastic* at everything you try. And that's just unrealistic. Experts say it takes 10 years to be great at something. You might have a safer pair of hands than other kids your age, but you're not as good as a professional goalkeeper for a simple reason: you haven't logged enough hours to truly perfect your positioning.

It's hard for your grownups not to gush over every little thing you do. But there are serious consequences to being constantly pumped up with false praise. Kids who get used to a steady stream of *brilliant!* are more likely to cheat – because they worry that their grownups *need* them to be exceptional. They're also more likely to brag, which is not the most appealing quality when it comes to making and keeping friends. Worst-case scenario for kids who feel like they can't be accepted for who they truly are? Depression, eating disorders, and anxiety.

Most people have both natural talents *and* challenges. If sitting still during lessons is hard for you, then it's a genuine accomplishment to finish a long novel or to write a report. And I hope your grownups tell you that the effort you are making is terrific and that they cheer for you when you try hard at sports or learn a new song on the flute. But I also hope you'll tell them you want to celebrate being ordinary. Admitting that you aren't exceptional won't make you a loser. Instead it will help you see that you are just like everyone else you know.

Illustration by Heather Kasunick

Need some help turning off the *brilliant!* tap? Try these tips:

Don't expect junk praise for cutting the grass or walking the dog

Unless you are doing them for the very first time, those tasks are just part of being a family and only merit a simple though heartfelt *thank you*.

Be patient

Don't expect to be even passably good at something you're attempting for the first time. Mastering a new skill takes practice.

Be realistic

No one is perfect. The ability to be honest about your strengths and your challenges is a more important life skill than being the best at something.

Make the most of your mistakes

Instead of working yourself into a frenzy to avoid messing up, embrace your mistakes as a normal part of any learning process.

Remember that life is full of disappointments

Every person on the planet gets seriously bummed out from time to time. Things won't always go the way you hope they will. Your grownup should comfort you without making an ordinary disappointment into a huge deal.

Gag the bragging

Sure, you should celebrate when you've done something well, but blabbing about your successes – especially if you're puffing them up to be more than they really are – just keeps people at a distance. Your friends should like you for who you are, not because you've tricked them into thinking you're exceptional at something.

Lead by example

Instead of bragging about yourself, try complimenting others when you think they've tried hard or done something particularly well.

FROM A-1
TO WICKED

You've told your grownups to stop calling you 'brilliant' so what do they do instead? They sneakily use synonyms for the B-word, of course. Don't let them get away with it! Stay on guard against the following 80 stealth terms of admiration.

- A-1
- Ace
- All that and a bag of chips
- Amazing
- Astonishing
- Astounding
- Awesome
- Bad
- Bang-up
- Bazzin'
- Beast
- Best thing since sliced bread
- Bestin'
- Boss
- Breathtaking
- Buck
- Champion
- Choice
- Cool
- Corking
- Crazy
- Cushty
- Doozie
- Dynamite
- Epic
- Excellent
- Fabulous
- Fabu
- Fantastic
- Far out
- First rate
- Fly
- Gnarly
- Grand
- Great
- Greatest
- Groovy
- Humdinger
- Incredible
- Inspired
- Jamming
- Kewl
- Killer
- Legendary
- Magnificent
- Marvellous
- Mega
- Mind-blowing
- Mint
- Nang
- Off the hook
- OMG
- Out of this world
- Outrageous
- Peachy
- Phat
- Phenomenal
- Premo
- Pwn
- Rad
- Radical
- Rainbow Dash
- Remarkable
- Rockin'
- Ronus
- Sick
- Smashing
- Splendid
- Stellar
- Stunning
- Super
- Sweet
- Terrific
- Top
- Unbelievable
- Unreal
- Wicked
- Wicked Awesome
- Winner
- Wonderful

BEST EVER
DIY FICTION

By Josh

So you've read the Harry Potter series, the Wimpy Kid series, and the Percy Jackson series? YAWN.

It's not as though these and other popular series are *terrible*. But if you enjoy books about young wizards-in-training, grumpy young teens who rebel against grownup authority and get into trouble, semi-mythical kids who carry swords, and other independent-minded adventurers and dreamers your age, there are superior options available to you.

I guarantee you'll find these DIY novels funnier and sadder, more exciting and scary, and also better-written than most of today's popular series books.

1938
THE SWORD IN THE STONE
Written and illustrated by T.H. White
A boy named Wart, who lives in medieval England, is tutored (which involves being transformed into animals and going on an adventure with Robin Hood) by a time-travelling wizard named Merlyn. The novel teaches you about falconry, jousting, and hunting a Questing Beast, without making the Middle Ages sound better than they really were – and without making Arthur seem different from any other kid. Although it's funny and exciting, it wasn't written for a young audience – so try inviting a grownup to read it aloud.

Despite a few good songs, the Disney movie version simply can't compare.

White wrote three sequels: *The Queen of Air and Darkness* (1939), *The Ill-Made Knight* (1940), and *The Candle in the Wind* (1958). They're terrific, too, but they're tough going for most kids. Instead, you might pick up *Mistress Masham's Repose* (1946), White's fantasy novel about a 10-year-old orphaned girl who discovers a race of tiny, dangerous people living in her garden.

1962
THE DIAMOND IN THE WINDOW
By Jane Langton
Eleanor and Eddy Hall, who live in Massachusetts, discover the secret attic playroom from which their aunt and uncle had disappeared at the same age. A mysterious Prince Krishna has left behind literary clues – related to the writings of former Concord residents Louisa May Alcott, Ralph Waldo Emerson, and Henry David Thoreau – which may help them free the missing children from an enchantment, and save the family home from being repossessed by the bank.

The Hall Family Chronicles are suspenseful and smart – particularly the first five. After *Diamond*, read *The Swing in the Summerhouse* (1967), *The Astonishing Stereoscope* (1971) and *The Fledgling* (1980). In the fifth book, *The Fragile Flag* (1984), five Concord kids lead an anti-nuclear-weapons Children's Crusade to Washington DC.

1962
A WRINKLE IN TIME
By Madeleine L'Engle
Madeleine L'Engle was shy and awkward as a child; so is 14-year-old Meg Murry, who wears glasses and has braces and is too good at maths to be considered cool by her classmates. When her scientist father disappears, Meg and her oddball baby brother, Charles, enlist the help of two weird neighbours (Mrs Whatsit and Mrs Who), and a basketball-playing jock. They travel through space and time to an alien planet which is dominated by IT, an evil disembodied mind that serves an evil, nearly all-powerful cosmic force called the Black Thing. Yikes!

At the time, there weren't many science-fiction books with female heroines. Also, the book explores both science and spirituality. So *Wrinkle* was rejected 26 times before it was published. In 2003, Disney made a TV version of the book, which is bad; an excellent graphic novel version came out in 2012.

L'Engle wrote three other books about Meg and Charles Murry: *A Wind in the Door* (1973), *Many Waters* (1986), and *A Swiftly Tilting Planet* (1978); and a second series about Meg's children. Good versus evil, time and space travel, science and spirituality – phew!

1964
HARRIET THE SPY
Written and illustrated by Louise Fitzhugh
Harriet is a smart, obsessive, obnoxious 11-year-old who dons a disguise every day after school, spies on eccentric neighbours, then writes judgemental, unintentionally hilarious observations about them (not to mention her family and friends) in a secret notebook that gets discovered by her schoolmates, who then gang up on her. Harriet seeks revenge.

Do *not* watch any Harriet the Spy movies – a good adaptation of the book has not been made yet.

Not quite as funny, but worth reading, are two sequels: *The Long Secret* (1965) and *Sport* (1979). Fitzhugh also wrote *Nobody's Family Is Going to Change* (1974), the heroine of which is a smart, obsessive, obnoxious girl who happens to be African-American. While you're at it, try to track down *Suzuki Beane* (1961), which Fitzhugh illustrated; it's about a girl who gets tired of her beatnik grownups, and a boy who gets tired of his stuffy grownups… so they run away.

1968
A WIZARD OF EARTHSEA
By Ursula K. Le Guin
A wizard discovers a boy with tremendous untapped magical abilities, and takes him on as an apprentice (think: Anakin Skywalker and Qui-Gon Jinn). Nicknamed Sparrowhawk, the boy enrols at a wizard school, where he makes friends and enemies (think: Harry Potter at Hogwarts). As a teenager, Sparrowhawk roams the world of Earthsea performing feats of magic until he's forced to confront his greatest nemesis: his own dark side (think: Luke Skywalker). Yes, this novel has been influential!

Sparrowhawk's grownup saga continues in *The Tombs of Atuan* (1971), *The Farthest Shore* (1972), and other books. Le Guin is also one of the greatest living science-fiction authors, though none of her sci-fi novels are written for children.

Sparrowhawk is described as having reddish-brown skin, so when the Earthsea novels were adapted for TV in 2004, Le Guin and her readers were upset that he was portrayed by a white actor.

1970
ARE YOU THERE, GOD? IT'S ME, MARGARET
By Judy Blume
Margaret, a girl in Year 7, worries about getting her first period, buys her first bra, gets crushes on boys, and tries to stick up for her opinions around her mean girl friends. What's more, she wrestles with deciding which religion (if any) she believes in; but her grownups aren't much help.

Because it deals frankly with sexual development and religion, it's one of the most frequently banned or challenged books in American schools and libraries. Whatever – it's terrific!

Blume's *Then Again, Maybe I Won't* (1971), about a 13-year-old boy who moves from a working-class, ethnic urban neighbourhood to a wealthy, snooty suburb, and who has wet dreams about a teenage girl next door, and whose new best friend is a shoplifter, is also great.

1976
THE BORRIBLES
By Michael de Larrabeiti
If you're too old and/or wised-up for Mary Norton's Borrowers series (1952–1982), which concerns a family of tiny people who live in the walls of an English house and survive by 'borrowing', then you should read this subversively unromantic take on such children's fantasy classics. Unlike the Borrowers, the Borribles (tribes of runaway children) don't borrow, they steal. Like Peter Pan

and his Lost Boys, they never get old and they're constantly at war with the grownup world – but instead of living in Neverland, they squat in London's abandoned buildings; and instead of fighting pirates, they're eluding the police. *The Borribles* and its sequels, *The Borribles Go for Broke* (1981) and *The Borribles: Across the Dark Metropolis* (1986), are violent and dark. However, the series's message – comradeship and adventure are more important than piling up material possessions – is, if you ask me, a valuable one.

PS: The Borribles' antagonists, the Rumbles, rat-like creatures who pile up wealth in an underground bunker, are a parody of the Wombles. Napoleon Boot is a parody of the Womble named Wellington, Bingo is a parody of Bungo, and so forth.

1987
WISE CHILD
By Monica Furlong
Wise Child is a nine-year-old girl living in Scotland during the eighth century, an era that historians used to call the Dark Ages because science and Christianity weren't widespread, which supposedly meant that most people were ignorant and narrow-minded. Because her grownups are missing, the villagers hand Wise Child over to Juniper, a wise, compassionate healer believed to be a witch. Though in fact she does turn out to be a *doran* (a magic-user who gets her power from the natural world), the fiercely independent Juniper isn't one bit ignorant; the village's priest, who attempts to have Juniper burned at the stake, is truly narrow-minded. Juniper teaches Wise Child magic, which involves observing nature as closely as a scientist.

Furlong also wrote *A Year and A Day* (1990; sometimes titled *Juniper*), a prequel to *Wise Child* that tells Juniper's coming of age story; and *Colman* (2004), in which Juniper, Wise Child, and a young boy struggle to save a kingdom from an evil queen.

COMING OF AGE
CELEBRATIONS

By Helen Cordes

Many cultural and religious traditions have coming of age ceremonies for kids aged 12 or 13. If a formal ceremony isn't your kind of thing, what about a party?

Having a celebration in the tween and early teen years makes sense – you're not a little kid any more, and you're mature enough to take on more grownup responsibilities and talk about complicated issues.

Maybe this all sounds a little weird – throwing a party just to say, 'Hey, I'm not a little kid any more.' True, sometimes grownups may want a coming of age party for their kid more than the kid wants it. But it doesn't have to be a ceremony. And you might be surprised at how nice it makes you feel when a group of people who are important to you gather to applaud your journey to adulthood.

My daughters are big fans of the Moonsisters coming of age ceremonies they had when they turned 13, which had wee bits of spirituality (Jewish, Christian and pagan) and big doses of 'Hooray!' about being official teenagers. Not only were these events really fun parties, the ceremonies were designed to reflect their interests.

For centuries, cultures worldwide have honoured coming of age as a very important process. After all, it's the youngsters who'll soon be running the show as the adults get older, and they'll need to know what to do. So as kids show signs of approaching adulthood around the age of 12 or so – such as a girl's first period or a boy's deepening voice – they'll start preparing for one of the biggest parties of their lives. While the celebration specifics vary widely, many involve challenges that prove readiness for the adult world – and a big party too.

American Indian Apache sunrise ceremony

In this four-day event, a girl typically builds a shelter of saplings along with her specially selected 'godmother', who teaches her tribal traditions and expectations. On the last night, she dances without stopping to songs sung by spiritual leaders until sunrise – when she receives her adult Indian name and joins in a feast with her entire community. In a similar Navajo Kinaaldà ceremony, a girl must grind corn and bake a huge cornmeal cake in an earth oven and serve it to the crowds who'll gather to honour her coming of age.

Illustrations by Mister Reusch

as early as eight years old, when they move to the unmarried male community and start learning grownup skills. At their initiation ceremony, red-painted boys often endure body cuts to show they're able to face the challenges of adulthood.

Kuna ceremonies

When a girl in the Kuna culture in Panama gets her first period, the male villagers build her a hut of leaves, where her mother and community women keep her bathed in sea water for four days. They also paint her body in jagua fruit juice to symbolise her new fertility. At the coming of age ceremony held later, her new adulthood is greeted with two days of flute songs and chants and wafts of cocoa bean incense.

THROW A PARTY

People who study coming of age ceremonies around the world point out common themes: the honoree gathers wisdom from elders; spends time alone to grow their own wisdom; gives service to the community; and finally, has an amazing celebration! What's cool for you is that there aren't any rules. You decide: your ceremony could be anything from a low-key evening with your family to a group event with friends that goes all weekend.

Aborigine walkabouts

Many Aborigine boys in Australia head out on a weeks-long journey to visit extended family and sites sacred to the 'dreamtime' myths of their culture. Their coming of age process may begin

Each kid gets to create her dream party

Be creative

In our Moonsisters group of girls and mums, each girl gets to create her dream party when she gets her first period. Our honoured Moonsister emerges dressed in something absolutely amazing – if you've ever been to a quinceañera (the coming of age ceremony for 15-year-old Latina girls), you get the picture. And we have fab food that each girl chooses.

Get guests grooving

As the guest of honour, the spotlight should be on you. But it's fun to get everybody involved, too. For example, all eyes are on the Moonsister as she walks through an arch we decorate with seasonal flowers, but later all the girls join in a spiral dance (with linked hands that symbolise our place in the long line of foremothers) that has us swirling around until we're happily exhausted. We also do fun crafts, including making paper flowers and tin-can lanterns that brighten and lighten the path of the honoree. Mask-making is a group activity that can be part of Boys to Men weekends, where boys make masks of the 'face' they'd like the world to see as they become men.

Take it outdoors

Consider throwing an outdoor party – everybody likes the freedom to move around in someplace beautiful. At some coming of age getaways, kids gather at a beautiful forest, learn outdoor skills and take off hiking with grownups. Each kid proves that they can survive just fine alone, camping for a day away from the rest, and at the end, there's an initiation to adulthood ceremony.

Talk about important stuff

Coming of age groups often work best if they're all-girl or all-boy, simply because in our culture and in most cultures, girls and boys are expected to act in different ways.

Of course, groups can include both girls and boys. At the Unyago weekend retreat (inspired by a common African coming of age ceremony) that one group of African-American grownups and kids have created, girls and boys talk together with adults about everything from friendship issues to money management – kids receive a wad of pretend money and figure out what it might take to live on their own. Then there's a big feast and a traditional African kente cloth placed on each celebrant's shoulder to symbolise their coming of age.

Show off

Everybody's got something they're good at – chess champ? Deluxe dancer? Passionate poet? Or if you've done some super service project, a coming of age celebration is the place to share your greatness and get well-deserved kudos.

Keep the party going

Coming of age celebrations can be part of an ongoing group that helps kids deal with the bumpy process of growing up. Ask a grownup to help you find one if you're interested. Or start your own.

PUBERTY
ADVICE CLASSICS

If we said that kids' bodies go through a lot of changes between primary school and secondary school, would you be surprised to hear it? Probably not. Most kids are really interested in this topic, and not at all squeamish about it – quite the opposite, in fact! Many grownups, however, find it embarrassing to talk about these physical changes that you can expect soon. Which is where books written by puberty experts come in handy.

Here are a few well-known books on the topic. Depending on your age and your family's worldview, some of these might be more appropriate than others – so make sure that your grownups take a close look before they share these books with you. It's important to note that these books won't make you grow up faster; they'll help you grow up at the normal speed… but equipped with all the information you'll need to do so confidently.

LIVING WITH A WILLY: THE INSIDE STORY

By Nick Fisher, fourth edition, 2010
From circumcision to wet dreams… it's all here in this frank and very funny classic devoted to a boy's external organ. This book includes information for older boys, too, so be sure your grownups have checked it out and approve before you begin reading. If you're starting to like girls, Fisher offers some helpful insights.

THE BOY'S BODY BOOK: EVERYTHING YOU NEED TO KNOW FOR GROWING UP YOU

By Kelli Dunham, 2007
From voice and bodily changes to tips on coping with siblings, peer pressure, and other issues that adolescent boys face, everything's here. Dunham is a registered nurse and a comedian who has assembled experts – including a Coach of the Year and a professor who researches adolescence – to create an informative and fun-to-read resource.

THE GIRL'S BODY BOOK: EVERYTHING YOU NEED TO KNOW FOR GROWING UP YOU

By Kelli Dunham, 2008
As she does with her book for boys, Dunham gives girls aged 8–12 the scoop on both the physical and emotional aspects of adolescence. This fun-to-read resource covers everything from hygiene to exercise to body changes, to dealing with parents who drive you nuts. It also includes 'Notes from a Real Girl', by Dunham's 12-year-old niece.

THE LITTLE BOOK OF GROWING UP

By Victoria Parker, 2007
The perfect book for younger girls (and curious boys) who are just starting to wonder what's going on 'down there'. If you are feeling anxious about the changes that are on the horizon, this book is a calming reminder that we all grow and change on different timetables – and that's OK.

WHAT'S HAPPENING TO ME? A GUIDE TO PUBERTY

By Peter Mayle, 1975
Ask your grownups if they read this when they were your age. We did! Written by the British author of the best-seller *A Year in Provence* (a detail your grownups might be surprised to learn), this is a lighthearted but informative guide to your questions about puberty. It's written for ages 9 and older, although teenagers may feel it's too young.

GIRLS ONLY! ALL ABOUT PERIODS AND GROWING-UP STUFF

By Victoria Parker, 2004
Friendly advice on periods and the physical and mood changes associated with puberty. From buying your first bra to using a sanitary pad to some basic biology lessons about that time of the month, this illustrated guide is a comforting and reassuring read.

FARTING GAMES

By Josh

Though we might not recommend playing one of these farting games in front of grandparents, teachers or other 'polite company', gross-out humour dates back over 2,000 years.

In Aristophanes' fifth-century BC play, *The Clouds*, the elderly Strepsiades is lying in bed when he hears thunder; 'Oh! adorable Clouds,' he says. 'I revere you and I too am going to let off my thunder, so greatly has your own affrighted me.' Then he lets rip a fart.

The point is, everyone passes gas – so why make it a shameful thing, when you're among friends? Enjoy!

Fart-accusing phrases

If you smell a fart, instead of just yelling 'Pee-yew!' try to be more imaginative. 'Who cut the cheese?' is a classic. If you hear but don't smell a fart, try one of these phrases on for size: 'Who stepped on a frog?' 'Who sat on a duck?' Or use this phrase, which might have been inspired by the Beverly Cleary novel *Runaway Ralph*: 'Mouse on a motorcycle!' Or make up your own.

Fart-denying rhymes

When someone accuses you of farting, it's amusing to respond with a rhyming denial. For example: 'He who smelt it, dealt it.' Or: 'She who detected it, ejected it.' Or: 'He who denied it, supplied it.' In our carpool, we once came up with a call-and-response sequence:

'He who smelt it, dealt it.'
'Whoever said the rhyme, did the crime.'
'She who spoke last set off the blast.'
'He who spoke third, smells like a turd.'
'He who *thpoke* fourth, farted – *of courth*.'

The Safety Game/Doorknob

I learned this game from my nieces, though I've heard it was first invented in Army barracks.

The Safety Game begins whenever someone farts in the presence of others; even if the fart was silent, the game is on. The farter must loudly call 'safety' before anyone else in the room can call 'doorknob'. The farter cannot call safety while farting; however, all ties go to the farter.

If someone in the room calls doorknob before the farter can call safety, then everyone is allowed to attack the farter – gently, please – until the farter manages to touch a doorknob. That's a doorknob, not a door handle. (Also, the door must divide two spaces – for example, the door must allow you to move from one room to another, or from the inside of the house to the outside. So cabinet or refrigerator doors don't count.) If there are no doorknobs around, then whoever called doorknob must do a silly dance. To avoid this scenario, it's OK to call door-hinge or some object that is within reach.

Illustrations by Mister Reusch

Note that if the farter has never heard of the Safety Game before, it doesn't matter – she *must still obey its rules.*

A variation on the game permits the farter who has succeeded in calling safety to challenge the others in the room to a contest of some kind. For example, everyone has to yell the name of a British Prime Minister, and whoever is the last to do so must perform a silly dance. If two people yell the same Prime Minister, then they must both perform a silly dance.

Dutch Oven

A dutch oven is a cast-iron cooking pot with a tight-fitting lid. It's also a prank you can play on someone with whom you are sharing a bed – a sister or brother, say. You fart under the covers, then pull the blanket over your sibling's head, trapping them in the foul-smelling cavern of doom.

If you're not sharing a bed, you can get into someone's bed, fart, then slide out quickly while tucking the blanket down tight behind you. (My brother Patrick learned this trick at boarding school, and played it on me when he was home.) If you do this moments before your victim gets into bed, they'll be in for a smelly surprise.

A Reverse Dutch Oven is when you fart in the bedroom, then dive into your own bed and get under the covers where it's not stinky.

The 'Beans, Beans' song

At one time, every kid in the English-speaking world somehow knew the lyrics to this silly song.

> Beans, beans, the magical fruit
> The more you eat, the more you toot
> The more you toot, the better you feel
> So we have beans at every meal!
>
> Beans, beans, they're good for your heart
> The more you eat, the more you fart
> The more you fart, the more you eat
> The more you sit on the toilet seat!

Fart Touch

Whoever farts reaches out and touches someone nearby, saying 'fart touch!' The person who has been touched must now pass the fart touch along to someone else; they're not allowed to pass it back to whoever passed it to them. This game involves a lot of running and screaming, because everyone is trying to avoid getting the fart touch passed to them.

One version of the game allows you to block a fart touch by crossing fingers on both hands while saying 'Shields!'

FREAKY
FITNESS

By Helen Cordes

Exercise not only makes our bodies stronger and healthier, it relieves stress, makes us feel happier, and shrinks the risk of getting a chronic disease as we get older.

Too many kids suffer from weight and health problems that keep them feeling bad physically and emotionally. Exercise can change that.

While team sports are great, if they're not your thing, there are plenty of physical activities you can do on your own. All your body needs to stay strong is about 30 minutes of activity a day – and it doesn't have to happen all at once. In fact, your workout doesn't even need to feel like exercise.

> **IMPORTANT!** Before you start moving, do a few minutes of warm-up, by walking or doing star jumps. Save the deep stretching for afterwards.

Wacky walks

Type 'Ministry of Silly Walks' and 'Monty Python' in a search engine for some inspiration (doing a Simon Says with wacky walks is fun with friends, too). If you don't want to get too silly, put on your headphones and set off strolling. If you walk to music you love, you're likely to go further and not feel as tired.

Crazy cardiovascular

Consider alternating normal walking with short but super-fast sprints. Exercise experts say these 'short-burst intervals' supercharge your heart and muscles. Try walking for three minutes and then doing a fast burst for one minute. Repeat. When that gets too easy, cut the rest time in half. You can also sprint around the streets and time yourself. Or count how many times you can jump a skipping rope without missing.

Illustrations by Mister Reusch

Dancing is another great way to get your heart rate going. Crank up your favourite music and rock out like no one's watching. Try to get every body part going at some point during your one-of-a-kind dance.

Amazing aim
Wad up a sock and try to shoot it into a waste-paper basket – edge back further as you get better.

Profitable pastimes
Want to get paid to keep your body strong? Do jobs that give you a great workout and some serious cash: walk dogs; cut grass (use an old-fashioned push-mower for extra upper-body toning); wash cars. You can also jump on your bike to fetch small items for your grownups or neighbours from the shop for a fee – tell your employer that they get to feel virtuous about reducing pollution from driving.

And don't forget that your healthy activity can benefit lots of people. Volunteer to pick up litter in the park or maintain a footpath in the countryside. Join a charity walk or charity run to help out your favourite cause.

Coordination crankers
To build ball-handling dexterity, blow up a balloon, toss it into the air, and see how long you can keep it from hitting the floor. Add another balloon and see how long you can keep them both aloft. Improve your leg muscle strength by getting in the crab position (all-fours but with belly up) and keep that balloon in the air with foot kicks. Write down your personal best and then try to beat it.

Mini-marathons
You can do a mini-workout in just 10 minutes. Try star jumps for one minute, march in place for one minute, and step up and down a stair for one minute. Then lie down, stick your feet under the sofa, and do five sit-ups. Repeat until 10 minutes has zipped by.

Group games
A recent study by a children's hospital found that kids used the most energy when they played simple games they considered fun, including Stop and Go (two teams try to get their ball to the other side's goal line) and Dragon's Tail (everyone tucks a handkerchief or rag into the back of their waistband and tries to grab another player's 'tail' while protecting their own).

Lots of games need no props at all – try Freeze Tag (you're frozen when tagged and unfrozen when a free player touches you) or Blob Tag (kids tagged join hands with the 'it' person to help chase). Or take whatever's around – rocks, pine cones – and hide them behind trees in the park to compete in a timed 'find them all' hunt. If the weather's bad, play Time Bomb inside, where players run from room to room to find a hidden item while the kitchen timer ticks away.

Relay races offer more endless options – balance a pillow on your head as you hurry to your partner, or bat a balloon back and forth with a friend as you rush towards the line. Build muscles with Tug of War or Playground Olympics – have competitions for monkey bar swinging and roundabout pushing. Make an obstacle course outside or inside by piling items contestants need to swerve around or jump over to win.

Freaky flexibility
Stretch and shake off stress with quickie yoga sessions. Check out a book or video on yoga for kids from a library or bookshop to get details. You'll learn that in just a few minutes you can fit in a few tension-taming deep breaths and some strengthening yoga stretches such as the cow pose (get on all fours and tilt your head up – mooing is optional) and the back-arched cat pose. Add a pose a week until you're limber as an acrobat.

GIVE YOURSELF A HAND

It's not just your legs, arms and heart that need a workout. Your fingers and hands also have to be able to move with skill. Manual dexterity - that's the technical term for hand coordination - is the key to being able to write in a notebook, draw comics or landscapes, play an instrument, even type on a computer or smartphone keyboard. Playing games is a fun way to make your hands and fingers more agile.

Jacks is a classic game that requires some serious dexterity. Here's the inside scoop on how to play.

You'll need:

- 10 jacks
- A small rubber ball

Ones

Scatter all jacks upon the playing surface with your strong hand. Using the same hand for all these moves, toss the ball into the air, pick up one jack, and - after the ball has bounced once - catch the ball in the same hand. Transfer the jack you picked up to your other hand, and repeat. When all jacks are picked up, you're ready for the next step.

If you make any mistakes (see Fouls & Misses), you must start Ones from the beginning.

Twos to Nines

For Twos, follow the same procedure as Ones, except this time pick up two jacks at a time. If you make any mistakes, start Twos again. The same rules apply to Threes, Fours, etc.

All Jacks (Tens)

Hold all the jacks, and the ball, in your strong hand. Using the same hand for all these moves, toss the ball up in the air, lay down (don't scatter) the jacks, then catch the ball before it bounces. Then toss the ball up again, scoop up all the jacks, and catch the ball. If you make a mistake, you can either do Tens over, or go all the way back to Ones.

Eggs in Basket

The trick here is transferring the jacks to your other hand before catching the ball. Using the same hand for all these moves, scatter the jacks, toss the ball, pick up one jack, and - allowing the ball to bounce once - transfer jacks to the other hand. Then catch the ball. When all jacks have been picked up and transferred, proceed through Twos, Threes, etc.

Crack the Eggs

Using the same hand for all these moves, scatter the jacks, toss the ball, pick up one jack, tap it sharply on the playing surface, then catch the ball after it bounces once. And so forth.

Fouls & Misses

- Using wrong hand to catch the ball, or catching the ball with both hands.
- Failure to pick up proper number of jacks required by ones, twos, etc.
- 'Clothes Burn'. Allowing the ball or jacks to touch the body (except hand) or clothing.
- 'Drops'. Failure to hold onto the ball or jacks until movement is completed.
- 'Touch'. Touching any other jack while attempting to pick up a jack or jacks.

Illustrations by Mister Reusch

BEST EVER
SPORTS MOVIES

By Josh

Sports films – about boxing, football and athletics – have been popular ever since the silent-film era (prior to the late 1920s).

Later, films about other sports became popular: sculling and horse racing in the 1930s and 1940s, rugby and cricket in the 1950s and 1960s; surfing and martial arts in the 1970s; gymnastics and motorcycle racing in the 1980s; football in the 1990s and the 2000s. Alas, too many sports films are uninspired… so watch these films instead.

PS: Since the 1970s, athletic opportunities for girls and women have increased; you'll notice that there weren't many girls' or women's sports movies made before the 1980s.

1915
THE CHAMPION
Directed by Charlie Chaplin
Before the English comic actor-director Charlie Chaplin famously put on boxing gloves in the 1931 classic *City Lights*, he poked fun at sports clichés and underdog stories in this short film about a boxer's sparring partner who stuffs a horseshoe into his glove. Once he starts knocking everyone out with his super-punch, he is booked for a championship fight with a much larger, stronger opponent. Only his rubbery physical abilities – and pet bulldog – can help him triumph.

1931
THE CHAMP
Directed by King Vidor
A washed-up, drunken boxer is accompanied by his nine-year-old son, Dink (played by Jackie Cooper, the first child star of the 1930s), as he travels from one fight to the next. When Dink's mother, who's now married to a wealthy man, shows up, the boxer pretends he doesn't want his son around – but really, he just wants Dink to be happy. It's a heart-warming, if melodramatic and kitschy film. So is the 1979 remake, in which Ricky Schroder plays the son.

1949
IT'S NOT CRICKET
Directed by Alfred Roome
Discharged from the military in disgrace, British intelligence officers and cricket enthusiasts Major Bright and Captain Early (Basil Radford and Naunton Wayne) set up a detective agency. Having accidentally come into possession of a cricket ball with a diamond hidden inside, Bright and Early (get it?) play in the barmiest cricket match of all time, one that is infiltrated by a jewel thief who also happens to be an escaped Nazi!

PS: Radford and Wayne were a cricket-mad double act in ten films, beginning with Alfred Hitchcock's *The Lady Vanishes*.

1950
THE JACKIE ROBINSON STORY
Directed by Alfred E. Green
This biographical picture stars Jackie Robinson, who was not only an amazing athlete but instrumental in bringing an end to racial segregation in Major League Baseball after he became the first black MLB player. While playing for the Brooklyn Dodgers, and going through a hitting slump, Robinson must ignore all slurs – but can he pull it off? Will the team win? (Yes and yes.)

1952
PAT AND MIKE
Directed by George Cukor
The athletic Katharine Hepburn plays Pat, whose attempt to become a professional golfer and tennis player is thwarted by her overbearing fiancé. She falls in love instead with Mike (Spencer Tracy), a slightly shady sports promoter who tries to bribe her to lose (so he can bet money on her opponent), only to become her manager and champion. Several real-life women golf and tennis champions, including Babe Zaharias, Gussie Moran and Alice Marble, make cameo appearances; it's exciting to watch them play.

1976
BAD NEWS BEARS
Directed by Michael Ritchie
Many grownups won't let kids watch this film because of the fighting,

swearing, cigarette-smoking, beer-drinking, racial slurs and bad sportsmanship. All the same, it's not only the funniest but perhaps the most inspiring kids' sports movie ever made. The grownups are overly competitive jerks who forget that kids' sports are supposed to be fun; the kids are feral, unscheduled and unsupervised. The scene in which the son of the mean coach (Vic Morrow) allows the Bears to get an inside-the-park home run is unforgettable; the final scene is wild.

PS: Avoid the 2005 remake.

1979
BREAKING AWAY
Directed by Peter Yates
Dave, a teenager unsure what to do with his life, pretends that he's really an Italian pro bicyclist – which upsets his narrow-minded (but loving) father. Meanwhile, his 'Cutter' friends are trying to figure out what to do with their lives. Not only is it an exciting sports film, *Breaking Away* captures what it felt like when the United States first began to transform from an industrial society (in which anyone with a high-school education could earn a good living) to a post-industrial society. When Dave and his unemployable friends are invited to compete against the town's snooty university students in a gruelling bicycle race, they finally get a chance to prove themselves.

1981
CHARIOTS OF FIRE
Directed by Hugh Hudson
Harold Abrahams, who faces prejudice because of his Jewish ancestry, and Eric Liddell, a devout Scottish missionary to China, transcend their outsider status when they compete as runners in the 1925 Olympic Games in Paris. Even before the climactic final races, there are many exciting athletic scenes, including: Abrahams dashing around the yard at Trinity College (Cambridge), and Liddell winning a race even after being tripped.

1983
GREGORY'S GIRL
Directed by Bill Forsyth
John Gordon Sinclair plays Gregory, an awkward teenager at a secondary school in Cumbernauld, Scotland. When Dorothy (Dee Hepburn), an athletic teenage girl, replaces him as centre forward on the school football team, Gregory is crushed… and he develops a crush on her. Gregory asks Dorothy to teach him how to be a good goalie, which she does willingly; but when he asks her out on a date, she plays a bluff.

PS: This coming of age film has a few scenes that are mildly inappropriate for younger viewers.

1994
HOOP DREAMS
Directed by Steve James
Named one of the best films of the 1990s, and one of the best documentary films ever, *Hoop Dreams* chronicles five years in the life of William Gates and Arthur Agee, African-American teens from inner-city Chicago recruited to play basketball at a mostly white suburban school. Will they make it to the pros?

2001
DOGTOWN AND Z-BOYS
Directed by Stacy Peralta
The Z-Boys were a gang of 11 young, free-spirited surfer boys (and one surfer girl) from Santa Monica and Venice, California, who – in the mid-1970s – transformed skateboarding from a passing fad into the athletic, stylish, attitude-filled sport it is today. Director Stacy Peralta was himself one of the famous Z-Boys.

2002
BEND IT LIKE BECKHAM
Directed by Gurinder Chadha
When tomboy Jules (played by Keira Knightley of *Pirates of the Caribbean* fame) convinces Jess (Parminder Nagra), a football-loving teen growing up in a traditional Indian family that does not approve of girls playing sports, to join a semi-pro women's football team in west London, things get complicated for everyone.

2003
WHALE RIDER
Directed by Niki Coro
Pai (Keisha Castle-Hughes) is a 12-year-old New Zealand girl descended from the whale-riding founder of her Maori tribe; as such, she ought to inherit the tribe's leadership. Her grandfather instead trains the tribe's boys, looking for a new leader among them. But the athletic Pai is better than the boys at just about everything. Will she get her chance?

2009
INVICTUS
Directed by Clint Eastwood
After Nelson Mandela was elected president in South Africa's first multi-racial election, he worked to reconcile the country's white and black populations. One way in which he did so was to support the national rugby team, the Springboks, in the 1995 Rugby World Cup. This biographical film will leave you cheering; and the Victorian-era poem it gets its title from is pretty inspiring too.

2011
SOUL SURFER
Directed by Sean McNamara
When she was 13, talented surfer Bethany Hamilton lost an arm in a shark attack. This family-values-heavy biographical film (starring AnnaSophia Robb) recounts how Bethany realised that she could use her story to inspire others. The surfing scenes are brilliant.

2011
REAL STEEL
Directed by Shawn Levy
In the near future, when robot boxing has replaced the human sport, a struggling promoter (Hugh Jackman, who plays Wolverine in the X-Men films) and his 11-year-old son train a rusty old robot to beat much more powerful competitors the old-fashioned way – thanks to heart and soul. A bit cheesy perhaps, but exciting.

CIRCUS TRICKS

Kids have always performed in circuses. In fact, the first human cannonball was a 14-year-old girl called 'Zazel' – real name Rossa Matilda Richter – who literally shot to fame at the Royal Aquarium in London in 1877. She later toured with the P.T. Barnum circus.

Today, bands of performers still move from town to town to put on their shows, but circuses are considered more controversial now than they were when your grownups were kids. That's because some people are concerned that the animals used in certain shows aren't treated well. There are plenty of circuses that have no animals. These spectacles – the most famous is the Canadian Cirque du Soleil – feature stunning acrobatic feats, artistic dance moves, and street entertainment such as juggling and plate spinning.

'Circus' has also become a popular non-competitive sport in its own right, with special schools that teach kids how to walk on a wire, swing on a trapeze, and do double backflips on a trampoline. Like dance and gymnastics, circus skills are an excellent way to develop strength and coordination.

BALANCE POSES FOR TWO PEOPLE

One of the hallmarks of the artsier professional circuses is what the pros call 'balance poses', which combine strength, concentration, and a seemingly impossible amount of flexibility.

Don't try these at home! Instead, start with these introductory poses.

The Box

The aim of this pose is to create a box shape with the bodies of two people. Start by deciding which person will lie on the floor on your back and which person will be on top. The top person definitely has the tougher job and needs strong stomach muscles.

1. If you are the person on the floor, lie on your back on a rug or mat. Raise your arms towards the ceiling with your fingers pointing up.

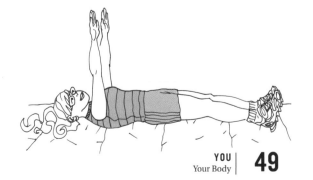

Illustrations by Mister Reusch

2. If you are the partner, stand over the person on the floor facing her feet. Now bend over and grab her ankles. Carefully lift one of your feet and place it in your partner's hand that's on the same side of her body as your foot. Don't laugh or your box will fall apart.

3. Now, carefully lift your other foot and place it in your partner's other hand. Both partners need to keep their stomach muscles tight. How long can you hold this pose?

The shape you're going for is a rectangle, so the bottom person will have to keep her arms straight and strong. The top person will have to keep her arms and shoulders straight and strong, like a plank pose in yoga.

The shape of this trick will depend on people's body sizes. If one person is a lot taller than the other, your shape might look more like a lopsided house. It's common to have to try different people in different positions until it works.

The Knee Handstand

Choose one person to lie on the ground on his back with arms up, fingers pointed towards the ceiling. Next, get that person to put his knees up while keeping his feet on the floor.

Now get a grownup or older kid to be a spotter. The second person stands facing the person on the floor and puts his hands on the floor partner's knees.

Keeping his hands on his partner's knees, the standing partner now bends over and kicks up as if he's doing a handstand. A grownup or big kid should catch his feet and support him. The floor partner will now also support the handstand partner by placing his hands on the handstand partner's shoulders. How long can you hold this pose?

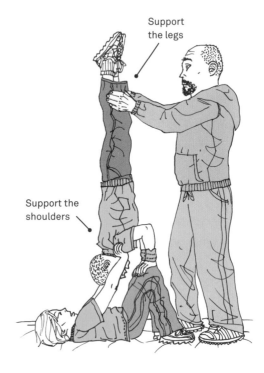

Support the legs

Support the shoulders

SCARF JUGGLING

Juggling is another classic circus act. While it looks hard, keeping all those balls in the air is actually fairly easy once you learn a few insider tips.

Circus pros often introduce juggling to their students with scarves instead of balls because they glide slowly through the air and give the juggler more time to catch and toss. You can buy special juggling scarves at a circus suppliers, but any lightweight scarves you have around the house or can find at a jumble sale or second hand shop will work just as well.

Try this:

1. Start with one scarf. Hold the scarf at one corner and lift your arm as high as you can across your body. Toss the scarf with the palm of your hand facing outwards. Reach up with your other hand and catch the scarf as you bring that hand down in a kind of clawing motion. Repeat this move by throwing the scarf back to your first hand.

2. Add another scarf. Hold a scarf in each hand. If you are right-handed, throw a scarf from that hand (do the opposite if you are a lefty). When the scarf is at its highest point in the air, throw the second scarf. Don't throw or catch both scarves at the same time. Instead repeat this rhythm: *throw, throw, catch, catch*. Practise until it feels like it's easy.

3. Add a third scarf. Start with two scarves in your dominant hand and the other scarf in the weaker hand. Throw one scarf from your dominant hand. When it reaches its high point, throw the scarf from your weaker hand. When that scarf reaches its peak, throw the third scarf. Keep alternating throws between hands.

HOW TO MAKE
A CLOWN FACE

While being a clown might look simple, it takes a lot of skill to convey all those emotions without using any words. That's why a clown's face is so important.

Try this:

1. Go online or check out books from the library that show different types of clown faces. Decide which appeal to you. Do you like happy clown faces? Sad? Wacky? Scary? You'll probably want to invest in a rubber or foam clown nose, which you can get at fancy dress shops.

2. Next, get a mirror and look at your own face. What kind of expressions does your face naturally make? Some people, for example, have natural frowns while others look more mischievous. Your clown face should bring out your natural expressions. It's not a mask but a tool for you to express your inner clown.

3. Wash your hands and face. Spread white face makeup (available at fancy dress shops) on your face. You don't need to use much. Some clowns just use white paint around the lower half of their face. Set it with white face powder (also available at fancy dress shops).

4. Use eyeliner to draw around the edges of your white makeup. You can also use eyeliner to create expressions – add forehead lines, teardrops, huge eyebrows, anything that you want.

5. Now put on your nose. If you don't want to buy one, a circle of red makeup on the tip of your nose will also work.

6. Top off the look with a hat and any clothes you think your clown would wear.

KITCHEN CURES

By Josh

For mild everyday ailments, you can often find remedies in your kitchen cupboards instead of in the medicine cabinet.

If you can't find some of the following supplies in your local supermarket, you and your grownup might want to take a trip to a health food shop.

PS: If you're allergic to any of these substances, don't use them for medicinal purposes!

Scrapes

Powdered turmeric, a plant that is used as a mustardy-peppery spice in curries (and also as a dye), is a natural antiseptic. Mix ½ teaspoon turmeric with a few drops of water, then spread it onto a mild scrape.

Cayenne is a spicy red chilli pepper named after a city in French Guiana. Powdered cayenne may sting when you sprinkle it onto a scrape, but it helps stop bleeding.

When honey spread on a clean cloth or bandage is applied to a scrape, it mixes with bodily fluids and slowly produces low levels of hydrogen peroxide – an anti-bacterial agent. The higher-quality and 'rawer' the honey, the better.

Sunburn

Aloe vera is widely believed to be useful in treating mild sunburn. One of the earliest recorded medicinal uses of the plant can be found on 4,000-year-old Sumerian clay tablets. If you have *bad* sunburn (e.g. with fever, eye pain, nausea, blisters or clammy skin), you should see a doctor immediately; but if your sunburn is mild, break off a leaf from an aloe vera plant and spread the gooey sap over the burn.

Aloe

Mosquitoes

Natural repellents might need to be applied more frequently and in higher concentration than the toxic kind you're accustomed to using, but they're much better for your health.

Mosquitoes don't like the following volatile plant oils, which carry a distinctive scent of the plants they're distilled from. You can use these to make your own repellents.

- Citronella
- Lemon Eucalyptus
- Cinnamon
- Rosemary
- Lemongrass
- Cedar
- Peppermint
- Clove

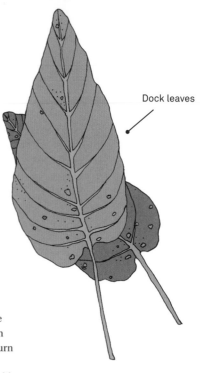

Dock leaves

For dealing with itchy mosquito bites, use Busy Lizzie. Or gently rub the puncture with a moist cake of soap. Some people also rub the juice of a cut onion onto bites.

Stinging nettles

A hike – or even just a run through your garden – can go seriously awry if the needle-like hairs of a stinging nettle make contact with your bare skin. The hairs are actually hollow tubes, called trichomes, and are filled with a concoction of natural chemicals. When the tip of the trichome gets broken, a sharp point is revealed. That point then stabs those nasty chemicals into your skin. For a natural cure, grab a small bunch of dock leaves – they usually grow near nettles. Scrunch them up and rub them on the irritated area until it turns green. Some people say that dabbing vinegar on the sting also calms the rash.

PS: Did you know that nettles contain more iron than spinach and are rich in vitamin C? That explains why some people go to so much trouble to pick these prickly plants. Simmering nettles for 30 seconds will take the poison out of them. From there you can make soup or tea.

Illustrations by Heather Kasunick

Bee stings

Remove the stinger and venom sac. Scrape the stinger out gently, with a fingernail or the edge of a credit card – don't squeeze the venom sac!

If you're having an allergic reaction (e.g. difficulty breathing or swallowing, hives, swelling around the face or throat, dizziness), seek emergency medical attention. Otherwise, make a paste out of bicarbonate of soda and water, and smear lots of it onto the sting.

Wasp stings

Wasps and hornets usually retract their stingers so you don't have to worry about taking one out. Apply ice wrapped in a towel or napkin to the sting for 20 minutes to ease the pain and swelling. Some people say that applying a freshly cut onion to the sting draws out the venom while others like to soak the sting in a mixture of bicarbonate of soda and vinegar.

Headache

Headaches have lots of causes, and not all of them can be treated with kitchen remedies. But try this: dissolve 1 teaspoon bicarbonate of soda in a cup of warm water and add 60ml freshly squeezed lemon juice. Drink it.

Also try placing a bag of frozen vegetables on the back of your neck. Sometimes it helps to pinch the fleshy area where your index finger and thumb meet.

To prevent headaches, drink plenty of water. Dehydration is the most common cause of headaches.

Head lice

Instead of using the pesticide shampoo they sell at the chemist – which burns the scalp – get your grownup to buy a little bottle of essential oil of thyme from a health food shop. PS: Make sure you're buying pure essential oil (not 'aromatherapy oil'), and read the safety instructions.

Add four drops of the oil, which is high in an anti-parasitic compound called phenol, to 60ml olive oil. Instruct your grownup to rub it into your scalp, then cover your head with plastic wrap for half an hour. Then wash your hair with normal shampoo.

Meanwhile, your grownup can wash all the blankets and sheets and generally freak out. Once you've washed your hair, get your grownup to comb through it with a fine-tooth comb, looking for lice and nits (louse eggs); the term 'nit-picking' comes from this very activity. PS: If you happen to have one of those magnifying lamps that people use for hobbies, it's very helpful!

Nausea & motion sickness

Crystallised ginger is yummy and helpful. Ginger snaps, real ginger ale or ginger powder in water also work. Sucking on hard sweets (peppermints, etc.) can work too. If the cause of nausea is unknown and persists for more than a day, see your doctor.

Feel a cold coming on?

Crush (don't chop) a couple of cloves of garlic, wait patiently for 10 minutes, then add 1 tablespoon olive oil and gulp the mess down without tasting it.

The active component of garlic is allicin – a sulphur compound produced about 10 minutes after garlic is crushed. It's a powerful antibiotic which can help the body inhibit the ability of germs to grow and reproduce.

Ginger root

Sore throat

Half-fill a tablespoon with honey, then fill the rest of the spoon with lemon juice, sprinkle on a little cayenne pepper and suck the mixture slowly down your throat. The idea is that the honey soothes and disinfects; the lemon contracts inflamed tissues in your throat and provides vitamin C; and the cayenne pepper stimulates circulation and encourages healing.

You can make a soothing hot drink by squeezing a lemon into hot water and adding honey. You can also mix ½ teaspoon cayenne pepper into that drink. Slices of ginger root, boiled gently, also make a nice tea.

TRICK YOUR MIND
AND ACCOMPLISH
GREAT THINGS

By Elizabeth

You might imagine you make decisions in an entirely rational way. However, you're influenced by how choices are presented to you. We all are.

For example, if you're craving an ice cream and your grownup is willing to buy it, then you will likely decide to eat one; but if you know that you'd have to buy that ice cream with your own money, that fruit bar at the back of the fridge might suddenly look a bit tastier.

The study of how people's decisions – including your own – can be influenced goes by many names, including 'behavioural economics' and 'choice architecture'. But let's just call it 'tricking people's minds so that they make one decision instead of another'.

This sounds sinister, and it sometimes is. But tricking your mind can be used for good purposes, including persuading kids to choose a healthier lunch. Researchers who study customer behaviour in canteens have discovered that moving the salad bar front and centre – in front of the cash register, say – can increase the sale of salads by 50 per cent. Want to encourage people to buy more white milk, and less chocolate- and strawberry-flavoured milk (which aren't as good for you)? Just put the chocolate and strawberry milk behind the white milk on the fridge shelf.

Do you want to improve the way people – or you – behave?

Take the high road

If you are raising money for your school, plant yourself at the top of an escalator instead of at the bottom. Researchers have found that twice as many shoppers who had just ridden an up escalator contributed to the Salvation Army than shoppers who had just ridden the down escalator. In another study by the same team, people watched film clips of scenes taken either from an aeroplane above the clouds or through the window of a car. Participants who had watched the clip of flying above the clouds were 50 per cent more cooperative (in a computer game which they played after watching the clip) than those who had watched the car ride on the ground.

What do escalators and flying have to do with being generous and cooperative? Researchers suspect that our brains may unconsciously associate height with behaving well; for example, when we say that we 'look up' to someone, it means we respect them. Because height and good qualities are connected in our mind, when we're high off the ground we may be more inclined to behave in a generous, cooperative way.

Illustrations by Heather Kasunick

Gross yourself out

If you've got a bad habit you want to break, try making the habit so unpleasant that your brain will scream 'stop' the next time you try it. A great example of this technique is 'no bite' nail polish, which tastes so disgusting that nail biters eventually stop their chomping. You can also try hypnotising yourself – for example, telling yourself over and over that fizzy drinks taste gross and make you sick.

Invent a sales slogan

When a school canteen labelled carrots 'X-ray vision carrots', sales of the normally unpopular veggie spiked by 50 per cent. That's the power of suggestion in action. When advertisers do this sort of thing, we don't like it. But if your little sister hates bedtime, it can't hurt to invent a new, more appealing term for it, such as 'snuggle time'. If the same little sister doesn't like eating broccoli, try renaming the broccoli 'trees', then tell her that she's a dinosaur, and beg her not to eat all the trees.

Label it

Even though we all know that leaving the lights on and neglecting to unplug our tech chargers sucks up energy, it's difficult for grownups to change their habitual behaviours. Try posting signs that say 'CO_2' above light switches, or drawing leaky taps with £-signs on posters stuck up near the shower; that should get your grownups' attention. And if they're fed up with boys spraying pee all around the toilet, then they can try a labelling trick of their own. Using a red permanent marker, they can write 'AIM' on a sticker and put it inside the toilet bowl. This strategy works wonders.

Invite peer pressure

If you have a goal you want to achieve – running a mile, maybe, or saving up to buy a snowboard – research shows that telling friends and family what your goal is, and then checking in with them every week to report on your progress (via an email or photographs, or even a video documenting how far you've come) will help you get there. There are even online and smartphone apps to help you check in with your support team.

Give positive feedback

If you've ever trained a dog, you know that giving positive rewards such as a treat or a scratch behind the ears every time he sits or comes when you call helps cement the behaviour you want. The same is true for people. If you don't like how stressed-out your grownup gets during the school run, then compliment him *every* time you notice him chilling out in the morning by saying 'Thanks for staying so calm.' Praising someone for doing something *right* helps them change bad habits; harping on at someone whenever they mess up is less effective.

HOW TO TEASE YOUR
BRAIN

AN EXCERPT FROM

ALICE'S ADVENTURES IN WONDERLAND

by Lewis Carroll

Lewis Carroll's 1865 fantasy tale is one of the greatest examples of 'literary nonsense'. Why was Carroll so skilful at sneaking maths and logic puzzles into his fiction? Because he was also a gifted professor of mathematics and logic, who enjoyed inventing games.

The Cheshire Cat's answer to Alice's first question demonstrates the limitations of logic. Logic can't tell us what we should or shouldn't do, because these sorts of decisions are ethical ones; logic is a useful tool only *after* we've made these key decisions.

The Cat only grinned when it saw Alice. It looked good-natured, she thought: still it had *very* long claws and a great many teeth, so she felt that it ought to be treated with respect.

'Cheshire Puss,' she began, rather timidly, as she did not at all know whether it would like the name: however, it only grinned a little wider. 'Come, it's pleased so far,' thought Alice, and she went on. 'Would you tell me, please, which way I ought to go from here?'

'That depends a good deal on where you want to get to,' said the Cat.

'I don't much care where—' said Alice.

'Then it doesn't matter which way you go,' said the Cat.

'—so long as I get *somewhere*,' Alice added as an explanation.

'Oh, you're sure to do that,' said the Cat, 'if you only walk long enough.'

Alice felt that this could not be denied, so she tried another question. 'What sort of people live about here?'

'In *that* direction,' the Cat said, waving its right paw round, 'lives a Hatter: and in *that* direction,' waving the other paw, 'lives a March Hare. Visit either you like: they're both mad.'

'But I don't want to go among mad people,' Alice remarked.

'Oh, you can't help that,' said the Cat: 'we're all mad here. I'm mad. You're mad.'

'How do you know I'm mad?' said Alice.

'You must be,' said the Cat, 'or you wouldn't have come here.'

Alice didn't think that proved it at all; however, she went on: 'And how do you know that you're mad?'

'To begin with,' said the Cat, 'a dog's not mad. You grant that?'

'I suppose so,' said Alice.

'Well, then,' the Cat went on, 'you see, a dog growls when it's angry, and wags its tail when it's pleased. Now *I* growl when I'm pleased, and wag my tail when I'm angry. Therefore I'm mad.'

'*I* call it purring, not growling,' said Alice.

'Call it what you like,' said the Cat. 'Do you play croquet with the Queen to-day?'

'I should like it very much,' said Alice, 'but I haven't been invited yet.'

'You'll see me there,' said the Cat, and vanished.

[…]

Alice waited a little, half expecting to see it again, but it did not appear, and after a minute or two she walked on in the direction in which the March Hare was said to live. 'I've seen hatters before,' she said to herself; 'the March Hare will be much the most interesting, and perhaps as this is May it won't be raving mad – at least not so mad as it was in March.' As she said this, she looked up, and there was the Cat again, sitting on a branch of a tree.

'Did you say "pig", or "fig"?' said the Cat.

'I said "pig",' replied Alice; 'and I wish you wouldn't keep appearing and vanishing so suddenly: you make one quite giddy.'

'All right,' said the Cat; and this time it vanished quite slowly, beginning with the end of the tail, and ending with the grin, which remained some time after the rest of it had gone.

'Well! I've often seen a cat without a grin,' thought Alice; 'but a grin without a cat! It's the most curious thing I ever saw in all my life!'

YOU HAVE ADHD?
CONGRATULATIONS!

By Elizabeth

Attention Deficit Disorder (ADD) and Attention Deficit Hyperactivity Disorder (ADHD) are extremely common. In fact, one or two – sometimes more – of the kids in your class probably have it.

Though they didn't diagnose it back then, I'm sure that I had ADHD when I was a kid (in fact, I still have a hard time sticking to one single task). I didn't get any help; instead, teachers called me a troublemaker and even some kids thought of me as a pain.

Having ADD/ADHD can make it really hard to concentrate at school. So hard that some kids need to take medication to be able to stay focused. You may feel like you need to get up and run or jump or do *anything* that's more physical than sitting at a desk. Or you might blurt things out when you should be listening. That was my biggest challenge at school – my nickname was 'motor mouth'.

Others kids with ADD/ADHD get really antsy at the dinner table. Still others are forgetful or disorganised – their school bags are crammed with random papers. (A lot of kids who don't have ADD/ADHD do these things, too; being messy and disorganised is very common for kids your age. But if you aren't doing as well as you could at school or are getting in trouble a lot and it's making you feel bad about yourself, you might want to talk to a counsellor or doctor about whether you could have ADD/ADHD.)

Even though ADD/ADHD can make a kid's life tougher than it already is, there are a lot of benefits to having such a busy brain. As my favourite ADD expert, Dr Edward Hallowell, likes to say about those of us with ADD/ADHD: 'You've got a Ferrari race car for a brain. But you have bicycle brakes.' What he means is that it's brilliant that you've got a powerful brain that can go really fast when you want it to. But not having equally powerful brakes can mean that you struggle sometimes.

If you have ADD/ADHD, you are in good company. Although the diagnosis didn't exist when they were alive, experts believe that legendary talents including Albert Einstein, Sir Walter Raleigh, Wolfgang Amadeus Mozart, Leonardo da Vinci, Beethoven, Galileo, Oscar Wilde and Abraham Lincoln might have had ADD. Justin Timberlake, Mary Kate Olsen, Will Smith and Olympic swimmer Michael Phelps all have talked publicly about having ADD/ADHD.

Got ADD/ADHD? Then you may be…

Creative
All that energy means you might do things you aren't supposed to more often than other kids you know. That ability to 'colour outside the lines' and see connections that other people often miss can mean that you have a lot of juice for creative projects.

Curious
Professionals who help kids with ADD/ADHD all agree that it's not true that people like us can't focus. Instead, it's hard for us to concentrate on something we don't find interesting. But if a topic captures our imagination, we can easily spend hours, days, weeks and months absorbed in it.

Illustrations by Heather Kasunick

Eager

Who wants to feel ho-hum about life? People like us are often very, very enthusiastic about the people and activities we love.

Persistent

If you have a goal, whether it's running a mile or launching your own babysitting businesses, you won't give up until you've made it happen.

Energetic

Having a lot of physical energy is good for anything where you need stamina, including playing sports or doing physical activities like hiking. It's also good for time-intensive projects – such as woodworking or learning lines for a play.

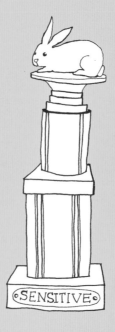

Sensitive

People with ADD/ADHD are often super-intuitive, which means we have what Dr Hallowell calls a special feel for life that gives us almost a sixth sense about people and situations. We are often able to see straight to the heart of a matter instead of having to think it through bit by bit.

TRAIN YOUR GROWNUP
TO SWEAR WITHOUT SWEARING

By Josh

'Gosh', 'Blimey', 'Crikey': these and other similar expressions are known as 'minced oaths'. This means they're slightly altered versions of swearwords.

'My goodness!' and 'My gosh!' are altered versions of 'My God!' (which some people still consider strong language), while 'Crikey!' and 'Cripes!' are altered versions of 'Christ!'

Harmless-sounding ancient Greek expressions like 'By the dog!' and 'By the goose!' are called 'Rhadamanthine oaths', after a mythical Cretan king who prohibited his subjects from uttering the names of deities in anger: 'By the beard of Zeus!'

Minced oaths didn't really take off in English until the late sixteenth century, at which time the uptight Puritans compelled the English to stop taking the Lord's name in vain. This is why Shakespeare's plays are crammed with then-new expressions like 'Zounds!' ('By God's wounds!').

The expressions 'Gad!' and 'Egad!' ('God!') date to the late seventeenth century; the particularly grim utterance 'Gadzooks!' ('God's hooks!') does too. In the eighteenth century, a new set of minced oaths appeared in English: 'Gosh!' and 'Golly!' substitute for 'God!', while 'Darn!' and 'Dash!' substitute for… well, you work it out.

Does your grownup sometimes swear? Tsk-tsk. Train her to use minced oaths instead.

Alliteration

Repetition of a sound in a word or words' first syllables makes it easy to switch from a bad word to a substitute word in the middle of saying the bad one. If your grownup often says 'Jesus!' suggest he imitate Velma from *Scooby-Doo* and say 'Jinkies!' A good resource for words that start with the same letter as other words is the website onelook.com.

Rhyming

Instead of calling your brother a 'jerk', which might get you into trouble, why not call him a 'Captain Kirk'? You could play it even safer, and shorten the phrase to just 'Captain'. This is how Cockney rhyming slang (which originated in London in the nineteenth century) works. 'Fart', for example, in Cockney rhyming slang becomes 'raspberry tart', which finally becomes the inoffensive 'raspberry'.

Invention

Help your grownup invent her own swearwords! This works for kids, too. I used to drive my little brother crazy by calling him 'Soap-on-a-Rope'. When he'd tell my mother on me, she'd just laugh. Real words that sound naughty but aren't – like *gubbins, scuttlebutt, carbuncle* – are the best.

Illustrations by Mister Reusch

CLAPPING GAMES

Clap your right hands

Kids – especially girls living in cities – have invented clapping games and rhymes for generations.

Clapping game basics

Sit across from your partner. Clap your hands together at the same time, then reach with your right hand to clap your partner's right hand (Figure A). Now, clap your own hands again (Figure B). Then reach with your left hand and clap your partner's left hand (Figure C). Repeat until you fall into a rhythm.

Make them trickier

Instead of clapping one of your hands to one of your partner's hands every time, you can try a lot of other moves including: slapping your own thighs, or the ground; clapping both of your hands to both of your partner's hands at the same time; clapping with the back of your hand instead of your palm; snapping your fingers instead of clapping; tapping your fist on top of your partner's fist; clapping with your hand turned sideways.

Clap your own hands

Rhyming

Most clapping rhymes have a regional variation. Why? Because the rhymes are part of an oral tradition – meaning they are passed down by telling instead of reading. Which means there is no single correct version, so there's no point in arguing about it with your friends. If you can come up with a rhyme that works, you're creating history!

⌂■□⊠⊠‡□⊞ ⊞□✦□⊡ □□⊡ □✗⊥ ■✳□⊥
□✗⊡ ⊞‡⊡■⊡□

⊛✗⅄⊡ □■□✗ ■‡■⊡ ⊥✗ ⊠■□⅄ ⊥⊠⊡⇥

Clap your left hands

Illustrations by Mister Reusch

TRY THESE STANDARDS

My Boyfriend

My boyfriend gave me an apple
My boyfriend gave me a pear
My boyfriend gave me a kiss
    on the lips
And threw me down the stair.
I gave him back his apple
I gave him back his pear
I gave him back his kiss on
    the lips
And threw him down the stair.
I threw him over Scotland
I threw him over France
I threw him over London Bridge
And he lost his underpants.
I made him scrub the china
I made him scrub the floor
I made him wipe the baby's
    bottom
In nineteen-eighty-four.

Miss Susie

Miss Susie had a steamboat
The steamboat had a bell
Miss Susie went to heaven
The steamboat went to…
Hello operator
Please give me number nine
If you disconnect me
I'll kick you from…
Behind the refrigerator there
    was a piece of glass
Miss Susie sat upon it and cut
    her little…
Ask me no more questions
Tell me no more lies
The boys are in the bathroom
    zipping up their…
Flies are in the meadow
The bees are in the park
Miss Susie and her boyfriend
    are kissing in the…
Dark is like a movie
A movie's like a show
A show is like a TV screen
And that is all I know.

Did you know? Sometimes
'Miss Susie' is called 'Miss Lucy'.

Miss Lucy

Miss Lucy had a baby
She named him Tiny Tim
She put him in the bathtub
To see if he could swim.
He drank up all the water
He ate up all the soap
He tried to eat the bathtub
But it wouldn't go down
    his throat.
Miss Lucy called the doctor
Miss Lucy called the nurse
Miss Lucy called the lady
With the alligator purse.
In came the doctor
In came the nurse
In came the lady
With the alligator purse.
Mumps said the doctor
Measles said the nurse
Hiccups said the lady
With the alligator purse.
Miss Lucy punched the doctor
Miss Lucy kicked the nurse
Miss Lucy thanked the lady
With the alligator purse.

Say, Say, Oh Playmate

Say, say, oh playmate
Come out and play with me
And bring your dollies three
Climb up my apple tree.
Slide down my rainbow
Into my cellar door
And we'll be jolly friends
Forevermore, one two three four!

*Clap both hands straight
across with your partner when
counting.*

Here's another version:
Say, say, oh playmate
I cannot play today
My dollies have the flu
Boo hoo hoo hoo hoo hoo.

Pretend you are crying.

My apple tree is dead
My rainbow's gone away
My cellar door is locked
Forevermore, one two three four.

*Clap both hands straight
across with your partner when
counting.*

A Sailor Went to Sea Sea Sea

*Tap the side of one hand into
your forehead so you look like a
sailor gazing out at sea whenever
you say the word 'sea' or 'see'.*

A sailor went to sea, sea, sea
To see what he could see, see, see
But all that he could see, see, see
Was the bottom of the deep blue
    sea, sea, sea.

**Now, substitute the following
words and motions for 'sea sea
sea' and 'see see see':**
Chop, chop, chop

Chop the air with one hand.

Knee, knee, knee

Lift one knee.

China

Say it long: Chiiiiiiiinaaaaaaa.

Finally, put them all together.
A sailor went to sea, chop,
    knee, China.

Nobody Likes Me

Nobody likes me
Everybody hates me
Guess I'll eat some
worrrrrrmmsss.
Fat ones, skinny ones,
    oochygoochygooey ones
Ones that squiggle and
    squirrrrrmmmm.
First you cut the head off
Then you suck the juice out
Then you throw the skin
    awaaaayyyy.
Nobody knows how girls can live
    on worms
Three times a daaaayyy.
Boom ba de ah da…
    boom boom!

Have You Ever, Ever, Ever?

When you say 'short-legged', make a short distance between your hands. When you say 'long-legged' make a longer distance between your hands. When you say 'knock-kneed', touch your elbows together.

Have you ever, ever, ever
in your short-legged life
seen a short-legged sailor
with a short-legged wife?
No I've never, never, never
in my short-legged life
seen a short-legged sailor
with a short-legged wife.

Have you ever, ever, ever
in your long-legged life
seen a long-legged sailor
with a long-legged wife?
No I've never, never, never
in my long-legged life
seen a long-legged sailor
with a long-legged wife.

Have you ever, ever, ever
in your knock-kneed life
seen a knock-kneed sailor
with a knock-kneed wife?
No I've never, never, never
in my knock-kneed life
seen a knock-kneed sailor
with a knock-kneed wife.

Have you ever, ever, ever
in your short-legged life
seen a long-legged sailor
with a knock-kneed wife?
No I've never, never, never
in my short-legged life
seen a long-legged sailor
with a knock-kneed wife.

The Strangler

Each verse of this rhyme adds a new move, which is then repeated again and again.

My mother owns a bakery shop
Yum-yum.

Rub your tummy.

My father drives a rubbish truck
Yum-yum, pee-yew.

Hold your nose like something stinks.

My sister talks on the phone
    all day.
Yum-yum, pee-yew, la-de-la-de-
    la-de-dew.

Raise your hands and wiggle your fingers.

My brother is a cowboy
Yum-yum, pee-yew, la-de-la-de-
    la-de-dew, roll 'em up, stick
    'em up, bang-bang!

Roll hands up from imaginary holsters, make your fingers look like guns, shoot, shoot.

My auntie is an operator
Yum-yum, pee-yew, la-de-la-de-
    la-de-dew, roll 'em up, stick
    'em up, bang-bang, may I
    have your number please?

Pinch your nose while speaking.

My uncle is a strangler
Yum-yum, pee-yew, la-de-la-de-
    la-de-dew, roll 'em up, stick
    'em up, bang-bang, may I
    have your number please?

Playfully and gently grab your partner's throat.

Double Double

Double double ice ice
Double double cream cream
Double ice, double cream
Double double ice cream.

Coca-Cola

Coca-Cola went to town
Pepsi-Cola shot him down
Dr Pepper fixed him up
And changed him into
    Seven-Up.

STOP WORRYING
EXERCISE

breathe

Do you ever have a hard time falling asleep? Do you worry too much about your homework or what your friends think about you? Do you ever have a hard time making bad or scary thoughts go away?

Lots of kids worry, so if you're one of them, you are not alone! One easy way to help calm your body and mind is a technique called Progressive Muscle Relaxation. It only takes a couple of minutes and helps you either wind down before bed or prepare yourself to start your day.

Try this:

Lie down or sit somewhere comfortable where you won't be disturbed. That's usually your bedroom, but another quiet place in your home will also work. Have someone you trust read this script aloud. Pause five seconds after each line.

Become aware of your breathing. Notice it going in and out. Notice your stomach going up and down. Can you make it go slower?

Now bring your attention to your head.

- Breathe in and soften your scalp.
- Breathe in and soften your forehead.
- Breathe in and soften your cheeks.
- Breathe in and soften your jaws.
- Breathe in and soften your tongue.
- Breathe in and soften your chin.
- Breathe in and soften your neck and throat.
- Breathe in and soften your shoulders.
- Breathe in and soften your arms.
- Breathe in and soften your hands and fingers.
- Breathe in and soften your chest.
- Breathe in and soften your ribcage.

Take a moment to notice your breathing. Let your body breathe in and breathe out all by itself.

- Breathe in and soften your abdomen and stomach.
- Breathe in and soften your pelvis.
- Breathe in and soften your back.
- Breathe in and soften your hips and bottom.
- Breathe in and soften your thighs.
- Breathe in and soften your knees.
- Breathe in and soften your legs.
- Breathe in and soften your ankles.
- Breathe in and soften your feet.
- Breathe in and soften your toes.
- Breathe in and soften your whole body.

You may notice your arms and legs feeling heavy and relaxed.

Let yourself become familiar with this feeling of relaxation.

GIVE YOUR GROWNUP A BREAK

Instead of having someone read the script to you each time, you can record yourself or someone else reading it. A grownup with a soothing voice is a good idea.

If you've made a digital recording, and if you or your grownup knows how to use Garage Band, Audacity, or other audio software, you can download free surf, rain or fan sounds to use as a calming background noise behind the reader's voice.

Illustration by Heather Kasunick

GET FOCUSED
MAKE A KUMIHIMO BRAID

By Elizabeth

Research shows that doing crafts, whether it's crocheting an afghan or creating a portrait from ice lolly sticks, focuses your mind and helps you chill.

While my family are fans of pretty much any kind of craft, we really love the ancient Japanese tradition of making kumihimo braids. Samurai used kumihimo cords to lace up their armour. Today, people create intricate braids that can be turned into anything from friendship bracelets to shoelaces to necklaces to key chains.

You can make kumihimo braids of almost any thickness; a lot of people add beads to the braids to make them even fancier. To get started, here's an easy friendship bracelet, which uses only seven strands of embroidery floss. It can be completed in under an hour.

You'll need:

- For the loom: a 5cm x 5cm square of stiff felt or cardboard. (Stiff felt, which is available at craft shops, is better because it bends without losing its shape.) You can buy pre-made kumihimo looms but it's more fun to make your own.
- Up to seven colours of embroidery floss. (You don't need to have seven colours, but use at least three to create a noticeable pattern.)
- Scissors

Try this:

1. Cut off the corners of the stiff felt or cardboard square to make an octagonal (eight-sided) shape.

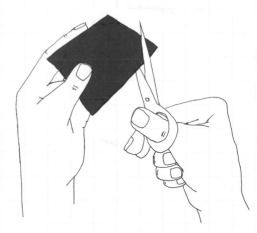

2. Cut small slots (about 6mm) into the middle of each side of the octagon. You'll have eight slots.

3. Make a small hole in the centre of the octagon. How to find the exact centre? Fold the octagon in half and cut a tiny slot. Then fold it in half the other way and cut another tiny slot in the same place – only going in the opposite direction. Now you've got a simple kumihimo loom.

4. Cut seven 45cm-long pieces of embroidery floss.

5. Put all of the strings together so that they are next to each other and are the same length. Tie them together by making a knot 5cm down from the top.

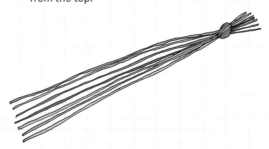

6. Pull the knotted string through the hole in the middle of the loom so that the knot rests on the other side of the hole. The loose strings will be on your side of the loom.

7. Pull one string through each of seven slots on the loom. The string shouldn't feel loose when it's in the slots. There will be one empty slot.

8. Turn the loom so that the empty slot is at the very bottom. If you imagine the loom as the face of a clock, then the empty slot will be at six o'clock.

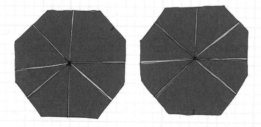

9. Count up three threads (from the empty slot) on the right side of the loom. Move the third thread (at about the two o'clock position) down into the empty slot.

10. You now have a new empty slot; rotate the loom so that the new empty slot is at the bottom (six o'clock) position. Count up three threads and move that thread into the empty slot. Repeat, again and again. Soon, your bracelet will start growing on the other side of the loom.

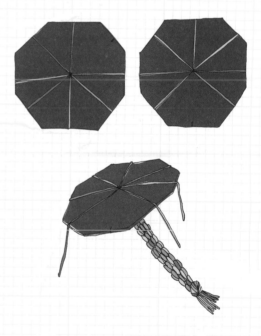

11. If you want to make a bracelet, cut the cord off the loom when it is long enough to fit around a kid's wrist. Leave 10cm extra thread to make it easy to tie into a bracelet. Once it's tied around your wrist (or a friend's), trim off the loose strings.

BEST EVER

PUZZLER & MAKER FICTION

By Josh

Puzzlers and makers build stuff without following instructions, investigate mysteries and crack codes, and use their wits (and materials at hand) to solve problems.

Here are some terrific novels about kids who experiment, fail… and try again. Failure, they know, isn't anything to be ashamed of – in fact, it's a great way to learn faster.

1952
THE BORROWERS
By Mary Norton

Pod and Homily Clock, and their 14-year-old daughter Arrietty are Borrowers – tiny folk who live under the floorboards of an English house. Pod makes daring raids on the 'human beans' to borrow what his family needs to survive. When Arrietty joins him on her first borrowing trip, she encounters one of the big people – an unnamed 10-year-old boy – and befriends him, which is against the rules. The boy gives the Borrowers some doll's house furniture, but in doing so he accidentally helps a less understanding human bean discover them! Will the Borrowers be able to escape?

The Borrowers Afield (1955), *The Borrowers Afloat* (1959), *The Borrowers Aloft* (1961) and *The Borrowers Avenged* (1982) are also fun.

1956
KNIGHT'S CASTLE
By Edward Eager

Siblings Roger and Ann, and their cousins Eliza and Jack discover that a toy castle and a set of figurines allow them to magically enter the world of *Ivanhoe*, a knights-in-armour adventure (written by Sir Walter Scott) set in twelfth-century England. Their appearance on the scene makes the story turn out badly. It's up to them to figure out how the magic works and fix everything.

The magic in each of Eager's Magic series – in addition to *Knight's Castle*, there's *Half Magic* (1954), *Magic By the Lake* (1957), *The Time Garden* (1958), *Magic Or Not?* (1959), *The Well-Wishers* (1960) and *Seven-Day Magic* (1962) – works according to laws whose strict but odd rules require figuring out. They're puzzles wrapped in adventures.

1958
HAVE SPACE SUIT – WILL TRAVEL
By Robert A. Heinlein

Having won an obsolete space suit in a contest, teenager Kip Russell (who wants to study engineering and space-suit design) fixes it up – and, while wearing it, gets kidnapped by an evil alien in a flying saucer. Outer-space action ensues.

Though his best-known sci-fi books are for grownups, Heinlein also published classic sci-fi novels for kids and teens. You might enjoy:

Rocket Ship Galileo (1947), *Space Cadet* (1948), *Red Planet* (1949), *The Rolling Stones* (1952) and *Starman Jones* (1953). PS: Heinlein's 1963 novel, *Podkayne of Mars*, features a teenage girl protagonist.

1958
DANNY DUNN AND THE HOMEWORK MACHINE
By Raymond Abrashkin and Jay Williams

When Professor Bulfinch builds an early computer, adolescent Danny Dunn and his pal Irene work out – through trial and error – how to program it to do their homework. They learn the hard way that computers aren't really any cleverer than the humans who program them.

There are 15 books in the Danny Dunn series (1956–77), but the first four, illustrated by the great Ezra Jack Keats, are the best. In addition to *Homework Machine*, read *Danny Dunn and the Anti-Gravity Paint* (1956), *Danny Dunn on a Desert Island* (1957), and *Danny Dunn and the Weather Machine* (1959).

1963
ALVIN'S SECRET CODE
By Clifford B. Hicks

Like the Danny Dunn books, Hicks's Alvin Fernald series (1960–2009) recount the adventures of a talented young inventor. This one is my favourite. A former spy teaches Alvin the history and basics of writing and cracking coded messages. Soon,

Alvin must crack a 100-year-old code that leads to treasure.

Fun fact: Clifford B. Hicks was an editor of the American magazine *Popular Mechanics*; he wrote the magazine's *Do-It-Yourself Materials Guide* and also edited the *Do-It-Yourself Encyclopedia*.

1965
THE MAD SCIENTISTS' CLUB
By Bertrand R. Brinley

Jeff, Henry, Dinky and other members of the Mad Scientists' Club tinker in a makeshift electronics lab above their town's DIY shop, and use whatever materials they can find to pull off various pranks and stunts. A remote-controlled lake monster is just the beginning.

The author of the Mad Scientists story collections (published in 1965 and 1968) and the novels *The Big Kerplop!* (1974) and *The Big Chunk of Ice* (2005) directed an Army programme for assistance and safety instruction for amateur rocketeers. Brinley also wrote *Rocket Manual for Amateurs* (1960). So he knew his stuff.

1967
FROM THE MIXED-UP FILES OF MRS. BASIL E. FRANKWEILER
By E. L. Konigsburg

Claudia, an 11-year-old geek who feels unappreciated at home, takes her nine-year-old brother along when she runs away to live at New York's Metropolitan Museum of Art. It's impossible to read about how Claudia and Jamie survive by their wits (for example: they steal coins from a fountain, in which they bathe, to pay for their meals) without wanting to do exactly the same thing. To top it off, the siblings help crack an art provenance mystery.

Konigsburg won the prestigious Newbery Medal (for *Mixed-Up Files*) and a runner-up Newbery Honor (for *Jennifer, Hecate, Macbeth, William McKinley, and Me, Elizabeth*, about proto-goth girls) in the same year.

1971
MRS FRISBY AND THE RATS OF NIMH
By Robert C. O'Brien

One of the great maker adventures of all time! Under a rosebush on Farmer Fitzgibbon's farm, a group of super-intelligent former laboratory rats have developed their own technologically advanced society. In exchange for their help moving her home out of the path of the farmer's plough, the field mouse Mrs Frisby helps save them from disaster. But the rats still face a philosophical decision: is it better to live as parasites or should they strike out on their own?

You will also enjoy O'Brien's 1968 novel *The Silver Crown*. His daughter, Jane Leslie Conly, has published two Rats of NIMH sequels.

1978
THE WESTING GAME
By Ellen Raskin

Who 'took the life' of multi-millionaire Samuel W. Westing? That's what the crafty 13-year-old Tabitha Ruth 'Turtle' Wexler wants to find out. So do the other 15 heirs to Westing's fortune; whoever cracks the case will inherit his fortune. The answer to the mystery is concealed in a complex word-puzzle.

Ellen Raskin won a Newbery Medal for this novel, and a Newbery Honor for her 1974 mystery, *Figgs & Phantoms*. Also well worth reading is Raskin's *The Mysterious Disappearance of Leon (I Mean Noel)* (1971), and *The Tattooed Potato and Other Clues* (1975).

1979
ALAN MENDELSOHN, THE BOY FROM MARS
By Daniel Pinkwater

Unhappy at their conformist and unchallenging school, two misfit friends – Leonard Neeble and Alan Mendelsohn – visit a funky urban neighbourhood, where a bookshop owner sells them a kit for learning telekinesis and mind control. Though he didn't realise it before, Mendelsohn is a Martian.

Pinkwater writes convincingly and hilariously about young misfits whose unhappiness with ordinary life leads them into wild adventures. Other favourites: the children's books *Lizard Music* (1976) and *Fat Men from Space* (1977); and the young adult books *The Worms of Kukumlima* (1981) and *The Snarkout Boys and the Avocado of Death* (1982).

1998
HARRY POTTER AND THE CHAMBER OF SECRETS
By J.K. Rowling

The true hero of the Harry Potter series – to those of us who really enjoy doing research – is Hermione Granger, the brightest student at Hogwarts. Her encyclopaedic knowledge saves the day every time. In *The Chamber of Secrets*, not only does Hermione assemble the Polyjuice Potion which permits her (along with Harry and Ron) to infiltrate Slytherin and learn about the Chamber of Secrets, she also hits the library and figures out that the serpentine monster in the Chamber is a basilisk.

Fun fact: Rowling has claimed that the character of Hermione is based, at least in part, on what she herself was like at the same age.

2007
THE MYSTERIOUS BENEDICT SOCIETY
By Trenton Lee Stewart

Twelve-year-old Kate Wetherall is a resourceful, athletic orphan who always carries useful stuff: a Swiss Army knife, a rope, a magnet and so forth. Along with 11-year-old puzzler Reynie Muldoon, 11-year-old mnemonist (look it up) Sticky Washington, and a precocious brat called Constance, she is recruited for a dangerous mission by the mysterious Mr Benedict. Logic puzzles galore!

So far, there are two sequels: *The Mysterious Benedict Society and the Perilous Journey* (2008), and *The Mysterious Benedict Society and the Prisoner's Dilemma* (2009).

AUTHOR, AUTHOR!

Q&As WITH KATE DiCAMILLO & DAVE McKEAN

KATE DiCAMILLO

Asked to explain what inspires her to write such award-winning novels as *Because of Winn-Dixie*, *The Tiger Rising*, *The Tale of Despereaux*, *The Miraculous Journey of Edward Tulane* and *Bink and Gollie*, Kate DiCamillo quotes *Charlotte's Web* author E.B. White: 'All that I hope to say in books, all that I ever hope to say, is that I love the world.'

That doesn't mean her books are always warm and fuzzy. DiCamillo's characters – from Opal, a 10-year-old girl adjusting to life in a new town and coming to terms with the fact that her mother has left her, to a quirky mouse named Despereaux – suffer the same kind of pain, heartbreak and abandonment that people go through in real life.

DiCamillo lives in Minnesota, where she says she writes two pages a day, five days a week. We asked her where she gets her ideas, and for tips for aspiring young writers.

UNBORED: Your fiction often explores the theme of parental absence and loss. So do many classic children's books. Why are we so drawn to stories where the parents are gone?

DiCAMILLO: I had a teacher who used to say that once the parents are out of the way, the action can start. So, there's that. But – for me, at least – there

is this deeper issue of having grown up in a single parent home. I'm always kind of working through that in my stories.

UNBORED: You've said that before you start writing a new book, you wait 'for the thing that makes the divining rod tremble'. Can you explain what this means, what it feels like?

DiCAMILLO: Eeek! I sound silly in that quote, don't I? What do I mean? I mean that when an image or a voice comes for a story, I can feel it in my gut. It almost makes me tremble. I am that certain about having found something… a way in.

Illustrations by Mister Reusch

UNBORED: You got the idea for *The Miraculous Journey of Edward Tulane* from a dream. Are there any techniques you can offer for those of us who have trouble remembering our dreams?

DiCAMILLO: First I received a rabbit doll as a gift. And then I dreamed about the rabbit doll underwater, naked and waiting to be found. I write in my diary every morning. And so a lot of what I dream gets written down – and remembered – that way.

UNBORED: How else do you come up with ideas, especially for your characters?

DiCAMILLO: I write down anything that moves me or surprises me or delights me. A gesture or a saying or an interaction between people… all those things can turn into characters, stories.

UNBORED: Do your characters ever surprise you? If so, can you tell us about one in particular who really changed as you were writing his or her story?

DiCAMILLO: I wait for them to surprise me. That's when I know I'm finally 'in' the story. Opal (in *Because of Winn-Dixie*) was named Bea in the beginning. It surprised me when I figured out that I had the wrong name for her. And there are characters who show up who you don't expect at all. Sistine Bailey, in *The Tiger Rising*, for instance. She stepped on the bus and I was like, 'Whoa, where did you come from?'

UNBORED: Do you ever get stuck when you're writing? What do you do to get writing again?

DiCAMILLO: I'm stuck all the time. Most of the time. But I just keep going. I pretend that I'm not stuck.

UNBORED: You have said that rewriting is an extremely important part of being a writer. Do you do rewrites after you've shown a story to someone else? Have you ever had feedback that bummed you out?

DiCAMILLO: I *do* do rewrites after I've shown the story to someone else. I rewrite and rewrite. And some of the hardest feedback to take is also the most helpful feedback for the story. Sigh.

UNBORED: How do you know when you've finished a story?

DiCAMILLO: It's the same feeling I used to get in college at 3 a.m. when I had been up all night studying and I would suddenly realise that if I studied any more I would be unlearning. I get to the point with a story where I feel like I need to let it go or else I will mess it up.

UNBORED: Have you ever wanted to change anything about your books – even after they've been published?

DiCAMILLO: Oh, yes. Sometimes when I'm reading aloud from one of my books, I'm actually changing words as I read. It's never perfect. You always want to change things. And you always let it go out into the world, anyway, imperfect.

DAVE McKEAN

Dave McKean is a comics artist who has collaborated on some our of favourite comic books and graphic novels, including *The Savage* and *Slog's Dad* (with David Almond). He also illustrated Neil Gaiman's fantasy novels *The Graveyard Book* and *Coraline*; he designed and directed the fantasy film *MirrorMask*; he has illustrated and designed many CD and book covers. Oh, and he was a concept artist on *Harry Potter and the Prisoner of Azkaban* and *Harry Potter and the Goblet of Fire*!

We asked him for a few tips for aspiring cartoonists and illustrators.

UNBORED: What's the difference between a comics artist and an illustrator?

McKEAN: A comics artist has to think in narrative, whereas an illustrator is usually dealing with a single stand-alone image – or a series of them. Comics guide you through time and space – like good film storytelling, you have to understand the spatial relationships between characters. You have to express how they move and talk, how the characters relate to each other. You can also express how they are feeling, and how those feelings change over time. You can express all of this within the content of the image – and also formally, that is, by using the composition, style, size, colour, and proportion of the panels and the images and type within the panels. When used to its full extent, the comic can be a complex form.

I don't want to suggest that illustration is a lesser form at all. The ability to compact a novel or a CD into a single cover image is a real challenge. It takes skill and empathy. But the sheer scale of expressing a whole life of emotions in a graphic novel – while not only maintaining the technical storytelling requirements, but creating beautiful and challenging images – is more daunting. There are very few people who can really do it.

UNBORED: Should a beginner carefully plan each panel of a comic before starting to draw, or just get started?

McKEAN: Everyone should evolve a method that works for them. There are some who prefer to dive straight in, and feel that the immediacy of that method pays dividends. I prefer a more thoughtful approach, so I like to plan everything. Not in very great detail, but I need a plan. I need to see rough doodles on paper before I can make a judgement as to whether they work or not.

UNBORED: In addition to doodling on paper, do you use a computer?

McKEAN: I don't like to use a computer. There is an organic energy that is often very important to keep in a pen-and-paper design. With a few exceptions, as soon as you start using computers, everything becomes gridded and constricted and lacking in humanity.

UNBORED: What role does curiosity play in telling your stories?

McKEAN: Telling a story is all about curiosity! I can only write a story if there is something there that I need to explore, and if I feel that the subject is compelling enough that I need to show it to others. As the story evolves, I leave each day's work open-ended, so that I'm discovering where I go with the story each day.

UNBORED: Our book encourages kids and their grownups to collaborate on fun projects. You work with a lot of writers – what do you enjoy about doing so?

McKEAN: I like getting to know that person, getting to wander around their mind for a while, live in their world and see through their eyes. It's an empathic exercise, to understand their worldview and help express it. But the best part for me is coming up with ideas to start with. That's when everything is fresh and could be perfect. Realising these ideas is when the compromises start. But when you first start throwing ideas on the table and piecing something together, that's pure alchemy.

FICTIONALISE
YOUR LIFE

AN EXCERPT FROM

LITTLE WOMEN

by Louisa May Alcott

Family life is one of the great themes of world literature. And when it comes to writing about sisters, no one does it better than Louisa May Alcott.

Born in 1832, Alcott was raised in New England. Her father, Amos Bronson Alcott, was a DIY educator and a transcendentalist (which means he believed that the key to an honest and noble life comes from within the human spirit instead of the rules of governments or organised religions). Alcott was tutored about the natural world by the now-famous authors Henry David Thoreau and Ralph Waldo Emerson, but it was her father who encouraged her to write fiction.

Little Women (1868) is loosely based on Alcott's experience growing up with three sisters. Here's the opening scene.

'Christmas won't be Christmas without any presents,' grumbled Jo, lying on the rug.

'It's so dreadful to be poor!' sighed Meg, looking down at her old dress.

'I don't think it's fair for some girls to have plenty of pretty things, and other girls nothing at all,' added little Amy, with an injured sniff.

'We've got Father and Mother, and each other,' said Beth contentedly from her corner.

The four young faces on which the firelight shone brightened at the cheerful words, but darkened again as Jo said sadly, 'We haven't got Father, and shall not have him for a long time.' She didn't say 'perhaps never,' but each silently added it, thinking of Father far away, where the fighting was.

Nobody spoke for a minute; then Meg said in an altered tone, 'You know the reason Mother proposed not having any presents this Christmas was because it is going to be a hard winter for everyone; and she thinks we ought not to spend money for pleasure, when our men are suffering so in the army. We can't do much, but we can make our little sacrifices, and ought to do it gladly. But I am afraid I don't,' and Meg shook her head, as she thought regretfully of all the pretty things she wanted.

'But I don't think the little we should spend would do any good. We've each got a dollar, and the army wouldn't be much helped by our giving that. I agree not to expect anything from Mother or you, but I do want to buy *Undine and Sintran* for myself. I've wanted it so long,' said Jo, who was a bookworm.

'I planned to spend mine in new music,' said Beth, with a little sigh, which no one heard but the hearth brush and kettle-holder.

'I shall get a nice box of Faber's drawing pencils; I really need them,' said Amy decidedly.

'Mother didn't say anything about our money, and she won't wish us to give up everything. Let's each buy what we want, and have a little fun; I'm sure we work hard enough to earn it,' cried Jo, examining the heels of her shoes in a gentlemanly manner.

'I know I do – teaching those tiresome children nearly all day, when I'm longing to enjoy myself at home,' began Meg, in the complaining tone again.

'You don't have half such a hard time as I do,' said Jo. 'How would you like to be shut up for hours with a nervous, fussy old lady, who keeps you trotting, is never satisfied, and worries you till you're ready to fly out the window or cry?'

'It's naughty to fret, but I do think washing dishes and keeping things tidy is the worst work in the world. It makes me cross, and my hands get so stiff, I can't practise well at all.' And Beth looked at her rough hands with a sigh that any one could hear that time.

'I don't believe any of you suffer as I do,' cried Amy, 'for you don't have to go to school with impertinent girls, who plague you if you don't know your lessons, and laugh at your dresses, and label your father if he isn't rich, and insult you when your nose isn't nice.'

'If you mean libel, I'd say so, and not talk about labels, as if Papa was a pickle bottle,' advised Jo, laughing.

'I know what I mean, and you needn't be statirical about it. It's proper to use good words, and improve your vocabilary,' returned Amy, with dignity.

'Don't peck at one another, children. Don't you wish we had the money Papa lost when we were little, Jo? Dear me! How happy and good we'd be, if we had no worries!' said Meg, who could remember better times.

'You said the other day you thought we were a deal happier than the King children, for they were fighting and fretting all the time, in spite of their money.'

'So I did, Beth. Well, I think we are. For though we do have to work, we make fun of ourselves, and are a pretty jolly set, as Jo would say.'

'Jo does use such slang words!' observed Amy, with a reproving look at the long figure stretched on the rug.

Jo immediately sat up, put her hands in her pockets, and began to whistle.

'Don't, Jo. It's so boyish!'

'That's why I do it.'

'I detest rude, unladylike girls!'

'I hate affected, niminy-piminy chits!'

'Birds in their little nests agree,' sang Beth, the peacemaker, with such a funny face that both sharp voices softened to a laugh, and the 'pecking' ended for that time.

'Really, girls, you are both to be blamed,' said Meg, beginning to lecture in her elder-sisterly fashion. 'You are old enough to leave off boyish tricks, and to behave better, Josephine. It didn't matter so much when you were a little girl, but now you are so tall, and turn up your hair, you should remember that you are a young lady.'

'I'm not! And if turning up my hair makes me one, I'll wear it in two tails till I'm twenty,' cried Jo, pulling off her net, and shaking down a chestnut mane. 'I hate to think I've got to grow up, and be Miss March, and wear long gowns, and look as prim as a China Aster! It's bad enough to be a girl, anyway, when I like boy's games and work and manners! I can't get over my disappointment in not being a boy. And it's worse than ever now, for I'm dying to go and fight with Papa. And I can only stay home and knit, like a poky old woman!'

And Jo shook the blue army sock till the needles rattled like castanets, and her ball bounded across the room.

'Poor Jo! It's too bad, but it can't be helped. So you must try to be contented with making your name boyish, and playing brother to us girls,' said Beth, stroking the rough head with a hand that all the dish washing and dusting in the world could not make ungentle in its touch.

'As for you, Amy,' continued Meg, 'you are altogether too particular and prim. Your airs are funny now, but you'll grow up an affected little goose, if you don't take care. I like your nice manners and refined ways of speaking, when you don't try to be elegant. But your absurd words are as bad as Jo's slang.'

'If Jo is a tomboy and Amy a goose, what am I, please?' asked Beth, ready to share the lecture.

'You're a dear, and nothing else,' answered Meg warmly, and no one contradicted her, for the 'Mouse' was the pet of the family. […]

The clock struck six and, having swept up the hearth, Beth put a pair of slippers down to warm. Somehow the sight of the old shoes had a good effect upon the girls, for Mother was coming, and everyone brightened to welcome her. Meg stopped lecturing, and lighted the lamp, Amy got out of the easy chair without being asked, and Jo forgot how tired she was as she sat up to hold the slippers nearer to the blaze.

'They are quite worn out. Marmee must have a new pair.'

'I thought I'd get her some with my dollar,' said Beth.

'No, I shall!' cried Amy.

'I'm the oldest,' began Meg, but Jo cut in with a decided, 'I'm the man of the family now Papa is away, and I shall provide the slippers, for he told me to take special care of Mother while he was gone.'

'I'll tell you what we'll do,' said Beth, 'let's each get her something for Christmas, and not get anything for ourselves.' […]

They talked over the new plan while old Hannah cleared the table, then out came the four little work baskets, and the needles flew as the girls made sheets for Aunt March. It was uninteresting sewing, but tonight no one grumbled. They adopted Jo's plan of dividing the long seams into four parts, and calling the quarters Europe, Asia, Africa, and America, and in that way got on capitally, especially when they talked about the different countries as they stitched their way through them.

SIGNIFICANT OBJECT
WRITING EXERCISE

By Josh

The least enjoyable thing about creative writing is the experience of facing a blank page or empty computer screen.

It is difficult to be imaginative on command; your mind freezes up. So here's a handy way to un-freeze your mind and get those creative juices flowing: *Tell a story about a random object in your home.*

Pick an object

Don't choose a special, deeply meaningful object – like your great-grandfather's war medals, say, or the urn containing your dead cat's ashes. Why not? Because if you do, the free play of your imagination might be restricted by the object's history, not to mention your own feelings and memories. Instead, choose an insignificant thing about which you don't care. Maybe it's a travel souvenir from a holiday your grownup took without you; or a toy from a car boot sale or charity shop; or a supposedly cute animal figurine that your aunt bought at the airport gift shop for you the last time she visited.

Invent the object's significance

Before sitting down to write, spend a few quiet minutes simply gazing at the object while your imagination roams freely. Hold the object in your hands, look at it from all sides. What kind of *vibe* do you get from it?

Try to see the object through the eyes of a character, not your own eyes. Maybe the object is evidence from a crime scene. Or did it play a role in a historical (or just meaningful) event? Does the object serve as a reminder – to one of your story's character's – about their childhood, or about a place or time that's vanished? Is the object a kind of messenger from the natural world (animal, vegetable, mineral)? Does the object possess lucky or magical properties? Is it alive? Can it move or talk?

If you clear your mind and sit patiently, the object might tell you something about itself. Listen!

Write a story

Fill up a page or two with a short story in which the object you've chosen – and which you've placed where you can see it while you write, and to which you have listened – plays an important role.

What kind of story? It doesn't matter! Maybe it's science fiction, fantasy, romance or a mystery. Maybe it's realistic. It can be sad, funny or scary. Your story can take the form of a series of emails between two or more characters; or it can be the narrator's diary entry or memoir; or perhaps it's written in the third person (i.e. 'He/She'). Maybe your story will allow readers get to know a character or characters really well (how they look, what they think about, how they talk and behave); or maybe your story is more about an action-packed sequence of events.

Don't worry about spelling, grammar, making a diagram of the plot, or anything else. Just write. Let the words flow from your mind through your fingers and onto the page or computer screen.

Once you've finished this exercise, ignore the object and keep writing. You're in the groove now.

SECRET HISTORY OF YOUNG ADULT NOVELS

By Anindita Basu Sempere

Before *Twilight* and *Harry Potter*, even before *The Princess Diaries* and *The Outsiders*, what sort of novels did young adults read?

The idea of a 'young adult' – a person between childhood and adulthood – wasn't invented until 1802. Sarah Trimmer, a writer and critic, coined the phrase to refer to anyone aged between 14 and 21.

Level up (or down)

When young adults were first defined as an age group, they had two choices: read *up* to adult novels (some of which featured child and young adult characters) or *down* to children's books.

1812	*The Swiss Family Robinson*, by Johann David Wyss
1814	*Waverley*, by Sir Walter Scott
1838	*Oliver Twist*, by Charles Dickens
1857	*Tom Brown's Schooldays*, by Thomas Hughes
1860	*Great Expectations*, by Charles Dickens
1865	*Alice's Adventures in Wonderland*, by Lewis Carroll
1868	*Little Women*, by Louisa May Alcott
1876	*The Adventures of Tom Sawyer*, by Mark Twain
1877	*Black Beauty*, by Anna Sewell
1880	*Heidi*, by Johanna Spyri
1883	*Treasure Island*, by Robert Louis Stevenson
1884	*Adventures of Huckleberry Finn*, by Mark Twain

Coming of age

Many novels published in the late nineteenth century featured young adult characters and we can date the unofficial start of YA literature to this era. In the first half of the twentieth century, more and more authors wrote coming of age stories; this remains a popular theme in YA fiction today.

1886	*Kidnapped*, by Robert Louis Stevenson
1894	*The Jungle Book*, by Rudyard Kipling
1898	*Moonfleet*, by J. Meade Falkner
1903	*Rebecca of Sunnybrook Farm*, by Kate Douglas Wiggin
1908	*Anne of Green Gables*, by L.M. Montgomery
1909	*The Secret Garden*, by Frances Hodgson Burnett
1938	*Brighton Rock*, by Graham Greene
1941	*My Friend Flicka*, by Mary O'Hara
1942	*Adam of the Road*, by Elizabeth Gray Vining
1943	*Johnny Tremain*, by Esther Forbes
1949	*I Capture the Castle*, by Dodie Smith

Illustrations by Mister Reusch

Meet the rebels

Two novels are most often credited with establishing YA literature as we now know it: *The Catcher in the Rye* and *The Outsiders*. Rather than merely telling a story *about* a young adult, a few pioneering YA novels of the 1950s and 1960s captured a sense of what it was like to *be* young.

1951	*The Catcher in the Rye*, by J.D. Salinger
1954	*Lord of the Flies*, by William Golding
1955	*The Chrysalids*, by John Wyndham
1959	*A Separate Peace*, by John Knowles
1959	*My Side of the Mountain*, by Jean Craighead George
1960	*To Kill A Mockingbird*, by Harper Lee
1960	*Owls Do Cry*, by Janet Frame
1961	*The Bronze Bow*, by Elizabeth George Speare
1962	*A Wrinkle in Time*, by Madeleine L'Engle
1963	*It's Like This, Cat*, by Emily Cheney Neville
1967	*The Outsiders*, by S.E. Hinton
1967	*The Chosen*, by Chaim Potok
1967	*The Contender*, by Robert Lipsyte
1968	*The Pigman*, by Paul Zindel

Welcome to the dark side

The 1970s and 1980s were known for 'issue' or 'problem' YA novels. These books explored topics so dark and edgy – including drug addiction and suicide – that some critics didn't think they were appropriate. Others argued that they reflected the lives of modern adolescents and teens. At the same time, young adult science fiction and fantasy for teens began to take off.

1970	*Bless the Beasts and Children*, by Glendon Swarthout
1970	*Are You There, God? It's Me, Margaret,* by Judy Blume
1971	*Go Ask Alice*, by Anonymous [Beatrice Sparks]
1974	*House of Stairs*, by William Sleator
1974	*The Chocolate War*, by Robert Cormier
1975	*Forever*, by Judy Blume
1976	*Dragonsong*, by Anne McCaffrey
1978	*The Borribles,* by Michael de Larrabeiti
1979	*Alan Mendelsohn, The Boy from Mars,* by Daniel Pinkwater
1982	*Secret Diary of Adrian Mole, Aged 13¾,* by Sue Townsend
1982	*The Blue Sword*, by Robin McKinley
1982	*Annie on My Mind*, by Nancy Garden
1983	*Me Me Me Me Me: Not a Novel*, by M.E. Kerr
1984	*The Changeover*, by Margaret Mahy
1985	*Ender's Game*, by Orson Scott Card
1988	*Hatchet*, by Gary Paulsen

Fresh voices

Now that young adult novels have a wider range of topics, they've begun to experiment with various new forms of storytelling – from verse novels to manga to the paranormal. Also, new voices have emerged in the past two decades, featuring characters of once-overlooked classes and ethnicities.

1990	*Maniac Magee*, by Jerry Spinelli
1990	*Wolf*, by Gillian Cross
1991	*Preludes and Nocturnes*, by Neil Gaiman
1995	*Tomorrow When the War Began*, by John Marsden
1995	*Northern Lights*, by Philip Pullman
1996	*Junk*, by Melvin Burgess
1997	*Harry Potter and the Philosopher's Stone*, by J.K. Rowling
1998	*Holes*, by Louis Sachar
1998	*If You Come Softly*, by Jacqueline Woodson
1999	*Speak*, by Laurie Halse Anderson
2001	*Noughts and Crosses*, by Malorie Blackman
2002	*Feed*, by M.T. Anderson
2002	*Lucas*, by Kevin Brooks
2005	*The Lightning Thief*, by Rick Riordan
2005	*Twilight*, by Stephenie Meyer
2005	*The White Darkness*, by Geraldine McCaughrean
2008	*The Hunger Games*, by Suzanne Collins
2008	*The Knife of Never Letting Go*, by Patrick Ness
2009	*Bog Child*, by Siobhan Dowd

YOUR FUNKY FAMILY TREE

By Elizabeth

Crazy Uncle Tony (Omar's dad, my dad's bro)

Omar (my fave cousin)

Li (my BF since year one)

Auntie Kiara (Mum's BF)

Abuelita Rosita (dad's mum)

Talia (my older sister)

Ruby (my little sister)

Grandad Peter (mum's dad)

Sara (my birth mum)

Mary (my mum)

Pablo (my dad)

me

For centuries – ever since judges started making legal decisions about family life – most governments have set the maximum number of parents a kid can have at two. Today, we know that's a pretty limited view of what makes a family.

Some kids have two mums. Others have four dads. Still others have a connection to their sperm or egg donor or their surrogate mother. In this book, we mostly use the term 'grownup' instead of 'parent' because stepparents, birthparents, grandparents, foster parents, babysitters, 'aunts' and 'uncles' who aren't even related to you can and do play important roles in loving and raising you.

Take my daughter, Luisa, who was adopted when she was a baby. Not only does she have an entire family in Guatemala, who we visit every few years, but she also has an American mum and dad, two brothers, five cousins, three aunts, and two uncles. Luisa also has three American grandfathers, three grandmothers, 12 step-cousins, an ex-step grandmother who is still family, and a half-aunt. That's a lot of love.

Unfortunately, our funky extended families aren't that easy to chart on a family tree. That's because genealogy is obsessed with, well, genetics – biological kinship. While your kinship history can be fascinating to explore, it can also leave out a lot of the people who matter most to you. Here are some ideas for how to expand what a family tree can be.

Make a family fan

Instead of creating a family tree, which emphasises biological kinship, try charting your extended family and close relationships by drawing an upside-down pyramid. If you arch the top edge, it'll look like an old-fashioned folding fan.

Write your own name, or paste a photo of yourself, at the bottom tip of the upside-down fan. Then, just above that, add the people to whom you are closest. Keep going upward and outward until you've filled out the entire fan with family members, friends, and other people you care about. If you have a large network of loved ones, you can even make a circular chart with yourself at the centre.

If you're interested in creating a more inclusive family tree, try doing a web search for 'alternative family tree' or 'adoptive family tree'. You can get a printable adoptive family tree at the site familytreemagazine.com and there are other websites and apps out there too.

Do your homework

Let's say you're interviewing a member of the generation above your grownup – or trying to find out more about members of your extended family who lived a long time ago. First, go to a library or do some online research about the era in which he or she lived. If the person in whom you're interested immigrated to Britain from the Caribbean in 1948, try to find our what songs were popular in both countries back then, how men and women dressed, what was going on politically, culturally, and economically. What was the context for their story?

Collect images, music, and other material from your research and make a presentation of some kind – a scrapbook, PowerPoint presentation, or even a time capsule in a shoebox.

Become a 'family' detective

Most grownups have a few old photos, documents, bits of jewellery, or school projects stashed away somewhere. Ask your grownups, your grownups' grownups, or other adults you are close to if you can check out their memorabilia. You'll hear some eye-opening stories. For example, when I was at school and my dad was pushing me to get better marks, my grandmother showed me his old report… including one where the best mark he got was a C-minus. In PE!

It's also fascinating to see how much things have changed since your grownups and their grownups were your age. That 1956 postcard from Italy may open the door to an era when families took the train to Europe – instead of driving. Military records can make wars come alive in a very personal way. Wedding albums, baby books, baby clothes, obituaries, letters (written on paper with ink!), passports, record albums, recipes – they're all ways to catch glimpses of your loved ones' pasts.

Bring a pencil and notepad to take notes – or you might prefer to make an audio or video recording of your conversations. If you don't live near the grownup whose stories you want to hear, you might try video conferencing; get them to hold objects up to the camera.

Interviews are a good way to encourage storytelling. You can use these interviews for many different projects – from source material for characters in a novel to school projects, to an actual family tree to embarrassment blackmail for your grownups.

HOW TO
INTERVIEW

Take it from a professional journalist – the best way to get an interviewee to tell you something is to give them enough time to answer your questions. Even if there's a long and uncomfortable pause, don't say anything! Let them be the one to break the awkward silence. Remember, this isn't an ordinary conversation; you should mostly be listening, not speaking. These sample questions can get you started:

- Do you know anything about your name and how you got it?
- Can you describe your childhood home?
- What did you do during the summer when you were a kid?
- How did your family make money? Did you grow up rich or poor, or somewhere in the middle?
- Where were you born? When did you, or your family, arrive in this country?
- Did you like school? Why or why not?
- What makes you happy? What about when you were a kid?
- How did you first meet my family?
- Can you describe what the word 'family' means to you?

Illustrations by Heather Kasunick

KEEP A
DIARY

By Elizabeth

10 NOV 2013

A diary is a personal record of your life. While some people write a diary with the intention of sharing it with others, most are private spaces to confide your secrets, express your creative side, jot down random thoughts, obsess and just be yourself.

When I was a kid, diaries for girls were little hardback books that came with a lock and key. (My younger sisters picked the lock on mine with a safety pin about 12 seconds after they discovered it under my mattress.) Boys weren't encouraged to keep diaries, though some did anyway. A few visionary kids drew comics or painted watercolours depicting their riding lessons or skateboard expeditions, or whatever. But most of us were stuck in the 'Dear Diary' rut.

Today, blogs, vlogs (video blogs) and digital photography let you instantly tell your story in living colour, not to mention shout it out to the world if that's your thing.

Diary basics

Always put the date (including the year) on your diary entries. Part of what's fun about keeping a diary is that you can go back to it years later and see what was important to you when you were 10 or 15 or even 30 years old.

Make it a habit. You don't have to write in your diary every day. But if you do it as often as possible, you'll find that your mind opens up, and what you create is often more interesting, and the process is more fun.

Don't worry about spelling, punctuation, blurry images, smudge marks, choppy videos. A diary isn't a finished piece of art, but rather a casual way for you to chart your life.

You can use anything from a notebook to digital diary software. If you are going to draw or paint in your diary, artists' sketchpads are best. Diaries can also be:

Scrapbooks

Cut and paste images from newspapers, magazines, even unwanted books. Also save movie and concert tickets, bird feathers, leaves, flower petals, friendship bracelets, notes from friends – anything important enough to remember.

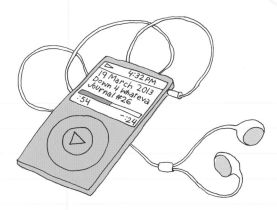

Voice diaries

If you have an iPod or an MP3 player with recording capabilities, you can just say your thoughts or talk about what you've done that day. Then, every time you sync to your computer, name the latest files, and keep them in a 'Diary' folder in your iTunes account or (less likely to be discovered) on your hard drive. Besides recording the way you speak for your future enjoyment – not only will your voice change, but the slang you use will also be different as you get older – this option saves a lot of paper.

Picture-a-Day

Take a photo – you hanging out with friends, a gorgeous autumn landscape, a goofy shop sign – every day. Download the photos to a folder on your computer, and give them a name that includes the date and subject, like so: 2013Oct31_Halloween. If you are 13 or older, you can upload your photos to a blog, or else to a photo-sharing website like Flickr or snapfish.co.uk; apps like Instagram are fun too. You can do the same sort of things with a daily video. Low-tech version: draw a one-panel cartoon daily.

Diary topics

Staring at a blank page can send you into a shame spiral. On days when you don't have anything general to say, here are some themes to help get you writing or talking.

Special interests

From travelling to sports to fashion, keep a record of what you love.

Dreams

That dream you had where you were surfing and then all of a sudden were stuck inside your wardrobe? Write it down or record it. If you have a hard time remembering your dreams, just write whatever you can remember immediately after you wake up. If you do that for several days, you will start recalling your dreams more clearly.

Lists

If you don't want to waste time with things like introductions and conclusions, making lists is a great way to record what's interesting to you. Lists can be about anything, including: your favourite places; things that annoy you; things you like most about yourself; what you'd do if you were head teacher of your school; books you have read or want to read; favourite songs; favourite videogames.

The one sentencer

Write or speak a line a day, nothing more. Or pick one adjective to describe each day and try not to repeat that word, ever again. A thesaurus will help.

Illustrations by Heather Kasunick

FAN FICTION

By Flourish Klink

If you've ever made up a story about your favourite character, or maybe imagined yourself into the world of Oz, then you've taken the first steps to writing fan fiction.

If you write a story about Jasmine's next adventure after the *Aladdin* film ends – that's fan fiction. A story about how a boy from Rio de Janeiro becomes Batman's next Robin? Fan fiction!

Fan fiction has been around as long as storytelling, but we've only had a name for the genre since the 1960s – when fans would write stories (for mimeographed fanzines) about TV shows like *Star Trek*. Today, thanks to the ease of sharing stories online, lots of people publish fan fiction. There are even online role-playing games that make use of fan fiction: one group of writers has created online diaries for all the Harry Potter characters; working together, they're telling a story in which Lord Voldemort rules Britain!

Most fan fiction authors are adults, but kids can join in too. Here are some pointers.

Think like a villain

Why do villains do what they do? Why do they think it's OK? Remember that almost every villain thinks they're doing the right thing, even when they're most in the wrong. Rewrite your favourite heroic story from the villain's perspective.

Pick a story you hate and make it better

Is *Transformers* boring because nobody has a real family with real problems? Write a better *Transformers* story. Think that Cinderella should've given her stepsisters a piece of her mind? Write it! Why not give her superpowers while you're at it?

Write a sequel to a story that you love

What happens after the credits roll? Do Han and Leia ever get married? Do Beauty and the Beast ever get bored with each other? What's going to happen after they find Nemo?

Give your characters interesting flaws

For example, Wolverine (of the X-Men superhero team) is strong and fast and clever, but he can sometimes make bad decisions in the heat of the moment. Professor X is wise and he can get around very well in his wheelchair – but he can't fight one-on-one the way Wolverine can. That makes Professor X and Wolverine much more interesting than if they were 100 per cent perfect!

Get your grownup involved

Many blogging services don't permit kids to have their own accounts… plus, there is quite a bit of fan fiction that isn't appropriate for kids. So if you want to share your fan fiction online, you'll need to do so with your grownup. Which means you'll have to get your grownup writing fan fiction, too. Figure out which books, movies, TV shows, legends or comic books you both enjoy (series like Harry Potter, Star Wars: Clone Wars, Spider-Man, or perhaps an epic like the legend of Gilgamesh) and go from there.

Make a fanvid!

Write a piece of fanfic, and then turn it into a film. Just for your family and friends, of course.

Illustration by Mister Reusch

BEST EVER
GRAPHIC NOVELS

By Josh

In the 1930s and 1940s, a few artists used comics to tell longer stories. Published not as magazines, but books, these were pioneering examples of what are now known as graphic novels. Today the format is widely popular – and it's taken seriously as a form of literature too.

Though a lot of graphic novels aren't appropriate for kids, the following favourites are. It's important to note, however, that although Tintin, Lucky Luke, Asterix, and other titles published before the late 1960s often feature ethnic and national stereotypes, their heroes aren't prejudiced. In most cases, those stereotypes were being mocked by the author.

1941
CALICO THE WONDER HORSE

By Virginia Lee Burton
Because her sons enjoyed comic books so much, the author of children's classics like *Mike Mulligan and His Steam Shovel* ended up writing one of the very first graphic novels – about a horse who outwits a gang of cattle rustlers who've hijacked a stagecoach full of Christmas presents. It's a gorgeous, epic story.

1942–1976 series
THE ADVENTURES OF TINTIN

By Hergé
The Belgian cartoonist Hergé, whose flat, simple style of drawing became hugely influential, told thrilling, funny adventure stories about the journalist Tintin and his dog, Snowy. The series (which began to be collected in 'album' form in 1942) becomes particularly great with *The Crab with the Golden Claws*. That's when Tintin first befriends the courageous, loyal, yet bumbling and foul-mouthed Captain Haddock.

1950–1971 series
BLAKE & MORTIMER

By Edgar P. Jacobs
These sci-fi adventures first appeared, from the mid-1940s on, in the Belgian comics magazine *Le Journal de Tintin*. Professor Mortimer is a brilliant scientist who runs afoul of enemy agents, time travellers and aliens; his friend, Captain Blake, is a British secret agent.

1951–1952 series
THE RED MOON MYSTERY

Created by Frank Hampson
Colonel Dan Dare, chief pilot of the Interplanet Space Fleet, was the hero of a beautifully drawn British science-fiction comic set in the then-future era of the 1990s. Along with his gormless sidekick Digby, and the brilliant professor Jocelyn Peabody, Dare explored outer space in his spaceship, *Anastasia*, and battled his arch-enemy the Mekon, an evil Venusian scientist with an enormous green head. This adventure was reprinted in a single volume in 2005.

1957–1986 series
LUCKY LUKE

Written by René Goscinny, illustrated by Morris
Lucky Luke is a noble cowboy who can shoot faster than his own shadow; his horse and sidekick, Jolly Jumper, has a mind of his own. Together, they roam the Old West – capturing dastardly villains and encountering historical figures from Calamity Jane to Billy the Kid.

You might also enjoy The Bluecoats, a funny series of Belgian graphic novels about US cavalry soldiers. You should try Goscinny's Little Nicholas novels as well.

1959–1979 series
ASTERIX

Written by René Goscinny, illustrated by Albert Uderzo
Asterix and his friend Obelix are Gauls (an ancient Celtic people) who live in what is now France; their village is surrounded by Roman soldiers but it has refused to surrender. Armed with a potion of invincibility, the two friends defend their village and travel around Europe causing trouble for the Romans. Grownups will enjoy the sophisticated jokes.

PS: The Asterix books after 1979 aren't as great as the earlier ones.

1963–1992 series
THE SMURFS
Created by Peyo

Forget the childish, annoying films, cartoons and videogames! The original Smurfs graphic novels (including *King Smurf*, *The Smurfette*, and *The Astrosmurf*), which were originally serialised beginning in the late 1950s, are far superior to the spinoffs. They've recently been reissued: read 'em all!

PS: The Belgian cartoonist Peyo didn't write and illustrate The Smurfs series, but he invented the characters, who first appeared in his own great Johan and Peewit series. Only two Johan and Peewit books have so far been published in English.

1966–1967 series
SIBYL-ANNE VS. RATTICUS
By R. Macherot

Long before Brian Jacques' similar Redwall series, the cartoonist R. Macherot told the story of a peaceful mouse (Sibyl-Anne) who is forced to band together with an unlikely assortment of animals (a crow, a rabbit, a porcupine) and defend her homeland against the land, sea, and air invasion of the villain Ratticus and his rat army. I've waited for years for this all-ages Franco-Belgian comic strip to appear in English; in 2011, it finally did.

1975
FATHER CHRISTMAS GOES ON HOLIDAY
By Raymond Briggs

A curmudgeonly Father Christmas travels around the world (on his sleigh) looking for a vacation spot far from the North Pole, where he can relax and live it up. Briggs's *Father Christmas* (1973) is also great.

Though perhaps best known for his powerful anti-nuclear graphic novel, *When the Wind Blows* (1982), Briggs's other graphic novels for kids are terrific: *Fungus the Bogeyman* (1977), *The Snowman* (1978), and *UG: Boy Genius of the Stone Age* (2001).

1987
FRED
By Posey Simmonds

Schoolchildren Sophie and Nick's ancient cat spends his days sleeping; when he dies, they sadly bury him in the garden. Late that night, however, they are awakened by dozens of top-hatted cat mourners who have assembled to eulogise 'Famous Fred'. Sleepy old Fred – it turns out – had spent his nights singing 'Meeyowley-yowley-yowl!' with his cat rock band, the Heavy Saucers.

PS: Simmonds is also the author of such kids' graphic novels as *Bouncing Buffalo* (1984), *Lulu and the Flying Babies* (1988) and *The Chocolate Wedding* (1990). The 1996 film adaptation of this book, titled *Famous Fred*, was nominated for the Academy Award for Animated Short Film. Comedian Lenny Henry voiced Famous Fred.

1998–present series
DUNGEON
Created by Joann Sfar and Lewis Trondheim

Although it spoofs the Dungeons & Dragons game, this sprawling series is not only funny but packed with thrills and chills. In the Zenith sub-series, the Dungeon Master's assistants Herbert the Duck and Marvin the Dragon get into scrapes. The Early Years series concerns the Dungeon Master's youthful adventures; the Twilight series follows Marvin the Red, a rabbit who teams up with Marvin the Dragon against Herbert the Duck, who has turned evil!

PS: Each book contains panels whose content is on the racy side.

2000–2007 series
SARDINE IN OUTER SPACE
Written by Emmanuel Guibert, illustrated by Joann Sfar

Sardine and her uncle, the pirate Captain Yellow Shoulder, battle Supermuscleman and Doc Krok, who run a space orphanage where children are taught to behave. The universe is rapidly becoming a law-abiding, boring place and it's Sardine's mission to keep it weird.

PS: The post-2007 Sardine books, which are written and illustrated by Guibert on his own, are not quite as terrific as the others.

2000
ASTRONAUTS OF THE FUTURE VOL. 1
Written by Lewis Trondheim, illustrated by Manu Larcenet

Martina and Gilbert are school-children who argue over whether grownups (and everyone else) are robots or aliens. Either way, they're convinced that something is terribly wrong. Several surprising plot twists later, they discover exactly how right (maybe) they are. The further adventures of Martina and Gilbert haven't yet appeared in English.

You will also enjoy Trondheim's McConey series of graphic novels, of which only *The Hoodoodad* and *Harum Scarum* have been translated into English so far.

2001
THE GOLEM'S MIGHTY SWING
By James Sturm

An all-Jewish baseball team tours small-town America in the 1920s, where they battle prejudice on and off the field. Looking to drum up publicity, the team outfits a Negro League ballplayer with a monster's costume, and advertise him as the scary golem of Jewish legend.

Sturm wrote a graphic-novel biography of Satchel Paige that is terrific. And he's the co-author of a graphic novel that teaches kids how to make comics: *Adventures in Cartooning* (2009).

2003
PEANUT BUTTER & JEREMY'S BEST BOOK EVER!
By James Kochalka

Peanut Butter is a kitten who wears a collar, tie and fedora (hat) because she thinks she works in an office – which is actually her owner's home office. Jeremy, a crow who lives in the tree next door, is determined to steal the fedora. Considering how cute their premise is, these stories are remarkably edgy.

2006
BILLY HAZELNUTS
By Tony Millionaire
Becky, a kid scientist, and Billy, a living manikin created out of rubbish, travel across the sea to discover where the moon goes when it sets. Along the way, they battle a giant Noah's Ark toy that's populated by toy animals, and a flying pirate ship crewed by robotic buccaneer alligators.

Tony Millionaire's Sock Monkey books for younger kids are gorgeous and strange, too.

2006
THE ARRIVAL
By Shaun Tan
In this wordless story, a lone immigrant leaves his family (who are threatened by dark shapes) and homeland, and journeys to a beautiful city in a new place where he struggles to find friends and work. His profound bewilderment is symbolised by, for example, floating elevators, dog-sized hermit crabs, and an unreadable alphabet made up of random shapes.

Tan's 2011 collection *Lost and Found* offers three more great stories.

2006
AMERICAN BORN CHINESE
By Gene Luen Yang
Who knew 2006 was such an amazing year for kids' graphic novels? This prize-winning book tells three intertwined stories: about Chinese folklore hero The Monkey King, shape-shifting master of kung fu; about Jin Wang, adolescent child of Chinese immigrants to America; and about Danny, an American teen who hates it when his Chinese cousin visits his school. Together, the stories thematise balancing self-respect with the desire to fit into mainstream culture.

PS: This book's publisher, First Second, has a website at firstsecondbooks.com that offers lesson plans and activity kits to teachers interested in using *American Born Chinese* and other First Second graphic novels in the classroom. Alert your teacher!

2006–2009 series
THE FOG MOUND
Written by Susan Schade, illustrated by Jon Buller
Thelonious is a chipmunk who explores a post-apocalyptic world in which humans are a legend. Over the course of the trilogy – of which each instalment is part novel, part graphic novel – he gathers friends, discovers a peaceful animal commune known as Fog Mound, battles ratminks and investigates the true cause of the humans' disappearance. Too bad all novels aren't part graphic novel, like this one – it's pretty cool.

2007–present series
MOUSE GUARD
By David Petersen
Kenzie and Saxon the swordmice, young Lieam, and the deadly Sadie are members of a medieval brother- and sisterhood of mice warriors. They have sworn an oath to protect all mousedom against snakes, crabs, weasels, bats, owls… even a few traitorous mice. The series has been collected in two volumes, so far.

Mouse Guard: Legends of the Guard (2010) is a collection of Mouse Guard stories by artists and writers handpicked by Petersen.

2008
LITTLE VAMPIRE
By Joann Sfar
Because all the other monsters in his haunted mansion are grownups, Little Vampire befriends a boy named Michael. He helps Michael with his homework, uses his supernatural powers to help him deal with a bully – and he enlists his fellow ghouls to rescue dogs from an animal testing laboratory. Spooky, sometimes gruesome, but always brilliant stuff from the great Sfar.

2010
SLOG'S DAD
Written by David Almond, illustrated by Dave McKean
This short but intense story – which is a collaboration between a well-known comic-book artist (McKean) and a well-known author of Young Adult fiction (Almond) – is part novel, part graphic novel. Before Slog's dad dies of cancer, he promises he'll be back for a visit in the spring; in the spring, Slog becomes convinced that a homeless man is a reincarnation of his father. Slog's friend isn't so sure, though: Is the man really who he says he is? Is he a dangerous nut? Or is he just trying to make Slog feel better?

PS: Almond and McKean also co-authored *The Savage* (2008) and, most recently, *Mouse Bird Snake Wolf.*

2011
WANDERING SON (BOOK 1)
By Shimura Takako
A sensitive and gently humorous Japanese manga (in translation) about two friends: Shuichi, a boy who wants to be a girl, and Yoshino, a girl who wants to be a boy. Spoiler alert: it's not just a phase. As the series progresses (11 volumes have been published in Japan), Shuichi and Yoshino will continue to grapple with gender identity and sexual orientation issues.

2012
THE ADVENTURES OF VENUS
By Gilbert Hernandez
In this collection of funny stories, a spunky Latina kid named Venus writes and collects comic books, goes on an adventure through a scary forest, plays football, schemes to get the boy she likes, and (maybe) travels to a far-off planet.

PS: Grownup fans of the magical-realist Love & Rockets series of comics by Gilbert and his brother Jaime know how much Los Bros Hernandez admire powerful women. Venus is a powerful *young* woman!

ROCK OUT

By Chelsey Johnson

Too cool to rock?
Too bad for you.

Put your heart
into it!

Eighty girls stand hand-in-hand in a circle in a room just large enough to hold them. It's the first day of the Rock'n'Roll Camp for Girls, a summer camp where I work every year. I am trying to get the girls to scream. 'OK,' I say. 'Let's do this.'

What is supposed to happen is we send one long continuous scream around the circle, like a wave. You scream, and before you've finished screaming you squeeze the hand of the person next to you, and her scream starts and overlaps with yours, and so on. When it works, it's earsplitting and hair-raising and funny and powerful all at once. On the first day of camp, it never works.

When all the girls plug their ears and close their eyes for a big unison practice scream, a mighty roar goes up. But once we're in the circle looking at each other, the campers shrink into shy little things. Some of them open up and go for it. But most of them fumble out a worried 'aaaah?' or a deflating 'eeeee', or emit a scared little peep.

I think we're afraid of what would come out if we really let loose, and how loud that could get. Would it be scary? Would it be ugly? Would it sound stupid? Mostly, I think we're afraid we will not look *cool*.

But rocking out is not about coolness. Want to know what will make you a rocker? Read on.

Be uncool

We have a saying at rock camp: 'Too Cool To Rock.' This describes people who are so busy trying to look cool – standing at the back of the crowd with their arms crossed, half-heartedly mouthing the lyrics to the camp song, showing up late to band practice and contributing 'I don't care' and 'whatever' to the songwriting process, and yes, refusing to scream – that they miss the part where you actually rock out.

When it comes to music, you have to be uncool before you can be cool. Kids who try to play it cool end up writing nothing, and looking terrified or bored when they finally take the stage. The kids who really rock are the ones who throw themselves into it all the way, who put their heart in it.

Let yourself be bad

Until I was 16, I played classical music that was written by someone else. The point was to reproduce it accurately, memorise the sheet music, and hit every note perfectly. But I was in love with rock and punk and if I wanted to ever make such music, I needed to learn guitar. Because I played piano and flute, and sang in two choirs, I thought that it would be easy.

Illustrations by Mister Reusch

So I signed up for guitar lessons. But my fingers would barely stretch to press the hard steel strings of my dad's big acoustic guitar. My chords were clunky, my riffs limped. I did not rock.

I swiftly gave up. I was used to doing things perfectly, or close to it. That feeling of badness scared me.

Here's what I wish I had known then: if you keep playing, you develop protective calluses on your fingertips that feel amazing, like little coats of armour. Also: there's this thing called the barre chord, where you can just mash your fingers down on two frets and basically play any punk song ever written (hello, Ramones!).

Perfect is a demon whose mission is to keep you from doing things you could potentially love. It's true in music, in art, in writing, in anything you create. It's especially true (I think) if you're a girl. Perfect hates messiness, weirdness, the discordant note, the accidental stumble. But not only are those things essential to learning anything, they often turn out to be the coolest part.

I picture Perfect as a little pristine white ghost with a satisfied smirk on its face and a fake halo floating over its head. But it might take the form of your enemy, your friends or your frenemy. And sometimes it will even make itself look exactly like you yourself, the you that is highly sceptical that you can pull this thing off.

When Perfect comes around to give you a hard time, tell it, 'Go away now, because I'm not finished yet.' Then allow yourself to write a stupid lyric, to play the world's clumsiest fill or riff, to keep stumbling forward with a trail of broken chords and off notes in your wake.

You don't have to be good to start a band, or to write songs. You learn by doing it.

Make your own sound

Learning how to play other people's songs teaches you a lot, but it is actually easier to make up songs yourself than to try to imitate someone else.

So invent your own songs, and turn your limitations to your advantage. If you only know three notes on the bass, make up a song that only needs those notes. If your band consists of two drummers and two singers and a violin player, don't worry that you're 'missing' a guitar or whatever – see what kind of totally new sound you can make.

If you think you're not a good singer, a) check out Bob Dylan, b) shout, c) fake your singing until you hit upon a vocal style that actually works, or d) do all of the above. Don't worry too much about the way things are 'supposed' to sound.

Here's a story. A seven-year-old girl in North Carolina (USA) named Elizabeth Cotten learned to play the banjo and then scraped together enough money to buy her own guitar. Because she was left-handed, Elizabeth played the guitar the way that felt natural to her – she picked and strummed with her left hand and played the notes with her right. The guitar was essentially upside-down – but for Elizabeth, it was a perfect fit. When she was 11, she wrote 'Freight Train', which turned into an American classic.

What matters is making music that's yours. Not copying what you hear on the radio, not singing or playing what you think other people want to hear. Your music comes from the same place that your scream comes from, a sound that is distinctively your voice, that comes from your body.

Community, not competition

Rock is not a competition where only one band can win. In fact, the more bands around you, the better.

Most great bands and artists come from a *scene*, which means a specific place and time where people play in each other's bands and put shows together and help each other out. Not only is there plenty of room for more than one band or musician, but the more bands there are, the better your town/school/universe will be.

Never tear down other people you know who are making music – instead, join forces with them! Play shows together. Form an alliance and all of you will be stronger.

Do it because you want to

The things you love the most in life will probably not make you mountains of money. This is definitely true for music. You have to do it out of sheer love.

Your bands are probably not going to become famous; they might not ever play outside a basement or garage. But playing in them will be one of the

BAND BASICS

Choose your bandmates
Being in a band requires people to work together in a way that's more intense than team sports or a school project. The best kind of bandmates are hardworking but willing to compromise.

Set up a practice space
Find a place where you can leave heavy gear like amps and drums. Cellars are best in order to avoid noise complaints. You could also ask your school (the band room after hours, for example), or, if you can, rent a shared space with other bands. When space is scarce, quiet practice (unplugged, in your bedroom) also works.

Set up a practice schedule
Decide a regular time (or more) each week for your band to practise. If you keep it looser than that, you'll rarely practise.

Record your practices
If you come up with a brilliant jam, recording your practice will ensure you don't forget the song by the next rehearsal.

Gear up
Get these basics if you can: a microphone (Shure SM58 is a classic); an amplifier (Peavey is an inexpensive workhorse); a 4-channel powered mixer (this allows you to have four different voices and instruments amplified – Peavey is a good bet); a microphone stand and cord (surprisingly expensive – buy them second-hand). Get your gear from a shop that will buy back your old stuff; that way you can get better stuff later. Hang out at the music shop to ask for tips on using your gear properly.

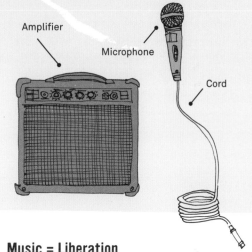

Amplifier

Microphone

Cord

most fun things you will ever do. Sure, the applause and the attention that come from playing in shows are exciting. But in a way, the best part of rocking out is not the performance, but the practice – the part where it's you and your friends in a room laughing, solving problems, inventing something that is more than the sum of your individual parts, making a glorious racket that turns into a song you just can't get out of your head.

It's never too soon or too late
You are not too young to play!

I have seen kids who are smaller than their guitars turn up the distortion and bang out a killer riff. I have danced to bands where you cannot see the drummer's head over the crash cymbal. I have seen 17-year-olds own the stage with a bass they picked up for the first time six days ago, and 50-year-old mums form their first band and write a song in one weekend.

Music = Liberation
A word to the shy: if you think rock is not for you, you're wrong. Yes, some people are born performers. If you're one of those people, lucky you! Most of us, though, harbour fears and doubts that come from our upbringing, our gender, our peer culture, ourselves. This is where making music can change your life.

In the squall of distortion or the power of a drumbeat that thumps in your own chest, in a jagged scream or a joyful unison shout, in rhyme and in rhythm, you can dig into feelings and ideas that are otherwise hard for you to express. You can say it in lyrics or you can say it with the sound of your instrument. You can do it by yourself or bolstered by the collective power of your band. And you can be messy and loud in the process – in fact, you have to be.

You will get there. Even if you think you're really bad at rocking out. Even if at first, you open your mouth to scream and only a squeak comes out.

QUIZ: WHAT INSTRUMENT ARE YOU?

By Elizabeth

These days, a lot of kids start violin just after they turn three years old... so it might seem like you need to choose an instrument early and stick with it through years and years of practice. But many professional musicians who play in bands and orchestras didn't start their instruments until they were 13 or older.

Although learning an instrument requires a commitment to work hard, it should also be fun. So choosing an instrument according to your personality and physical traits helps. While there's no guaranteed way to determine the perfect instrument for you, when helping my kids make this decision I consulted *The Right Instrument for Your Child*, co-authored by flautist Atarah Ben-Tovim, and I also took the advice of my music-teacher husband. Here's the process my kids ended up using.

Ask yourself these questions:

1. **What kind of music do you like?** You may want to download a few songs or watch videos on YouTube to give you an idea of the music you can make on the instruments you are considering.

2. **What do people who play certain instruments like about them?** If your aunt loves the trumpet because it gives her a chance to be loud and bossy, that's good to know – especially if you're quiet and shy.

Drums

Do you bang sticks, forks, knives, and your fingers on any surface you can find? Does your body feel like it needs to be constantly moving? Can you stick with the same physical task for a long time? Then drums might be the perfect fit.

If you want to play in a rock band, a standard drum kit is for you. But to drum in an orchestra or school band (if you've taken music lessons already), you'll need to try percussion, which includes playing timpani, a drum you tune.

Flute

This band and orchestra standard is easy to learn, which makes it a great choice if you are the kind of person who likes to see quick results. But you have to be able to hold the flute horizontally (harder than it looks if you're too small!) with your left arm comfortably stretched across your chest.

Clarinet

Clarinets are reed instruments – that is to say, the sound you make is increased by a thin strip of material that vibrates in the mouthpiece. Reeds are very fragile, so if you don't have the patience to care for them, your grownups will get very frustrated.

Saxophone

Saxophones are heavy. That's why most kids don't start playing them until they are at least 12. Easier to play than the flute or clarinet, this is an instrument that can produce almost instant satisfaction.

Trumpet

Do you like to be the centre of attention? Are you independent – meaning that you don't need to go along with a group of kids? Trumpet players have the guts to play solos in front of groups.

Trombone

Most kids don't start playing trombone until their right arm is long enough to stretch the slide all the way out. That's usually around 12 years old. Note that full lips are a bonus for the trombone, which has a larger mouthpiece than other brass instruments.

Electric guitar or bass

You've got to really, really enjoy loud noises if you want to commit to an electric instrument; in fact, you should always wear earplugs when you play to protect your hearing. Playing the electric guitar or bass is a great way to get together with friends and make your own music; however, practising is also important.

Piano

Like the guitar, the piano is a wonderful instrument to play on your own. And like the violin, it requires a tremendous amount of practice. So if you rock at school (especially calculating maths problems in your head), like to work hard and practise something every day, and enjoy being alone, piano may be for you.

Violin

Do your teachers comment on how well-behaved you are? Can you spend hours alone in your room reading? Do you like to do homework? And finally, do you have good balance? If your answer to all of these questions is Yes, then the violin could be the perfect fit for you.

Illustrations by Mister Reusch

BEST EVER
MUSICAL MOVIES

By Josh

So you've watched *High School Musical 3*, *Camp Rock 2*, *The Lion King 1½*... and also some oldies like *The Wizard of Oz*, *Singin' in the Rain*, *The Sound of Music*, *Mary Poppins*, *The Aristocats*, *The Jungle Book* and *Peter Pan*. And now you want more?

Here's a list of musical movies, and films about music and musicians that kids and grownups can enjoy together.

1935
TOP HAT
Directed by Mark Sandrich
This is the best-known film by legendary dance partners Fred Astaire and Ginger Rogers. He plays an American dancer in London; she's the girl in the hotel room downstairs annoyed by his tap-dancing. Two of Irving Berlin's tunes for the movie – 'Top Hat, White Tie and Tails' and 'Cheek to Cheek' – went on to become classics.

1940
FANTASIA
Produced by Walt Disney
Eight wild and gorgeous animated segments set to pieces of classical music, including 'The Rite of Spring' and selections from *The Nutcracker Suite*. The movie – not only its art, but its recording techniques – was way ahead of its time, and audiences weren't impressed. It didn't begin to make a profit until students, who appreciated its far-out animation, rediscovered it in the late 1960s.

1942
YANKEE DOODLE DANDY
Directed by Michael Curtiz
Song-and-dance man George M. Cohan (a real person, who wrote the First World War anthem 'Over There,' not to mention the patriotic 'You're a Grand Old Flag') tells stories about growing up in a performing family. James Cagney, an actor best known for his tough-guy roles, does a swell job here portraying Cohan.

1948
A SONG IS BORN
Directed by Howard Hawks
Along with bandleader Benny 'King of Swing' Goodman, the great singer-dancer-comedian Danny Kaye plays a fuddy-duddy scholar researching an encyclopaedia of music. When a nightclub singer (Virginia Mayo) on the run introduces them to jazz and swing (performed by Louis Armstrong, Lionel Hampton, and others), things get hectic – in a good way.

PS: The film is a remake of the black-and-white *Ball of Fire* (1941), which features legendary jazz drummer and bandleader Gene Krupa, and trumpeter Roy Eldridge. Watch both, and decide which you like best.

1951
AN AMERICAN IN PARIS
Directed by Vincente Minnelli
If you loved Gene Kelly in *Singin' in the Rain*, then watch the movie that won him an Oscar. Kelly plays an American looking for success as a painter in Paris; French actress Leslie Caron, who'd dance in other movies with Fred Astaire, Mikhail Baryshnikov, and Rudolf Nureyev, plays his love interest.

1956
THE GIRL CAN'T HELP IT
Directed by Frank Tashlin
Jayne Mansfield plays a mobster's girlfriend who is forced to be a singing star even though her voice is so bad it breaks lightbulbs. That's the whole plot; what's important about the film is that Little Richard performed the title song, and other early rock'n'roll stars (Eddie Cochran, Gene Vincent) also show up.

1957
JAILHOUSE ROCK
Directed by Richard Thorpe
Fast-forward past the disturbing scene where Elvis Presley gets sent to jail for killing a man with one punch (and the scene where he gets whipped by a jailer) and enjoy the amazing 'Jailhouse Rock' dance sequence. It's been described as the prototype for the modern music video.

1963
SUMMER HOLIDAY
Directed by Peter Yates

During a wet London summer, bus mechanic Don (singer Cliff Richard, who dominated the British pop music scene in the pre-Beatles period of the late 1950s and early 1960s) converts a double-decker bus into a holiday caravan… and drives it across Europe. He and his two pals, one of whom is played by Jeremy Bulloch (the actor inside the costume of the bounty hunter Boba Fett in the original Star Wars trilogy), are joined by three girls and a runaway singer pursued by her mother and agent. Four of the movie's songs became chart-toppers; and several are accompanied by dance numbers – which contributed to its wild success.

PS: The irreverent 1980s sitcom *The Young Ones* takes its name from another Cliff Richard musical. The success of these films led Cliff to be named the No. 1 cinema box office attraction in Britain… beating James Bond!

1964
A HARD DAY'S NIGHT
Directed by Richard Lester

In this pseudo-documentary, the Beatles must get to a TV studio in time to record a show – but John, Paul, George and Ringo keep sneaking away from their uptight manager. It's a wild ride: George is mistaken for a teenage actor, Paul's grandfather gets into mischief and Ringo gets thrown in jail. The movie influenced 1960s spy films, the Monkees' TV show and pop music videos. Most importantly, the music is terrific and the Beatles are charming.

1965
HELP!
Directed by Richard Lester

When a sacrificial ring gets stuck on Ringo's finger, the Beatles are chased across London, the Austrian Alps and the Bahamas by an eastern religious cult (stereotype alert:

the cult is a parody of the south Asian Thuggee cult). The film, which spoofs the James Bond spy movies, isn't quite as amazing as *A Hard Day's Night*, in part because the Beatles weren't given as much creative input. But the group house in which the Beatles live is amazing, and the scenes in which the Beatles perform their songs are terrific. How could they not be?

1967
MAD MONSTER PARTY
Directed by Jules Bass

A spooky-kooky stop-motion movie in which Dracula, the Werewolf, the Creature from the Black Lagoon and other monsters team up to destroy kind-hearted Felix, to whom his uncle, Baron von Frankenstein, has left the secret of total destruction. You'll groove to the spoof-Swingin' Sixties tunes, like 'Do the Mummy'.

PS: Jules Bass co-founded Rankin/Bass Productions, who in addition to feature films like this one produced classic American animated TV specials like *Rudolph the Red-Nosed Reindeer* (1964), *Frosty the Snowman* (1969), and *Santa Claus is Comin' to Town* (1970).

1968
YELLOW SUBMARINE
Directed by George Dunning

In this far-out animated movie, the Beatles – whose music provides the soundtrack, but who didn't record the voices for 'John', 'Paul', 'George' and 'Ringo' – must travel via a yellow submarine to Pepperland, a music-loving paradise under the sea which has been invaded by the evil Blue Meanies.

The film – which was inspired in part by Walt Disney's *Fantasia*, though its style is more abstract and unrealistic than Disney's exquisitely detailed animation technique – has been credited with helping audiences take animation seriously as an art form.

1971
BEDKNOBS AND BROOMSTICKS
Directed by Robert Stevenson

This adaptation of English author Mary Norton's wartime books *The Magic Bed Knob; or, How to Become a Witch in Ten Easy Lessons* (1943) and *Bonfires and Broomsticks* (1945) stars Angela Lansbury as apprentice witch Eglantine Price, and David Tomlinson as con artist Emelius Browne. During the Blitz, three children are evacuated to Miss Price's countryside home. She bewitches a bedknob, and the children's bed turns into a flying machine. The five characters use it to gather more spells, which Miss Price then employs against German soldiers who have invaded England.

PS: The film won an Academy Award for Best Visual Effects, and 'The Age of Not Believing' received a nomination for Best Original Song.

1976
BUGSY MALONE
Directed by Alan Parker

Though it's kinda weird to hear the characters sing with dubbed-in adult voices, this all-kid musical gangster movie is a lot of fun. Scott Baio and Jodie Foster, both of whom were famous child actors, play boxing promoter Bugsy Malone and a gangster's moll (girlfriend). Nobody dies; they just get 'splatted' by custard-shooting tommy guns.

1977
THE HOBBIT
Directed by Arthur Rankin Jr and Jules Bass

Although the goblins are perhaps a bit too cute, and although many plot details are left out, this Rankin/Bass animated version of the classic fantasy novel is scary and thrilling. Plus, it sets the songs that J.R.R. Tolkien wrote to music – and they're actually catchy! You'll dig the dwarves' song teasing Bilbo for being so fussy about his kitchen, and the orcs' song 'Where There's a Whip There's a Way' is brilliantly evil.

1978
THE WIZ
Directed by Sidney Lumet

The urbanised version of *The Wizard of Oz*, with an African-American cast and Munchkins turned into graffiti, was a good idea that didn't work out; the film was a flop. Still, Michael Jackson makes a terrific, agile and graceful Scarecrow (made of rubbish); Dorothy is played by Diana Ross, one of the great R&B, soul and disco singers of all time; and turning the Munchkins into graffiti was an inspired idea. Plus, the song 'Ease on Down the Road' is much more danceable than 'Follow the Yellow Brick Road'.

1982
THE LAST UNICORN
Directed by Arthur Rankin Jr and Jules Bass

When evil King Haggard (voiced by Christopher Lee, the actor who plays Saruman in the *Lord of the Rings* trilogy and Count Dooku in *Star Wars II* and *III*) exiles her species, the last unicorn (voiced by Mia Farrow) teams up with a bumbling wizard named Schmendrick (voiced by Alan Arkin) to find out where they've gone. Transformed into a human, the unicorn falls in love and nearly abandons her quest.

1988
HAIRSPRAY
Directed by John Waters

The original *Hairspray* is funnier and edgier than the 2007 remake. Ricki Lake plays Tracy, a 'pleasantly plump' pupil in 1962 Baltimore who wins a spot on a TV dance show. Soon, she's agitating to integrate black and white dancers on the programme. Real-life pop stars Sonny Bono and Debbie Harry play the pushy parents of Tracy's rival, Amber Von Tussle. The director makes an appearance as a quack psychiatrist hired to brainwash Tracy's friend Penny into dating only white boys.

1992
NEWSIES
Directed by Kenny Ortega

Based on the true story of the Newsboys Strike of 1899, a youth-led campaign to force the New York newspapers published by Joseph Pulitzer and William Randolph Hearst to pay their child labour force fairly, *Newsies* follows the adventures of Jack 'Cowboy' Kelly (played by Christian Bale, now known as the star of recent Batman movies). Though not intended as a musical, there are a dozen songs and many athletic dance sequences.

PS: This is the first film directed by choreographer Kenny Ortega, who went on to direct the High School Musical trilogy.

1998
SPICE WORLD
Directed by Bob Spiers

Perhaps you've never heard of them, but once upon a time, the Spice Girls (Sporty, Scary, Ginger, Baby and Posh – who is now married to David Beckham) were a very big deal. In this celebrity-filled (Elton John, Meat Loaf, Elvis Costello) farce inspired by the Beatles' *A Hard Day's Night* and *Help!*, the girls race around London in a brilliant custom-built double-decker bus on their way to a big show. It was panned by critics but it has gained a cult following.

2003
SCHOOL OF ROCK
Directed by Richard Linklater

Jack Black plays Dewey, a slacker and failed rock musician who masquerades as Mr Schneebly, a substitute teacher at a snooty school. His true identity is discovered, but not before he has transformed a class full of diligent, goody-two-shoes students into a rock band and crew – and taught them the importance of 'sticking it to the Man'. The sequence with Black teaching his students the history of rock is educational, and the song 'School of Rock' is pretty excellent.

2004
BRIDE AND PREJUDICE
Directed by Gurinder Chadha

Loosely based on Jane Austen's classic novel *Pride and Prejudice*, this Bollywood-style English movie tells the story of farmer's daughter Lalita Bakshi (Aishwarya Rai) who resists the advances of handsome and wealthy American Will Darcy (Martin Henderson). Darcy must learn to appreciate Indian culture before Lalita is won over. In the meantime, there is singing and dancing galore!

2005
LINDA LINDA LINDA
Directed by Nobuhiro Yamashita

When their band's singer and lead guitarist quits two days before the school talent show, two Japanese schoolgirls (played by Shiori Sekine and Aki Maeda) force a keyboardist friend to play guitar and recruit a Korean exchange student as their new vocalist. The only problem is... she doesn't speak Japanese.

2006
NACHO LIBRE
Directed by Jared Hess

Jack Black, who plays Nacho, a monk who moonlights as a masked wrestler, only sings a couple of (silly) songs: 'Singing at the Party' and 'Encarnación'. But music – a hybrid of traditional Mexican folk music and American indie rock – is key to this funny movie's general atmosphere.

2007
TAARE ZAMEEN PAR (LIKE STARS ON EARTH)
Directed by Aamir Khan

Because he's not getting good marks, eight-year-old Ishaan (played by Darsheel Safary) is mistreated at home and school. Then a teacher discovers that Ishaan is dyslexic – and a great painter too. The soundtrack to this Indian film is lovely, and one of the songs, 'Bum Bum Bole', became a huge hit with kids in India.

CIGAR BOX
GUITAR

By Walter Schleisman

Building a guitar is a complex process so it's more fun to do it with your grownup than alone. Even working with a grownup, it's unlikely that you'll build an instrument that you can use to perform; to do so, you'd have to thoroughly understand how intonation (always being in tune) and equal temperament (a complex tuning system) operate. Instead, why not build a guitar that is fun to play, makes some really cool sounds – and looks brilliant.

You'll need:

- A piece of wood for the neck: 2.5cm thick x 5cm wide x 90cm long. Use poplar or another soft wood; doing so will make the job easier. Also, the finished guitar will feel more balanced.
- **Optional:** Metal frets, wood burner or marker pen
- A cigar box. A fancy cigar shop will often give you one for free, or for a small price. Pick one with heavy wood and a thick cover. You can also use a biscuit tin, though you'll have to modify these instructions.
- 3 guitar tuning machines (also known as pegs) To save money, look for them on eBay.
- 3 acoustic guitar strings, gauged .024, .016 and .011; or gauged .042, .032 and .024
- Router (or wood file)
- Drill with different size bits
- Sandpaper and/or power sander
- Power saw, wood saw or wood file
- Ruler
- Wood glue
- Clamps
- **Optional:** Hammer and 6 small nails
- 3 small screw eyes
- 2 large bolts
- Dust mask and safety goggles

> **WARNING!** It's always important to use safety goggles or safety glasses when operating power tools. Work in a well-ventilated place and wear a dust mask to avoid breathing in particles. Grownup supervision is a must.

Try this:

1. Shave about 1–2cm off the thickness of the neck's top 10cm – to make room for the tuning machines. (They have to be lower than the neck so the strings can lie flat.) Some guitar builders insist that you use a wood file; but a power router makes doing this part easy.

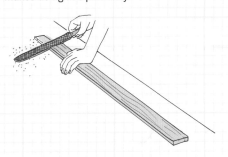

2. Drill three holes for the tuning machines. If the tuning machines you buy don't specify what size hole to drill, or how thick the wood needs to be, use a ruler to measure how wide and thick the tuning machines are, then guesstimate.

Illustrations by Mister Reusch

3. Sand down the entire back, front and sides of the neck thoroughly so it won't give you splinters when you play. If you can, round the edges on the back of the neck for a more professional look.

4. Decide whether or not you want frets – the skinny metal bars that tell you where the different notes are. If you do, you'll have to do some serious maths and woodworking to place and pound them in; the cigarboxguitars.com website offers some pointers. An easier route is marking frets along the neck with a wood burner or permanent marker. An even easier route is going fretless.

5. Using a power saw, hand saw or wood file, cut out the parts of the cigar box where the neck will fit. This is a tricky procedure, because the neck must fit snugly, so 'measure twice, cut once', as they say. When you're measuring, remember that the neck will go through the cigar box, and stick out by a couple of centimetres from the box's bottom end – to hold the strings. If the lid of your cigar box closes on the inside, you may have to router out the neck where it goes into the box.

6. Attach the neck to the box; if you have a snug fit, this is pretty easy to do. Put wood glue wherever the two surfaces touch, close the box, and clamp everything down to dry overnight.

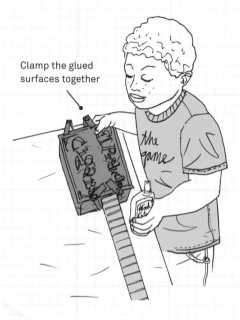

Clamp the glued surfaces together

7. Once everything is dry, you might want to ensure that the neck doesn't separate from the box by hammering in a few small nails around the edges of the box, and also in a few places where the neck touches the box.

8. Attach the tuning machines to the neck. Also, to hold the strings in place, screw three small screw eyes into the bridge (the part of the neck that comes out of the bottom of the box).

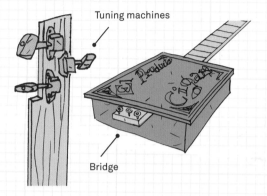

Tuning machines

Bridge

9. Using the large bolts, string the guitar. Place one bolt on the part of the neck where it drops down for the tuning machines (this is called the *nut*). Place the other bolt on the top of the bridge. To ensure that the strings sit at an even height the whole length of the guitar, you'll want the height of the bolts to be about the same. Thread one string through each screw eye (guitar strings have a 'ball end' that will catch on the screw eye) and attach its other end to its corresponding tuning machine; tighten the strings.

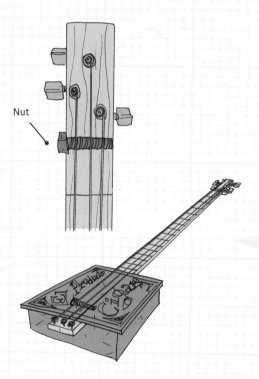

Nut

ICE LOLLY STICK
HARMONICA

You'll need:
- 1 wide rubber band
- 3 ice lolly sticks
- 2 thin rubber bands

Try this:

1. Stretch the wide rubber band (yellow) over the long edge of one ice lolly stick.

2. Using a damp sponge, wet the middle of the other two sticks; then carefully bend them in an arc. To make it easier to bend, you can also gently chew the middle of the two sticks.

3. Place the stick with the rubber band between the other two sticks. The arcs of the other two sticks should bulge outwards, away from the middle stick.

4. Using the thin rubber bands (red), secure the ends of the three sticks together.

Go ahead and blow through your harmonica. How many different sounds can you make?

Tuning your cigar box guitar
There are many ways to tune your cigar box guitar.

- Try D-G-B, which are the three middle strings of standard guitars that when strummed together create a major chord.

- For other tuning possibilities, do a web search for 'cigar box guitar tuning'.

- Use a guitar tuner (either a real one or an online one).

Did you make a fretless guitar?
Try using a slide (a metal cylinder worn over one finger); it makes a great sound.

YOU: RESOURCES

BUNK OFF

Art of Roughhousing, The: Good Old-Fashioned Horseplay and Why Every Kid Needs It (2011), by Anthony T. DeBenedet and Lawrence J. Cohen. Roughhousing moves, games and activities – by two parenting experts.

Backyard Ballistics: Build Potato Cannons, Paper Match Rockets, Cincinnati Fire Kites, Tennis Ball Mortars and More Dynamite Devices (2001), by William Gurstelle. The title says it all.

Banksy Bristol Tour (banksybristol tourapp.co.uk). This app is a tour guide to works by the famous street artist Banksy in his hometown of Bristol. Years ago, Banksy faced fines and other repercussions for his graffiti. However, when the Bristol City Museum exhibited his work in 2009, more than 300,000 people attended. He's become a local institution!

Big Book of Boy Stuff, The (2004), by Bart King. Games, explosions, magic tricks. Plus, the book can be disguised as a school textbook. Not just for boys.

Bro-Jitsu: The Martial Art of Sibling Smackdown (2010), by Daniel H. Wilson. Grownups may not approve of everything here. Not just for boys.

Games for All Occasions (1930, 2010), by Mary E. Blain. Classic parlour and outdoor games – for all ages.

Graffiti Research Lab (graffitiresearch lab.com). A group that's dedicated to inventing new street art and activist technologies – including LED Throwies.

How to Do Nothing With Nobody All Alone by Yourself (1958), by Robert Paul Smith. An amazing book of kid lore – with info about how to make your own toys out of everyday objects, and how to amuse yourself endlessly.

Magic Books & Paper Toys (2008), by Esther K. Smith. Lots of fun stuff to do, from making a 'Cootie Catcher' to much more complex paper creations.

Mini Weapons of Mass Destruction: Build Implements of Spitball Warfare (2009), by John Austin. You get the idea.

Mischief Maker's Manual (2009), by Sir John Hargrave. A guide to pranking and causing mayhem, written in the style of a military training manual.

Parlour Games for Modern Families (2010), by Myfanwy Jones and Spiri Tsintziras. Old-fashioned parlour games rediscovered and reinvented for today.

Ride UK BMX (rideukbmx.mpora.com). The website for the magazine *Ride UK BMX* showcases progressive BMX riding – from streets to trails to skate-parks – in Britain. Brilliant videos, featuring both up-and-coming riders and legendary ones.

Sneaky Book for Boys, The (2008), by Cy Tymony. For pranks, see the chapter 'Sneaky Tricks'. Not just for boys.

DO IT YOURSELF

Best of Instructables, The (2008). DIY projects from the editors of *Make* magazine and instructables.com

Best of Make, The (2007), by Mark Frauenfelder and Gareth Branwyn. Projects from the DIY magazine and website *Make*. Check out the sites makezine.com and makeprojects.com

Build It Yourself (build-it-yourself. com). Features many DIY projects.

D.I.Y. Kids (2007), by Ellen Lupton and Julia Lupton. The previous two books are mostly for grownups; not this one.

Fifty Dangerous Things (You Should Let Your Children Do) (2011), by Gever Tulley and Julie Spiegler. Fun! Also check out the website for Gever Tulley's Tinkering School (tinkeringschool.com).

Fix It, Make It, Grow It, Bake It: The DIY Guide to the Good Life (2010), by Billee Sharp. So DIY it's actually handwritten.

Free-Range Kids (freerangekids.com). Tips for grownups on how to bring up independent children, safely and boldly.

Geek Dad: Awesomely Geeky Projects for Dads and Kids to Share (2010), by Ken Denmead. DIY projects from the blog GeekDad (wired.com/geekdad). Note that it's not just for fathers.

Get Crafty (2004), by Jean Railla. The book that helped start the hip crafting revolution! Fun for grownups and kids.

Home Education Magazine (homeed mag.com). Cool homeschooler projects. Some articles are written by kids.

Kids Invent! (kidsinvent.org). Find ideas for projects and submit your own inventions too. From the author of the great DIY book *Unscrewed*.

Made by Hand (2010), by Mark Frauenfelder. Might inspire your grownups to make their own stuff.

Maker Shed (makershed.com). Shop for tools, electronics, and other components for your DIY projects.

Other Lab (otherlab.com). DIY ideas along with information and news about design, engineering and technology.

Pop!Tech (poptech.com). Find inspir-ation at this website run by some of today's leading technology innovators.

Popular Mechanics (popularmechanics. com/how-to). The website of this long-running magazine for hands-on enthusiasts features a How-To section.

Robot Builder's Bonanza, The (fourth edition, 2011), by Gordon McComb. An illustrated guide to building 100 robots.

TED (ted.com). Videos of speeches and lectures by today's leading innovators. These are who DIY kids grow up to be.

Unschooling Handbook, The (1998), by Mary Griffith. Use the entire world as a classroom – without any report cards.

Unscrewed: Salvage and Reuse Motors, Gears, Switches, and More from Your Old Electronics (2011), by Ed Sobey. A great deconstruction guide.

Upcycling: Create Beautiful Things with Stuff You Already Have (2011), by Danny Seo and Jennifer Levy. Yes, do it!

YOUR BODY

5 A DAY Meal Planner (nhs.uk/Tools/Pages/5aday.aspx). A healthy-eating app from the National Health Service. It offers ideas for meals, tasty recipes and shopping tips.

Circus Development Agency (circusarts.org.uk). An organisation that promotes circus training and the sharing of skills – including aerial, acrobatics, tight wire and juggling. Their online Youth Circus Workshop database allows you to search your area of the UK for circus training classes and schools.

Country Almanac of Home Remedies, The: Time-Tested and Almost Forgotten Wisdom For Treating Hundreds of Common Ailments, Aches and Pains Quickly and Naturally (2011), by Brigitte Mars. You get the idea.

Fitness for Young People (2003), by Simon Frost. Very detailed step-by-step instructions on fitness, flexibility, and stamina training for kids.

Girlology: A Girl's Guide to Stuff That Matters (2005) by Melisa Holmes and Trish Hutchison. A paediatrician and gynaecologist offer advice on dealing with everything from periods to boyfriends.

Herbal Kitchen, The: 50 Easy-to-Find Herbs and Over 250 Recipes to Bring Lasting Health to You and Your Family (2010), by Kami McBride. Identify and harvest edible and medicinal plants.

It's Perfectly Normal: Changing Bodies, Growing Up, Sex, and Sexual Health (2009) by Robie H. Harris, illustrated by Michael Emberley. Very useful info.

Jamie Oliver's Food Guide. This smartphone app by celebrity chef Jamie Oliver, known for his campaign against the use of processed foods in schools, celebrates brilliant places to eat, buy and enjoy food around Britain.

New Games Book, The (1976), by the New Games Foundation. A super-groovy book that helped introduce the play-hard, play-fair, nobody-hurt trend.

Official Fart Book, The (2010), by Craig Yoe. An entertaining and – believe it or not – informative book on farting.

YOUR MIND

ADHD Workbook for Kids, The: Helping Children Gain Self-Confidence, Social Skills, and Self-Control (2010), by Lawrence E. Shapiro. That says it all.

Braidweaver (braidweaver.com). Inspiration and tips for kumihimo braiding.

EpicWin (rexbox.co.uk/epicwin). A cross between a digital organiser and a role-playing videogame, this app lets you win points by accomplishing tasks.

Google Calendar (google.com/calendar). An easy way for kids with or without ADHD to keep track of homework. Share it with your grownups!

Koi Pond. This smartphone app is a relaxation tool disguised as a game.

Nudge Blog (nudges.org). This site investigates the process of making good decisions – about eating, for example – through 'choice architecture'.

Putting on the Brakes: Taking Control of Your ADD or ADHD (2008), by Patricia O. Quinn and Judith M. Stern. Helpful!

Self-Esteem Trap, The: Raising Confident and Compassionate Kids in an Age of Self-Importance (2008), by Polly Young-Eisendrath. Kids urged to be extraordinary can suffer from fear of failure. It's great to be ordinary!

TELL YOUR STORY

Artists Journals (artistsjournals.com). Get inspired by lots of visual diaries. Then make your own artist's diary, and submit it to this website!

Bird by Bird: Some Instructions on Writing and Life (1995) by Anne Lamott. Tips from a well-known writer on how to get started – without stressing out.

Climbing Your Family Tree: Online and Off-Line Genealogy for Kids (2002), by Ira Wolfman. A comprehensive, kid-friendly guide to genealogical research.

Daisy Yellow (daisyyellow.squarespace.com). A blog about writing in your diary. Lots of beautiful examples.

Drawing Words and Writing Pictures: Making Comics: Manga, Graphic Novels, and Beyond (2008), by Jessica Abel and Matt Madden. Step-by-step advice from two well-known cartoonists.

Family Tree Kids (kids.familytreemagazine.com/kids). Find downloadable family tree forms, including options for stepfamilies and families formed through adoption.

Flickr (flickr.com). Search this photo-sharing website for examples of artist diaries, and prepare to be amazed.

Journal Craft (blog.journalcraft.co.uk). A great blog filled with tips on keeping a journal – along with examples of various different types of journals.

Significant Objects (significantobjects.com). A project – co-founded by one of the editors of this book – in which over 200 writers made up stories about charity-shop and second-hand objects.

ROCK OUT

All Music (allmusic.com). More details about your favourite band or album than you probably wanted to know.

Cigar Box Nation (cigarboxnation.com). Find free plans, how-tos and parts for building your own cigar box guitar.

Magic Fiddle (smule.com/magicfiddle). An app that turns your smartphone screen into a fiddle. Share your songs with other Magic Fiddle fans.

Ocarina (ocarina.smule.com). An app that turns your smartphone into a flute-like instrument. Listen to what people are playing across the world.

Right Instrument for Your Child, The (2005), by Atarah Ben-Tovim and Douglas Boyd. Choose an instrument based on your personality and build.

Rock&Roll: Year By Year (2003), by Luke Crampton and Dafydd Rees. A massive book that will teach you everything about pop music, from rock to rap.

Rock'n'Roll Camp for Girls: How to Start a Band, Write Songs, Record an Album, and Rock Out (2008), by Rock'n'Roll Camp for Girls. This book puts the 'amp' in summer camp. It's not just for girls.

Shazam is a mobile-based music identification service. Its free-to-try and pay-to-play apps use a mobile's built-in microphone to sample music being played, then compare the tune's 'acoustic fingerprint' against its massive database.

get crafty
CRAFTIVISM MANIFESTO
DESIGN YOUR OWN PATTERN
BIRCH BARK HOUSES
ILLUSION
KNITTING
GLUE GUN BASICS
MAKE A SECRET BOOK SAFE
Transform an Old Record into a Nifty Bowl
DÉCOUPAGE
DECORATE YOUR TRAINERS
HOME
TOASTER SCIENCE
EXPERIMENTING IN THE KITCHEN
pantry experiment
READ A FOOD LABEL
COOKING
WEIRD FACTS ABOUT CONDIMENTS
TRAIN AN ANIMAL KINDLY
HOME ALONE RECIPES
Conserving water
CLEAN YOUR DOG
HIGH AND LOW-TECH PET SEARCH
HEEL, ROBOT!
your pets
BEST EVER ANIMAL MOVIES
SECRET HISTORY OF PETS
MAKE A ROBOT PET CONTROLLER

HOME QUEST

By Geoff Manaugh

The day after he turned 16, a boy was asked by an architect – a friend of the family – to describe what kind of home he would someday like to live in. 'I don't know,' the boy whispered, embarrassed by the answer. 'I've lived in one kind of house my entire life. What other kinds of houses are there?'

The architect smiled. 'Remember that you can be home anywhere,' she said, 'not just inside houses.' After all, people have lived on drawbridges, in lighthouses, under the sea in submarines, in research stations across the Antarctic, on interconnected bamboo platforms high up in giant trees – and, the architect added, someday people will even be living on other planets.

The architect explained that, at the request of the boy's parents, she would spend the next few weeks teaching the boy all about homes – what homes could be and what homes have been. They would take numerous field trips around the city, and, at the end of it all, the boy might finally know what kind of home he'd like.

First, he had to learn what sort of houses exist.

Bone houses of the Ice Age

Two days later, the architect sent the boy off with a packed lunch to visit the natural history museum. The boy went alone. He was instructed to go inside and learn about the very origins of home building – the first houses ever built by human beings.

Deep inside the museum, the boy approached a full-scale replica of a 15,000-year-old house made from the piled skeletons of giant Ice Age animals, many of which were now extinct. Their bones, as white as snow, had been assembled like puzzle pieces to form strange domes and other structures for the Ice Age hunters nearby. The bones had then been covered with animal skins to block the freezing winds – and, because they were built with bones, the houses sometimes *left their own fossils*.

Your house, the architect told the boy, could leave traces even 15,000 years from now: think about that as you consider what you'll build.

Behind the basement wall

The next day, the architect told him a story. Thousands of years ago, she said, in what is now Turkey, in a region known for its soft soils, there lived a group of people whose cities were almost entirely underground. The soil there – called *tuff* – is so easy to excavate you can actually scoop it out by hand; it then reacts with fresh air, growing as hard as concrete.

Today, these underground cities are periodically rediscovered. Indeed, the architect said, in 1963 a man living in the region walked downstairs one day to do some cleaning in his basement – only to accidentally break through the cellar wall, revealing another room behind it. This room, in complete darkness and a total surprise to the man, led to yet other rooms, which led to more rooms. Soon the man, returning with a torch, had discovered stairways, deeper levels, and hundreds of corridors, one of which, incredibly, was six miles long. Engineers now estimate that the underground city behind this man's basement wall could have housed up to 30,000 people.

Today, the city is a tourist destination. 'You should visit it,' the architect said, 'before deciding what sort of house you want to build. You should also think about what's underground.'

The man who lived in the sky

Now imagine turning all this upside down, the architect said; imagine someone accidentally discovering a home in the sky.

As it happens, the architect's next story began, the tallest building in the world had to be constructed by *someone* – but, in order to operate all that heavy equipment high in the air, it would take the workers far too long to travel up and back again every day. If they did so, the building would never be finished.

But the crane operator suddenly had an idea: he could simply *stay up there*, amidst the I-beams and the unfinished rooms of the world's tallest skyscraper, three times higher than the Empire State Building, even if it meant living there alone. The crane operator thus moved into his machine for more than a year, looking out over the world from the highest home ever built, watching distant storms form in the desert, as the building below him was gradually completed.

And when it was finished, it was less like a building, the architect said, and more like a bridge: a connection between him and the earth's surface he had left so long ago.

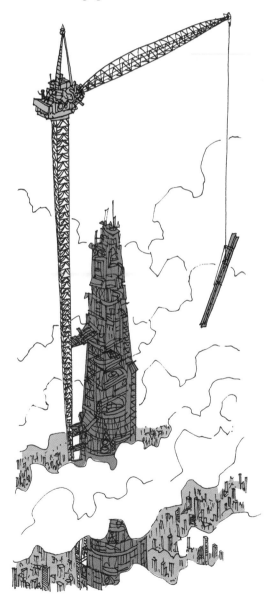

The wall

Several days went by before they saw each other again. In the meantime, the architect got the boy to look through books full of drawings and pictures of houses: houses on cliffs, houses in cities, handmade houses, houses made from brick. The boy learned about houses in London that had been extended far below street level, forming spectacular super-basements; he read about haunted houses in films and ghost stories; he discovered that a team of famous scuba divers had once built a strange kind of house, called Continental Shelf Station Two, at the bottom of the Red Sea, near Sudan; he laughed when he saw photos of an unhappy married couple who had physically built a wall to divide one home into two.

The house that was prone to tornadoes

The next time they met, the architect had lunch with the boy in a park near his father's office. 'A few blocks away from us,' her next story began, 'a young couple once moved into a very old building. It was full of tiny rooms and narrow hallways, and there were dozens of cupboards on every floor.'

But the couple wasn't happy with the house, so they had it renovated. They removed entire walls to make certain rooms bigger; they turned the massive living room into two separate guest bedrooms; and that was only the beginning of their many, expensive changes. Most important for what happened next was one small detail: they added air-conditioning.

Something very strange then began to happen inside the house. The couple had accidentally done something to the layout that meant that whenever they turned the air-conditioning on, small tornadoes would appear: tiny whirlwinds of air moving slowly through the hallways, gathering dust and scattering paperwork. Some days these miniature tornadoes

got so intense that fragile glassware could be sucked off the kitchen shelves, shattering dangerously on the floor.

The house had its own internal weather system, the architect explained, laughing; no one had ever seen anything like it. The dining room, for instance, would dry out due to crosswinds and the living room had become so humid that no one could spend more than 10 minutes there; meanwhile, these strange tornadoes, like ghosts, would turn in slow spirals all around them. Eventually, someone from Hollywood flew in to make a documentary about the house; it was called *The House that Was Prone to Tornadoes*.

'Your house needn't only have rooms,' the architect advised the boy. 'Your house can even have its very own storms.'

A home against ageing

Towards the end of their time together – after they had looked at mobile homes, at campsite homes, at castle homes, at boat homes, at homes in outer space, at homes built for animals – the architect took the boy for a walk. She walked so slowly, however, that the boy became impatient.

'We all grow old,' she said. 'We all get weak. We forget things – and we begin to walk slowly. It will happen to you, as well, I'm afraid. It happens to all of us.'

In fact, *ageing* was the premise of the final house she wanted to tell him about.

Many years ago, a house was built in Japan for a couple who never wanted to grow old – or, more accurately, they never wanted to go senile. They wanted to remember everything that had happened to them, and they never wanted to lose their minds. They thus came up with a bold plan: they hired an unusual architect, someone who could design a house that would never let them settle into an everyday routine. The idea was that everything could be changed so that the couple would always be kept on their toes; they would always be paying attention. The house itself would keep them focused, aware and constantly active.

Another house, the architect continued, was specially built to cure a woman of her chronic déjà vu – the haunting sense that whatever you're now experiencing has happened to you before. What the woman did, however, was unexpected: she hired architects to create a house for her where everything felt like déjà vu. *Everything* felt like it had already happened. Entire rooms were identical and there were strangely angled mirrors on every wall. By making each moment of the day feel like déjà vu, *nothing* felt like déjà vu. Eventually, the house cured the woman of her strange affliction.

'In the end,' the architect said, 'when you've grown old and feeble, you should remember that your house might be the only thing that you have left. Your house can be your closest friend – or your worst enemy. Imagine a house that guarantees you will age badly, for instance, or one that guarantees you will lose your mind. No one wants to live in a house like that.'

'You will have many houses over the course of your life,' the architect reminded the boy as they said goodbye. 'Not all of them will feel like home. The ones I've told you about are just examples. The important thing is to find the home that's right for you – and then, someday, to build it.'

The architect then sent the boy back to his parents, where he might finally begin to answer the original question: 'What kind of home would you like to live in someday?'

⬜⊠ ⬛⊠✦⬜ ⬜⬛⬜⬛⬜⬜⬜⊠ ⌐⬛ ⬜⊠⬛⬛ ⊠✳⌐⊥
⬜⊠⬗⬜⊠ ⊠⬓ ⌐⬜⬛ ⊠⊠✦⬜⬛ ⬗⬜⬛⬗⊠⬜⬜⬜
⬗⬜ ⌐⊠✳⬜ ⬜⊠⬛⬜⋋ ⬜⬜⬜ ⬜⬜⬛⬛

LIVE IN A TREE

'Green architecture' is good for the planet, but a house that's a living ecosystem might be even better!

Designed by the Human Ecology Design team at the Massachusetts Institute of Technology, the Fab Tree Hab is an 'edible prefab home for humanity'. Instead of being built like a normal home, using resources and energy, the Fab Tree Hab would be grown from living trees.

How would it work? You'd put a carefully designed scaffold where you wanted the house to be, and grow trees over it; the scaffold would force the tree's branches into a durable woven pattern. The structure's inside walls would be clay and plaster, and the outside walls would be covered with a thick layer of vines; any gaps in the vines would be filled with pockets of soil used to grow gardens. The entire home would be edible – whether by people, animals or insects.

Sounds like science fiction, but in fact the MIT team was inspired by a centuries-old technique called 'pleaching', in which a gardener (or an artist with a green thumb) weaves together tree branches to form living archways, lattices or screens, even sculptures, then encourages the branches to fuse together permanently in that form.

So when do we get to live in a Fab Tree Hab? Unfortunately, it could take several decades to grow such a house – particularly in a non-tropical climate. Besides, in most areas, planning laws won't permit you to live in a home constructed this way.

Garden follies & cottages

If you can't yet grow your own house, then why not a garden folly? A folly is an ornamental structure, not meant to be permanently inhabited, which wealthy people used to build on their estates.

In sixteenth-century Italy, and later in France and England, there was a fad for building artificial caves called 'grottos'. Outside, the grotto might look like a boulder or rocky overhang; inside, you might find fountains, artificial stalactites and statues.

In the early nineteenth century, there was a fad in Europe for poets' bowers, hermitages and other follies. In America, whose inhabitants prided themselves on being more practical than Europeans, they had rustic cabins, like the one Henry David Thoreau built by Walden Pond in Concord, Massachusetts. His 1854 book *Walden; or, Life in the Woods* inspired many people to get away from crowded cities and 'rusticate' in a summer cottage.

In fact, Thoreau helped Bronson Alcott (father of Louisa May, the author of *Little Women*) build a summer cottage in Concord for their mutual friend, the poet and thinker Ralph Waldo Emerson. They used hemlocks from Walden Pond, and they designed the cottage's rafters to curve in a way that mimicked tree branches. It was, perhaps, the original Fab Tree Hab!

Illustrations by Mister Reusch

HOME AWAY FROM HOME

AT FESTIVALS

By Matthew De Abaitua

The festival season is an ancient rite. Since the Stone Age, Britons have gathered in the hundreds at enclosed causeways to drink, eat and share skills with different tribes for a few days and nights. In the Neolithic era, chiefs and priests presided over the festivals and sacrificed cattle in service of the ancient urge for revelry. A festival is a time of excess and a time when everyone can paint their faces, put on a stupid hat, dance, stay up late and be playful.

When I was a lad, music festivals seemed like scary places, full of wild-eyed grownups and disreputable types. But, over the last fifteen years, they have smartened up their act, particularly during the daylight hours. At festivals, my children have learned new crafts, including pottery, knitting, even how to build a miniature city out of blocks. They've run in a three-legged race, ridden a helter-skelter, then learned to write a sonnet – all in a single hour.

My children have been going to festivals since they were babies, sometimes four or five over a summer: Alice, my eldest, even met Doctor Who at Glastonbury – he had a temporary tattoo of the time vortex on his arm. She swam wild at Wilderness Festival and Port Eliot, went backstage to meet Pulp (ask your parents who they are), ran around at sundown with a large pair of homemade wings, skated at a replica of a 1970s roller disco, climbed trees, and hung out with new friends at the liquorice stall: it's at festivals that we learned to trust her with more freedom and she has never let us down.

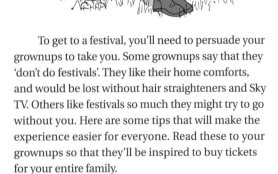

Mark your pitch with a unique flag

To get to a festival, you'll need to persuade your grownups to take you. Some grownups say that they 'don't do festivals'. They like their home comforts, and would be lost without hair straighteners and Sky TV. Others like festivals so much they might try to go without you. Here are some tips that will make the experience easier for everyone. Read these to your grownups so that they'll be inspired to buy tickets for your entire family.

Choose your camping style

There are no hotels at festivals. Most now offer pre-pitched tipis or yurts, which are expensive but also luxurious. For the classic festival experience, you'll be pitching your own tent. If it's your own little tent, practise pitching it at home beforehand. If it is a pop-up tent, practise taking it down. Pop-up tents take a second to pitch, but folding them back into the bag can consume the best part of a morning. When your tent is surrounded by other tents, consider putting up some homemade bunting or even a unique flag to mark your pitch.

Illustrations by Mister Reusch

Be smart about your gear

It's always a hike from the car park or bus drop-off to the camping field and there's always a lot of gear for everyone to carry. You'll need a decent rucksack with padded straps. A really decent rucksack – as opposed to your school bag – can even have a sleeping mat and a sleeping bag attached to it. Don't take a big blow-up bed. They are heavy, a pain to inflate, and not even that comfortable. A thin sleeping mat that you can inflate by mouth will do just fine. Also, bring along a small foldable day bag in which you can fit the following: a waterproof jacket, a roll of toilet paper, your phone, a torch and some glow-sticks, wet wipes and a bottle of water. Arrive ready to walk in rain or shine for a mile or two. Your sun hat, sunscreen and waterproof jacket should be in accessible pockets. Don't arrive wearing your best gear. Getting into a festival, lugging your stuff, and pitching your tent can be muddy and sweaty work, so save your going-out clobber for later in the weekend.

Break out the wellies

I know that the very mention of sensible footwear – such as wellies or walking boots – sounds like no fun, but there is no way around it. Festivals can get very muddy. Like, unbelievably muddy. At one particularly notorious year at Glastonbury, I saw a woman in kitten heels and a fur bikini sink up to her knees in liquid mud. It doesn't matter if it's sunny on the day you set off, there will always be rain, and, invariably, quite a lot of it. Wellies are a big part of festival fashion ever since Kate Moss was photographed wearing them at Glastonbury, but don't forget you'll need to wear thick sports socks with them. Otherwise, chafing will result.

But don't forget your fun clothes

You will get plenty of advice about taking sensible clothes. But don't forget to take something stupid to wear. Festivals are a world of different rules, and what is cool on the high street is the height of naffness according to the topsy-turvy logic of the festival. What you wear is as much to amuse other people as it is to project the right image of yourself. Many festivals have a big dressing-up area where you can try and buy all manner of vintage clothing. Having said that, do not let your grownup wear a jester's hat.

Don't rely on the mobile

Mobile reception at festivals is patchy. All you need is a phone that can send and receive texts and go a couple of days without recharging. If you have a fancy phone, switch off the wireless connection and automatic syncing, as both will quickly eat through the battery. Limit communication to texting. And don't forget to check your phone regularly if you are exploring alone – you might not necessarily hear a phone call from your grownups amidst all that noise. If you have an old mobile, it's worth moving your sim over to it for the course of the weekend. Also keep in mind that it's easy to lose a phone by dropping it into the mud or down the toilet.

Explore

When heading out without grownup supervision, stick to two or three areas that you have agreed to beforehand. Make definite plans on when and where to meet and keep to them: your meeting place should be somewhere manageable and not – say – at the main stage. Try to get your adventures in during the daytime. At night, festivals become difficult to navigate and it's best to stick close to your grownups once the sun is down. If you get really lost, speak to a steward; they will often be in groups of three or four, wearing high-visibility jackets and equipped with a walkie-talkie.

Practise your (festival) etiquette

A good festival is a world unto itself. So it is bad form to remind grownups of the world outside. Try to stay inside the bubble of the weekend and don't call friends who aren't there or talk too much about home.

Go with the flow

Festivals are designed to surprise you. Plan your day around two or three acts that you want to see and then surround those times with periods of aimless wandering. Everyone in your family should get a chance to see and do what they want to. The weather will affect what you can or cannot achieve too.

Tip! Work your way up to Glastonbury

If you and your grownups have not been to a festival before, then do not start with Glastonbury. With around 135,000 tickets sold every year, it is ten times the size of the new crop of festivals. It can take a long time just to walk around the site, and some of the crowds of human traffic are overwhelming during the big acts.

FAMILY FESTIVALS

Festivals come and go, and sometimes take a year off to let the grass grow. Plus, there are festivals that aren't appropriate for kids, including Reading Festival, Creamfields and V Festival: all places where you can expect to see drunk weeping students slumped around a tiny campfire made of burning plastic bottles. The festivals that I prefer don't have big bands; instead they host lots of interesting events and activities scattered around a beautiful location. Here are a few of my favourites:

End of the Road Festival

endoftheroadfestival.com
The music at End of the Road is very grownup friendly, particularly if your grownups like the kind of alternative rock championed by websites like pitchfork.com. The site itself is in Larmer Tree Gardens, a peaceful maze where peacocks roost on the roofs. As the name suggests, the festival is at the end of the summer, and so has an appealingly easy-going atmosphere.

Port Eliot Festival

porteliotfestival.com
Set in grounds of a stately home in Cornwall, alongside a tidal estuary where festival-goers can swim wild, Port Eliot has many hubs to it and no dominant central stage. With a garden maze, small stages beside the river, literary talks tucked away in a walled garden, and a reputation as a fashion hotspot, Port Eliot is the perfect place for you to explore and have adventures.

Wilderness Festival

wildernessfestival.com
Set in the grounds of the Cornbury Estate, next door to Blenheim Palace in Oxfordshire, Wilderness Festival tends to mix popular bands from the 1990s with interesting talks and, invariably, an attempt to break the world record for the highest number of people swimming nude. More corporate than the other two festivals, it still has plenty of hidden delights – from film screenings to a faux-museum of insect wrestling.

Camp Bestival

campbestival.net
Specially designed for grownups with younger children; as a consequence, bits of it will be too young for you. With so many moppets running around, the children are always getting lost, and the grownups must push around their empty buggies of despair. Worth considering if you want to treat your younger siblings. (As if.)

TURN YOUR HOME
INTO A SPA

By Elizabeth

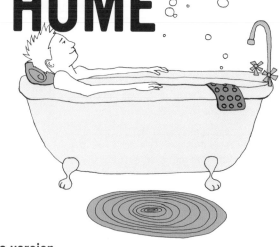

You can create your own spa treatments using foods (available at health food shops and elsewhere) and everyday items.

Before you get started, make sure you have plenty of clean towels and flannels to hand.

BATH SALTS

Bath salts have been used for centuries to soften bathwater and relax tired muscles. They are really easy to prepare and make great gifts.

You'll need:

- 900g coarse salt (sea salt and Dead Sea salt work)
- 300g Epsom salts
- 10 or so drops of essential oil, either one scent or a combination of scents
- Stainless steel bowl
- Stainless steel mixing spoon

> **IMPORTANT!** Because they are so concentrated, essential oils can be toxic. Never apply an essential oil directly to your skin or put it near your mouth, eyes or private parts. Avoid these oils: basil, oregano, thyme, nutmeg, clove, cinnamon, black pepper and bay. Keep essential oils away from your pets.
>
> Don't use a plastic or wooden bowl or spoon, because they will absorb the essential oil.

For fancy version, you'll need:

- Dried rose petals
- Dried lavender
- Muslin spice bags

Basic version

1. Pour the coarse salt and the Epsom salts into the bowl. Mix them together with the spoon.

2. Work out what scent or combination of scents you prefer. You can use ordinary household baking ingredients such as vanilla and peppermint extracts. Or try a few essential oils, which are super-strong concentrations of plant oils. My family likes to combine lavender, lemon and a tiny bit of ylang ylang. Other popular scents include eucalyptus and rosemary.

3. Put 10 drops of essential oils into the salt. Mix thoroughly with the stainless steel spoon.

4. Store your new bath salts in jars with lids or in sealed plastic or paper bags. Wait several hours (24 if you can stand it) before using; give the salt time to absorb the scents.

5. Scoop several spoonfuls of salts into a warm bath.

6. Play your favourite calming music and relax.

Fancy version

1. Follow steps 1–3 from the basic directions.

2. Mix in a handful of dried lavender and a handful of dried rose petals.

3. Don't put the fancy version directly in your tub: the petals will clog your drain. Instead, scoop the mixture into muslin spice bags. Tie the bags tightly. Let sit for several hours.

4. When you take a bath, toss a bag into the tub. The salts will absorb into the water immediately and the rose petals and dried lavender will stay in the bag, which you can now rub all over your body like a flannel. Hold the bag close to your nose and breathe in the smell of lavender and roses.

5. Empty, dry and reuse the bag.

FOODIE FACE MASKS

Make your own beauty masks from common kitchen staples.

You'll need:

- Foods for your mask. Use bananas, honey, avocados, porridge oats, plain yogurt, olive oil – whatever you want as long as you're not allergic to it!
- Hair bobble, if you have long hair
- Blender
- Flannels
- Towel

Try this:

1. Combine the foods in a blender. (If the mixture begins to clump like dough, add a tiny bit of water.) Experiment with different combinations – an easy option is to mix one tablespoon of honey with one tablespoon of plain yogurt.

2. Pull your hair back into a ponytail if you need to.

3. Apply a thin layer of mask mixture to your face.

4. Wait 3–5 minutes. Rinse and towel your face dry.

SOOTHING FOOT SOAK AND STRAWBERRY FOOT SCRUB

This is a two-part activity. First, soak your feet to get them feeling soft.

Make the soak
You'll need:

- 600g sea salt
- 300g Epsom salts
- **Optional:** A few drops of essential oil
- Stainless steel bowl
- A bucket or small tub of warm water
- **Optional:** Marbles or smooth rocks
- Towel

Try this:

1. Mix the ingredients together in a bowl.

2. Pour the mixture into a bucket or small tub of warm water. For added luxury, put marbles or smooth rocks in the bottom of the bucket.

3. Place the bucket onto a towel in front of a relaxing chair.

4. Put your feet in the water, sit back and enjoy.

Make the scrub
You'll need:

- 8–10 fresh strawberries
- Vitamin E capsule, punctured
- 1 teaspoon sea salt
- Small mixing bowl
- Fork

Try this:

If you can get a friend or family member to do this for you, then you'll *really* feel relaxed.

1. Put the strawberries in a small mixing bowl and mash them with a fork.

2. Mix in the vitamin E capsule's oil, and the salt.

3. Massage the strawberry foot scrub into your feet, and continue rubbing them for several minutes to remove dead, dry skin. Concentrate on your heels and any other dry areas.

4. Rinse your feet with warm water and dry them thoroughly with a soft towel.

Illustrations by Heather Kasunick

MAKE A FAMILY
PORTRAIT

By Elizabeth

Family portraits have been used throughout history to celebrate special events like weddings and graduations, or simply to remember what people looked like at different stages in their lives.

Your family portrait reveals a lot of information about you. When King Charles IV of Spain hired the famous painter Francisco Goya to paint his family in 1800, the fancy clothes, medals and huge paintings in the background symbolised that this family was very, very powerful. However, art historians have also said that there are clues in the painting that Goya didn't really respect the king or his corrupt policies – which is why their faces and postures look a little dumpy, despite all that bling.

When your grownups were kids, family photos were in what we'll call a 'high awkward' phase of overly posed cheesiness. Need proof? Here's me (upper left, just got my braces off) with my sisters – yes, the dude on the right is my sister Anne – in 1975, just casually hanging out in a tree in Florida.

A great family portrait should give you a feel for the people in it. If you spend all your free time on your skateboard, it doesn't really make sense to wear a fancy dress for this lasting memory. Sure, sometimes you have to put on a dress or coat and tie and smile for the camera. But don't stop with what your grownups prefer. You can also create alternative family portraits that are as relaxed and fun as you want.

Elizabeth
(upper left)

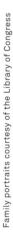

Family portraits courtesy of the Library of Congress

Shoot a lot of photos

One of the great things about digital cameras is that you can experiment with different poses and settings because you don't have to worry about wasting rolls of film, which can get expensive because they have to be developed.

Natural light is the best

Shooting outside is great because you don't have to use a flash, which can make people look pale and startled. Early morning (before 10 a.m.) and late afternoon (a few hours before the sun goes down) are best because the sun isn't too harsh and people won't squint as much.

Get close

Put the camera much closer than you think you need to. A portrait should focus on people's expressions, not the empty field or house behind them.

Stay in the picture

Learn how to use the self-timer on your camera. You can invest in an inexpensive mini-tripod, which is a three-legged piece of equipment that holds the camera steady. If you don't have one, prop your camera on a rock, fencepost or anything that's sturdy and won't move. Set the timer, run to your place, say cheese!

Get funky with the setting

Shoot your family portrait in your favourite restaurant or sporting event or on a footpath. Or go super-realistic and take the portrait of your family eating breakfast – no fluffing out that bed hair.

Pack into a photo booth

Yes, the prints are small, but you can't beat the close-up focus on your faces or the fun that comes from cramming your entire family together into a tiny space. Some newer photo booths allow you to download your photos onto your computer, where you can then order larger prints.

Share your thoughts

Cover a wall with blackboard paint (or just stand in front of a blackboard or white board). Then let everyone in your family write out their own thought bubble in chalk and stand next to them so people can literally read your thoughts.

Special effects

Most computers have photo programs where you can add cool effects to your portraits. Want something to look old-fashioned? Turn it black and white, or sepia – which is that brownish look that was popular back when women wore bustles.

So this:

Becomes this:

Plus, there are lots of smartphone apps that create super-saturated colours and a cool retro feel.

‡▢ ⅄✖✳ ▢✳‡▢ ▢ ✖✖▢▢ ✖✖✖⅄✖ ◉⅄
▢⅃‡▢⊞ ▢▢⅃ ‡▢ ⅃✖▢ ◉▢⅃⬛⊞▢✳▢ ▢
‡⅃ ‡▢ ⬛▢▢✖▢ ▢▢ ✖✖✖⅄✖◉✖⬧◉‡▢⊞

Photography by Stephanie Sorenson

Accessorise

Have every person hold one item that's really important to them. Mobile phones, stuffed animals, biscuits, enormous water blasters – include them. Some families take their portraits during Halloween so that they can wear their costumes.

Take the focus off faces

Close-ups of everyone's hands, feet – even knees – tell their own stories about each person.

Go abstract

Instead of showing actual people in your portrait, choose a theme – flowers or animals or vegetables, whatever you like. If you can, photograph them together (although who can get five breeds of dog?). Otherwise cut out images from magazines, or download them off the internet. Then paste them onto a piece of poster board to make a collage of your 'family'. Or skip the visual images altogether and record your voices having a family conversation.

MAKE FAMILY
PORTRAITS FUN
By Henrik Schleisman

As you can see from the photos on these pages (in which I am almost invisible), I'm not into family portraits. I like it when my mum takes my picture, and I like school pictures. But when it comes to standing around posing with my family, I'd rather ride my bike, play videogames, or be out having fun at a friend's house. Here's how grownups can make the experience better for kids – and themselves:

Get out of the sun

Nothing is worse than getting hot and squinting into bright sun. Stand in the shade instead.

Turn off the flash

It hurts your eyes, too.

Bring sweets

It helps to have a little reward. My mum says to make sure the sweets aren't blue in case you want to take a few more photos after the reward time.

Toys not combs

This is my sister Luisa's idea and it's more about school pictures (which I actually like because at least they are quick and you know what to do) than family photos. I think toys any time are a good idea.

GROSS FACTS ABOUT
BEDROOMS

boing.

By Elizabeth

Having your own bedroom - or even a space that you share with only your brother or sister - was, until recently, very rare.

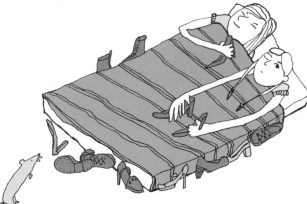

In the past, grownups and children would often bunk together in the same room, with the kids sharing beds with their grownups or snoring away on trundle beds that pulled out from under a bigger bed.

While this might sound like a slumber party, and although the 'family sleep' tradition continues in many parts of the world today, the reality wasn't always fun. Sometimes kids slept with servants on straw-covered boards in whatever room had space. If you were a slave, of course, it was much worse: it's likely that you slept on a pile of rags in an attic or in the slaves' quarters behind your master's home.

It wasn't just people crowding into these bedrooms, either. In his book *At Home: A Short History of Private Life*, Bill Bryson reports that in 1867, an American girl named Eliza Anne Summers and her sister took piles of shoes to bed so that they could use them to protect themselves from rats! Sleeping so close to the floor, Bryson writes, made kids 'especially familiar with the whiskery closeness' of those scratching and scurrying pink-eyed rodents.

The beds themselves weren't great. Spring mattresses weren't invented until 1865, and in their early days the coils would sometimes pop through the fabric and – boing! – poke the sleeper. Before then, mattresses were stuffed with all kinds of things. According to *Goodholme's Domestic Cyclopedia of Practical Information*, an instruction book for everyday life that was widely read in the 1800s, the following were the most popular options, ranked from most comfortable to least:

- **Down:** The layer of super-soft feathers underneath a bird's tougher outer feathers.
- **Feathers:** It took 30–40kg feathers to fill a mattress and pillows. Some families had their own flocks of geese, which they plucked three times a year to keep the beds nice and fluffy. The featherbeds (basically huge pillows that cover a mattress) were so high that most beds had little step stools so you could climb into bed. While this might sound like your own private fluffy cloud, diaries show that these beds were also extremely lumpy.
- **Wool**
- **Wool-flock:** A blend of fleece from different types of sheep.
- **Hair:** Horse and otherwise.
- **Cotton**
- **Wood shavings**
- **Sea-moss**
- **Sawdust**
- **Straw**

Illustrations by Heather Kasunick

Stink bombs

The beds weren't the only unpleasant parts of bedrooms. In her 1878 book *The Bedroom and the Boudoir* (a boudoir is a woman's private bedroom or sitting room), Lady Mary Anne Barker writes about the importance of bedrooms staying fresh and clean. 'People do not half enough realise… how the emanations from the human body are attracted to the sides of the room and stick there.' In other words, the greasy, rotten fumes of all your farts and burps and dirty socks hang around long after you've gone to school.

In the days before plumbing, people took their midnight pees – not to mention poos – in chamber pots, which only made the stink problems worse.

It's no wonder, then, that Lady Barker insisted that whenever possible, her readers should sleep in rooms with open windows. Getting fresh air was extremely important before the days of immunisation because communal bedrooms were breeding grounds for yellow fever, typhus and other illness – including something particularly awful called 'black vomit' – that killed millions of grownups and kids.

Kids' zone

In the early 1800s, well-to-do kids of all ages – not just babies – began sleeping together in a room or suite of rooms called a nursery. This practice started in Britain, where the nurseries included a sleeping room, play room, and sometimes a classroom. This part of the house was supervised by nannies and a governess, who was the woman in charge of the children's education.

You can see such nurseries in the film versions of *Mary Poppins* and *Peter Pan*. But while both of them show these kids' zones as places of magical wonder, it's important to remember that the truth was a little less Hollywood. One mother in 1848 described her family's nursery as 'a damp gloomy division of the basement storey'.

Going solo

The idea of kids having their own rooms started in the mid-1800s, when people began to think that children would stay more innocent if they weren't around grownups so much. People also worried that it was improper for brothers and sisters to sleep in the same room.

From the late 1800s and early 1900s onwards, grownups in America and the UK started having fewer kids. At the same time, children went from being thought of as handy workers to precious beings who were the centre of their grownups' lives. For families who could afford it, giving your kid her own room symbolised that shift in thinking.

Displacement and upgrades

As the Second World War got under way, millions of city children were evacuated to the country. While some wealthier children and their mums moved to hotels, country homes and even overseas, others had to become accustomed to completely new environments, including sleeping in already-crowded children's rooms and even cellars.

Meanwhile in America kids were spending as much time as they could at cinemas. This greatly worried grownups and the experts who studied kids, who – now this is a shock – didn't think all that time in front of a screen was such a grand idea. Those experts urged parents to make their homes more fun by doing things like getting ping pong tables. As a result, parents started to try to make children's bedrooms more fun too, by letting kids play in them with their friends.

As rooms got more fun, they also started being more of an expression of each kid's unique personality. In 1971, Greg Brady, the oldest son of the popular American TV show *The Brady Bunch*, decided he was too mature to keep sharing a room with his two rowdy younger brothers. So he transformed his dad's office into a 'far-out pad' complete with mobiles, a strobe light, and glow-in-the-dark posters. (Do a web search for 'Brady Bunch Our Son, The Man' and see it for yourself.)

My space

Today, your room is not only a place to sleep but also your own personal space where you can relax, study, enjoy your hobbies and sit around with your friends. Even if you share a room, it's a space that you care about.

And you know what? Although we have indoor plumbing and heating and all kinds of bleaches and scrubs, your room probably gets pretty gassy and stinky from time to time. So put your dirty clothes in the washbasket, open your windows and door, and let the fresh air circulate. Better yet, hang your duvet and pillows halfway out the window to breathe in fresh scents.

Then get out the hoover and wash your sheets and duvet cover every week. Your bed is a major nesting area for dust mites – microscopic bugs that live on your dead skin cells. That's not a big deal for most of us. But some people are allergic to dust mite poo and wake up sneezing and wheezing.

Taking care of your room will not only make you happier and healthier, but your grownups will probably keel over with happiness.

DITCH YOUR TV

Research shows that 60 per cent of kids your age have TVs in their bedrooms and that more than half of you fall asleep to the soothing tones of your favourite programmes. That's depressing!

Why? Because TV is an entirely passive entertainment. (A computer can be passive, or interactive, depending on how you use it.) Also, if you're sitting in front of the TV, chances are you're by yourself. And even though you enjoy watching TV, being isolated can make you feel down and anxious.

It's also been suggested that kids with TVs in their rooms are more likely to score lower in tests, sleep badly and be overweight. They're also at an increased risk to start smoking.

Don't get us wrong: technology can be brilliant. But when you've got a computer, phone, iPod, videogame console, tablet, and internet connection all in one 3m x 3m space, you're living in a digital cave. And then technology is controlling you instead of the other way around.

And that's too bad because a bedroom should also be your place to rest; and it ought to be a refuge where you can feel artistic or angry or sad or like you want to invent the planet's most complicated LEGO city ever. Whether you're thinking up new rap lyrics or designing a costume, your room is your getaway where you can cultivate your creative life.

So get rid of the TV! And you might also experiment with keeping all your tech in another room. If you only use your tech stuff in this area, then your own room – and any other tech-free rooms in your house – will become places to sleep, draw, read, build, cry, dance, read, practise foreign accents, play games, play fight, read and make stuff up in your head. And you'll sleep better at night.

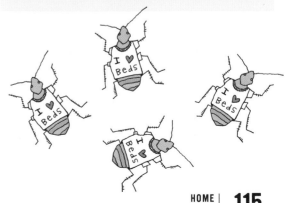

DECORATE YOUR ROOM

What's Your Taste?

By Elizabeth

Warm colours

Do you prefer cool or warm colours?

In her 1897 book *The Decoration of Houses*, Edith Wharton – the author of *Ethan Frome* and *The Age of Innocence* – warned grownups about the dangerous effects a badly decorated room would have on kids. 'The daily intercourse with poor pictures, cheesy "ornaments" and badly designed furniture may, indeed, be fittingly compared with a mental diet of silly and ungrammatical story-books,' she wrote.

Wharton's solution to the potential tragedy of ugly art and daft knickknacks? She wanted grownups to encourage their kids to decorate their rooms with reproductions of famous art, including a painting of a pudgy, lute-playing cherub by Italian Renaissance painter Giovanni Bellini.

OK, so Wharton didn't have kids and might have been a little clueless about what they actually liked. But it's cool that she passionately believed in the importance of young people developing their own taste.

What is taste? Simply put, it's a personal preference or liking. You might prefer salt on your popcorn, or Taylor Swift's twangy but cute singing voice. Your favourite colour, skirt style, pizza topping, brand of trainers – all are a reflection of this instinct inside you about what feels right.

Developing your own taste is important because it helps you understand yourself. And there's no better laboratory for experimenting with what you like and don't like than your bedroom. The great thing about taste is that there is no right answer: it's up to you.

Decorating your room doesn't have to be expensive. You can find great furniture at car boot sales, flea markets and charity shops. Or you can score hand-me-downs from grownups you know. Used furniture can usually be spruced up with a coat of paint or varnish. But as a rule, it's best not to get a second-hand mattress. Old ones are more likely to have dust mites or – even grosser – bedbugs.

Show off your stuff

One cheap and easy way to start discovering what looks good to you is to try different ways of displaying your collections. Do those football stickers look better framed in a group or one at a time? Are your seashells more appealing in a basket or arranged on a shelf? Try lots of options!

Keep it real

Don't decorate your room according to a theme, such as 'Country Cottage' or 'Wicked Princess' or 'Sci-Fi Recharge Pod'. Chances are your interests will change and that boat-shaped bed will no longer be the jam. Instead, focus on the colours you like, the kind of furniture that appeals to you, and how the sheets and fabrics feel when you touch them. You don't want a bedspread that itches.

Illustrations by Heather Kasunick

Also think about the size of your space. A room crammed with too many pieces of furniture doesn't feel restful. If you need a desk but don't have room, consider building or buying a loft for your bed and arranging one or two pieces of furniture underneath it.

Put up a fight

Finally, grownups are usually pretty intense about their own taste and may have a hard time letting you choose that wicked stripe pattern over some flowered option. No matter what posters you hang, if your grownup chooses the bedspread and curtains, it's not going to feel like your room.

Do you like organic or geometric patterns?

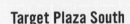

Geometric pattern

MY TASTE
By Peter Schleisman

I like to learn about architecture and really love skyscrapers. In fact, I used to spend hours building models of them; so my room's décor is skyscraper-dominated. Here are a few of my favourite buildings.

Burj al Arab

This ultra-luxury hotel in Dubai (United Arab Emirates) is a modern skyscraper with some classic features. It's 321 metres tall, making it the second tallest hotel in the world (not including buildings with mixed uses). The design of the skyscraper is supposed to mimic a classic Arabian sail.

Target Plaza South

I usually prefer very tall buildings (known as *supertalls*), but the 150-metre-tall corporate headquarters of Target in my hometown of Minneapolis, USA, is cool because of its lighted screen on the upper floors. On Halloween, different images – pumpkins, bats, the moon, witches – seem to float up into the sky. The building's design is relatively simple, which gives it a very modern look.

Shanghai World Financial Centre

Located in Shanghai, China, this building is a true supertall. It's 492 metres high: 101 storeys above ground. The sleek building is made of glass and steel. It has a twisting design, and it looks – from pictures I've seen of it – as though there is a handle on top. It has the world's tallest observation deck.

Kingdom Tower

This tower in Jeddah, Saudi Arabia, hasn't been built yet – but I love the sharp edges in the proposed images. I also love the fact that at 1,000 metres high, it will be the world's tallest building. Note that this measurement is from the top of the tower's antenna, which is the way skyscrapers should always be measured.

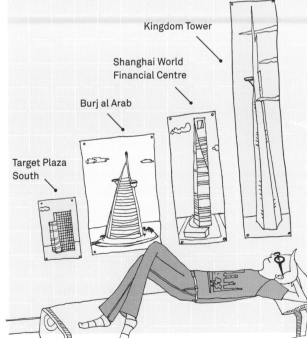

Kingdom Tower

Shanghai World Financial Centre

Burj al Arab

Target Plaza South

SPRAY PAINT
YOUR ROOM

Spray paint is right up there in the pantheon of Most Fun Things. However, though some grownups might be OK with you going freestyle on your bedroom walls, most would like your room to look a little less chaotic. That's why using stencils is a good compromise.

You'll need:

- Plain card
- Spray paint. Use with grownup supervision. If you don't want to risk a mess, use a roller instead.
- Cutting board
- Precision knife for crafts (e.g. an X-Acto knife). Use with grownup supervision.
- Ruler or tape measure
- Painter's masking tape
- **Optional:** Double-sided tape for more complicated stencils
- Newspaper
- Old sheets
- Painting clothes, gloves, safety goggles, mask or respirator

Try this:

1. On the card, draw a black-and-white image that you'd like to stencil on your bedroom wall, or download a black-and-white image from the internet (try a search query like "spray paint stencil" or check a website like spraypaintstencils.com) and print it out on card. The simpler the image, the better.

2. Tape the image securely to a cutting board. Using the precision knife, cut out all parts of the image that are black. If there is white in the middle of a black part, cut out the entire section. Then cut the white part out from the black section and set it aside.

3. Take a look at your room's walls – with your grownup. Do you want to spray paint the image in just one spot? Or repeat it several times? If you want to use the image to create a border around the top edge of your room's walls, you'll need to carefully measure how far down from the top of the wall to place the stencil each time you spray paint. You'll also have to decide how many centimetres apart the images will be – and measure to make sure they are distributed evenly.

4. Using painter's masking tape, attach your stencil where you want it. If you've set aside any white pieces, use double-sided tape to attach them to the wall now. Then use newspaper, old sheets and painter's tape to mask the wall, ceiling and floor for a metre in every direction from the stencil – and make sure you tape the newspaper onto (not next to) the stencil's edges.

5. Open the windows – proper ventilation is important when working with spray paint. Put on your painting clothes, gloves, safety goggles and mask or respirator. Make sure there are no open flames or pilot lights in the vicinity because spray paint is flammable. Lay down an old sheet as a drop cloth.

6. Follow the instructions on the spray paint label for how long you should shake the can, and also for how far you should stand from the wall while you are spraying. If you stand too close, the paint could drip; too far away and you won't get a dense, rich colour. Spray!

7. Let the spray paint dry before removing the newspaper and stencil.

Illustration by Heather Kasunick

ORGANISE YOUR ROOM

If your bedroom doesn't look like it could be photographed for a catalogue or magazine, that's because you're living in it. Those super-perfect rooms are staged by professionals who are paid to make rooms look that way.

Sometimes that's done by artfully arranging 10 years' worth of *National Geographic* magazines into calming yellow blurs placed in chunks throughout a bookshelf. More often, the minimalist look is accomplished by taking 80 per cent of a person's possessions and dumping them in the hall or bathroom until the photo shoot is finished.

Rooms with lots of stuff are the best because they are real-life reflections of who you are. But sometimes all those stuffed animals, trophies, posters, clothes, pillows, papers, books, magazines, shoes, award certificates, ribbons, seashells, birds' nests, feathers, coins, bracelets, socks, model aeroplanes, boardgame pieces, pencils, plants, clocks, LEGO pieces, folders, photos, frames, catalogues, fish tanks, gerbil cages, hermit crab terrariums, dog beds, rulers, glue sticks, pens, head bands, hair clips and oh, yes, dirty underwear can look just a tiny bit cluttered.

That's why it's good to know a few simple tricks to keep things organised.

File don't pile

If you've got stacks of random papers, take 10 minutes every week to sit down and sort through the stuff in your bag and room. Throw away anything that you don't need or want to keep. Then sort the rest into different categories. Make a file for each and write the category on the file tab – 'Maths homework', 'Drawings', 'Song lyrics', or even just 'Random stuff that's cool'. Put those files in a filing drawer or wire rack on your desk or shelf.

Break out the bins

There are always going to be those special items – that well-loved blanket, brilliant Polly Pocket house, particularly engrossing comics – that you won't want to throw away even though you don't use them any more. While there is a place for permanent purges, throwing everything away can lead to regrets. (Josh, for example, still misses his Micronauts' Microrail City set.) Instead, set up a schedule with your grownup – once every one or two months – to put a few selected items away in a clear plastic bin that you then place in storage. Never store books or clothes in the cellar unless they are in 100 per cent air-tight bins because they can get mouldy.

⬚✖♦⬚ ✖⬚ 人✖✳⬚ ⬚⬚⬚⬚✳⬚⬚⬚
♦人⬚⬚⬚ ⬚✦✖✳⬚✖⬚人 ⬚✦⬚⬚✖✖⬚⬚⬚⬚ ⬚✖⬚
✖人 ⬚▵▵✦⬚⬚⬚ ✖✖⬚ ⬚✦▵✖✳⬚⬚ 人✖✖⬚
⊞⬚✖⬚⬚⬚✖ ▵⬚⬚♦♦⬚⬚ ⬚⊠⬚♦ ✦⬚⬚✖ ⬚
⬚✖✖✖✦⬚⊠ ⬚⬚⊞ ⬚⊠✦■⬚ 人✖✖ ⬚⬚⬚⬚
✖✖⬚ ✖⬚ ⬚⊠⬚ ⊠✖✖⬚⬚⬚

Cull your clothes

Nothing feels more disorganised than prising open a drawer crammed with too many shirts or pants or jumpers or mismatched socks. Your body is growing really fast right now, so make sure that you regularly get rid of clothes that either don't fit or you don't wear. If they're destined for a younger sibling, put them in clean plastic bins with the size of the clothes clearly marked on the front. Otherwise, bag them up for friends, cousins or a charity you support.

Label

It's easier to find something if it always goes in a specific place. Label makers are not only a blast to use, but also help you clearly mark where things should go. Once you use something, always put it back in the place where it's supposed to be.

Illustrations by Heather Kasunick

MAKE A NO-SEW
STUFFED ANIMAL

By Elizabeth

You probably have a lot of stray socks strewn uselessly around your home. Give those slackers a reason to live by turning them into stuffed animals.

A lot of sock animal projects are quite complicated and involve not just sewing and cutting but also fairly detailed embroidery. It's great to develop those crafting skills, and activities like that can be very rewarding.

But if you want something that's so easy it feels almost wrong, try this no-sew version that my kids and I improvised one day when we didn't want to set up the sewing machine.

Adjust your expectations. Most craft projects that you see in magazines and books are created by experts and then photographed by professionals; they look so perfect you could sell them in a shop. Real sock animals made by most kids and grownups are usually a little bit lumpy and rough. The great thing about this sock hamster is that it can also be a sock whale or even just a grumpy old human face. Experiment!

You'll need

- Piece of paper
- Old sock (no holes!)
- 4 rubber bands (hair bobbles will also work)
- Uncooked rice
- Pom-poms, googly eyes or fabric for eyes
- Adhesive tape
- Glue

Try this:

1. Bend a piece of paper into a funnel and tape it closed; magazine covers work well because they are a little heavier and can hold the rice more easily.

2. Put the small end of the funnel into the sock. Pour or scoop rice into the sock until it's slightly more than half full.

3. Put a rubber band on the open end of the sock. Put a rubber band around the toe end of the sock to form a nose. Then add two more rubber band lumps on top to create ears.

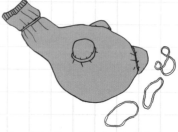

4. Take the rubber band off the end of the sock and fill with more rice until you have a couple of centimetres or less of unfilled sock left. Put the rubber band back on and tuck the end of the sock into it to create a little hamster tail.

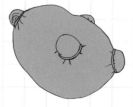

5. Using small pom-poms, googly eyes, or pieces of fabric, make a mouth and eyes for your hamster. Glue them on, wait for them to dry, and you're done.

Illustrations by Mister Reusch

CHECK OUT MUSIC ONLINE

Many kids retreat to their rooms in order to go online. While you're online, why not explore and develop your taste in music?

Sample & download music

There are plenty of reputable online music stores, most of which – including Amazon MP3 and the iTunes Store – offer millions of songs, and each of which permits you to sample a tune before purchasing it. Once you download a song, you own it.

Stream music

Subscription music services – for example, Spotify, Napster, We7 and Deezer – are more like customisable radio stations than music stores. These services charge a fee. Depending on the service and how much you're paying for it, you can stream a certain number of tunes each month.

The upside of streaming music is that for the price of a dozen new songs from iTunes or Amazon, you get access to all the music you could possibly want to hear. (Some services let you listen to music for free, as long as you listen to ads.) The downside of streaming is that if you stop paying the monthly fee, all of that music you don't own will vanish – along with your playlists.

How to choose between these services? Besides cost, look into how many songs each service has in its catalogue, how many songs you can listen to each month, and whether the service's functionality appeals to you. Spotify works seamlessly with Facebook, making it easy to see what your friends are listening to, and vice versa. However, although Spotify has the biggest and deepest music library, Napster and We7 aren't too far behind.

Cloud music

Cloud music services combine the functions of an online music store and an online radio station. Here are two examples. For a monthly fee, Amazon's Cloud Player permits you to upload tunes you own to its servers; you can then press 'play' from any device with an internet connection. Apple's iTunes Match will scan the songs in your iTunes library, match them to songs in its catalogue, and then – for a monthly fee – you can download these songs to any computer or Apple device via Apple's iCloud service.

SHARE IT, DON'T STEAL IT

Practically every song ever recorded is available online. This is great not only for music fans, but for musicians – whose potential audience has been vastly expanded in recent years. But if you download songs without paying, you're ripping off those musicians. So resist the temptation!

If you use a song clip as a soundtrack to a movie you've made, use just a few seconds of it.

Also: check the terms of service for any online music store or service. If you are younger than permitted, don't lie about your age. Instead, you and your grownup will just have to explore your musical tastes together. Which is also fun.

Illustration by Mister Reusch

APPLE-PIE BED

If you've ever been on holiday with friends, you may already be familiar with this prank. Try it on your grownup.

Your sleepy grownup will slide into her cosy, perfectly made-up bed, only to discover that she can't stretch her legs out all the way to the end of the bed. Oh, the horror!

This prank works particularly well on visiting relatives, because unlike your grownup, your grandma or uncle or cousin won't find a neatly made-up bed suspicious. The only problem is that next time you visit them, they'll get revenge.

Practise making 'hospital corners' with a top sheet.

1. Fit the bottom ('fitted') sheet – the one with elastic edges – over the mattress.

2. Spread the top sheet evenly across the mattress, so that it hangs down equally on both sides. Make sure the wide hem is at the head (pillow end) of the bed.

3. Tuck the bottom edge of the sheet beneath the foot of the mattress.

4. Grasp a handful of one of the sheet's edges, about 30–45cm from the foot of the bed and pull straight up.

30–45cm

5. A triangular drape (hanging down at the foot of the bed) will form.

Triangular drape

6. Tuck this triangle under the mattress.

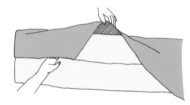

7. Then hold it in place as you lower the sheet's edge back down.

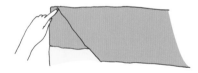

8. Now tuck in the remaining edge, tightly.

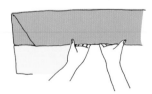

9. Repeat on the other side of the mattress.

Illustrations by Heather Kasunick

Now it's time to make an apple-pie bed!

1. Strip the bed, leaving only the bottom sheet on the mattress.

2. Spread the top sheet across the mattress, so that it hangs down evenly on both sides. This time, however, make sure the sheet's wide hem is at the foot of the bed. Tuck the other end beneath the head (pillow end) of the mattress.

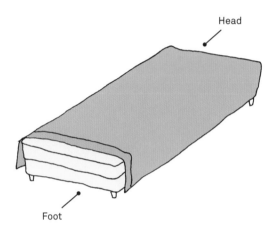

Head

Foot

3. Make tight hospital corners... only do it at the head of the mattress this time.

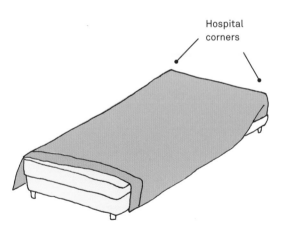

Hospital corners

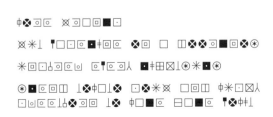

4. Instead of tucking in the sheet's edges all the way down the sides of the mattress, pull the wide hem of the sheet back up to the bed's pillow end.

Pull the sheet back up to the head of the bed

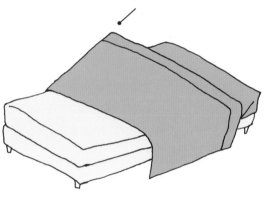

5. Loosely tuck in the hanging edges, so it will be easy for your victim to slide into bed.

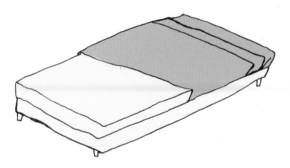

6. Put everything else back onto the bed exactly how it was before.

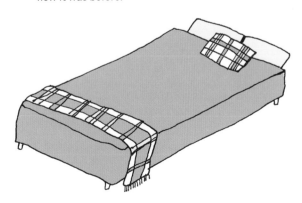

SHARE
YOUR GARDEN

Did you know that it's illegal to kick someone off your countryside property in Norway? Norwegians believe their mountain paths and sea views should be able to be enjoyed by everyone, not just the people who own the land.

British people like their privacy. It's hard to imagine anyone in this country wanting their garden to be so crammed with visitors that it feels like a public park. But there's a downside to keeping our green (or cement or brick) spaces to ourselves – if doing so means we don't get to know our neighbours. Knowing our neighbours not only gives us more opportunities to make friends, but also keeps us safer because friends look out for each other more than strangers do.

That's why it's important to share your garden. We don't mean throwing open the gates and posting a 'Trample our grass!' sign. Instead, we're talking about creating a welcoming feeling that honours a neighbourly spirit and celebrates the fact that your garden can be a place where you have fun with others. Here's how:

Illustrations by Mister Reusch

Throw a gnome party

Get your grownups to organise a revolving 'Gnome Party' in your neighbourhood. Some communities have this kind of party every week during the summer. People sign up for the date they want to host on a website and are expected to provide a garden or patch of street and access to an indoor toilet. On the day of the party, the host family puts a garden gnome out so that people know where to go. Every neighbour who joins the fun brings something to drink or eat. If it rains, the party is cancelled until the next week.

A Gnome Party is a blast. You can set up a rock band in the garage or crank up the karaoke. Or let all the kids jump on your trampoline. But mostly, a Gnome Party is an opportunity for the adults to hang out and get to know each other. And you know what goes on when that happens: all the kids get together and set up their own games, which are much cooler and more fun because the adults are 'watching' them in only the loosest sense of the word. Whether it's Kick the Can or a water balloon fight in the street, the kids will inevitably stay up way past their bedtimes. And they'll make friends with the people their age who live near them.

Put a garden gnome out on the day of the party

Start an eruption

Bicarbonate of soda and vinegar volcanoes are fun. But they're messy and the volcano can be a pain to build, so take the activity outside and make the volcano construction easier by using mud or (even better) snow.

You'll need:

- Empty plastic bottle
- 2 tablespoons of bicarbonate of soda
- Washing-up liquid
- Red food colouring
- Vinegar

Try this:

1. Use your hands or a shovel to mould snow or mud into a volcano – the size is totally up to you. The top of the volcano needs to be fitted around the empty plastic bottle. Make sure you don't cover the bottle's hole.

2. Fill most of the bottle with warm water (or hot water if you're working with snow) and add 2 drops of red food colouring.

3. Add 6 drops of washing-up liquid to the bottle contents.

4. Add 2 tablespoons bicarbonate of soda to the liquid.

5. Slowly pour the vinegar into the bottle.

Build an obstacle course

Inviting your neighbours to make and run an obstacle course is a great way to spend an afternoon.

Try this:

1. Survey the grounds. Check out your garden to make sure there aren't any huge holes; you don't want your contestants to twist an ankle. Mark the beginning and the end of the course with traffic cones.

2. Find good stuff. Those unwanted soft toys are as good as bean bags for tossing through hula hoops. Rubbish bins, cardboard boxes, paddling pools, skipping ropes, scooters – whatever you've got, you can find a way to use it. You can get items such as tyres and planks for free at scrapyards.

3. Set up your events. Come up with activities that use different muscle groups. Categories could include: crawling, jumping, hopping, pulling, riding, tossing and splashing. If you and your friends are into gymnastics or parkour, incorporate tricks like jumps and flips into a few of the stations. And don't limit yourself simply to physical activities. People may also have to sing songs or do dance moves or put on and take off daft costumes. If you're into woodworking, make an activity where contestants have to saw through a board or hammer nails into a log. Space each activity 3–5 metres apart.

4. Do a test run. This will help you make sure the course is safe.

5. Get out the stopwatch. You don't need to time contestants if you don't want to, but sometimes it's more fun to make it a competition.

6. Break out the awards. Prizes can be anything from sweets to homemade certificates. Use your imagination.

Anything can be an obstacle!

Make it a competition!

Mark the end of the course

Play with fire

Few activities are as satisfying as mucking around with real leaping flames. While campfires are great, they're impractical for gardens. If your grownups have built or bought a fire pit, you can experiment with turning the flames different colours.

> **WARNING!** Grownups need to supervise this activity. Also, never do this on a barbecue – the chemicals will taint your food.

You'll need:

- Pine cones or sawdust
- A bucket of water for each colour
- Colourant (see right)
- A fire pit
- Fire-making supplies

Fire pit

Try this:

1. Gather a bunch of pine cones or a pile of sawdust.

2. Fill a bucket with water for each colour that you want to use. Make sure you have enough water to completely soak your sawdust or pine cones.

3. Mix in your colourant (see right) until it is fully dissolved.

4. Add some pine cones or sawdust to each bucket and coat them evenly in coloured mixture. Let them soak overnight.

5. Set the pieces out to dry for several hours. Pine cones can be arranged on a flat surface or hung in a mesh laundry bag. Sawdust can be spread out in a thin layer on wax paper. Whatever surface you choose, make sure it is something you can throw away after your experiment.

6. Build and light your fire.

7. Toss pine cones and sawdust into the fire one handful a time.

FLAME
COLOURS

Most of these ingredients are easy to find online, and some of them are available in the supermarket. Add as much colourant as will dissolve in the bucket (you need about 60g colourant per litre of water, usually).

 Red
Strontium chloride

 Yellow
Sodium chloride (table salt)

 Yellow/green
Borax

 Green
Copper sulphate (hair dye)

 Blue
Copper chloride

 Violet
3 parts potassium sulphate and 1 part potassium nitrate

 Purple
Potassium chloride

 White
Magnesium sulphate (Epsom salts)

GARDEN CASTLES & DENS

By Josh

More permanent than a tent, less permanent than a treehouse, garden castles and dens can be built in a day (once you've gathered the materials, that is) and taken down in an hour.

Mention these facts to your grownups, and they will be forced to say OK to your plans… and maybe they'll even lend a hand too.

As you'll see, many of these castles require tree branches and evergreen boughs. Are we suggesting that you take an axe to the trees in your garden and neighbourhood? We are not! You might need to wait until your family, or another family in the neighbourhood, is having a tree trimmed or cut down; or you can collect fallen branches after a storm.

Site your castle/den

The point of building a shelter is staying warm and dry; and the point of building a castle is defending it from invaders. Here are a few questions to ask yourself before you begin construction:

- In what direction does the wind usually blow? Which way should your shelter's entrance face?

- Where in the garden should you build? Will you need to use a fence, tree, garage wall or some other garden feature as part of your structure?

- How many friends do you want to fit inside?

- How can you prevent your enemies from spying on you? Do you have an escape route planned?

Answer these questions, then get building.

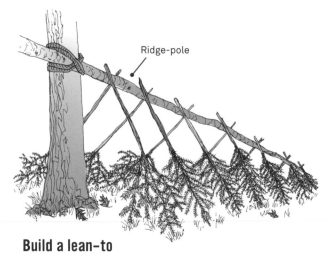

Ridge-pole

Build a lean-to

1. Collect a straight, sturdy pole, or a plank, or a tree branch (with twigs trimmed off) to use as your ridge-pole – it should be at least 2 metres long. Also collect a pile of poles, floorboards (without nails), hockey sticks, branches with the twigs still on, and any other objects that could be used to construct a sloping roof/wall. (Several of these objects must be as long as the lean-to is going to be tall – so you'll need some roughly 2-metre-long objects.) Finally, collect either a pile of evergreen boughs or a couple of large waterproof tarps.

2a. Lash the uppermost end of the ridge-pole to something solid – a classic example is a tree branch or tree fork that's a bit higher up than the head of the tallest person who'll be using the lean-to. You can also lash the uppermost end of the ridge-pole about 2 metres up a tree trunk. Don't lean the pole against anything whose surface you wouldn't want to scratch; and don't lean the pole against something to which you can't fasten it. For added stability, bury the bottom end of the ridge-pole in the ground.

    PS: Vikings and Maori decorated their ridge-poles – go ahead, give it a try!

Illustrations by Mister Reusch

2b. Otherwise, drive two sturdy, 2-metre-long, Y-shaped tree limbs about 30cm deep into the ground, about 2 metres apart from each other; make sure that their forks are the same distance above the ground, or else your roof will be crooked. (If you're lucky, you'll find two trees growing about 2 metres apart, and you can use them instead.) Place a ridge-pole between the two forked ends. Lash if necessary.

3. Build the sloping roof/main wall by leaning poles and branches and other things against the uppermost part of the ridge-pole; if you're using tree limbs, the thicker ends should be on the ground. For added stability, lash the objects' top ends to the ridge-pole and/or bury their bottom ends 3cm deep in the ground. You could stop here, but why not keep going?

4. Fortify the roof/wall, to keep the sun and rain off your heads. One old-school method involves laying evergreen boughs over the roof/wall – place them side by side, beginning at the bottom and working your way up. Make sure the part of the bough that was attached to the tree is pointing up; each new row of boughs should slightly overlap the one beneath. You might want to tie the boughs down, but it's not 100 per cent necessary. If you don't have evergreen boughs, you can block up gaps in the roof/wall with leaves, grass and other material.

5. If you want side walls on your lean-to, they should not be sloping but vertical. So sharpen the ends of some sticks and drive them into the ground in parallel rows, then fill the gap between the rows in with other sticks, grass, etc.

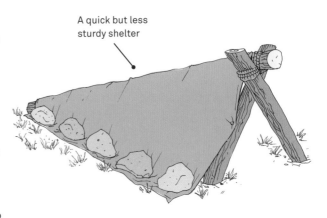

A quick but less sturdy shelter

Build a tarp shelter

1. Set up a ridge-pole using one of the methods described above. Because the tarp is light, you can use a rope for a ridge-pole; if you're just trying to stay warm and dry while you're sleeping in the woods, you can use a fallen tree.

2. Throw a tarp over the ridge-pole, then fasten the top end to the ridge-pole (with string, if the tarp has holes for that purpose; or with clothes pegs).

3. Fasten the bottom end to the ground (with tent pegs or sharpened sticks if the tarp has strings, loops or holes for that purpose; if it doesn't, use large rocks to weigh it down). If you have a large enough tarp, you can peg it to the ground on both sides.

   The structure you've just built is also called a 'wedge tent'. It's fun to build, but... a real tent is a lot sturdier.

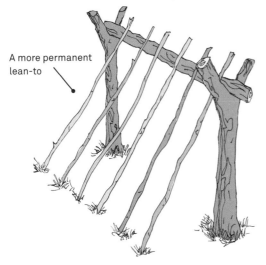

A more permanent lean-to

3. Raise the lashed-together poles in the air and separate them – now you've got a tripod. Wrap the tarp around the tripod, and fasten it from as high as you can reach to about a metre off the ground – and make a door.

   FUN FACT: The tripod (Greek for 'three feet') is geometrically the stablest structure around, because when you push down on one side, the pressure is distributed to all three sides, which actually increases the structure's tensile strength.

4. Instead of using a tarp, you could also lash branches, poles and other stuff to the tripod (leaving room for a door), then insulate the walls.

   TIP: Don't confuse a wigwam with a tipi. A tipi is a tripod, while a wigwam is either six- or eight-sided. Also, a wigwam – associated with Native Americans from the north-east of America – is formed from a framework of arched poles, so its roof is domed, not conical.

Build a tipi

A tipi (Lakota Sioux for 'house') is a portable, durable tent associated with nomadic Native Americans of the Great Plains of America.

1. Gather the same materials that you would for a lean-to; except you'll need three ridge-poles, and you might want to use poles that are more than than 1.5 metres long.

2. Lash the tops of three long branches, poles, or planks together; make sure the thicker ends of the branches, if that's what you're using, are on the bottom. Attach a tarp to the top of one of the poles.

Build an igloo

The only materials you need are a shovel and about 30cm of heavy snow on the ground.

1. Choose an igloo site, and mark a large circle in the snow – about 2 metres across is a nice size. Dig out the circle to a depth of 10cm. Establish a snow quarry near your igloo site, then trample down the snow in that area to make it nice and firm. Using your shovel, mine the quarry by cutting rectangular snow bricks about 60cm long by 40cm wide.

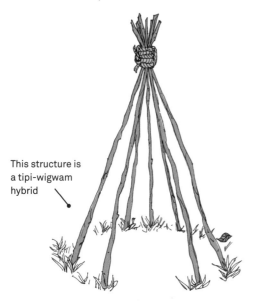

This structure is a tipi-wigwam hybrid

2. Leaving a space for an entrance, build a layer of snow bricks around the edge of the circle. (Some people claim you should shape the bricks so they end up a little shorter at one end of the semi-circle.) Fill in the cracks between the bricks. Build a second layer of bricks, then a third. By this point, your entrance ought to be tall enough to crawl through, so finish the circle by making two well-packed bricks meet over the entrance. Keep filling in the cracks.

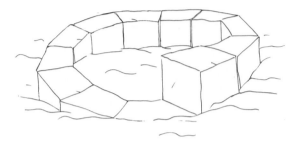

3. Carry on until the igloo is complete except for a smallish hole in the roof. Cut a 'capstone' block of packed snow that's wider than the hole and

hoist it into place. Pack snow around the capstone, and smooth the edges down so it looks right. Smooth the inside and outside walls of the igloo, and cut a couple of small windows near the igloo's top and bottom – not so much for looking out of as for breathing.

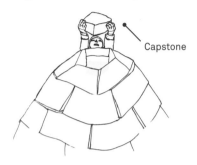

Capstone

TIP: Want to see a pro build an igloo? Watch the 1922 documentary *Nanook of the North*, which depicts the struggles of an Inuit named Nanook and his family in northern Quebec (Canada). It's viewable for free on YouTube.

SNOW CASTLE
AND OTHER SHELTERS

A snow castle makes snowball fights a lot more exciting – just ask Charlie Brown (from *Peanuts*) or Calvin (from *Calvin & Hobbes*). Every winter, my family makes a snow castle in our tiny front garden because once we've shovelled the pavement and drive out, there's a big pile of snow in the garden. Pile up a mound of snow in one corner, and dig a cave inside it – just be careful, it can collapse. Build walls radiating out from the cave mound. If the snow is compact enough, you can make small windows in the walls, or even tunnels through them.

You can also dig a trench in the snow, cover it with boards or branches, then pile snow on top of them – this makes a tunnel to wriggle through.

The photo here shows a brilliant snow castle that my father helped me and my brother Patrick and our neighbours build in our driveway during the Blizzard of '78 in Boston. That's Patrick on top; our friend Michael is in the entrance.

Humpy & Wickiup

A humpy is a small, temporary shelter made by leaning tree branches against a standing tree. The word comes from an Australian Aborigine language; another term for it is a 'wurley'.

A wickiup is like a wigwam, only usually less permanent. You can build one by sticking a bunch of long, limber poles (like willow wands) into the ground in a circle, then bending them towards one another in opposing pairs and lashing the ends together. Throw a tarp over the top.

Boston's Blizzard of '78

SECRET HISTORY
OF THE GARDEN

5000 BC Ancient Egyptians toss polished rocks at a target. The game eventually catches on with the Roman Empire and becomes the Italian game *bocce*, from the Latin word *bottia*, which means boss.

1817 In Germany, Baron Karl von Drais invents the two-wheeled *Laufmaschine*, or running machine. With a few tweaks, this wooden contraption will one day become the bicycle.

1827 Englishman Edwin Budding invents the first lawn mower, which cuts grass more efficiently than swinging a scythe or grazing animals.

1847 In Germany, Hermann von Arnswald invents the sandpit.

1868 The All England Croquet Club is founded in Wimbledon.

1882 Members of the Bury Fen Bandy Club in Wales publish the rules of a game played on ice with sticks. The game is a precursor to hockey.

1902 Beatrix Potter publishes *The Tale of Peter Rabbit*, which was influenced by her childhood spent playing outdoors.

1905 Harry C. Bunnell steals his friend's idea for a comfortable outdoor chair and patents the wooden Adirondack chair. It quickly becomes an icon of relaxed summer living.

1920 The first climbing frame is invented by an American lawyer named Sebastian Hinton. An original model is still standing at the Crow Island School in Winnetka, Illinois.

1935 California citrus farmer Orton Englehardt patents the first prototype of the impact sprinkler, which waters lawns automatically with a circular spray pattern.

Illustrations by Mister Reusch

1941 Gymnasts George Nissen and Larry Griswold start up the world's first trampoline manufacturer in Iowa. They invented and trademarked the word 'trampoline' during a 1937 exhibition tour in Mexico, where *trampolin* means springboard.

1947 The rules of Capture the Flag are listed in the Boy Scouts' *Scoutmaster's Handbook*. Kids beg their grownups to stay out past dark – because the game is way more fun when you can't see your opponents.

c. 1950 Skipping ropes – often washing lines – become extremely popular, as do skipping rhymes such as 'Sausage in a Pan'.

1952 George Stephen decides to invent a garden grill that cooks food more evenly and stays lit even in the rain. His dome-shaped Weber Kettle Grill is nicknamed 'Sputnik' by his neighbours, a reference to the first earth-orbiting artificial satellite.

1958 After demonstrating them on playgrounds across southern California, a company called WHAM-O sells 25 million hula hoops in four months.

1961 WHAM-O helps millions of American kids stay cool and get goofy with the invention of the Slip'N Slide.

1970s American Brooke Miller of Anaheim, California, patents the Pooper Scooper, a metal box on a stick that scrapes dog poo off the grass.

1976 Vert skateboarding is born when California skateboarders Ty Page, Bruce Logan, Bobby Piercy, Kevin Reed and the Z-Boys skate the walls of swimming pools that are empty because of drought.

1993 Swing sets get fancy when Rainbow Play Systems launches its first climbing frame/treehouse hybrids.

2000 Razor (originally a Swiss product) sells its first microscooter.

2000s The campfire gets an upgrade as people across the UK start warming themselves over shop-bought fire pits.

2004 Omlet launches a line of colourful plastic 'Eglu' henhouses, igniting a craze among city-dwellers for chicken-keeping.

GARDEN
PARKOUR

The term *parkour* comes from a French word meaning 'obstacle course'. Also known as *freerunning*, parkour was invented in the Paris suburbs in the 1980s by teenagers who turned their childhood chasing games into quick and graceful vaults over common urban obstacles like fences, walls and rubbish bins.

Thanks to YouTube videos and a cool chase scene through a construction site in the James Bond film *Casino Royale*, parkour became world-famous. A noncompetitive sport that requires strength and agility, parkour teaches you to see the everyday world of objects around you as a puzzle to solve, a challenge to overcome.

WARNING! Parkour can be dangerous. Parkour classes that teach safety and proper techniques are sprouting up all over the country, but a good rule of thumb is: Don't try anything fancy that you've seen in a video unless you've had proper coaching! Grownup supervision is a must.

Landing

Even if you are just jumping off a chair, landing is extremely important in parkour. If you don't do it properly, you can hurt your legs, knees, ankles and back. Always bend your knees when your toes make contact with ground. And always land on the balls of your feet – never land flat-footed.

the game

Bend your knees!

Land on the balls of your feet

Illustrations by Mister Reusch

Parkour Roll

This move will lessen the impact of a fall or landing. Practise it – in slow motion – on the carpet or grass (first clear away any sticks or sharp objects).

1. Bend down close to the ground.

2. Place your hands, palms down, in front of you on the ground. Your hands should face forward.

3. Look toward your waistline and tuck your chin in.

4. Roll on one shoulder, diagonally across your back. To get the feel of where you should be rolling, get someone to trace a diagonal line from the shoulder you want to roll on down across your back. Curl into a ball when you roll.

5. Keep your legs tucked as you roll. Your body should feel tense and strong.

6. As you come out of the roll, put your knee on the ground or stand up.

7. If you want to do a roll *after* a jump, squat so your legs form a 90-degree angle when you land. This will keep your momentum moving forward.

Monkey Vault

This is an extremely common and useful vault that can be used to clear rails or walls up to chest-height.

1. Pick an obstacle (rails and benches work well) that is not too high. Knee-height is good.

2. Run towards the obstacle.

3. Put both hands on the obstacle.

4. Push down with your shoulders. At the same time, bring both legs together up towards your chest into a squat position.

5. Move your legs through your hands. Lean forward as you execute the vault.

6. Once you've cleared the obstacle, keep running.

SOAK AND DESTROY

Remote-Controlled Water Blaster

By John Edgar Park

Want to keep your brothers, sisters and friends from breaking into your secret den to dig through your comic books? Build a remote-controlled motorised water blaster so you can soak them while sneakily savouring the moment from a safe distance!

You'll need:

- Super Soaker
- 12V DC relay switch kit
- 2 dead AA batteries (to be used as 'dummies' or spacers)
- Heat-shrink tubing (3mm diameter) cut into two 15mm-long sections
- A 9V battery and a 9V-battery holder OR (for longer shooting time) 6 AA batteries and a 6 x AA-battery holder
- Small Phillips screwdriver
- Wire strippers
- Electrical tape
- Soldering iron and solder
- Cable ties
- **Optional:** Lighter
- **Optional:** Strong string
- Goggles
- Grownup supervision

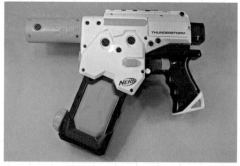

Battery-powered Nerf Super Soaker Thunderstorm. You can use another motorised blaster but you may need to modify some steps of these instructions.

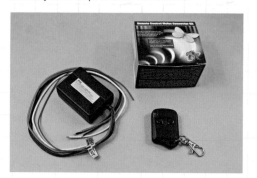

Remote-controlled 12V DC relay switch kit.

Illustration by Mister Reusch   Photography by John Edgar Park

Here's the plan. We'll strap the water blaster's trigger into a permanently pulled position, and insert a remote-controlled relay switch into the power supply. At the push of a remote transmitter's button, you'll be able to start and stop the flow of electricity running between the battery and the motor that powers the water blaster's pump.

Hotwire the blaster

First, we'll splice the relay into the water blaster's battery circuit. A relay is a switch that is opened and closed by applying an electrical current; the remote-controlled relay switch can be opened and closed from a distance by a transmitter. By splicing the relay into the battery circuit, we'll be able to make the blaster shoot by pressing the transmitter's 'on' button.

1. Unscrew the blaster's battery cover and remove the battery pack (Figure A). Remove its batteries. On the back of the pack you'll see two metal tabs; the one connected to the coiled spring is the negative (–) tab, the other is the positive (+) tab.

2. Find the 12V OUT wire on the relay switch (your colours may vary from the photos); it will contact the positive tab. (The GND OUT wire is the 'earth', which will contact the negative tab.) Use the wire strippers to remove 25mm of insulation from both of these wires.

3. Cover the positive (+) end of one of the dummy batteries with the exposed 12V OUT wire. Cover the negative (–) end of the other dummy battery with the exposed GND OUT wire. Wrap electrical tape around each battery to hold the wire in place, as shown (Figure B).

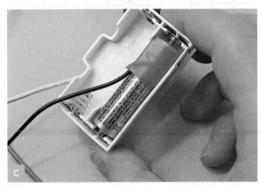

4. Insert the positive dummy battery into the blaster's battery holder; make sure the exposed 12V OUT wire is touching the positive (+) tab (Figure C). Insert the negative dummy battery into the battery holder; make sure the exposed earth wire touches the negative (–) tab. Now we have a dummy power insert. Stick the dummy power insert into the blaster, and close the cover – allowing the relay switch's two wires to run out from the top (Figure D). They'll get lightly pinched by the cover but it's OK.

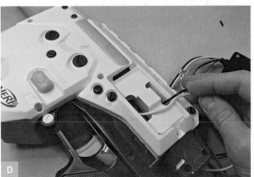

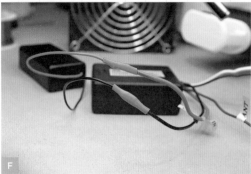

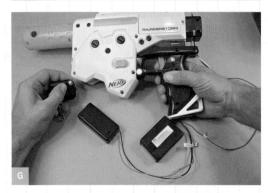

Power the relay switch

Next, we'll give the relay switch some power. Put on your goggles, and make sure you're in a well-ventilated space, because we're going to use the soldering iron to splice the battery holder and the relay unit together.

1. If necessary, use the wire strippers to remove 30mm of insulation from the battery holder's red and black wires.

2. Slide a 15mm-long section of heat-shrink tubing over the relay unit's 12V IN wire, leaving the wire's stripped end exposed.

3. Twist together the ends of the battery holder's red voltage wire and the relay unit's 12V IN wire.

4. Heat the joined wire ends with the tip of your hot soldering iron, then solder them together – by touching a length of solder to the joint (Figure E).

5. When the soldered joint is cool, slide the heat-shrink tubing into place over the joint. Using a lighter, or the side of your soldering iron, heat up the tubing so it shrinks. We've just insulated the joint, which will help avoid a short circuit if the wires get wet.

6. Repeat the above steps to solder together and insulate the battery holder's black earth wire and the relay unit's GND IN wire (Figure F).

Test the blaster

The circuit is complete! Time to test it.

1. Make sure the relay switch kit's remote control unit is working.

2. Insert a 9V battery into the 9V-battery holder (or, if you used a 6 x AA-battery holder, insert 6 AA batteries). If the battery holder has an ON/OFF switch, turn it on.

3. Pull the blaster's trigger – nothing happens yet. Keeping the trigger pulled, press the ON button on the relay switch kit's remote control unit. The blaster should start firing! Press the remote control unit's OFF button to stop it (Figure G).

4. Use a cable tie to secure the blaster's trigger in the pulled position (Figure H). Press the ON button on the relay remote – the blaster should now start firing without your finger on the trigger.

Deploy and destroy

Finally, we need to deploy the remote-controlled water blaster.

1. Fill the water blaster's tank, and insert it into the blaster.

2. Place the blaster somewhere sneaky. In your garden, for example, you could use some strong string to lash the blaster to the side of a den – or to a tree branch (Figure I).

3. When your victim walks into the blaster's line of fire, turn the remote control unit on (Figures J & K)! Because the remote works from over 30 metres away, you could even hide indoors.

MORE
DANK PRANKS

Kitchen Cabinet

Tie a short length of string or thread around a large plastic cup, and secure it with strong tape – you'll want to leave about 5–10cm of string hanging down. Fill the cup halfway up with water, open the door of a kitchen cabinet, and place the cup on a shelf inside. Shut the cabinet door most of the way, then tape the other end of the string to the inside of the door. Shut the door. The next person who opens the cabinet will be splashed – this prank is particularly effective if the shelf is above the victim's head.

Toilet

Remove the lid of your toilet's tank, and set it aside – be careful not to drop it. If you see a small water feed tube leading from the inlet valve (at the edge of the tank) into the overflow tube (sticking up at the centre of the tank), you're in luck! Flush the toilet, and you'll see that water comes shooting out of the small tube. Unclip the tube and redirect it, so that it's sticking out over the edge of the tank, aiming straight at you. Carefully replace the tank's lid, so that it holds the tube in place; you may need to enlist an accomplice to assist you.

Sink

If your kitchen sink has a handsprayer, wrap a rubber band a few times around the spray head, so that the trigger is forced down. Aim the sprayer nozzle at yourself, then skedaddle. The next person who turns on the sink will get soaked.

Bedroom Door

Fill a large plastic cup about halfway with water, and carry it sneakily into your room. Using several drawing pins, fasten a 15cm-long piece of cardboard above the door, to the underside of the doorframe; make sure that you do this on the opposite side of the doorframe from the hinges! About 10cm of the cardboard should extend into the room. Take the cup of water outside your room, and close the door behind you until it's slightly ajar; the cardboard will now be supported by the top edge of the open door. Stick your arm through the opening and carefully place the cup of water onto the cardboard platform – you may need to stand on something to reach that high. Lurk nearby.

CRAFTIVISM MANIFESTO

By Jean Railla

Getting crafty doesn't require lessons, expensive materials or equipment, or kits. The only requirement is a willingness to dive in.

Craftivism, as I call the movement, is all about the process of making stuff. It doesn't matter so much what the end result is – it's all about the activity of using your hands, your brain and your creativity to make something from nothing.

You can get crafty by sewing, embroidering, knitting, crocheting, cooking, building stuff, woodworking, painting – the list goes on and on. I fiercely believe there's nothing more important in life than getting crafty. When we get crafty, we start to see ourselves as creators, not just consumers. When you get crafty, you tap into a force that says *I can change my life, my world*.

How do you get started? By making things yourself, one little project at a time.

Free your mind!

When I was 12, I wanted to decorate my room according to my own sense of style, not my parents'. But my mum refused to buy me posters from the shopping centre. So I covered the walls with collages made from magazine pages and photos of my favourite bands. For the first time, my room became a sanctuary – a place where I could not only do my homework, but also listen to music, write poetry and let my imagination roam free. Slapping up a couple of posters bought from a shop wouldn't have had the same effect. The kitchen, meanwhile, became a laboratory where I'd experiment with after-school snacks tailored to my taste buds.

Crafting was not only liberating, it was calming. While crafting, I felt less worried about fitting in (among other adolescent anxieties). Studies have shown that knitting puts your brain into the same state that meditating does – how cool is that?

Express yourself

Getting crafty made me feel powerful. I no longer needed to beg my mum for all the things I wanted – including clothes. Saving up my pocket money, I would ride my bike to a cheap clothes shop and carry home jumpers and T-shirts. I would cut off the necklines or sleeves, dye them new colours and

Illustrations by Heather Kasunick

decorate them. Or else my friends and I would take the bus to charity shops, where we'd buy vintage skirts and dresses that we could wear with combat boots. Although I had to wear a uniform to school every day, I had a great time creating outfits that expressed who I was – even if I mostly wore those outfits at home.

Become self-reliant

I desperately wanted independence from my grownups, and crafting taught me to rely on my own skills to create a wardrobe, room décor and meals I wanted to eat. It also taught me that I didn't need much to make a fun life for myself – that I could start small and build from there. These lessons really came in handy when I got older and moved away from home. Growing up means creating a life that you – not your grownups, your school, a major corporation, or anyone else – want for yourself. If you're not self-reliant, it's hard to grow up!

Find your craft

A craft can be something that you do to relax on a daily basis, like knitting, needlepoint or embroidery. Or it can be a one-off project, like planting a herb garden or making candles. It's fun to learn a craft from your grownup, or a friend, but you can also browse the crafting section of your local library for inspiration. There are also lots of crafting magazines and websites. If you try a craft and don't like it, that's OK – there are plenty of others out there.

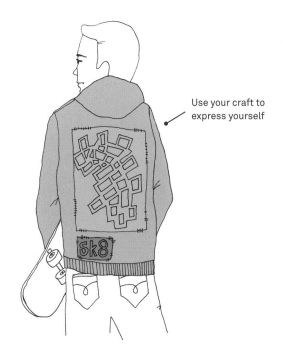

Use your craft to express yourself

Start a craft swap

Here's how a craft swap works. Gather a group of friends, and put everyone's name into a hat. Each person picks a name. Over the next week, make a handmade object for the person whose name you picked. Set a budget for the craft materials: no more than three pounds, for example.

Flaunt your creations

Show off your work and inspire others at the same time. How? You could set up a crafts fair or gallery exhibition at your house, and send out invitations. Or start a blog. If none of your friends seem to be interested in what you're doing, there are plenty of crafting communities out there. Visit a crafting website, or pick up a crafting magazine – some of which feature Craft Challenges in which you might be old enough to participate.

Hit the charity shops

Charity shops, not to mention car boot sales and flea markets, are treasure troves for crafty folk. You'll find old clothes that can be re-purposed in spectacular ways, as well as tools, handbooks, sewing patterns – even wool and knitting needles. Old books and magazines contain cool graphics and photos that you can use in an artwork, while plates can be painted and hung on the wall. Even old vinyl records can be used to make all sorts of fun things.

TRANSFORM AN OLD RECORD
INTO A NIFTY BOWL

To get you started thinking like a craftivist, here is a simple project that takes less than an hour and costs almost nothing. The material for this project comes from something you can find at almost any charity shop – an old vinyl record. Your grownups might even be willing to give you a scratched, unplayable record that they don't want any more.

You'll need:
- 12" vinyl record. Or a 7" single works, too.
- Baking tray
- Tin foil
- Oven-safe bowl (or colander), about 25cm across the top and 10cm across the base
- Oven
- Oven glove

Try this:

1. Preheat the oven to 200°C/400°F.

2. Cover your baking tray in tin foil.

3. Place the oven-safe bowl on the baking tray, top side down.

4. Balance the record on top of the bowl.

5. Place the baking tray with the bowl and record into the oven, and bake for five minutes.

IMPORTANT! For anything to do with a hot oven, ask your grownup for help.

6. Using the oven glove, remove the baking tray from the oven and place it on the stove-top. Your record should now be flexible but not too hot to handle – however, the bowl and baking tray will be quite warm – so be careful!

7. Quickly remove the record from the top of the bowl with one hand, and – using the oven glove – flip the bowl the right way up with the other hand (or with your grownup's help). Push the record down into the bowl to give it shape.

8. Manipulate the record's sides until you're satisfied with how they look.

9. Let the record cool. Hey presto! You now have a cool bowl that can hold playing cards, jewellery and all sorts of other stuff. If you want to cover the hole in the record, use clear parcel tape.

DÉCOUPAGE

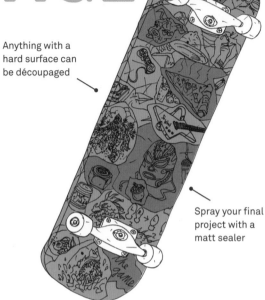

Anything with a hard surface can be découpaged

Spray your final project with a matt sealer

The art of covering paper cutouts with clear varnish was a huge craze in the eighteenth century. Members of some royal courts découpaged everything from hat boxes to wig stands.

You, too, can découpage anything that has a hard surface: non-upholstered furniture, lamp shades, boxes, picture frames, the bottom of a skateboard, a wooden bracelet, glass jars… the possibilities are endless.

You'll need:

- An item to découpage
- Any kind of paper with images: comics, photos, wrapping paper, magazine pages, fabric, foreign currencies, tissue paper (especially nice on glass because light will shine through), maps – you name it.
- Scissors
- Precision craft knife (e.g. an X-Acto knife). Use with grownup supervision.
- White glue
- Stirrers; we like ice lolly sticks.
- Foam brushes
- **Optional:** Hand roller (known as a brayer)
- Matt sealer spray

Try This:

1. Pick an item to découpage. Make sure it is clean and dry before you start découpaging. If you have painted the item before découpaging it, make sure the paint is completely dry.

2. Cut out the images you're going to découpage. Use a precision knife (with grownup supervision) for more intricate images.

   TIP! Do not découpage images printed from an inkjet printer because the ink will smudge when it gets wet. Instead, print the image, then photocopy it and use the photocopied image for your project.

3. Make the découpage medium by mixing three parts glue to one part water. Stir the solution. More water makes it thinner; less water makes it thicker.

4. Arrange the images onto the item you are découpaging. They can overlap, or not.

5. Working in small sections, remove the pictures and apply a thin layer of glue solution onto the item you are découpaging.

6. Stick the picture on the glue solution. Gently press the image into place and push out any wrinkles and excess glue solution using your finger, a foam brush or a hand roller. Repeat until all your images are glued into place.

7. Let the découpage medium dry.

8. Using the foam brush, coat the entire item with glue solution. Let dry again. Recoat, dry and repeat as many times as you need in order to get the item to look the way you want it to. More coats will create a thickly varnished appearance.

9. Let dry overnight.

10. Spray the surface of your masterpiece with a matt sealer. Let dry.

Illustration by Mister Reusch

ILLUSION KNITTING

By Anindita Basu Sempere

Illusion knitting, or shadow knitting as it's sometimes called, involves knitting a design across stripes using two contrasting colours: a main colour and a background colour. If you hold an illusion knit project vertically, you'll only see stripes, but if you hold it at an angle, the design will appear.

Magic? Not exactly. Illusion knitting works through texture – purling makes bumps in the pattern while knitting lies flat. By knitting some parts of the pattern and purling others, you can create a 3D image that only appears at an angle.

You need to know:
- How to knit
- How to purl
- How to switch between two colours of wool

You'll need:
- 100g each of two contrasting wool colours (double knit, smooth texture)
- 4.5mm knitting needles

Here's a sample pattern

There are 24 columns and 15 rows. Each column represents one stitch, and each row represents four rows of knitting (2 rows in each colour), so this pattern describes 60 rows with 24 stitches in each.

To knit any illusion knitting pattern, cast on as many stitches as you have columns. In this example, that means casting on 24 stitches. Every row will be knitted as follows:

- Row 1-1: Knit the main colour.
- Row 1-2: Knit the white boxes. Purl the green boxes.
- Row 1-3: Switch to the background colour. Knit.
- Row 1-4: Purl the white boxes. Knit the green boxes.

For the first row of the sample pattern, this means:

- Row 1-1: Using the main colour, knit 24 stitches.
- Row 1-2: Knit 5, Purl 3, Knit 3, Purl 2, Knit 3, Purl 3, Knit 5.
- Row 1-3: Switch to the background colour. Knit 24 stitches.
- Row 1-4: Purl 5, Knit 3, Purl 3, Knit 2, Purl 3, Knit 3, Purl 5.

What would Rows 2-1 and Rows 2-4 translate to?

Answer:
Row 2-1: Using main colour K24. Row 2-2: K3, P3, K1, P1, K2, P1, K2, P1, K2, P1, K1, P3, K3. Row 2-3: Using background colour K24. Row 2-4: P3, K3, P1, K1, P2, K1, P2, K1, P2, K1, P1, K3, P3.

Illustrations by Heather Kasunick

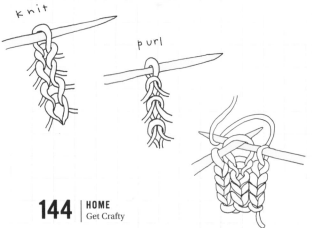

knit

purl

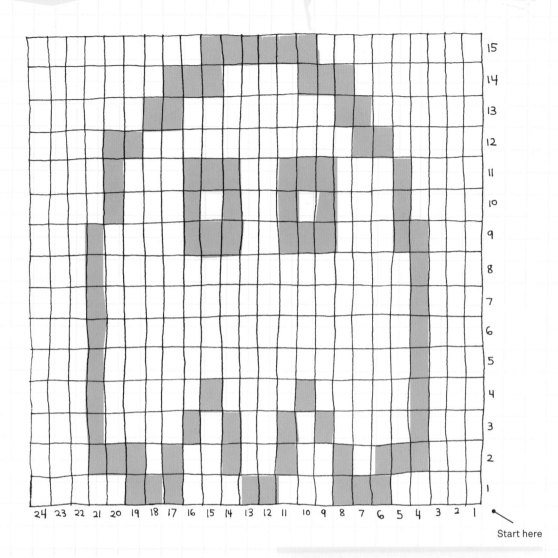

Start here

As you work the pattern, you can see that you're making the image bumpy with the main colour, and emphasising the background with the background colour. You're increasing the contrast between the colours so the secret image will stand out.

What next?

If you're knitting a scarf, you can knit the same pattern several times until it's long enough. Leave space between repetitions by knitting a few 'white' rows, meaning you'll knit Rows 1 and 2 in the main colour, switch to the background colour, knit Row 3, and purl Row 4.

To mix things up, you can knit the pattern once, turn the pattern upside down, knit the pattern in reverse to switch directions, and then switch back. Sneaky.

DESIGN YOUR OWN PATTERN

Do a web search for 'illusion knitting pattern' or else, using graph paper, colour in boxes to create a new pattern.

If you or your grownup knows how to use a Microsoft Excel spreadsheet, you can use Excel to design an illusion knitting pattern.

Try this:

1. Open Excel and then select the entire spreadsheet. Under 'Format' set the row and column dimensions to 6mm, making perfect squares.

2. Click the divided square button to create cell borders. Use the paint bucket button to shade boxes and design your pattern.

3. When it's done, print the pattern.

MAKE A SECRET
BOOK SAFE

Need a place to stash your money, sweets and other valuables – where brothers, sisters and other burglars won't find them? A hollowed-out book makes a cheap, handy and effective safe.

You'll need:

- A hardback book, preferably one with a dust jacket. Make sure the book is wide, tall and thick enough to fit whatever it is you want to conceal inside. Even if you pick up a book at a charity shop or library sale for this purpose, check with your grownup to make sure it's OK to use. Another thing to think about: don't use a book which will look out of place on your bookshelf – or one whose title is so fascinating that people will want to read it.
- 2 plastic bags, the kind you get at the supermarket
- **Optional:** Large rubber bands
- PVA glue, mixed with a small amount of water (about 3 parts glue to 1 part water) to make it more easily absorbable by the edges of the book's pages. If you have craft glue, use that instead.

- Brush for applying the glue
- A heavy weight or vice to hold the book shut
- Ruler for marking the outline of your book safe's secret compartment
- Precision craft knife (e.g. an X-acto knife) with extra blades. Use with grownup supervision.

Try this:

1. Remove the dust jacket. Open the book to about the fifteenth page. You won't carve up these pages – that way, if anyone opens the front cover, the book will look normal.

2. Wrap one plastic bag around the book's front cover and the first 15 pages or so. Wrap the other plastic bag around the back cover. If you have large rubber bands, use them to hold the bags in place. The plastic bags will prevent the pages from sticking to the front and back covers; this is important, because you'll want to get the dust jacket back onto the book.

3. Using the brush, spread the glue solution smoothly and evenly on the outside of the book's pages, all around the book's three edges. You might ask your grownup to assist you by holding the book firmly shut while you brush. Do this several times, so there's plenty of glue on the pages. Smooth out any blobs or globs.

4. Cover up the glue solution, and wash the brush off thoroughly with hot water so that it doesn't get ruined.

5. Place a heavy weight on top of the book so the pages won't warp as the glue dries. (You can place the book in a vice instead, but doing so might leave marks on the cover.) Let the book dry for about an hour. If the pages are still wet, let it dry for longer.

6. Open the book to reveal the first glued page. Using a ruler, trace an outline of the secret compartment on that page. You'll want to leave a border within the page's edge of at least 12mm. If you're going to hide paper money in the book, make sure that your compartment is large enough for that purpose.

7. Using the precision knife, and being careful of your fingers, cut along the outline of the secret compartment. Don't try to go too deeply, or you'll end up with messy edges. Try to make the cut as vertical as possible; and try to cut in a straight line: using the ruler as a guide can be helpful. The corners are very tricky – you'll need to clean them up every now and then.

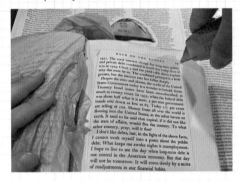

8. Keep at it until you're finished. Remove the bits of paper that accumulate from the cutting. Make sure you don't cut a hole in the back cover. It's OK to leave a few glued pages uncut at the bottom of the compartment.

9. Brush the glue solution onto the inside edges of the compartment, and apply another layer of the solution to the book's outside page edges. Leave it to dry overnight.

10. Once every part of the book is dry, replace the dust jacket and hide your valuables inside.

BIRCH BARK
HOUSES

Going on a family holiday where you'll be spending a lot of time in nature? Make a house of birch bark.

Birch bark has been used for centuries to make everything from baskets to roofs to canoes. In the American Midwest and parts of southern Canada, the Ojibwa (or Anishinabe) people made entire homes out of this versatile material; Louise Erdrich's *The Birchbark House*, about a nineteenth-century Native American girl, is set in one such structure.

If you aren't holidaying where birches grow, then improvise! These instructions can be adapted for, say, a miniature house of coconuts and shells.

You'll need:

- One or more 'tubes' of birch bark – intact, hollow cylinders of bark that have fallen off birch trees.
- Decorative elements that can be found outdoors, without causing harm to living nature: e.g. fallen pine cones or acorns, dry moss, leaves, dead bark, sticks, feathers, rocks
- **Optional:** Scraps of leather
- Cardboard
- Fibrefill
- Table knife
- Scissors
- Precision craft knife (e.g. an X-Acto knife). Use with grownup supervision.
- Glue gun. Use with grownup supervision.
- A workspace with electricity, so you can plug in the glue gun.

Try this:

1. Gather birch bark 'tubes' from forest floors, or from woodpiles that include birch logs.

> **IMPORTANT!** Never strip the bark off a live tree, which could weaken or even kill it.

2. Gather the rest of your building materials. Choose a flat piece of birch bark, or something else flat, for a foundation. Be careful: If you use stuff that isn't dried up, it might be filled with bugs! Also, stay away from mushrooms, some of which are poisonous.

3. At your workspace, use a table knife to scrape any stray clumps of wood and dirt from inside your birch tube.

4. The tube will be the main part of your house so decide which side will look best as the house's front. Using scissors, create a door by cutting a rectangle from the tube's bottom edge. Then cut out very small rectangles of leather to create 'hinges'. Glue them on with a hot glue gun.

5. Use a precision knife to cut out windows (put cardboard underneath while cutting). To make window shutters, glue on hinges to the cut-out pieces as in the previous step.

6. Using a hot glue gun, put glue along the bottom edge of the birch bark house. Attach the house to its foundation (you can use cardboard or bark for this). First glue a thin layer of fibrefill to the bottom of the house, then glue the fibrefill to the foundation. Watch out: the fibrefill can get hot from the glue and stick painfully to your fingers.

Illustrations by Mister Reusch

7. Glue on the house's roof, using a piece of birch bark (flat or wavy, it's up to you); or you can roll and glue a piece of birch bark into the shape of a cone, and use it for a roof – just make sure it will fit the house. You can also use sticks, shells and other found materials to roof the house.

8. Start decorating. Dried moss and pebbles make beautiful ground coverings. Pine cones work well for chimneys. Flowers add a fairy-house vibe.

GLUE GUN BASICS

A glue gun is indispensable to crafters. Here's how to use a glue gun properly, so that you don't get burned.

- Grownup supervision is a must.

- Inspect your glue gun before plugging it in – tighten the nozzle, and don't use the gun if it has any cracks in it.

- Use your glue gun in an area that doesn't get much traffic. To avoid electrical shocks, don't work near a sink or a damp area.

- Wear safety gloves that are resistant to heat.

- Wear safety goggles.

- Wear long trousers or put a cloth over your lap.

- A glue gun is messy. Resting it on a large ceramic tile, for example, will prevent it from scorching the tabletop.

- Unplug your glue gun after you finish using it.

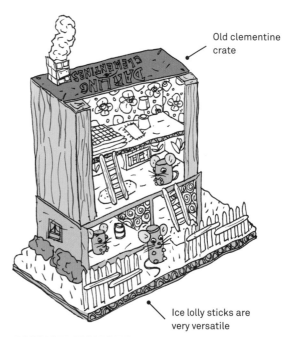

Old clementine crate

Ice lolly sticks are very versatile

MOUSE HOUSES

Our friend Madeline makes and collects felt and wool mice. In order to give them a block of flats to live in, she creatively upcycled stuff – from old clementine crates to ice lolly sticks – that would otherwise have been thrown out or recycled. She has even turned an empty dental floss container into the invention of Dr Squeaker, her evil scientist mouse. She gave us some pointers.

Try this:

You can use lots of different kinds of containers for rooms, including wine bottle boxes (good for stuffed animals or dolls) or shoeboxes. You should make sure that you are building something that proportionally fits whoever is going to live there. For example, if your creature is 15cm tall, then the ceilings should be between 20cm and 25cm high.

- For little houses, wine corks work well for table bases.

- Green felt makes great grass.

- Ice lolly sticks are incredibly versatile and can be used to make anything from fences to beds. Madeline attached pieces of ice lolly sticks to an empty Tic Tac container to make an exercise treadmill.

- Scrapbook paper works well for wallpaper.

DECORATE YOUR TRAINERS

By Elizabeth

When I was at school, one of my favourite hobbies was to use a ballpoint pen to doodle elaborate drawings on my trainers. My creativity, however, was lost on my grownups – who were none too pleased that I was 'defacing' an expensive item of clothing.

My choice of materials was also ill-considered… The drawings would smear and wash off every time it rained or I walked through a dewy patch of grass.

What my grownups didn't understand is that this activity is a great way to give a second life to a worn-out pair of shoes. Or to make a ho-hum new pair into something that perfectly expresses who you are. Thanks to all the gorgeous permanent markers out there, these days, your hard work won't wash off in the rain.

Shoe manufacturers know that decorating your trainers is cool, so they try to get in on the act. Some host events where you can have a (brand new) pair customised by an artist. Others rip off the DIY look with rhinestones and perfectly imperfect hearts and flowers. Sorry, but the homemade versions are way better.

Need inspiration? Start by choosing three or four of your favourite colours. Maybe they're the colours of your favourite flag or football team or your school. You could add the logo of your band, create a design that matches your coolest pair of leggings, or whatever you like.

PS: Your trainers don't need to match. If you have two favourite football teams, make a trainer for each one!

You'll need:
- Pair of trainers
- Pencil
- Permanent markers in a range of colours – some with an ultra-fine tip and other with just fine tips. If you want the colours to match, make sure to buy the same brand of markers so the tips match.
- Waterproofing spray

Optional:
- Rhinestones or metal studs with backs
- Hammer
- Ribbons or rickrack
- Safety pins
- Anything

Illustrations by Mister Reusch

Sketch out your design

Slip-on trainers are perfect for customising

My favourite option is also the easiest. Simply choose a pair of shoelace holes (the top or bottom pair) put the studs in them, snap on the backs, and you're ready. You can also decorate your shoes with safety pins – either on their own for a new wave look, or as a way to hold little charms or dangly things.

Try this:

1. Remove the shoelaces.

2. Sketch out the design you want to make and pick your colours.

3. Start colouring. If you are colouring on canvas shoes, then the ink will saturate more deeply if you stick a finger on your other hand inside your shoe, and press outwards against the tip of the marker. Use an ultra-fine tip for small details. Switch to a fine tip for bigger blocks of colour – but be careful! The ink spreads quickly when you use the larger tips. For darker trainers, try silver and gold metallic markers.

4. There are a lot of ways to add studs to fabric or leather, including buying a special stud-setting gadget that will do the work for you. You can also buy a less expensive eyelet tool set, which is a small piece of metal used to hammer holes into canvas or leather.

5. Put in the laces. You can either use the laces you already have or buy new laces in a different colour or pattern. You can also use ribbon or rick rack. (Just remember to tie knots at the ends or wrap the tops in a 13mm-wide piece of duct tape.)

6. Don't forget the inside! Write secret messages on the underside of your trainer's tongue or even the insides of the shoe – anything from your name spelled backwards to a joke you like, to the identity of a secret crush.

7. Take good care of your trainers. Even though the ink is permanent, your artwork could fade. Spray them with a waterproofing solution to give your designs extra protection when they get wet.

人✖✳ ◼✳·⊤⊥ ◼●✖·⊤⊥ ⊥◻⊙ ⊞◻⏀⊙

EXPERIMENTING IN THE KITCHEN

By Jeff Potter

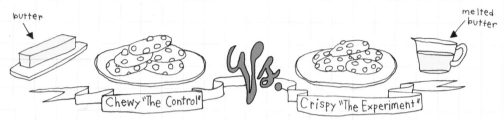

butter

melted butter

Chewy "The Control" Vs. Crispy "The Experiment"

We all eat, but have you ever stopped to think about what happens to food when you cook it? The secret to making great food is to understand what happens to it under heat.

Imagine you're eating a really good chocolate chip cookie. What does it taste like? Chocolatey? Buttery? Toasted, maybe even a little bit nutty? Chewy or crispy? Gooey and warm? Or a little dry, perfect for dipping in a glass of cold milk?

Now that you've described your perfect cookie, how would you make it? Sure, you could choose a recipe at random and give it a try. Or you could come up with a theory – a hypothesis – and put it to the test. This is where food science can help.

You see, cooking is really about chemistry and physics. When you heat foods, they change. Butter melts. Water turns to steam. Some ingredients turn brown and change flavour. All of this can be understood with science. When it comes to the perfect chocolate chip cookie – or any culinary creation – understanding the science means you can alter the recipe's outcome, or at least pick the right recipe.

Science relies on two important things: theories and data. Theories describe how we think the world works. Data are the observations of what actually happens when we do an experiment. Without theories, we can't make accurate predictions, and without data, we don't know if our theories are valid. Science – whether inside or outside the kitchen – needs both theories and supporting data.

Imaginary experiment

Imagine that you have some bits of dark chocolate in front of you. Your theory might be this: *If I hold this chocolate in my open hand, it won't melt; if I hold this chocolate in my mouth, it will melt.* Now imagine holding the chocolate in your open hand for one minute. Does it melt? If you're me, it doesn't; but you might have warmer hands. Either way, the result of the experiment is data. Now what happens when you hold dark chocolate in your mouth for one minute? It melts. (More data.) If your data supports the theory, then the theory is sound. That's how science works.

In search of… the perfect cookie

How would a scientist make a perfect cookie? They'd start by making a guess, writing it as a theory. Here's an example of such a theory: 'If I make cookies with melted butter, then they will be crispier than cookies made with cold butter.'

Then they'd test this theory by making two batches of cookies with just one difference: one with melted butter, the second with cold butter. This way, they'd know that there was no other 'variable' being changed in their experiment.

Finally, they'd bake the cookies and then look at them to see if their theory was supported. By studying (and eating) the cookies, they'd learn something: either their theory was correct, or the variable in question doesn't change the outcome as theorised. Either way, of course, the results of this particular experiment are delicious.

The following kitchen experiments, which involve hot stoves and ovens, should only be done with grownup supervision.

Illustrations by Heather Kasunick

COOKIES: CHEWY VS. CRISPY

Chewy or crispy? Creaming sugar and butter together changes the texture of the cookie dough by adding millions of little tiny air pockets into the dough. But if you melt the butter ahead of time, then you won't have any of these little air pockets. And if you mix melted butter in with flour, your dough will have more of something called gluten, which also changes the cookies' texture.

There are many different 'perfect' chocolate chip cookies because everyone has their own preferences. Chewy? Crispy? With or without nuts? I'll get you started with one theory. It's up to you to come up with more theories to test in your quest for your own perfect chocolate chip cookie.

Before jumping into the experiment, here's a quick note on reading recipes. Recipes sometimes tell you to 'cream the butter and sugar together.' This means mixing butter (not melted!) and sugar together with a beater until the sugar is completely mixed in. You can use a spoon if you don't mind stirring for a while, in which case you will also want to leave the butter out on the kitchen counter for a few hours beforehand to soften it. OK, now that you know what creaming sugar and butter together means, back to the cookies.

THEORY

If you make cookies with melted butter instead of creaming butter and sugar together, you will get crispier cookies.

EXPERIMENT

How to test our chewy vs. crispy theory? Make two batches of chocolate chip cookies. First make a 'control' batch, then make an 'experimental' batch.

For each batch...

Prepare a baking tray covered with greaseproof paper. Then, in a medium bowl, mix together:
- 260g flour
- 1 teaspoon salt
- 1 teaspoon bicarbonate of soda

For the 'control' batch only...

In a large bowl, cream together:
- 165g unsalted butter
- 175g light brown sugar
- 85g white sugar

For the 'experimental' batch only...

In a large bowl, mix together:
- 165g unsalted butter, MELTED
- 175g light brown sugar
- 85g white sugar

For each batch, add the following ingredients to the bowl of butter and sugar. Mix together until smooth.

- 2 large eggs
- 1 teaspoon vanilla extract

For each batch, follow these instructions...

Add the dry ingredients to the large bowl. Mix with a spoon or electric beater until completely blended.
- Add 350g chocolate chips and stir to combine.
- Spoon onto the baking tray, leaving room to spread.
- Bake in a pre-heated oven at 180°C/350°F for 12–14 minutes (longer for large cookies).

RESULTS

Take one cookie from each batch and compare them. After they have cooled down, try breaking them in half. How do they differ? What do you notice when eating them?

In a notebook, create a chart something like the one shown here, and record your data in it.

CONDITION	THEORY PREDICTION	YOUR DATA
Sugar & butter creamed	Chewier	
Melted butter	Crispier	

BROWN-ALL-OVER PANCAKES

Pancakes are easy to make. Mix your ingredients together, pour onto a hot pan or griddle, and *ta-da*, pancakes.

If you've ever made pancakes, you've probably noticed that they don't usually come out a smooth brown colour. How do you make pancakes brown all over? Let's do an experiment and work it out.

Here's a recipe my dad taught me.

In a large bowl, mix together:
- 150g flour
- 1 tablespoon baking powder
- A pinch of salt

In a second, small bowl, mix together:
- 1 large egg
- 240ml milk
- 1 tablespoon vegetable oil

1. Mix the wet ingredients into the dry ingredients, stirring until there are no lumps of flour.

2. Heat a non-stick frying pan and grease it with a small amount of butter. Don't wipe the pan down after you grease it (see Pancake Experiment 2).

3. Pour pancake batter into the centre of the pan (note that these are thick American-style pancakes). After 2–3 minutes, flip the pancake and cook its other side for another 2–3 minutes. Make sure to add a very tiny amount more butter to the pan – and don't wipe the pan down – before cooking each pancake.

THEORY 1

The temperature of your pan needs to be hot enough to turn the pancake brown. Too cold and the pancake will come out pale beige or white. Too hot and it will burn.

EXPERIMENT 1

Cook the pancakes at different temperatures.

- Low heat
- Medium heat
- High heat

(If you can't set the temperature accurately, try taking a guess.) What happens?

RESULTS

What did you learn? In a notebook, create a chart like the one shown here and record your data in it.

CONDITION	THEORY PREDICTION	YOUR DATA
Low heat	White/pale beige coloured	
Medium heat	Medium-brown coloured	
High heat	Dark with burnt edges	

THEORY 2

If your pan is too greasy, then the pancakes will come out with a splotchy brown-and-white pattern. The pancakes will turn out an even brown colour if you wipe the pan down after greasing it.

EXPERIMENT 2

Heat your pan using the best temperature that you learned from your first experiment. Make a pancake exactly the same way you did in the first pancake experiment. In science lingo, this first pancake will be your *control*. Without a control, you won't know if the change you're about to make – wiping the pan down after greasing it – actually does something.

Now make a second pancake. This time, grease the pan and then wipe it clean with a paper towel. Remove most of the grease, leaving only a very thin layer of oil behind.

RESULTS

What did you learn? In a notebook, create a chart like the one shown here and record your data in it.

CONDITION	THEORY PREDICTION	YOUR DATA
Greased, no-wipe (control)	Splotchy	
Greased, wiped down	Smooth	

Have fun experimenting!

If your pancakes or cookies don't come out the way you want at first, don't get frustrated. Success isn't about making the perfect cookie or pancake, it's about learning what works and doesn't work. As long as you learned something – even if it was 'Whoops, I burnt the cookies because the oven was too hot!' – then you're making progress.

TOASTER SCIENCE
By Josh

In 2011, a food researcher commissioned by a bread company investigated the optimal cooking time and thickness for bread slices, with the aim of achieving toast with a 'golden-brown' colour and the 'ultimate balance of external crunch and internal softness'.

After toasting and tasting 2,000 slices of bread, the researcher determined that toast should be 14mm thick; the outside of a perfect toast slice, he announced, should be 12 times crunchier than the middle. Therefore, the bread should be toasted for 216 seconds at 154°C/309°F; this can be roughly achieved by setting a toaster's temperature dial at the 'five out of six' mark.

The 'perfect toast' is a subjective question, of course. Here's an experiment that you can do using the same equipment. It aims to answer an objective question: *Which type of bread contains more sugar and protein – white bread or brown?* The answer is: *Whichever bread toasts more quickly.*

How do we know that bread with more sugar and protein toasts more quickly? Named after the French chemist who studied the reaction between amino acids and sugars in the 1910s, the 'Maillard reaction' is a chemical process in which meat, bread, coffee beans, maple syrup and other foods turn brown when cooked at certain temperatures. The more sugar and protein in the food, Maillard discovered, the more rapidly it browns when heated up. So that's how we know.

You'll need:
• Slice of fresh white bread
• Slice of fresh brown bread
• Toaster

Try this:

1. Place both slices of bread in the toaster.

2. Start toasting them at the same moment.

3. Check every 10 seconds to see which slice toasts first.

4. Record your results for future reference.

5. Spread jam on the experiment and eat it.

PANTRY
EXPERIMENT

You wouldn't want to eat the following science experiment but you can still perform it in the kitchen.

Because ethanol, a flammable liquid that can be produced by fermenting sugar (processed from corn or from unprocessed 'biomass') with yeast, emits cleaner emissions than petrol, ethanol-fuelled vehicles are becoming more common. So here's an ethanol-related puzzler: if we combine yeast and sugar in a bottle, how can we tell if the yeast is breaking down the sugar through fermentation?

Detecting fermentation

As yeast eats whatever sugar it finds in the bottle, the sugar will break down into not only ethanol, but also carbon dioxide. So we can solve our ethanol puzzler through a process that allows us to detect whether or not carbon dioxide has been produced. This will tell us whether the fermentation process is taking place.

The following fermentation-in-a-bottle experiment won't permit you to directly see ethanol, because if any is produced, it will mix with the water in the bottle. However, at least you'll be able to measure how much (if any) carbon dioxide is produced when you combine yeast with either processed sugar or an unprocessed biomass.

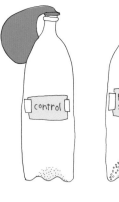

You'll need:

- 3 tablespoons yeast
- 3 clean 500ml plastic bottles. Save the caps.
- Permanent marker
- 4 tablespoons any sugar, e.g. granulated sugar or a cola drink
- **Optional:** Funnel
- 4 tablespoons unprocessed biomass, e.g. ground-up dried leaves; ground-up dried grass; sawdust
- Plenty of very warm water
- Several nine-inch balloons (use non-latex balloons if you are allergic to latex)

Formulate a theory

Will enough carbon dioxide be produced to inflate any of the balloons? If so, which balloons? Which balloons will inflate the most?

Try this:

1. Add 1 tablespoon of yeast to each bottle.

2. Mark the first bottle 'CONTROL' and set it aside.

3. Mark the second bottle 'PROCESSED SUGAR', and add 4 tablespoons of a sugar to it.

4. Mark the third bottle 'BIOMASS', and add 4 tablespoons of an unprocessed biomass to it.

5. Fill each bottle halfway with very warm (but not hot) water. Screw the cap on tightly and shake the bottles to mix the ingredients thoroughly.

6. Now remove each bottle's cap and replace it with a balloon, pulled firmly over the spout. (You really only need three balloons, but we've suggested you collect several in case you tear one.)

7. Observe, then record the data from your results.

8. Pour the (gross) contents of the bottles out. Recycle or reuse the bottles.

If your theory was incorrect, ask yourself why. And then start the process again – that's how science works.

Illustration by Heather Kasunick

READ A FOOD
LABEL

Ever wonder what you're really eating?

Although the Guideline Daily Amounts (GDA) and other info on nutrition facts labels are often calculated for grownups, it's smart for kids to learn how to read them. How else will you know if you are getting enough of what you need to stay healthy – or too much?

Servings

First, check out the servings per container information. If a frozen pizza contains three servings and you eat the entire thing, then triple the numbers on the label – because those percentages are based on a single serving only.

Energy

Depending on how much exercise and physical activity you get and how fast you are growing, kids up to the age of ten should eat 1,800 calories a day. Boys aged 11–14 should eat 2,220 calories a day, while girls the same age should eat 1,845 calories. If you eat something that has a lot of calories (a portion of chip-shop chips has 240), balance it with lower-calorie foods like fruit and vegetables.

Protein

Your body needs protein to build and repair essential parts of the body – including blood, muscles and organs. About 10–30 per cent of your daily calories should come from protein (that's about 20–30g if you consume 1,800 daily calories).

Sugars

One gram of sugar is the same as a quarter-teaspoon. Most experts agree that if your cereal has more than 9g of sugar per serving you might as well be eating a plate of chocolate biscuits for breakfast.

What's really in a tin of beans?

Fat

This is the number of calories that come from fat. It's good to limit fat intake to 25–30 per cent of the calories you eat (for example, that's roughly 70g if you consume 1,800 calories). Note that 20 per cent or more of the GDA is not a good sign!

Sodium

This is the amount of salt in your diet. You'll notice that frozen foods are often high in sodium, because manufacturers use salt to keep food tasty in a freezer for weeks. Kids should consume no more than 1.5g of sodium a day. As with fat, 20 per cent or more of the GDA for sodium/salt means it's too salty.

Ingredients list

On food labels, ingredients are listed from most to least. So if the first ingredient in your cereal is 'whole grain oats', you know you're eating a food that is mostly oats. But if one of the first three ingredients is something you can't pronounce, or sounds like a chemical from science class, you'll probably want to find another choice.

Illustration by Heather Kasunick

WEIRD FACTS ABOUT
CONDIMENTS

By Tom Nealon

The great thing about condiments is that – unlike meals, which grownups get to choose – they're entirely up to you. Don't like ketchup? No problem! Love mustard? Go for it! If clothes are one way to express our freedom and individuality, choosing condiments is how we do so with our mouths full.

This vital connection between condiments and freedom brings us to world history – because history is about struggles to control resources, and to gain liberty (or, if you're in power, to prevent people from gaining liberty). So here are some little-known facts about the origins of the condiments we take for granted… and also a few theories.

MAYONNAISE
The spread that started a war

Mayonnaise is an *emulsion*, meaning a mixture of two un-blendable liquids plus an emulsifier; that is, an ingredient which makes an impossible blend possible. *Allioli*, the Spanish precursor to mayonnaise, had been around at least since the Roman naturalist Pliny wrote about it 2,000 years ago. But how did the Spanish end up (probably during the Renaissance) transforming this paste made of oil, garlic and salt into emulsified mayonnaise? We now know that someone must have added an emulsifier (egg yolk) and an acid (vinegar or lemon juice) to the recipe, and… *ya está!* Mayonnaise. But its tasty recipe remained secret for a long time; it was the culinary equivalent of black magic.

This amazing, mysterious new sauce (*salsa mahonesa* in Spanish) was named after the town where it was first created: Port Mahón, on the

Spanish island of Minorca. And here's where world history enters the picture. In 1756, a French force under the command of the Duc de Richelieu captured Minorca from the British, who'd controlled it since 1708. This was the first event in a global military conflict that was later known as the Seven Years' War.

What was the true cause of the Seven Years' War? Could it be that the French wanted to capture Spain's secret mayonnaise recipe? If so, they succeeded brilliantly. They renamed the sauce *mayonnaise*, and wrote cookbooks claiming that it was a French recipe; they even suggested the word comes from an ancient French word (*moyeu*) meaning 'egg yolk'. Today, you'd be hard pressed to even find a resident of Minorca who thought mayonnaise was Spanish. That's something to chew over next time you're spreading mayo on a BLT.

KETCHUP
The brain-tricking sauce

Ketchup was invented in China as a vegetarian substitute for fish sauce. (Fish sauces were popular throughout the Roman Empire some 2,000 years ago and remain central to many Asian cuisines. They add a certain zing to a variety of dishes but they smell so bad that Romans passed laws forbidding their manufacture near towns and cities.) Originally, ketchup was made not with tomatoes but with beans and mushrooms, and later on with walnuts; the point of these recipes was to get savouriness (the 'fifth flavour' after salty, sweet, bitter and sour; it's also called *umami*) into foods. Glutamates, the chemicals that produce the umami flavour, trick your brain into thinking it's eating meat; like fish and cheese, mushrooms and ripe tomatoes are rich in the umami flavour.

In the late eighteenth or early nineteenth century, tomatoes made their first appearance in ketchup. Though other ketchup makers added preservatives to their products, Henry John Heinz, an American businessman who started manufacturing ketchup in 1876, didn't need them because he was using ripe tomatoes.

MUSTARD
Not just for peasants any more

Brown and black mustard – condiments made from the seeds of a mustard plant mixed with water, vinegar and other flavourings – have been served since the dawn of civilisation. The yellow variety with which we're familiar gets its colour from powdered turmeric (a spice). In the Bible, Abraham serves mustard on beef tongue (considered a delicacy) to visiting angels; and the seventeenth-century English diarist Samuel Pepys liked the flavour of mustard on neats' (cows') feet.

Today, we think of mustard as being a fairly classy condiment. However, for most of recorded history, only poor folk used mustard (which was cheap because, unlike many spices, it can be grown almost anywhere in the world) as a food. Wealthier people didn't eat mustard; instead, they used it for medicine.

The ancient Greek philosopher Pythagoras claimed that mustard would cure scorpion bite, and the Roman Pliny suggested it for 'improving lazy housewives'. In the first printed cookbook, *De honesta voluptate et valetudine* (On Honest Pleasure and Good Health, 1474), we read that mustard is good for dispersing the poison of snakes and fungi, for purging the head (by sneezing), and for burning away skin rashes and warts. During the Renaissance, the pioneering French obstetrician Jacques Guillemeau suggested that a good way to wean babies off a mother's milk was to smear mustard on her breast. Ouch! Don't try these remedies at home.

Illustrations by Heather Kasunick

GHERKINS
Are your pickles pickled?

Gherkins (known as pickles in the US) are pickled mini cucumbers. Or at least, the cucumbers are *supposed* to be pickled – by fermenting them in brine (salty water with a little vinegar in it). Recently, supermarkets have been invaded by cucumbers marinated in vinegar – which might be tasty, but it's not the same. Fermentation is a magical process that doesn't merely change how a cucumber tastes, but what it looks like and even what it's made out of.

You see, lovely little anaerobic bacteria that are normally out-competed by aerobic bacteria (which thrive on oxygen) are living all over almost any vegetable. The battle of the bacteria is what causes vegetables to spoil. However, if you sink a cucumber into a vat of brine, where the aerobic bacteria can't get oxygen, the anaerobic bacteria eat the parts of a cucumber that would normally spoil – and replace them with B vitamins. Fermentation also turns cucumbers bright green, sour and delicious. So make sure your gherkins are *pickled* pickles!

MARMITE
The primordial spread

That brown stuff that you smear on your toast with a bit of butter has something in common with the primordial goo that generated the first life on Earth a couple of billion years ago! Like the slime in which those single-celled organisms developed, Marmite is swimming in amino acids, which are the building blocks of protein, those complex molecules out of which muscle and DNA are made.

Scientists tell us that one amino acid in particular – glutamate – can trick your tongue into thinking that it is tasting something deliciously meaty. While it is naturally present in foods that taste curiously delicious (like Parmesan cheese, tomatoes and mushrooms, for example), it is difficult to acquire really substantial amounts of it. Because your taste buds can only taste the glutamate if it's 'free' (that is, floating around on its own), food scientists in search of large quantities of the elusive stuff have had to figure out how to spring it free from yeast and other glutamate-carrying microorganisms.

The glutamate that makes Marmite taste so meaty was hijacked from brewer's yeast. If you put enough salt on yeast, it goes through something called autolysis and explodes, leaving the amino acids floating around freely. The glutamate then bonds with the salt used to autolyse the yeast (sodium chloride) and forms a different salt called monosodium glutamate – which our taste buds think is the best thing ever. This is what gives Marmite its powerfully meaty flavour.

How powerful is Marmite's flavour, exactly? So powerful that during the First World War it was issued to British soldiers who didn't have enough meat to eat, in order to keep their spirits up.

SOUR CREAM
It's what made the Mongol Horde so tough

In the early thirteenth century, a Mongol army known as the Golden Horde took over Russia. Along with their fearsome horse archers, the invading Mongols introduced *kumis* – a drink made from fermented horse's milk – to the Russians from whom they collected tribute. Locked inside that strange drink was the secret of sour cream; Russians applied the same process of fermentation to cow's milk, and allowed it to thicken further. Russians paying tribute as a sign of allegiance to the Mongols – expensive. Being able to put sour cream on everything from soup to dumplings, even in their coffee? Priceless.

HOME ALONE
RECIPES

By Helen Cordes

Lots of kids in the UK are at home without a grownup before or after school. Being on your own is an opportunity to become more responsible and to discover that you can do things for yourself.

That includes making meals and snacks. Though you'll need help from your grownups at first, cooking is an extremely creative way to do your own thing. Here are some easy recipes – gathered from latchkey kids and their grownups – to help you get started. While they're all delicious, they're even better if you improvise. So experiment!

KITCHEN SAFETY BASICS

WASH YOUR HANDS Always clean your hands with soap and water before you prepare food. Also wash your hands after handling raw meat, chicken, eggs and fish. These foods can contain bacteria, which if it gets on your hands can make its way to your mouth and make you sick.

KNIFE SAFETY Point the blade away from your body and make sure to keep your fingers away from the blade when you're cutting. Curling your fingers into a claw shape will make the knife slide down your fingernails instead of cutting into the skin.

PREVENT BURNS Hot and boiling liquids are a major cause of kitchen burns. Prevent boil-overs by making sure you don't fill a pot too high. If you are taking a boiling pot of pasta to the sink to drain it, walk carefully.

If your stove or oven won't turn on, do *not* try to relight the pilot light. This is a job for a grownup. If you accidentally turn on the gas and the burner doesn't light, open the window and leave the room for a few minutes.

BREAKFAST

SCRAMBLED EGG MUFFINS

A breakfast food that can be eaten at any time of the day. Eggs are high in protein so they're great for keeping away hunger pangs.

You'll need:
- 2 eggs
- Salt
- Pepper
- English muffin, halved
- Butter

Try this:

1. Whisk eggs in a bowl. Add a pinch of salt and a pinch of pepper.

2. Put your breakfast muffin in the toaster so that it is ready when you are.

3. Melt a small amount of butter in a small pan over medium heat so that the bottom is lightly coated. Pour the eggs in the pan and then toast the muffin.

4. Use a spatula to scrape the eggs around until they are cooked.

5. Take the cooked eggs out of the pan and place them on top of your toasted (and buttered) muffin.

Illustrations by Mister Reusch

LUNCH

VEGGIE BURGERS

A yummy alternative to beef burgers. There are so many varieties that we won't offer a definitive list of ingredients. Create your own recipe!

1. Start with something 'gluey' like tofu, mashed beans or mashed potatoes. Adding cheese or a beaten egg can help hold your patty together.

2. Dice your favourite veggies in tiny pieces and sauté in a little oil until soft. Anything you like will work – mushrooms, carrots, onions, squash, broccoli. Cooked grains such as rice or uncooked quick oats add some bulk. Chopped nuts and seeds give you crunch and protein. Grated or crumbled cheese adds flavour.

3. Spice it up. Salt and pepper are fine, but how about garlic, any and all fresh or dried herbs or spices you like, salsa, mustard, or soy sauce?

4. Cook your veggie burger in a frying pan or bake it on a grill tray. Either way, coat the surface with olive oil – that will make it easier to flip the burger. Cook on a low heat on the hob, or at a low temperature (140°C/280°F) in the oven – usually they're done on one side after about 10 minutes. Flip the burgers and cook for another 10 minutes or so. Then break out the buns, load on your favourite burger toppings, and enjoy.

CHICKEN OR VEGGIE SOUP

Soup is a wonderful alternative to sandwiches. Here's a basic recipe for chicken or veggie soup – feel free to add other ingredients you like.

You'll need:

- 1 onion, chopped into small pieces
- A few tablespoons olive oil
- 2 cloves chopped-up garlic
- Chicken or vegetable stock, enough to half-fill a big saucepan
- Vegetables
- **Optional:** Rice or noodles
- **Optional:** Cut-up chicken breasts
- Salt
- Pepper

Try this:

1. Sauté (cook with low heat) the chopped onion in a few tablespoons of olive oil in a big pan. When the onion gets soft (usually about 10 minutes), add a few cloves of chopped-up garlic.

2. Fill the pot at least halfway full with veggie or chicken stock – add water to the stock if it tastes too strong.

3. Add the chopped-up veggies you like best – carrots, peas, corn, green beans, potatoes, broccoli, whatever.

4. If you like noodles or rice or any other grain in your soup, toss that in, too.

5. Ditto a boneless piece of chicken breast that you've cut into small pieces. After you've finished, be sure to thoroughly clean your knife and chopping board and any other surfaces that the chicken touched.

6. Cover your pot and simmer over a low heat for at least half an hour, and then add salt and pepper to taste.

⬚⬚⬚ ⬚⬚⬚⬚⬚⬚ ⬚⬚⬚ ⬚⬚⬚⬚⬚⬚
⬚⬚⬚⬚⬚⬚⬚

⬚⬚⬚⬚ ⬚⬚ ⬚⬚⬚ ⬚⬚⬚ ⬚⬚⬚
⬚⬚⬚⬚⬚⬚ ⬚⬚⬚⬚

⬚⬚⬚ ⬚⬚⬚⬚⬚⬚

⬚⬚⬚⬚⬚⬚⬚ ⬚⬚⬚ ⬚⬚⬚⬚⬚

⬚⬚⬚ ⬚⬚⬚ ⬚⬚⬚⬚

DINNER

PEANUTY NOODLES

Another easy-to-assemble meal that's a good choice when there's leftover chicken in the fridge. Vegetarians can skip the chicken. If you are serving this dish to friends, make sure they don't have peanut allergies.

You'll need:

- 250g pack of rice noodles
- Leftover chicken
- 1 carrot
- 1 cucumber
- 100g peanut butter
- 2 tablespoons soy sauce
- **Optional:** Pinch of dried ginger; salted peanuts; cashews; almonds; dried cranberries, apples or cherries.

Try this:

1. Heat a pan of water. When it's almost boiling, turn off the heat, and stick in the rice noodles. Let the noodles soak according to instructions on the packet, then drain them in a strainer or colander.

2. Tear the chicken into bite-size chunks. Peel the carrot and cucumber with a vegetable peeler. Discard the peels (they are great for compost). Then, use the peeler to make strips of carrot and cucumber.

3. In a small bowl, mix the peanut butter and soy sauce. If you like dried ginger, add a pinch. If the sauce is too thick, add a small amount of water.

4. Combine the drained noodles with the chicken, carrot and cucumber. Mix the sauce in thoroughly.

5. If you like, add some sweet and salty treats such as salted peanuts, cashews or almonds, dried cranberries, apples or cherries.

SUPERQUICK VEGGIE LASAGNE

Lasagne is one of those meals that grownups like more than kids. But that's because grownups don't use this brilliant recipe.

You'll need:

- 80g ricotta cheese
- Your favourite fresh or frozen vegetables, cut into small pieces
- Salt
- Pepper
- 80g grated Parmesan cheese
- 350g grated mozzarella cheese
- Jar tomato pasta sauce
- Pack of lasagne sheets

Try this:

1. In a mixing bowl, combine the ricotta cheese with the vegetables and add about a teaspoon of salt and several shakes of pepper.

2. Add the Parmesan and mozzarella cheese, but keep a nice handful of each to add to the top when you're done.

3. In a baking dish, spoon half the tomato pasta sauce in the bottom and cover with a layer of lasagna sheets. Spread half the ricotta mixture on top of the sheets. Now repeat the layers: tomato pasta sauce, lasagne sheets and ricotta mix.

4. Sprinkle the reserved mozzarella and Parmesan over the top.

5. Bake in a oven heated to 180°C/350°F for around 45 minutes. Take out, let cool a bit, and dig in.

SNACKS

GRILLED TOSTADAS

Also great for lunch or dinner.

You'll need:

- Tinned refried beans, either black or pinto
- Corn or flour tortillas
- 1–2 tablespoons chopped onion
- 1–2 tablespoons chopped peppers
- A handful of grated cheese
- **Optional:** Pinch of dried cumin
- Salsa

Try this:

1. Spread a layer of beans on top of a tortilla.

2. Layer on the onion, peppers and grated cheese. Sprinkle a pinch of dried cumin on top, if you like the flavour.

3. Grill (or microwave) until the cheese melts.

4. Top with salsa.

BAKED BEAN TOASTIES

A popular kids' snack. Also good for lunch or dinner.

You'll need:

- Tin of baked beans
- 2 slices of bread
- Butter
- A handful of grated Cheddar cheese
- **Optional:** Ketchup

Try this:

1. Butter both pieces of bread.

2. Place one piece buttered side down under the grill (make sure you have a tray or piece of tin foil underneath). You can also use a toastie-maker.

3. Put several tablespoons of the beans onto the bread.

4. Add cheese. You can also include a dollop of ketchup, if you like.

5. Top with the second piece of bread, buttered side up.

6. Toast until golden brown (around 3–4 minutes). Cut into two triangles and serve.

SMOOTHIES

There are hundreds of varieties of smoothies. They're great for breakfast, lunch or snacks. Just toss a few ingredients in a blender and push a button.

You'll need:

- Frozen fruit
- **Optional:** Fresh fruit
- Plain or flavoured yogurt
- **Optional:** Fruit juice; soya milk; 1 tablespoon honey; ½ teaspoon vanilla or almond extract; 1 tablespoon peanut (or other nut) butter

Try this:

1. Pick your fruit. A mix of different kinds works best. While some of your fruit should be frozen so that your smoothie is thick and cold, feel free to toss fresh fruit into the mix too.

2. Put your ingredients into the blender. Make sure you don't fill it up to the top – stop at three-quarters full. If the blender gets stuck, it means you need to add a little more liquid to your smoothie – water, fruit juice, milk and soya milk all work.

CONSERVING WATER

By Helen Cordes

Less than one per cent of all the water on Earth is drinkable. Every day, the average UK household uses a whopping 150 litres of water – which shrinks the water supply for fish and other water dwellers.

Proclaim a family contest to cut back your water usage by half! The following tips will make it easy.

Let it mellow
Bathrooms are the biggest household water hogs, with toilets at the top. Hear that sound? That's nearly two billion litres of water flushed every day in the UK. Maybe you've heard 'if it's yellow, let it mellow; if it's brown, flush it down'? Start doing just that. If your family needs to get a new toilet, make sure it is a water-saving model.

Hack your toilet
If you have an older toilet – i.e. not a high-efficiency model that saves water – you're using more water than necessary. Fill a leftover plastic bottle with sand or gravel and water, cap it, and place it in your toilet's water tank.

Turn off the tap
Who says you need to shower every single day if you haven't broken a sweat? You could save another 900 or so litres a month just by turning off the water while you brush your teeth.

Cut back on laundry
Washing machines are another top household water robber at over 150 litres a load, so only wash when the load's full. Don't throw clothes or towels in the washer just because you've worn or used them once – are they really dirty?

Do your own dishes
Consider switching from a dishwasher to cleaning dishes in the sink: a couple of sinkfuls of water (one soapy and one for rinsing) vs. 56 litres of water per dishwasher load. You do the maths.

Rethink your lawn
Water your lawn and gardens in the early morning or evening – otherwise, evaporation from the day's heat can steal half the water. Sweet-talk your grownups into slowly converting the lawn, which guzzles more water than even a food crop such as corn, to native grasses or other plants that require less water.

Make sponge bombs
Water play is a non-negotiable part of summer. But instead of letting the hose flow endlessly, fill a big container with water and use it for games like chucking sopping sponges at each other.

Turn off the lights and unplug your tech when it's done charging
Half our water use goes to electric and nuclear power plants (water is needed to cool equipment and run steam generators). So when you save energy, you save water.

Buy less stuff
The factories that make everything we buy use billions of litres of water to produce those goods. That graphic T-shirt you're eyeing? Growing and producing and shipping it requires around 1,900 litres of water.

Illustrations by Mister Reusch

SECRET HISTORY OF PETS

c. 10,000 BC In what is now Israel, a puppy is buried cradled in the hand of a human. It's the earliest clear evidence we have that humans and dogs, which 2,000 years earlier had been domesticated Asian wolves, share a special bond.

c. 7500 BC A cat resembling an African wildcat is buried with a human on the Mediterranean island of Cyprus. This early evidence suggests that cats were first domesticated in the Fertile Crescent (where the African and Eurasian continents meet) and later brought as pets to Cyprus and Egypt.

c. 3000 BC Ancient Egyptian paintings depict house cats, which were first allowed into houses to hunt mice after the Egyptians invented the idea of storing grain indoors. Cats, which were sacred in Egypt, were also depicted in many statues.

AD 168–190 Chinese Emperor Ling Ti falls so in love with his dogs that he gives them the rank of senior court officials. This allows them to eat the finest food available, sleep on oriental rugs and have special bodyguards.

c. AD 500–1500 Pets are not uncommon in Europe during the Middle Ages and the Renaissance, but they are kept for the most part by wealthy households. Near the end of this period, the word 'pet' (from 'petty', as in small) is introduced into English.

1369 Zhu Yuanzhang, known as China's Hongwu Emperor, establishes a porcelain company that produces tubs for goldfish. The shape of the modern goldfish bowl evolved from these tubs – but they weren't healthy environments for fish.

1493 On his return from South America, the explorer Christopher Columbus brings Queen Isabella of Spain a pair of Cuban Amazon parrots.

1542–1567 Before she is forced to abdicate her throne, Mary Stuart (Queen of Scots) surrounds herself with an entourage of tiny dogs, dressed in blue velvet suits. According to legend, when she was beheaded in 1587, a tiny pet dog was hiding inside Mary's dress.

1768 The royal governor of Britain's Virginia colony keeps 28 red birds (most likely cardinals) in cages. By the late 1800s, birds are the most popular indoor pet in America. Canaries won't achieve most-favoured cage-bird status until the 1930s.

1850 British chemist Robert Warington announces his discovery that plants added to a large container of water give off enough oxygen for fish to survive. A few years later the English naturalist Philip Henry Gosse starts the aquarium craze by creating a seawater aquarium for the London zoo; he also invented that word.

c. 1860 The first commercially prepared dog food is introduced in England.

c. 1870 World-famous actress Sarah Bernhardt loses her pet tortoises in a fire.

1877 English author Anna Sewell publishes *Black Beauty*, one of the best-selling books of all time. Her sympathy for working animals led to kinder treatment.

Illustrations by Mister Reusch

1881 The first pigeon race takes place in the UK. The birds fly from Exeter, Plymouth and Penzance to London.

1910 *Country Life* magazine tells readers that it's more affordable to get around by car than horse. However, miniature horses, including the stubborn Shetland pony, will go on to become popular pets for rich kids in the 1920s.

1931 German Shepherds Judy, Meta and Folly become the first seeing-eye dogs in Britain. Their new owners are veterans who were blinded during the First World War.

1944 Susan, a Pembroke Corgi, is given to Princess Elizabeth – who will go on to become Queen Elizabeth II – as a gift from her father the King for her 18th birthday. Even today, all of the Queen's many Corgis (and Dorgis, which are a cross between Corgis and Dachshunds) are descended from Susan.

1947 Sylvester and Tweety, who will become one of the most notable comedy duos in animation history, make their first appearance together in *Tweetie Pie*.

1950s Women go nuts for tiny dogs. Some even dye their miniature poodles to match their own clothes.

1956 British author Dodie Smith's novel *The Hundred and One Dalmatians* turns the spotted breed into a sensation. Many new owners, who weren't educated about handling such a high-energy animal, abandon their dogs at animal shelters.

1957 The Soviet Union fires a dog, Laika, into space on the *Sputnik 2*.

Лайка

1967 The TV show *Star Trek* airs an episode called 'The Trouble with Tribbles', starring fuzzy guinea-pig-like rodents who make trilling noises that irritate Klingons. The tribbles begin having babies like mad and they eat nearly all the ship's supplies. The episode makes a point about the dangers of introducing non-native species, such as when rabbits were released in Australia in 1859.

1975 Jason, the first *Blue Peter* cat, plays the part of the Cheshire Cat in the show's Christmas production of 'Alice in Blue Peter Land'. His voice sounds freakishly similar to that of the show's presenter, John Noakes.

1978 The animated film *Watership Down* spurs an interest in keeping rabbits as pets.

1984 The European Union bans the sale of wild-caught Mediterranean tortoises, tamping down the tortoise-as-pet fad.

1988 Australian Wally Cochran breeds the first Labradoodle – a cross between a Poodle and a Labrador Retriever – as a way to create a dog that won't aggravate her husband's allergies.

1990 The first *Teenage Mutant Ninja Turtles* movie is released, sparking a terrapin boom.

2005 Rome bans the giving away of goldfish and other animals as prizes at carnivals.

2006 New Zealand passes a law to ensure that all licensed dogs have a microchip inserted into the skin around their neck so they can be identified if they get lost.

2009 In the US, Pet Airways takes flight, upgrading cats and dogs (the airline calls them Pawsengers) from the cargo hold to the main cabin.

2011 Lupo, the Duke and Duchess of Cambridge's Cocker Spaniel, is born.

TRAIN AN ANIMAL
KINDLY

AN EXCERPT FROM
— BLACK BEAUTY —
by Anna Sewell

One of the most popular novels of all time, *Black Beauty* (1877), was written by English author Anna Sewell. Told from the point of view of the horse Black Beauty, the story follows his entire life – from his carefree days as a colt on an English pasture to his career as an overworked London taxi horse.

By writing from Black Beauty's point of view, Sewell hoped to draw people's attention to the cruelty inflicted on many horses during the late 1800s. But the book can also be read as a lesson on how people should treat other people. (Sewell's point is that it is better to inspire love and devotion than fear and sadness.) *Black Beauty*'s publication led to a movement for animal welfare in England; the novel was instrumental in abolishing the practice of using a 'bearing rein' to keep horses' heads high – for no reason other than fashion.

This excerpt takes place while Black Beauty is young and living on a lovely farm with his mother Duchess.

I was now beginning to grow handsome; my coat had grown fine and soft, and was bright black. I had one white foot and a pretty white star on my forehead. I was thought very handsome; my master would not sell me till I was four years old; he said lads ought not to work like men, and colts ought not to work like horses till they were quite grown up.

When I was four years old Squire Gordon came to look at me. He examined my eyes, my mouth, and my legs; he felt them all down; and then I had to walk and trot and gallop before him. He seemed to like me, and said, 'When he has been well broken in he will do very well.' My master said he would break me in himself, as he should not like me to be frightened or hurt, and he lost no time about it, for the next day he began.

Every one may not know what breaking in is, therefore I will describe it. It means to teach a horse to wear a saddle and bridle, and to carry on his back a man, woman or child; to go just the way they wish, and to go quietly. Besides this he has to learn to wear a collar, a crupper, and a breeching, and to stand still while they are put on; then to have a cart or a chaise fixed behind, so that he cannot walk or trot without dragging it after him; and he must go fast or slow, just as his driver wishes. He must never start at what he sees, nor speak to other horses, nor bite, nor kick, nor have any will of his own; but always do his master's will, even though he may be very tired or hungry; but the worst of all is, when his harness is once on, he may neither jump for joy nor lie down for weariness. So you see this breaking in is a great thing.

I had of course long been used to a halter and a headstall, and to be led about in the fields and lanes quietly, but now I was to have a bit and bridle; my master gave me some oats as usual, and after a good deal of coaxing he got the bit into my mouth, and the bridle fixed, but it was a nasty thing! Those who have never had a bit in their mouths cannot think how bad it feels; a great piece of cold hard steel as thick as a man's finger to be pushed into one's mouth, between one's teeth, and over one's tongue, with the ends coming out at the corner of your mouth, and held fast there by straps over your head, under your throat, round your nose, and under your chin; so that no way in the world can you get rid of the nasty hard thing; it is very bad! yes, very bad! at least I thought so; but I knew my mother always wore one when she went out, and all horses did when they were grown up; and so, what with the nice oats, and what with my master's pats, kind words, and gentle ways, I got to wear my bit and bridle.

Next came the saddle, but that was not half so bad; my master put it on my back very gently, while old Daniel held my head; he then made the girths fast under my body, patting and talking to me all the time; then I had a few oats, then a little leading about; and this he did every day till I began to look for the oats and the saddle. At length, one morning, my master got on my back and rode me round the meadow on the soft grass. It certainly did feel queer; but I must say I felt rather proud to carry my master, and as he continued to ride me a little every day I soon became accustomed to it.

The next unpleasant business was putting on the iron shoes; that too was very hard at first. My master went with me to the smith's forge, to see that I was not hurt or got any fright. The blacksmith took my feet in his hand, one after the other, and cut away some of the hoof. It did not pain me, so I stood still on three legs till he had done them all. Then he took a piece of iron the shape of my foot, and clapped it on, and drove some nails through the shoe quite into my hoof, so that the shoe was firmly on. My feet felt very stiff and heavy, but in time I got used to it.

And now having got so far, my master went on to break me to harness; there were more new things to wear. First, a stiff heavy collar just on my neck, and a bridle with great side-pieces against my eyes called blinkers, and blinkers indeed they were, for I could not see on either side, but only straight in front of me; next, there was a small saddle with a nasty stiff strap that went right under my tail; that was the crupper. I hated the crupper; to have my long tail doubled up and poked through that strap was almost as bad as the bit. I never felt more like kicking, but of course I could not kick such a good master, and so in time I got used to everything, and could do my work as well as my mother.

I must not forget to mention one part of my training, which I have always considered a very great advantage. My master sent me for a fortnight to a neighbouring farmer's, who had a meadow which was skirted on one side by the railway. Here were some sheep and cows, and I was turned in among them.

I shall never forget the first train that ran by. I was feeding quietly near the pales which separated the meadow from the railway, when I heard a strange sound at a distance, and before I knew whence it came – with a rush and a clatter, and a puffing out of smoke – a long black train of something flew by, and was gone almost before I could draw my breath. I turned and galloped to the further side of the meadow as fast as I could go, and there I stood snorting with astonishment and fear. In the course of the day many other trains went by, some more slowly; these drew up at the station close by, and sometimes made an awful shriek and groan before they stopped. I thought it very dreadful, but the cows went on eating very quietly, and hardly raised their heads as the black frightful thing came puffing and grinding past.

For the first few days I could not feed in peace; but as I found that this terrible creature never came into the field, or did me any harm, I began to disregard it, and very soon I cared as little about the passing of a train as the cows and sheep did.

Since then I have seen many horses much alarmed and restive at the sight or sound of a steam engine; but thanks to my good master's care, I am as fearless at railway stations as in my own stable.

Now if any one wants to break in a young horse well, that is the way.

My master often drove me in double harness with my mother, because she was steady and could teach me how to go better than a strange horse. She told me the better I behaved the better I should be treated, and that it was wisest always to do my best to please my master; 'but,' said she, 'there are a great many kinds of men; there are good thoughtful men like our master, that any horse may be proud to serve; and there are bad, cruel men, who never ought to have a horse or dog to call their own. Besides, there are a great many foolish men, vain, ignorant, and careless, who never trouble themselves to think; these spoil more horses than all, just for want of sense; they don't mean it, but they do it for all that. I hope you will fall into good hands; but a horse never knows who may buy him, or who may drive him; it is all a chance for us; but still I say, do your best wherever it is, and keep up your good name.'

CLEAN
YOUR DOG

So your dog is enjoying a romp in the garden. Good for her. That is until she paws her way into a muddy fox or rabbit hole or (much worse) gets into trouble with another animal's poo.

Many dogs don't need regular baths. Do some research on your dog's breed to see what's best for her in the bathing department. Sometimes, all that's needed to get a dog smelling better is a sprinkle of bicarbonate of soda brushed into her coat. Still, there are times when a bath is a necessity. If that's the case with your dog, here's a recipe for a homemade dog shampoo and some tips about how to clean her.

You'll need:

- 150ml clear washing-up liquid
- 150ml apple cider vinegar
- 100ml water
- 25ml clear glycerine
- Dog brush
- **Optional:** nail clippers or small pair of scissors
- Cotton balls
- An empty resealable plastic container
- Several old towels

Try this:

1. Make the shampoo by mixing the washing-up liquid, vinegar, water and glycerine in the plastic container. This amount of shampoo is enough to wash a medium-size dog. Note: Your homemade shampoo is thinner and less concentrated than the kind you'd buy in a shop.

2. If your dog isn't disgustingly dirty, brush her before her bath to get out the knots and matted areas. You may need to clip the matted hair with nail clippers or a small pair of scissors. Use this time to also look for ticks and fleas.

3. Gently put a cotton ball in each ear.

4. Place your dog in the tub and turn on the bathwater. Make sure it's lukewarm since hot water can burn a dog's sensitive skin.

5. Stay calm! Many dogs hate baths and wriggle and whine at this stage. Gently douse your dog in the warm water. You don't have to completely douse her – just make sure she's wet enough for the shampoo to do its work.

6. Lather your dog's coat. Be careful not to get shampoo in her eyes.

7. Rinse using the now-empty plastic container as a scoop to pour clean water over your dog until the shampoo is gone. Drain the water from the tub. Don't forget to remove the cotton balls.

8. Towel-dry your dog while she's still in the tub. Don't use a hair dryer since they are often too hot.

9. Keep your dog in the bathroom (or carry her to a mud room) until she's completely dry.

TIP: Give your dog her favourite treats throughout the bathing process to reinforce her good behaviour.

Illustration by Mister Reusch

BEST EVER
ANIMAL MOVIES

By Josh

There are a million cute animal films out there, most of them cartoons with cheesy endings, from *Dumbo* and *101 Dalmatians* to *Finding Nemo* and *Kung Fu Panda*.

True, some of the films on this list are cartoons. And yes, most of them end happily. But these movies aren't for little kids – they're neither sappy nor silly. So avoid *Marley & Me* and *Beethoven, Stuart Little* and *Free Willy*. Watch these instead.

1933
KING KONG
Directed by Merian C. Cooper and Ernest B. Schoedsack
Though the film is a thriller – and it *is* exciting and scary, even if the stop-motion animation isn't as 'realistic' as the digital effects we're used to these days – you will also find it quite tragic. Try to overlook the stereotyped island natives; focus on the gorilla and the girl he loves. Don't be surprised if you end up in tears.

1938
BRINGING UP BABY
Directed by Howard Hawks
The great Cary Grant plays a geeky palaeontologist; the equally great Katharine Hepburn plays a kooky rich woman with a tame leopard. When a dangerous leopard escapes from a nearby circus, they don't know which one is which. Hijinks ensue.

PS: The white-haired fox terrier in the film is Asta, one of Hollywood's most famous dogs.

1942
BAMBI
Directed by David Hand
Considered one of the three best animated movies of all time, *Bambi* is not for the faint of heart. Bambi's mother is killed by hunters, he has to fight a duel (nearly to the death) with another buck, and then the forest goes up in flames. It's a wild ride.

PS: The former Beatle Paul McCartney credits his animal rights activism to his having seen *Bambi* as a child. This sort of thing – outrage about killing cute animals, though not always un-cute ones – is so common that it's known as the Bambi Effect.

1943
LASSIE COME HOME
Directed by Fred M. Wilcox
A poor boy named Joe – played by Roddy McDowall, who'd grow up to portray a chimpanzee scientist in the *Planet of the Apes* movies – is forced to sell his beloved dog Lassie (a long-haired collie, bred for herding sheep) to a duke. Lassie keeps escaping to Joe, no matter how far away she's taken.

PS: Pal, the dog who plays Lassie in this movie, went on to portray Lassie in six other movies. In 1954, the first in a series of Pal's descendants played Lassie in a long-running TV show of that title.

1944
NATIONAL VELVET
Directed by Clarence Brown
Velvet, a 12-year-old girl, saves a horse named 'the Pie' from the glue factory – and helps train it for the Grand National steeplechase, a dangerous form of horse racing that involves jumping ditches and fences. Only male jockeys are allowed to ride in the race… so Velvet ends up disguising herself as a man. One of the greatest sports movies.

1954
ANIMAL FARM
Directed by John Halas and Joy Batchelor
Pigs lead a revolution against their farm's human owner… but soon they're treating their fellow farm animals even worse than he used to do. This adaptation of George Orwell's dystopian science-fiction novel was funded by the Central Intelligence Agency, which was trying to brainwash children in the name of national security and defence.

1962
SAMMY THE WAY-OUT SEAL
Directed by Norman Tokar

Two brothers smuggle a mischief-loving seal home from summer holiday and try to hide it from their parents. Like other live-action Disney movies from the 1950s and early 1960s – *That Darn Cat*, *The Shaggy Dog*, *The Three Lives of Thomasina* – its animal star represents the spirit of rebellion against everyday life.

1968
PLANET OF THE APES
Directed by Franklin J. Schaffner

Astronauts crash on a planet where apes rule and humans can't speak – and don't wear much clothing. They are captured by the apes, who cage them and treat them as cruelly as we humans often treat animals. There is some violent action, a couple of naked bottoms, and a surprise plot twist that will freak you out forever.

Between 1968 and 1973, five Planet of the Apes films were made. In the 1970s there were also two Planet of the Apes TV shows (one live-action, one animated) that weren't very good but which boasted amazing action figures. The 2001 remake of the original *Planet of the Apes* wasn't as good as the original; but the 2011 series reboot, *Rise of the Planet of the Apes*, was terrific.

1969
KES
Directed by Ken Loach

Billy is a neglected, bullied schoolboy who doesn't want to end up as a coal miner like his grownup brother. When he finds a young kestrel (falcon), he steals a book about falconry and trains the bird, which makes him happy for the first time. But then his brother gets angry with Billy, and takes revenge on his pet. Although it's a bleak film, it's well-made and worth seeing.

1970
DOUGAL AND THE BLUE CAT
Directed by Serge Danot

A weird, funny stop-motion animated French film (later dubbed in English) about a grumpy, sweet-loving dog named Dougal – and Buxton, a cat who helps sinister Madam Blue take over the Magic Garden. It's like the Beatles' *Yellow Submarine*, but with animals instead of a band named after insects.

PS: The movie is based on a French TV show, *The Magic Round-about*, whose English-language version (created for the BBC by Eric Thompson) is a cult classic.

1972
NAPOLEON & SAMANTHA
Directed by Bernard McEveety

When 11-year-old Napoleon is orphaned, he runs away to the mountains with his friend Samantha (played by the child actress Jodie Foster), a rooster, and Major, a retired circus lion. A cougar and a bear attack them, but Major saves the day.

PS: During filming, the lion playing Major grabbed Jodie Foster in his mouth, held her sideways, and shook her like a doll. She still has scars from this incident, not to mention a lifelong fear of cats.

1978
WATERSHIP DOWN
Directed by Martin Rosen

Adapted from a well-known novel by Richard Adams, the film tells the story of scrappy rabbits who form their own warren against all odds. It switches between stylised animation, for scenes about rabbit mythology, and more realistic animation.

PS: This animated film about fluffy bunnies is a lot darker – scary, sometimes violent – than you might expect. You might want to avoid it if you get scared easily.

1979
THE BLACK STALLION
Directed by Carroll Ballard

A boy named Alec is saved from a shipwreck by a wild Arabian stallion, in this beautifully filmed and mostly wordless adaptation of a classic 1941 children's novel by Walter Farley. Stranded on an uninhabited island, the horse (Alec calls him 'The Black') and the boy become friends. Once back in America, Alec and The Black enter a race. Who will win?

PS: The movie was followed by a 1983 sequel, *The Black Stallion Returns*; and by a 1990–1993 TV series. Neither of these is as compelling as the 1979 film. Ballard worked as second unit director on George Lucas's *Star Wars* before becoming known as a director of animal films.

1983
NEVER CRY WOLF
Directed by Carroll Ballard

The film dramatises the true story of Farley Mowat, a government biologist who is sent to the Canadian tundra to investigate the harm that wolves were supposedly doing to caribou herds. Tyler (the character based on Mowat) discovers that wolves aren't marauding killers; in fact, they play a key role in the Arctic ecosystem.

You'll enjoy the scene where Mowat pees on rocks around his campsite; and maybe the mouse-eating, too. What you will *not* enjoy is the unhappy ending.

1987
HARRY AND THE HENDERSONS
Directed by William Dear

On their way home from a camping trip, a Seattle family runs over a legendary cryptid: Bigfoot. They name him Harry and take him home. Though critics panned the silly comedy, John Lithgow's performance as the gentle, misunderstood Harry will remain with you – for better or worse – for the rest of your life.

1988

MY NEIGHBOUR TOTORO

Directed by Hayao Miyazaki

In this anime film by one of the genre's greatest directors, two girls befriend Totoro, a friendly spirit-creature with rabbit ears who represents and protects Japan's *satoyama* – the border zone between settled areas and mountainous wilderness. Totoro lives inside a camphor tree, rides around on a bus-shaped giant cat, and dances to help seeds sprout into new trees.

1991

WILD HEARTS CAN'T BE BROKEN

Directed by Steve Minor

It's 1930s America and Sonora, an orphaned tomboy, runs away from home and becomes the star of a Death-Defying Diving Horse Girl Show. Then she's blinded in an accident. But she doesn't give up! She keeps diving with horses! And the son of the show's owner falls in love with her! They live happily ever after! The craziest thing about this seemingly outlandish story? It's based on the real-life events chronicled in Sonora Webster Carver's 1961 memoir, *A Girl and Five Brave Horses*.

1995

BABE

Directed by Chris Noonan

Babe is a piglet raised by a sheepdog on Farmer Hoggett's farm. He turns out to be good at herding – particularly after Maa, an elderly sheep, suggests he ask politely ('Excuse me, ladies'), instead of chasing like a dog. So Farmer Hoggett enters Babe in a competitive sheep-herding contest. Trouble follows.

PS: The movie is an adaptation of the 1983 novel, *The Sheep-Pig*, by Dick King-Smith. The film was nominated by seven Oscars, and was followed by a 1998 sequel, *Babe: Pig in the City*, which some (but by no means all) fans claim is even more entertaining than the original.

1996

FLY AWAY HOME

Directed by Carroll Ballard

Amy, a 13-year-old girl, accidentally becomes a surrogate mother to a flock of Canada geese. To protect them from having their wings clipped by the game warden, Amy's inventor father works out a way to get the geese to fly to a bird sanctuary – with Amy to lead them, piloting an ultralight aircraft.

1997

MOUSEHUNT

Directed by Gore Verbinski

Two grownup brothers inherit a falling-down mansion and a failing string factory. They decide to fix up the mansion and sell it. But first they need to get rid of the mansion's inhabitant, a mouse. Even when they adopt an insane cat (Catzilla) and hire an exterminator, the brothers can't kill the mouse – who ends up saving the factory. Dark but funny.

2005

DUMA

Directed by Carroll Ballard

The director of *The Black Stallion*, *Never Cry Wolf*, and *Fly Away Home* adapts a real-life story about Xan, an African boy whose family has a pet cheetah, Duma. Xan must return Duma to the wild before the cheetah is put into a zoo. So the duo head out, by motorcycle and on foot, into the scorching desert and dangerous mountains.

2005

MARCH OF THE PENGUINS

Directed by Luc Jacquet

Forget *Happy Feet*. In this amazing and emotional French documentary, we watch the emperor penguins of Antarctica leave their usual habitat (that is, the ocean) and march inland to their breeding grounds, where they lay eggs. Both the male and female penguins are needed to keep the egg warm through the winter. And then it gets even tougher: life for an emperor penguin chick is a constant struggle for survival.

PS: The movie won, and richly deserved, an Oscar for Best Documentary Feature. The director later told an interviewer that no matter how human the penguins may seem, 'I find it intellectually dishonest to impose this viewpoint on something that's part of nature… You have to let penguins be penguins and humans be humans.'

2008

PONYO

Directed by Hayao Miyazaki

This lovely animated movie is about Ponyo, a fish-girl who lives beneath the waves, and her new friend Sosuke, a five-year-old human boy. Ponyo wants to become human so her sea-goddess grandmother tests them by flooding the land with water. It's up to Sosuke and Ponyo to rescue Sosuke's mother.

2008

BOLT

Directed by Chris Williams and Byron Howard

There are so many animated films about animals from Walt Disney – how to decide which ones to mention here? In the case of *Bolt*, the answer is: because of Rhino, the TV-obsessed hamster-in-a-plastic-ball character who steals the movie. Voiced by Mark Walton, Rhino is the ultimate fanboy and a surprisingly effective sidekick. In fact, Rhino should get his own movie some day.

2009

FANTASTIC MR FOX

Directed by Wes Anderson

When Mr Fox, a retired poultry thief, and his possum friend steal food from three farmers (Boggis, Bunce and Bean), his home gets destroyed and his nephew is captured. What to do now? This stop-motion adaptation of Roald Dahl's children's novel is rated PG (for action, smoking and slang humour) but it's innocent fun.

HIGH AND LOW-TECH
PET SEARCH

By Anindita Basu Sempere

Guide a lost dog by calling its name

Put up posters

The street team will actively search for your pet

Losing a pet can be heartbreaking but acting right away might increase your chances of finding your cat or dog.

Here are a few pointers from someone who has been through this ordeal herself.

PHASE ONE

First, call friends and family for help. Split your helpers into two groups: a street team and home team. The street team will actively search for your pet, so it should be made of people your pet knows and will approach. The home team will make calls, create posters, and post 'Lost Pet' notices online.

Street Team

- Grab some index cards and a pen. Make sure you have a photo of your pet, even if it's on your phone.

- A cat that escapes from home usually stays within a five-house radius, so ask your neighbours if you can check their gardens and garages, then divide up the search area. Look under bushes and into any small hiding places.

- Try to guide a lost dog to you by calling its name or squeaking a favourite toy. A dog that runs away because it was scared or attacked might travel up to two miles away, so don't limit the search too much.

- Talk to everyone you see. Let them know your pet is missing. Write a contact number and 'Lost Pet' on index cards and hand them out.

Illustrations by Mister Reusch

Home Team: making calls

While the street team is actively searching, the home team should spread the word to officials and online.

- Create a spreadsheet of contact information and log calls as you go. If you use Google Docs, multiple people can update the spreadsheet at the same time and help with follow-up calls later on. Also list websites and email addresses when available.

- Notify the Council Animal Warden about your pet in the area where it was lost and all of the neighbouring areas. You can find warden contact numbers at the website animalwardens.co.uk

- Call local police stations in the same places.

- Call shelters and vets in the same places in case someone finds and brings your pet in. Also call large regional animal shelters and hospitals.

For each of these calls, you'll need answers to the following questions:

- What does your pet look like? (Breed, size, weight, colour, short/long fur, etc.)

- Was your pet wearing a collar? If so, what tags are on the collar?

- Is your pet microchipped?

- Is your pet spayed/neutered?

For each of these calls, ask if you can email a photo of your pet, or have someone drop one off.

Look for patterns using Google Maps

The home team will make calls, create posters, and post 'Lost Pet' notices online

Notify your local Animal Warden, pet shelters and local police

Only include basic information on the poster

Don't list a reward amount!

Home Team: making posters

The home team should also quickly make a colour poster and print copies to post in the neighbourhood.

- The photo is the most important part of the poster. It should take at least half the page.

- Use a profile view of your pet. Most people will see your pet only in passing, so it's important that the photo show its body, not just its face. If you don't have a good profile photo, do an online image search for a photo of a cat or dog that looks like yours.

- Only include basic information on the poster: the photo, contact phone number, and the words 'Lost' and 'Reward'.

- Don't list a reward amount! If the amount is too low, some people might not be motivated to look. But if the amount is high, someone might decide your pet is valuable, and keep it – or try to sell it.

- Once the poster is printed, get the street team to pick up copies to distribute and put up.

- Get your grownup to post information about your pet to doglost.co.uk, nationalpetregister.org, foundandlostpets.co.uk, animalwardens.co.uk, dogstrust.org.uk, lostyourpet.net and elsewhere.

- Use the power of networking. Ask your grownup to post on Facebook, Twitter and any other social media he may use, while asking friends and family to help spread the word.

PHASE TWO

If your pet is lost for more than 24 hours, it's probably too frightened to come to anyone, even you. The street team should *stop* calling the animal's name. Instead you should ask animal control officers or animal rescue organisations for help with recovery. But there are still things you can do to assist the search.

- Keep walking the area where your pet was lost in case it catches your scent and follows you.

- Get your grownup to set up a Facebook page for your pet. Ask your friends and family to 'Like' the page and to share it on their own profiles. You can post updates on your pet's Facebook page and let people know how your search is going. The page is also a good way to ask for help – for example, putting up posters in new areas, or making follow-up calls to shelters, vets and police stations. You can post photos on the page and share stories to help others get to know your pet and get involved. Your grownup can add a friend or family member as a page administrator to help post updates.

- Your grownup can also spread the word by creating a Facebook ad. Facebook lets you set a budget and time limit for ads and select specific types of people who will see it. Choose people who live near where your pet was lost and who list interests such as cats, dogs, hiking, biking, running, and so forth. Outdoorsy people are more likely to see your lost pet! Keep the ad simple with an image of your pet, the word 'Lost', and a link to your pet's Facebook page so that anyone who clicks through will get up-to-date information on how the search is going.

- As people call in sightings, you or your grownup can drop pins in a Google map to figure out where your pet is hiding – and look for patterns.

- Once your pet is home, remember to call everyone on your contact list to share the good news and to thank them for their help. Celebrate by giving your pet extra treats and belly rubs!

HEEL, ROBOT!

Make a Robot Pet Controller

By John Edgar Park

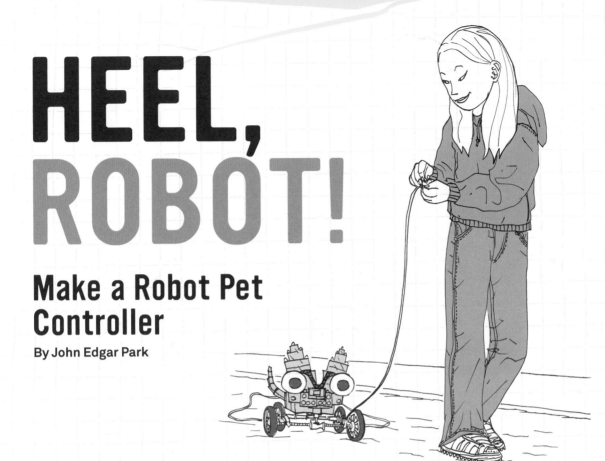

Illustration by Mister Reusch   Photography by John Edgar Park

Using two LEGO geared motors, you can build a simple yet effective robot pet control system – that is, a system that will transmit your steering instructions via a wire to a wheeled LEGO robot pet.

When you use batteries to turn a geared motor's shaft, it acts as a motor; however, when you turn the shaft by hand, a geared motor acts as an electrical generator.

So here's the trick: If you connect this electrical generator to a second geared motor via a wire, you can send power to the second motor by manually turning the first motor's shaft. So if the second motor is used to control your wheeled robot pet's steering, then by manually turning the first motor's shaft you can actually steer your robot pet around.

You'll need:

- 3 LEGO 9V geared motors. Use either Electric Technic mini-motors or Power Functions motors (size Medium or XL).

- 2 insulated alligator clip hook-up wires, with clips on both ends
- Voltmeter
- An LED
- 2 LEGO motor wires (they're also called connector cables)
- LEGO parts for building a wheeled robot. Technic vehicle kits or Mindstorms kits work well. Make sure you have wheels and a battery power pack.

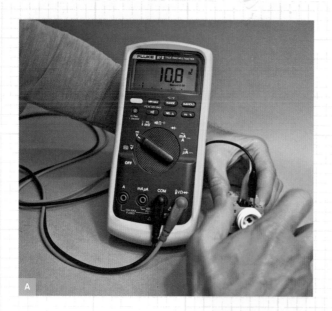

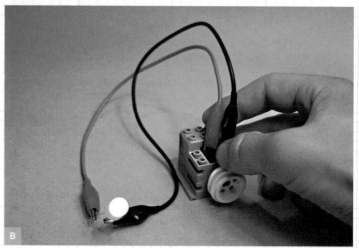

TEST THE CONNECTIONS

Measure the voltage

1. Clip one end of each alligator clip hook-up wire to one of the two contacts on your LEGO motor. Clip the other end of each hook-up wire to the voltmeter's probes (Figure A).

2. Set the voltmeter to measure DC voltage, then spin the LEGO motor's shaft. With a fast spin you should be able to generate up to 12 volts. If you generate negative voltage, try spinning the shaft in the opposite direction. Remember this 'positive' direction for the next step.

Generate a current

1. Swap the voltmeter for an LED, connecting the long leg of the LED to the same alligator clip wire that was connected to the red wire of your voltmeter. Connect the short leg of the LED to the other alligator clip.

2. Turn the motor shaft in the positive direction (from the previous step) until you see the LED start to glow (Figure B). LEDs only light up with the current flowing in one direction; if the LED isn't lighting up, try turning the shaft in the other direction. Careful: You can damage the LED if you spin too hard.

HOOK EVERYTHING UP

Wire the motors

1. Remove the hook-up wires.

2. Connect the two LEGO motors directly using the LEGO motor wires. Now, when you turn the shaft of one motor you'll see that the other motor turns nearly the exact same amount.

3. Connect a wheel to the shaft of one of the two connected motors; you'll spin this wheel when you want to send power to your robot pet's steering motor.

4. Spin the steering wheel as much as you want in either direction, and the other robot pet steering motor's shaft will do exactly the same thing (Figures C and D).

Steer your robot

1. Designing and building the wheeled LEGO robot pet itself is up to you; the robot in the photographs is just one example of what you might build.

2. When you build your robot, connect the third motor to the battery pack; you will use this motor to drive the robot pet forward. Use the steering motor (which is connected to the hand-turned steering wheel motor) for guiding your robot pet's wheels (Figures E and F). Enjoy!

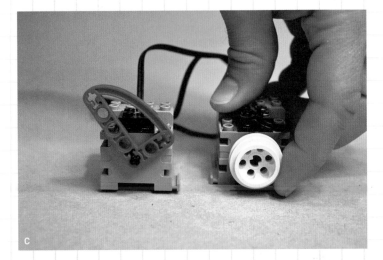

HOME: RESOURCES

YOUR HOME

13 Buildings Children Should Know (2009), by Annette Roeder. Thirteen architectural wonders of the world.

Architect Studio 3D (architectstudio3d. org). Design your own home at this website, which is sponsored by the Frank Lloyd Wright Preservation Trust.

Art of Camping, The (2011). This book by *UNBORED* contributor Matthew De Abaitua tells you everything that you'll ever need to know not only about sleeping under the stars – from packing to pitching camp, and from building a fire to campsite games – but its history. Did you know, for example, that mankind has slept in tents for at least 8,000 years? No wonder we enjoy it so much!

Awkward Family Photos (awkward familyphotos.com). A hilarious website filled with, yep, awkward family photos.

Google SketchUp (sketchup.google. com). Free 3D software for designers, architects and engineers that lets anyone design their own buildings.

Heights, The: Anatomy of a Skyscraper (2011), by Kate Ascher. How do skyscrapers sway in the wind? How do they get clean water hundreds of metres into the air? And lots more answers.

Hipstamatic (hipstamatic.com) is a smartphone app that turns ordinary photos into retro works of art, complete with super-saturated colours.

Music Download Review (music-download-review.toptenreviews.com). Side-by-side comparisons of iTunes, Napster, Amazon MP3, Rhapsody and other music downloading services.

Photobooth (2002), by Babbette Hines. This book features 700 beautiful photobooth photos from the late 1920s to the early 2000s.

Weald and Downland Open Air Museum (wealddown.co.uk) is a fascinating collection of old British 'vernacular buildings' (huts and houses) in West Sussex. Visitors can wander around the buildings, and learn about country crafts and industries in the process.

YOUR ROOM

DIY Art at Home: 28 Simple Projects for Chic Decor on the Cheap (2010), by Lola Gavvary. Room-by-room style guide.

D.I.Y Kids (2007), by Ellen and Julia Lupton. See chapters on 'Graffiti Furniture' and 'Decorated Boxes'.

Dollar Store Decor: 100 Projects for Lush Living that Won't Break the Bank (2005), by Mark Montano. Cheap style.

IHeart Organizing (iheartorganizing. blogspot.com). Check out the Project Gallery for photos of kids' rooms.

IKEA Hackers (ikeahackers.net). Creative ways to hack – customise, that is to say – your IKEA furniture.

Lazy Environmentalist, The: Your Guide to Stylish, Green Living (2007), by Josh Dorfman. For green bedroom design tips, see the chapter 'The Bedroom'.

Socks Appeal: 16 Fun and Funky Friends Sewn from Socks (2010), by Brenna Maloney. The title says it all.

Super Suite: The Ultimate Bedroom Makeover Guide for Girls (2002), by Mark Montano. By the author of lots of books about crafts and home décor.

YOUR GARDEN

Backyard Ballistics (2001), by William Gurstelle. PS: You'll need a big garden.

Boy's Book of Backyard Camping, The (1968), by Allan A. Macfarlan. As useful now as back in 1968. Not just for boys.

Cokesbury Game Book, The (1960), by Arthur M. Depew. For classic games, see the chapter 'Outdoor Games'.

Field and Forest Handy Book, The (1906, 2000), by D.C. Beard. See the chapters 'How To Camp Out in Your Backyard' and 'How to Make Snow Houses and Snow Men'.

Fix It, Make It, Grow It, Bake It: The DIY Guide to the Good Life (2010), by Billee Sharp. For DIY gardening tips, see the chapter 'Grow It: Get On My Land'.

Foxfire Book of Appalachian Toys and Games, The (1993), edited by Linda Garland Page and Hilton Smith. See the chapter 'Outside Games'.

Gardening Projects for Kids (2011), by Jenny Hendy. The author of this fun and useful guide, who runs a garden design consultancy and has a degree in Classical Botany, offers 60 practical tips for under-11s on cultivating flowers, growing fruit and vegetables, and attracting birds and insects.

Grow It, Eat It (2008). The experts at the Royal Horticultural Society (Britain's gardening charity) offer kids tips on both cultivating and cooking healthy and delicious food. Everything from photosynthesis to pumpkin pie.

Home Composting Made Easy (1998), by C. Forrest McDowell. A classic.

Householder's Guide to the Universe, A (2010), by Harriet Fasenfest. Step off the consumer treadmill, and start 'householding' instead. Enthusiastic advice on growing your own food.

Kids' Places to Play (2004), by Jeanne Huber. How-to instructions – for grownups and kids – on building treehouses and other play structures.

Make it Wild! 101 Things to Make and Do Outdoors (2010), by Fiona Danks and Jo Schofield. Danks, an ecologist from South Oxfordshire, and Jo Schofield, another Oxfordshire mother, make a playground out of wide open spaces. For example, they suggest digging clay, flattening it into dishes and tiles, and firing it in a homemade oven; pinning fiery red and gold leaves to old treetrunks to create a forest-fire illusion; and creating natural dyes from rhubarb roots and blackberry leaves, then painting your face with them.

Parkour.com. Videos, history, and news, plus an international directory of parkour and freerunning groups.

Pocket Guide to Games, The (2008), by Bart King. See the chapters 'Miscellaneous Active Games' and 'Contests, Feats, and Tussles'.

Primitive Wilderness Living and Survival Skills (1993), by John McPherson and Geri McPherson. See the chapter 'Primitive Semi-Permanent Shelters'.

Shelters, Shacks and Shanties (1932, 2003), by D.C. Beard. A great classic.

Tree Houses You Can Actually Build (1998), by David Stiles and Jean Stiles. The only question is: will you do it?

GET CRAFTY

101 Things for Girls To Do (1935), by Lillie B. Horth and Arthur C. Horth. Vintage crafting projects. Not just for girls.

Alternacrafts: 20+ Hi-Style Lo-Budget Projects to Make (2006), by Jessica Vitkus. Upcycle household items into things to wear, gifts and home décor.

Craft (craftzine.com). This magazine, and its website, are terrific resources for hip craft projects. PS: *Craft* and *Make* are from the same publisher.

Craftster (craftster.org). An online crafting community that shares craft ideas, projects and advice.

Etsy (etsy.com). Buy and sell handmade and vintage crafts. Or just get ideas for hip, upcycled craft projects.

Get Crafty (2004), by Jean Railla. The book that helped start the hip crafting revolution. Many projects. Railla is one of this book's contributors. Hooray!

Get Frugal (getfrugal.com). Tips on how to live frugally, including how to use household items in different ways.

Hyperbolic Crochet Coral Reef (crochetcoralreef.org). A cool project merging crocheting with 'hyperbolic' geometry to create reef-like forms.

Instructables (instructables.com). A site crammed with user-created and uploaded do-it-yourself projects, including all sorts of craft projects.

Kid's Crafternoon: Papercraft (2011), edited by Kathreen Ricketson. Twenty projects – most requiring normal A4 paper, tissue paper and paper napkins in different colours – that kids can tackle on a rainy weekend with minimal grownup assistance.

Last Year's Model (lastyearsmodel. org). A growing community of people dedicated to extending the life of products, by repairing, refurbishing or adapting them once they are outmoded – instead of tossing them.

Magic Books & Paper Toys (2008), by Esther K. Smith. Lots of fun craft projects – all of which involve paper, if that's what you're into. (We are.)

Make These Toys: 101 Clever Creations Using Everyday Items (2010), by Heather Swain. The title says it all.

Maker Shed (makershed.com). Everything you can imagine for young and old DIY makers and crafters.

Recycler's World (recycle.net). Connects you to people in your area looking to trade or sell scrap metal and other reusable materials.

Side by Side: 20 Collaborative Projects for Crafting with Your Kids (2012), by Tsia Carson. From giant newspaper snowflakes to a living tipi, many hours of family fun.

Super-Cute Chibis to Draw and Paint (2011), by Joanna Zhou. Are you into manga – that is, Japanese-style comics? This guide offers tips on how to create ultra-cute but distinctive characters of your own.

Vans Art (vansart.tumblr.com). Images to inspire you when you are decorating your trainers. Not just for Vans fans.

WhipUp (whipup.net). This DIY crafting and creativity blog by Kathreen Ricketson, author of a series of Kid's Crafternoon activity books, and editor of the kids' e-magazine *Action Pack*, is right up our alley. It's a wonderful resource for, among other things, reviews of the latest crafting books.

COOKING

300 Step-by-Step Cooking and Gardening Projects for Kids (2012), by Nancy McDougall and Jenny Hendy. Mostly aimed at younger kids, but lots of inspiration for older kids, too.

Cook School: Teach Your Child to Cook (2011), by Amanda Grant. Over 50 recipes and activities designed to teach core cooking skills to kids of every age.

Cooking for Geeks: Real Science, Great Hacks, and Good Food (2010), by Jeff Potter. A cookbook that applies your curiosity to invention in the kitchen. Check out the book's website (cookingforgeeks.com). PS: Potter is one of this book's contributors.

Get Crafty (2004), by Jean Railla. See the chapter 'Consuming Pleasures'. Also see Railla's great cooking blog (mealbymeal.blogspot.com). PS: Railla is one of this book's contributors.

Jamie Oliver's Food Guide. This smartphone app by celebrity chef Jamie Oliver, known for his campaign against the use of processed foods in schools, celebrates brilliant places to eat, buy and enjoy food around Britain.

Peas and Thank You: Simple Meatless Meals the Whole Family Will Love (2011), by Sarah Matheny. Over 80 recipes by the Peas and Thank You blog creator (peasandthankyou.com).

Redwall Cookbook, The (2009), by Brian Jacques. You don't have to be a fan of Brian Jacques' Redwall series of novels to enjoy such old-fashioned recipes as Mole's Favourite Deeper 'n' Ever Turnip 'n' Tater 'n' Beetroot Pie, or Great Hall Gooseberry Fool. Yum.

See Dad Cook: The Only Book a Guy Needs to Feed Family and Friends (and Himself) (2006), by Wayne Harley Brachman. Not just for dads. A very useful cookbook for grownups and kids who want to eat yummy meals that don't take a lot of time to produce.

YOUR PETS

50 Simple Things Kids Can Do To Save The Earth (1990), by John Javna. See the chapter 'Protecting Animals'.

Imagine Life with a Well-Behaved Dog: A 3-Step Positive Dog-Training Programme (2010), by Julie A. Bjelland. How to choose the right dog for your family – and how to live together.

Lazy Environmentalist, The: Your Guide to Stylish, Green Living (2007), by Josh Dorfman. For green pet tips, see the chapter 'Animal Accessories'.

Worst-Case Scenario Survival Handbook, The: Life (2006), by Joshua Piven and David Borgenicht. See the amusing chapter 'Pets'.

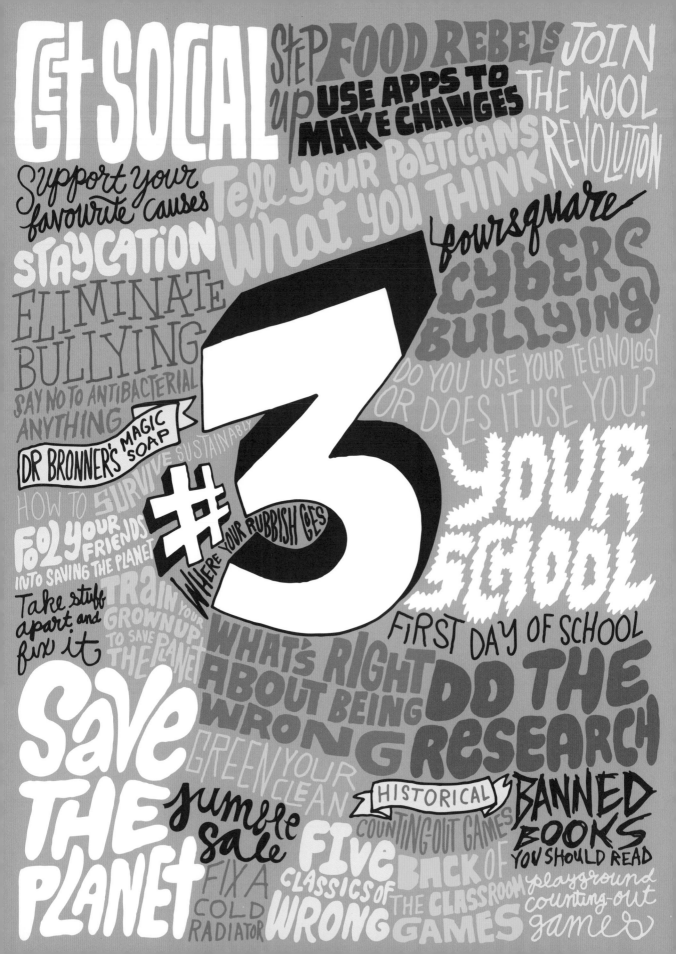

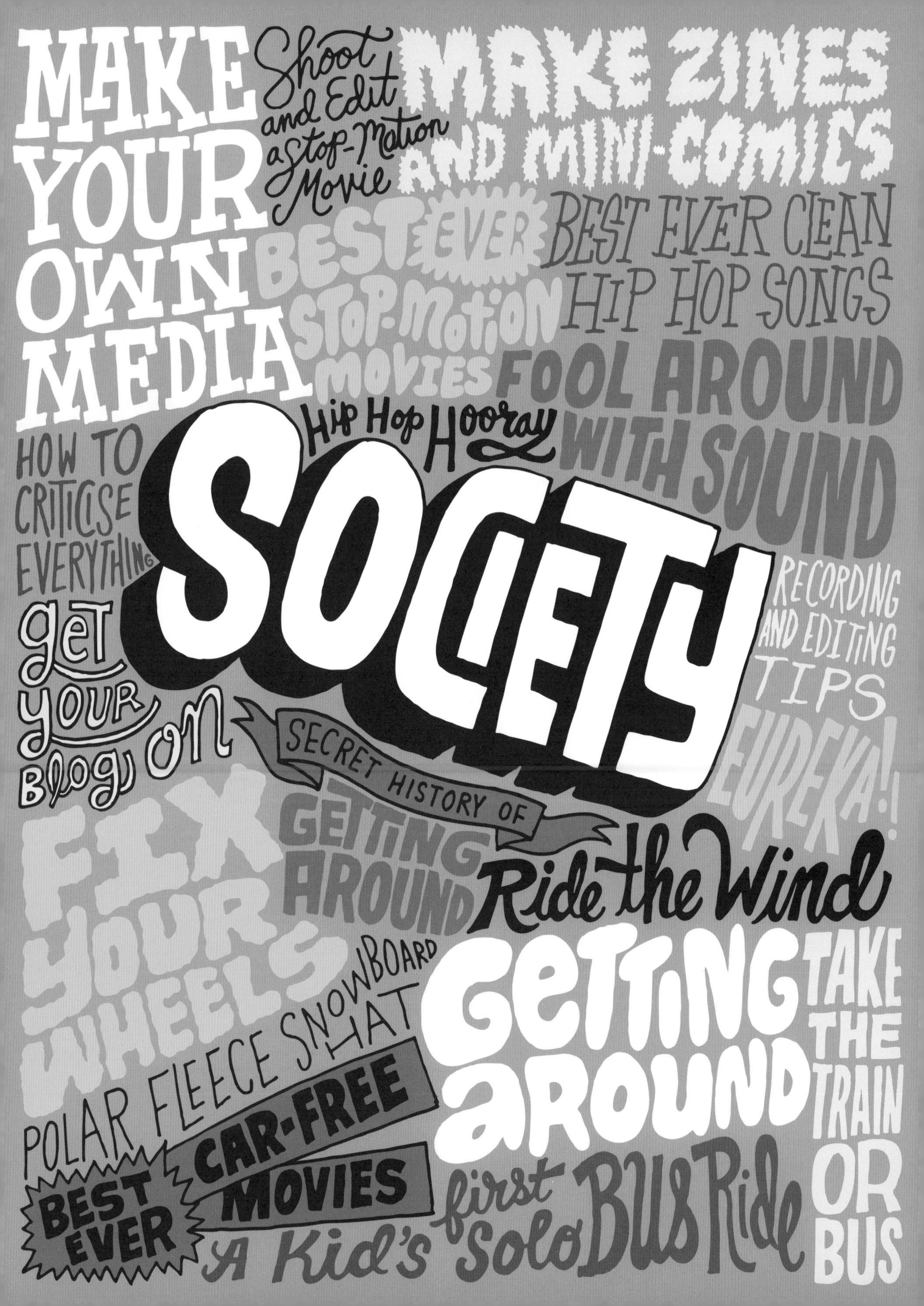

MAKE YOUR OWN MEDIA

Shoot and Edit a Stop-Motion Movie

MAKE ZINES AND MINI-COMICS

BEST EVER STOP-MOTION MOVIES

BEST EVER CLEAN HIP HOP SONGS

FOOL AROUND WITH SOUND

HOW TO CRITICISE EVERYTHING

get your blog on

Hip Hop Hooray

SOCIETY

SECRET HISTORY OF

RECORDING AND EDITING TIPS

EUREKA!

FIX YOUR WHEELS

GETTING AROUND

Ride the Wind

POLAR FLEECE SNOWBOARD HAT

GETTING AROUND

TAKE THE TRAIN OR BUS

BEST EVER

CAR-FREE MOVIES

A Kid's first Solo BUS Ride

STEP UP

Q&A WITH REBECCA WALKER

Rebecca Walker, the daughter of a white, Jewish dad and an African–American mum, grew up to be a leading voice of the multiracial and multicultural experience.

Walker is an author and activist who has spoken out on everything from women's (and men's) rights to racial discrimination and religious freedom. She's also a mum. We talked to her about what it's like to be a multiracial kid today; and we asked for advice on making a stand for what you think is right.

UNBORED: You have written about your life as a kid growing up in many different communities where you needed to switch back and forth between identities. What have you noticed about what it's like to be a multiracial kid today?

WALKER: When I was a kid, race was so primary – it came first. That's changing a lot. The kids I talk to these days seem to be having an easier time. I think having a president who is multiracial has helped. When I talk to kids today, there are so many ways that they are trying to define themselves: What

does it mean to be a boy? Am I a vegetarian? Race and culture are becoming just a part of a longer list of labels and identities.

UNBORED: Is there any advice you'd like to give to the grownups of today's multiracial kids?

WALKER: It's the same advice that I've always given: just talk to your kids about all these things. Realise they are watching you and taking cues from you about race and identity. It's important to be aware that there is so much peer pressure pushing on multiracial kids to identify themselves either one way or another. So it's up to a kid's grownups to explain what it means when you take on a label or an identity – and that kids don't have to choose any of it. They can be first and foremost whoever they are as human beings.

Illustrations by Mister Reusch

UNBORED: How can kids navigate a society that's still mired in prejudice and divisiveness?

WALKER: In my own family we talk about how a lot of things are private. We are Buddhist and people want to ask my son about what he's going to do for Christmas or other religious holidays. We tell him that he has a right to say nothing and that he doesn't have to explain himself. When we talk to him about race and colour, we explain that people have different colour skin just like they have different colour eyes and come from different cultures and speak different languages. He comes from a long line of all different kinds of people and the most important thing is to be the best person he can be – to be kind, compassionate, smart and strong. All the other stuff may seem really important to other people, but what we value has to do with how we treat each other and the kind of people we are. And that has nothing to do with race or skin colour. That has to do with what's on the inside.

UNBORED: How would you describe feminism, the history and context of feminism, to a kid?

WALKER: There was a time when it was difficult for a woman to get certain kinds of jobs just because she was a woman. People didn't have faith in her. They didn't feel like she could control herself or handle things that were really hard and difficult.

A lot of people – feminists – worked very hard for a long time to change that idea. They helped people see that idea of women as just an old, weird thought that came from people who were wrong. Today, we understand that all human beings have the potential to be powerful and deserve to be respected and protected by the government and the police. Feminists share that idea with others.

UNBORED: What can feminist kids do to change society?

WALKER: I've been doing a lot of teaching in Sweden and I'm really excited about a lot of things happening there. In Swedish primary schools, they are changing the language from 'boys' and 'girls' to 'friends'. So instead of saying, 'OK, boys and girls,' the teachers say, 'OK, friends.' If kids started to think of themselves and the other kids in their class as friends rather than as boys and girls, that is a feminist act – because it suggests that our gender isn't as important as our ability to be good friends. That's a mind shift. I'd love to see kids start that kind of movement in their schools.

UNBORED: What else can feminist boys and girls do – perhaps on a smaller, individual scale?

WALKER: Kids can make sure that they are reading a lot of books that are by women writers. And they – especially girls – can take a look at how much time they spend thinking about how they look as opposed

to what they think. It would be an interesting school project to look at that question (what you look like versus who you are) and try to change the culture of your school or classroom. You don't need to start something that's going to be a huge societal change to make an impact.

UNBORED: You've written that 'feminism is an experiment, and just like in science you have to assess the outcome of the experiment and adjust the results'. How has the experiment of feminism changed during your life?

WALKER: Part of the work I've done is to try and help feminism pay attention to what's happening with boys. The experiment is evolving as we realise that we can do a lot to address the needs of girls, and their ideas about what it means to be a girl, but we are just beginning to understand how limited boys can be about ideas about what it means to be a boy. Today, we have a lot of girls who are doing great and feel like they can do anything and be anything. And we also have a lot of boys who don't feel that way. The range has to be wider for them too. It's time to navigate what it means to be a boy to be a full human being and not just be good at sports.

UNBORED: Your advice is much more about changing hearts and minds than laws...

WALKER: The experiment of feminism has shown us that you can change laws but people also need to change their ideas. No matter how many laws you can change, there can still be a tremendous amount of discrimination. So when you think about changing the world, you need to think about not only how you can make political change but also how you affect people in such a way that they will have a shift in their consciousness. Unless there is real change in people's hearts, we won't see the results we want.

UNBORED: How did you become an activist?

WALKER: When I was 15, I was walking down the street and saw a woman getting beaten by a man. I went home and wrote about it and I published the essay in my school newspaper. That was my first activist moment. We had an assembly and talked about it. We formed a committee and brought in a speaker to talk about domestic violence. It was the first time I realised I could impact people's lives.

UNBORED: Is there a particular cause you think should be important to kids today?

WALKER: I think now is a good time to become an activist even about your own lunchbox. Kids should advocate for healthy and sustainable food in schools and at home. Understand where your food comes from. Try and eat less meat, because it's better for the environment and for you. And recycle! Kids can be part of a movement to change how we eat as a nation so that we can have enough food to feed people in 20–30 years. Not only does an individual kid need to eat healthily but all people need to eat healthfully. Food is a nexus for all kinds of social issues.

SUPPORT YOUR FAVOURITE CAUSES

Giving money is known as philanthropy, which means 'a desire to help humankind'.

Whether you donate a portion of your pocket money to the RSPCA, or use the proceeds of a cake stall to help children with cancer, you are using your money to benefit others and make a positive impact.

Give a portion of whatever money comes your way.

Whether it's your pocket money, money you earn by babysitting, or a gift you get from your grandparents, a good rule of thumb is to set aside 10 per cent of your cash for philanthropy.

Look into your heart

If you love animals, then supporting an animal shelter makes sense. If your favourite sport is football, maybe you want to see if your local youth league has a scholarship fund you can contribute to. If you've heard about earthquakes, tsunamis and other natural disasters and can't imagine what it would be like to suddenly be without a home, support the victims of those devastating events.

Newspapers, news programmes and websites will give you the information you'll need to be able to get your money to the people who need it. You can also search online for information about the millions of charities that take donations. You'll need to work closely with your grownups to do the proper research.

Hold fundraisers

Host an event to raise money for your favourite cause. You don't have to do anything fancy: anything from a fruit sale to a carnival in your garden will do the trick.

Set up a family foundation

Your money can make a greater impact if you combine it with other people's money. Have every kid in your family pool the 'give' portion of your pocket money (or gifts or earnings) into one larger savings pot. Then organise special family dinners throughout the year whose purpose is to decide where the money will go.

Include giving in your family rituals

Maybe you designate one night of Hanukkah, or Christmas Eve, as 'giving night'. On that night, you ask your grownups to give money to a charity of your choosing instead of buying you a gift. Some kids ask for donations to their favourite causes instead of birthday presents – which can be thought of as a 'Hobbit Birthday', because J.R.R. Tolkien tells us that hobbits give presents on their birthdays instead of receiving them.

Get creative

You can grow your hair long and then donate it to Little Princess Trust, a charity that makes wigs for children suffering from medical hair loss. Or you can collect tinned goods for a local food bank. You can even help present awards at your local Paralympics, which is a sporting event for people with physical or intellectual disabilities.

There are all sorts of ways to give, even if you don't have much money.

Illustrations by Heather Kasunick

TELL YOUR POLITICIANS
WHAT YOU THINK

Get started by finding out who represents your area

By Helen Cordes

You can't vote until you're 18, so politicians aren't going to listen to you, right?

Wrong. If you write a letter, email, phone or visit your local Member of Parliament, your concerns are taken just as seriously as a grownup's. You can make change in issues important to you. All you have to do is put a little thought into it.

Find your MP

If the issue you want to speak to a politician about concerns the whole country, then you will want to influence your MP – that is, your Member of Parliament. One way to talk directly to your MP is via a website such as theyworkforyou.com or an app such as MyMP. If the issue that concerns you is to do with your local community, then making contact with members of the local council will be more effective. The website writetothem.com will help you find the right representative in your area.

You can also write to a Lord in the House of Lords; the key is to find a Lord who has spoken about the issue you wish to discuss. Web searches make it easy to match up your concerns with speeches that Lords or MPs have made: for example, you can search speeches via WriteToThem.

Get your message straight

Before you email or do any other communication with your MP, your councillor or a Lord, jot down your concerns in a short, clear message. You should aim for three to four paragraphs to outline your feelings about an issue. Be sure to explain how it affects you and your family and community, and tell your MP what you'd like done about it. Use a friendly tone, and mention that you like to discuss issues and politics with friends, family, teachers and others – this lets them know that you are influencing voters even if you're not a voter yet!

Your letter will be counted to let your MP know what his or her constituents (residents of the MP's area) want only if there's full contact info, so include your address and full name – and mention that you're looking forward to a response.

Find examples of effective letters

Let's say you want your MP to help preserve forests. Organisations such as the National Trust issue petitions for you to sign up to on this issue. Perhaps you're interested in preventing a badger cull or another issue facing animals? A group like Viva (that is, Vegetarians International Voice for Animals) will suggest who you should contact and the best and most effective way to get your point across politely.

However, it's better to use the petitions provided by these organisations as a guide, because politicians pay closer attention to

Illustrations by Heather Kasunick

individualised letters. In fact, when politicians see the same email message over and over, they might assume it's 'astroturfing' – an email campaign masquerading as a grassroots effort – and ignore it. So personalise your letter and send it from your own email account, or write a letter (neatly) by hand and post it.

Pick up the phone

Phoning is a great way to practise voicing your opinions and asking for the changes you want. It can be easier to call a local councillor (who may even live in your neighbourhood), but the preparation and process is the same for phoning any office.

First, make sure you have a 'script' ready – if you already wrote an email, you can use it as your script. Don't ask to speak to your representative; grownup callers don't get to talk to them, either. Instead, tell the receptionist what your issue is, and then ask to speak to the person who works with your MP on that issue. If that person's not available, tell the receptionist your position and it will get passed along. For example, you could say, 'I'd like my representative to know that I'm asking her to vote "yes" on the Clean Air bill and also continue to decrease pollution in other ways.'

Meet in person

Don't be shy about visiting your representatives. Local officials will often meet personally with a kid (don't drop in; phone in advance to set up the appointment). Be polite, and have a to-the-point version of your views ready to say; memorise a few sentences, or key points you want to make.

USE APPS TO
MAKE CHANGES

You and your grownup can use websites and apps to register your opinions, network with other activists, start a cause or campaign, and make positive changes where you live. Here are a couple of examples.

Apps for Good (appsforgood.com) teaches young people how to create their own apps that address social issues, from bullying to being stopped and searched. The programme is being offered in schools across England. Ask your school to consider hosting a course!

Commute Greener (commutegreener.org) helps reduce your carbon footprint by helping you make smarter choices on your daily travels. If, for example, your grownup drives you to school, you can track the CO_2 output of that journey and then set a goal for how much you'd like to reduce it by. Then you can make another choice for one or more days of the week, including walking, biking or taking a bus or train and see what your CO_2 output is for those options. You must be 16 or older to use this app on your own. It's more fun to do it with your grownups, anyway.

MyMP (my-mp.org.uk) allows constituents to tell their MPs what they think about the important issues of the day. MPs share everything from news about their initiatives to their daily appointments. They also respond directly to constituents' comments.

Tweetminster (tweetminster.co.uk) is for anyone who's interested in politics and current affairs. The app tracks the links and information that politicians, civil servants, activists, professors and journalists on Twitter think is the most important news of the day. You can filter it by top stories or by news that's shared by government departments, or MPs, or the media. Important! You must be 17 or older to subscribe to Tweetminster. Use this app only with your grownups.

FOOD REBELS

Q&A WITH MARK WINNE

Mark Winne was an 18-year-old university undergraduate when a friend showed him photos of children starving from a famine in Africa. 'I felt I had to do something about it,' he says.

That's why he and his friends organised events to raise money for children in Africa, and also started a programme to provide breakfasts for American kids who couldn't afford them. Winne later organised local farmers' markets where people could not only buy fresh and healthy food, but also make personal connections with the people who grew it. Using methods that don't harm the environment, Winne made a positive impact on his community.

In addition to decades of hands-on work providing food to low-income and elderly people, Winne has written several books, including *Food Rebels, Guerrilla Gardeners, and Smart Cookin' Mamas: Fighting Back in an Age of Industrial Agriculture*. We asked Winne how kids can not only eat healthier, but see food as a way to make the world a better place.

UNBORED: What would you like kids to understand about the food they eat?

WINNE: As a society, we've been told for a long time that it's OK to eat 'processed food' – that's the term for food that is already prepared.

Crisps, frozen pizza, boxed macaroni and cheese, for example, have a lot of chemicals to stay tasty.

We've also gotten the message that producing food isn't something we need to do personally, and that we can rely on a small number of large farms and businesses to do that work for us.

Both those messages miss the fact that you make healthier eating choices when you prepare your own food yourself. You can also help smaller farms stay in business.

I use a term called 'getting your head above your plate'. It means knowing information about your food beyond whether it tastes good or not. For example, knowing that your Cheddar cheese was made by a farmer with an actual name helps you appreciate it more than if you think of cheese as coming from the supermarket's aisle. Food isn't just something you put in your mouth. Food has stories – about the people who produce it, the places it's grown, and the ways it's produced.

UNBORED: What's a food rebel?

WINNE: Anybody who doesn't accept what society considers 'normal' when it comes to food. It's somebody who says, 'I'm not going to eat processed food, or food that's easy to prepare, because it might not be healthy for me.' A food rebel learns how to cook, even if he has zero experience doing it. That might seem simple but a lot of people are forgetting how to cook. A food rebel says no to foods that are made cheaply and without regard to the environment or the welfare of animals.

UNBORED: What's a guerrilla gardener?

WINNE: Somebody who looks for unusual ways of producing food. A guerrilla gardener might take a piece of land that's not being used for anything and turn it into a vegetable garden. Today, guerrilla gardeners are planting gardens on rooftops, and even on paved lots covered with lots and lots of compost, which helps fertilise soil. Some people are collecting from their rainspouts to water their gardens. Others are building small greenhouses. Traditional agriculture uses large pieces of land and then covers it with chemicals to kill pests and weeds.

UNBORED: What about smart cookin' mamas?

WINNE: Somebody who cooks healthfully while also preparing delicious food.

A Texas woman I write about in my book has family from Mexico. She told me she had watched her mother 'cook with love', which means she cooked slowly and took a lot of time to create dishes that showed how much she cared about her family. But her mother didn't cook with knowledge. The food she made was fatty and salty and had a lot of sugar. As a result, her children gained too much weight and didn't get enough nutrition. So this woman decided to not carry on that particular family tradition. Instead, she learned how to cook well and healthfully *and* prepare delicious meals.

UNBORED: How can kids help end hunger?

WINNE: Donating food at harvest festival at your school or place of worship is one way to help people who don't have enough to eat. But we also need to understand why they can't eat, and why food donations by themselves will never be enough to end hunger.

It would be great to get any events you do involving food to highlight healthy food choices. Instead of holding cake sales, consider fruit sales. When my children were in their school band, they held an annual citrus sale to finance the band's trip. It enabled me to stock up on grapefruit for a couple of months.

UNBORED: What can kids do to help the food revolution?

WINNE: Get close to food! Get your hands in the soil, even if you are only growing cherry tomatoes in a pot in a city flat. Food preparation is a hands-on activity. Learn with your grownups how to prepare and cook food that's good for you.

Also, pay attention to where your food comes from. Shop at farmers' markets, grow food in your garden or a community garden, or pick your own at a nearby farm. Read your food packages. If there's no information where your food came from, ask the manager of your supermarket.

I know this next tip is tough for kids but it's best not to load up on sugar, salt and fat because your taste preferences are still evolving. Those tastes will take over and make it hard for you to start liking healthier choices that are delicious in a different way. Obesity is a huge challenge right now for families, so making healthy eating choices is especially important.

Illustrations by Heather Kasunick

ELIMINATE BULLYING

Bullying in schools and online is a worldwide problem. Some kids who are bullied are terrified to go to school. Others worry that mean girls and guys might gossip or spread lies about them on the internet or through texts. Some kids who are bullied are badly traumatised.

Bullying someone is not even remotely OK. In fact, physically or emotionally hurting someone to make yourself look better is actually a sign that you need help and should talk with your school counsellor or another grownup you trust.

More than half of bullying situations will end if a bystander – that's someone who watches without saying anything – takes a stand, even if it's as low-key as not encouraging the bully to continue.

You can do something about bullying – sometimes even before it starts.

If you are bullied, don't blame yourself

It's common for kids who get picked on to believe that they are somehow to blame when people are cruel to them. Whether you're tall, short, skinny, overweight, terrible at sports, unpopular or even super-great at school, you have a basic human right to be exactly who you are. It is *not your fault* if someone bullies you.

Text for help

If you feel unsafe, text a friend and ask them to come and find you – or put you in touch with someone who can.

Respect differences

Everyone is unique. When you value and respect differences, you give bullies less ammunition. So if someone teases you because you stutter or have ADHD or have a crush on someone, just smile and agree with them – say something simple like, 'Yes, I do jiggle my legs a lot' – and then walk away.

Don't be isolated

Bullies pick on people when they are alone. If you're worried about being bullied, stay with friends or near a grownup who can see what's going on.

Remain calm

OK, that sounds impossible. But if a bully shoves you, try not to show how afraid you are. Instead, look them in the eye and say 'Stop.' Do not yell or fight back. That will only make the situation worse.

Talk to a grownup

Bullies often threaten their victims that things will get worse if they tell someone. But the truth is that grownups really do have power over kids.

Illustrations by Mister Reusch

The problem is that bullying often takes place when grownups aren't around or can't see what's happening. Telling a trusted grownup if you are being bullied (or if you've seen another kid being bullied) allows them to take measures – like getting a bully kicked off the bus – that can actually make life better.

CYBER-BULLYING

Think before you click

- If you find yourself emailing or texting something cruel to someone else, put down your mouse or phone and count to five. Then don't do it.
- If someone sends you a message, do not forward it unless it's something factual, like which movie you are going to see. Anything personal should remain private between the sender and you.
- Never send a text or email pretending you are someone else.

Block jerks

- Never share your password with anyone, except your grownups.
- If you receive a threatening email, block all future incoming emails from that person.

Report it

- Report any cyber-bullying to a grownup you trust.

A little act of solidarity can make a huge difference

Befriend a kid who is a target of bullies

Little things like walking around the playground with a girl who doesn't have many friends, or eating lunch with someone who usually sits alone, can make a huge difference. You don't have to become best friends with this person. But a little act of solidarity will help take away a bully's power. You can also say something kind that acknowledges what this kid has gone through. A simple 'I'm sorry that happened' will help. Or: 'It's not your fault.'

Make sure your school has an anti-bullying policy

If they don't, talk to your teachers and head teacher about creating one. A good anti-bullying policy defines and forbids all kinds of bullying, including: threatening; unwanted teasing; intimidating; stalking; cyberstalking; cyber-bullying; physical violence; stealing things; sexual, religious or racial harassment; public humiliation; destruction of school or personal property; social exclusion; spreading rumours or false facts. Your school's policy should also have a process to verify if bullying actually happened and clear consequences about what will happen if a kid is found to have been a bully.

Educate others

Put together a programme with your school where you can educate other students about how to identify, stop and prevent bullying. Whether it's a written statement or a skit at assembly, there are lots of ways your school can start talking about how to end bullying. For more ideas, check out the ChildLine site (childline.org.uk/explore/bullying).

FOURSQUARE
THE SMARTPHONE APP

The social city–guide app Foursquare is a fun way to explore the place where you live using a smartphone or phone with a web browser, or via text messaging.

Foursquare's users around the world mostly use it to broadcast their current location to friends. But it's also a game that rewards you for discovering new places; and you can compete with others. It's these aspects of Foursquare – the ones that encourage users to get to know their town or city better – that you and your grownup might enjoy together.

Check in from
wherever you are

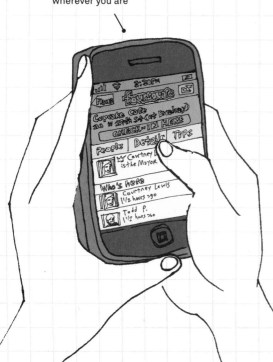

Check in

When you tell Foursquare where you are, that's called 'checking in'. The Foursquare apps for the iPhone, BlackBerry and Android use GPS to show you a list of nearby locations. You can check in from parks, museums, houses, shops, libraries… anywhere. If Foursquare doesn't have the place you're looking for, you can add it to the app's listings.

Don't worry, Foursquare doesn't know where you are unless you check in to tell the app your location; also, if you prefer, you can check in without broadcasting your location to friends. Though it requires a little more effort, you can check in via Foursquare's mobile website.

Learn about your town

Whenever you check in, Foursquare will recommend places to go and things to do nearby. If your friends use Foursquare, you'll learn more about their favourite spots and the new places they discover (and vice versa).

You the mayor

Foursquare is sort of like a videogame, but instead of playing the game indoors in front of a TV, you're visiting unfamiliar places near your own home.

Every Foursquare check-in earns you points. Find a new place in your neighbourhood? +5 points. Dragging friends along with you? +1. And so forth. As you start checking in to more and more new places, you'll unlock badges.

If you've been to a place more often than anyone else, you'll become the 'mayor' of that place on Foursquare – which can mean discounts and freebies. Or just bragging rights.

Illustrations by Mister Reusch

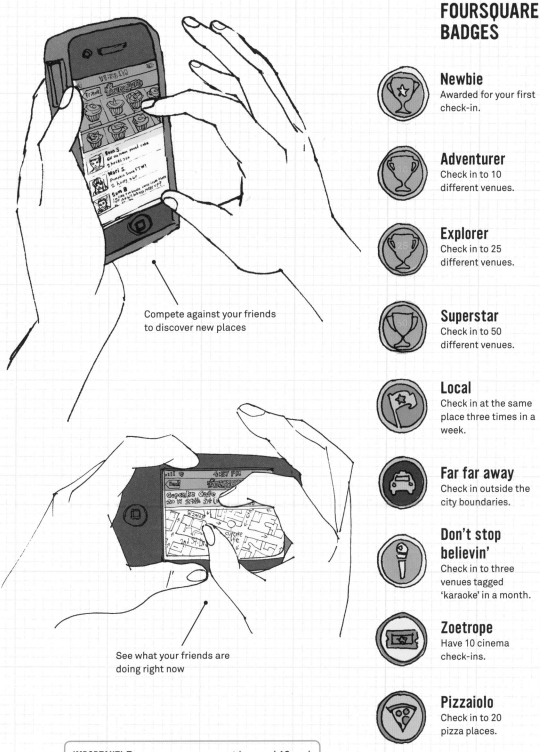

Compete against your friends
to discover new places

See what your friends are
doing right now

IMPORTANT! Foursquare users must be aged 13 and
over to subscribe, and the online interaction isn't
moderated. So kids under 13 can and should only
use this app with their grownup.

FOURSQUARE BADGES

Newbie
Awarded for your first
check-in.

Adventurer
Check in to 10
different venues.

Explorer
Check in to 25
different venues.

Superstar
Check in to 50
different venues.

Local
Check in at the same
place three times in a
week.

Far far away
Check in outside the
city boundaries.

Don't stop
believin'
Check in to three
venues tagged
'karaoke' in a month.

Zoetrope
Have 10 cinema
check-ins.

Pizzaiolo
Check in to 20
pizza places.

Babysitter
Check in to 10
playgrounds.

JOIN THE WOOL REVOLUTION!

BECOME A YARN BOMBER

By Elizabeth

No, yarn bombing isn't about pelting your enemies with balls of wool. It's a creative, fun, and easy way to add colour and beautiful textures to otherwise grey urban landscapes. The 'bombing' part comes from street slang; it means to 'tag' a public space with graffiti.

Also called *yarn storming, guerrilla knitting* and *graffiti knitting,* yarn bombing started in Houston, Texas, when knitter Magda Sayeg decided that the neighbourhood where she managed a clothes shop was ugly and depressing. To perk it up, Sayeg knitted a pink-and-purple cover for the shop's door handle. 'People wanted to come by and touch it and talk about it,' she says.

Those positive reactions were all Sayeg needed to start covering other public structures with yarn. She and her knitting group made striped sleeves for parking meters in Brooklyn (New York). They knitted caps for the pylons surrounding the Sydney Opera House in Australia. They inspired other needle crafters from Britain and elsewhere to start their own projects across the globe.

If anyone in your family knits or crochets, yarn bombing is a great way to use up leftover yarn. You can start your own yarn bombing projects to cover less-than-beautiful items in your house or garden or flat. Or you can head out and bring some woolly sunshine to other parts of your town. Posts, door handles, fences, street sign poles, statues, trees, bike racks: knit or crochet cosies for whatever's out there! (You can sew the ends together with a large embroidery needle, or use buttons if you know how to make buttonholes.)

Just remember to never cover the words on a street sign; you wouldn't want someone to drive dangerously because the Give Way sign was covered in an afghan.

Yarn bombing is also a fun way to leave something beautiful behind on your holidays. Photograph your tags (that's what yarn bombs are called) to keep a unique record of where you've been.

Illustrations by Mister Reusch

Graffiti bombing outside the Sydney Opera House

One of Magda Sayeg's favourite projects: a bus in Mexico City

Cover less-than-beautiful items in your own garden or building

Photography by Magda Sayeg and Cesar Ortego (bus). Reprinted with permission.

WANT TO GET
STARTED?
Q&A WITH MAGDA SAYEG

UNBORED: How did you get the idea for yarn bombing?

SAYEG: The city around us is made out of concrete and steel. I wanted to put something warm, fuzzy and handmade into it to remind people that everyone has responsibility for the world we live in.

UNBORED: Do you have a favourite project?

SAYEG: My favourite project was a bus in Mexico City. We wrapped the entire bus in knitting, and there were art classes inside the bus so that everyone in the community could be involved.

UNBORED: How can kids get started with yarn bombing?

SAYEG: Learn how to knit! The best way is to use your fingers instead of needles – it's called finger knitting. Search 'finger knitting' on YouTube for some demonstrations.

UNBORED: What do you say to people who say yarn bombing should be illegal, like graffiti?

SAYEG: Knit graffiti doesn't harm anything. It is not permanent, and it doesn't use anything like paint or glue that is bad for the environment. If someone doesn't like it, knitting is easy to remove.

UNBORED: How long should yarn bombs be left in place?

SAYEG: It depends on the place. If the knitting is exposed to bad weather and sunlight, it might start to fade after a month or two. If your installation starts to look like rubbish – if it's making things uglier instead of more beautiful – then remove it.

STAYCATION

Most of us are so busy going about our daily lives that we forget our city and county offer a lot of cool things to see and do. Taking a 'staycation' where you plan time on holiday but don't leave town is a fun and often inexpensive way to have a family trip.

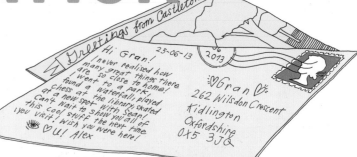

Treat your staycation like a holiday

That means no school, no homework, no errands, no chores for kids or grownups. Ease up on your tech, too. Don't waste your staycation texting.

Check in

If you can afford it, splurge on a hotel or bed and breakfast. Nothing makes you see your town in a new light more than waking up to the sights, smells and sounds of a new location. Cram everyone into the same room to make it feel more like a big party. Camping is another good option.

You can also swap houses with a family that lives in another part of town.

Do a little research

If you live in a place that's big enough to be mentioned in a guidebook, check one out of the library. Are there any museums, bike routes, botanical gardens, water parks, planetariums, book shops, bowling alleys or amusement parks that you never get to? Put them on your list! Check out your local entertainment listings to see if there are any special festivals or concerts.

Go behind the scenes

Police stations, fire stations, TV stations, zoos, sports stadiums and even cinemas often offer behind-the-scenes tours. If they don't, a polite phone call may persuade them to do so.

Break out the cameras

This is a holiday! Document it the same way you would if you'd travelled there by plane. Not just photos, but video, too.

Peek into history

Go seriously Olde Tyme and learn something about the history of where you live, whether it's a trip to a local historical society, an old house that's now a museum, or even reading roadside historical markers. The guides at historical societies have often lived in their town for decades. These guys really know their stuff and can help you get an idea of what it was like before you or even your grownups were born.

Go green

Few of us get enough time in nature. Find a green patch – a park, woods, a lake – and spend an entire afternoon there easing into the slower pace. Climb trees, burn a hole in a leaf with a magnifying glass, hunt for frogs or fireflies, or just spread out on a blanket and read a book.

Relax

Turn your home or hotel room into a spa. Take a bubble bath, paint your nails, light scented candles, dim the lights, and turn on your favourite music. Elsewhere in this book, you'll find instructions on making homemade facial masks and foot scrubs.

Illustrations by Heather Kasunick

DO YOU USE YOUR TECHNOLOGY OR DOES IT USE YOU?

By Douglas Rushkoff

I used to think that kids who grew up with computers in their homes and schools would understand them really well. Better than we grownups do, anyway. Most of us only had television sets when we were kids, and maybe a simple videogame console. Computers came much later, and when they did, they offered us a whole new world of possibilities.

Illustrations by Heather Kasunick

Television, you see, was a completely closed medium. We watched it all afternoon when we came home from school, but couldn't change anything about it. The only way we could affect what appeared on the TV was to change the channel. We could pick which programme we wanted to watch, but then we just watched it. Someone else, far away, made the programmes. We simply received them.

Maybe that's why it's so appropriate they called the stuff on television 'programming'. They weren't programming the TV sets; they were programming us viewers.

The Digital Revolution

The first computers most of us touched turned this whole situation on its head. They were basically like TV sets, except they also had keyboards. So now, instead of just watching what was on the TV, we could put stuff *onto* the monitor. Television changed from a thing that we watched to a thing that we made.

Imagine having a telephone for many years, but only using it as a radio. You'd pick up the receiver, and listen to the news or the weather or a song. And then imagine suddenly realising that you could talk through the thing, as well! That's how big a shift it was to see TV evolve into a computer.

But wait, there's more. Not only could we make our own content, the computer was an anything machine. You could make it be a typewriter, a paintbrush, a calculator… anything. All you needed to do was to give it a new set of instructions – a *program*. To use a computer was to create a program and then use it.

Sure, many of us got our programs from friends and schools instead of writing them ourselves, but we were aware that there were different programs for different jobs, and that we could have created any of these things ourselves, if we were willing to put the time in. (Just like we sometimes buy a sandwich at the delicatessen, even though we know how to put salami on a roll.) Using one kind of program encouraged us to work or play in a certain way, while using another encouraged something else; each program had tendencies, or biases, towards certain behaviours, mind-sets and approaches. We understood that, because we could read the commands in our programs, and alter them if necessary. That's why we enjoyed a sense of choice about what computers could do, and a feeling of command over them.

How programming got mysterious

Software companies didn't want computer users to make programs; they wanted to sell them software. So computers started getting more and more easy to use, thanks to pre-installed programs featuring attractive buttons and windows that made it possible for us to get things done without typing in any commands. But in the process, computers became more difficult to program for ourselves; we could no longer see how these programs were made. (It was like buying a pre-made sandwich, instead of choosing its ingredients at the delicatessen counter.) Now computers are so easy to use that we don't even need instruction manuals – but at what cost?

Today, people think of an 'app' as something that is downloaded from an App Store rather than something you build yourself. To those of us who know what a program really is, that's almost like saying a sand castle is something you buy. Or that swimming is something you go to the pool to watch. Or that telephones are for listening to music, instead of talking to friends.

As I watched computers becoming easier to use but more difficult for non-programmers to understand, I wrote books for grownups explaining that, as with any family immigrating to a new culture, it's the kids who learn the language and customs the best. I described grownups as slightly disoriented 'digital immigrants' and young people raised with computers and the internet as 'digital natives', who would instinctively know how digital technology works. Kids would be so good at programming, I predicted, that they would one day program humanity itself out of the terrible hole into which we have dug ourselves.

Oddly enough, however, most kids today seem to know – or care – less than grownups do about how computers and the internet, not to mention websites, smartphones and videogames, really work. Kids write with computers, make friends through Facebook and other online social networking services, and find information through Google. Having grown up with digital technology all around them, as a part of their 'natural' environment, kids tend to accept it exactly as it is, without question.

Don't take your tech for granted

Studies have shown that kids and young adults are less likely than grownups to be able to tell the difference between a news story and an advertisement. Kids also are less able than are grownups to figure what their digital technology wants from them – which is to say, to recognise the biases with which the technology was programmed.

All technologies have biases. It's true that 'guns don't kill people; people kill people.' But guns are much more likely to be used to kill people than, say, pillows are. Yes, a pillow can still be used to commit a murder, but it is much more biased towards sleeping. Guns are more biased towards killing.

Knowing the biases of a technology *before* you use it can save a lot of headaches later on. If we had really considered all the biases of the automobile before we made it a way of life, things might have turned out differently. People used to walk to work and back home for lunch. Cars are biased toward distance. So as we have built neighbourhoods around the needs of the car, we ended up having to travel long distances to get to work. Now we just take that for granted as a fact of life. We need cars, and we have to work hard to pay for the car to get us there.

When we use technologies in a passive, unthinking way, we risk changing our world and behaving in ways driven by our technologies' built-in biases. For example, think of the difference between the websites Amazon and Facebook. What does Amazon want you to do? Buy stuff. So every button, every paragraph, every pop-up window you see when you visit Amazon is designed to get you to buy stuff. Facebook, on the other hand, wants you to share information about yourself, because that information is valuable to the marketing companies and research firms who pay Facebook for access to it. That's why Facebook encourages you to list the bands and brands you like, and to 'friend' and 'like' everything in your universe. You aren't Facebook's customer; those businesses are. Your information is Facebook's product.

The people who program websites and TV shows and other technology and media – I mean the people who decide what these media should do, and for whom – do so on behalf of their real customers. For example, who is the customer of *X Factor*? Not you, the viewer, but Samsung's Galaxy phones, and London's luxury Corinthia Hotel, who advertise through the show and want viewers to buy their stuff. That's why the *X Factor* contestants talk to their celebrity mentors with Galaxy phones and stay at the Corinthia Hotel.

Apple's App Store encourages you to think of all your online purchasing as something that has to be orchestrated by Apple. The online stock trading platforms your grownups use are configured to make them want to trade more frequently, earning the companies behind them more commissions.

By figuring out the way your digital world is really put together, you gain the ability to see what your media and technology want from you. Only then will you be able to consciously choose which of these websites, entertainments and gadgets are worth your time and energy.

Program or be programmed

I hope some of you choose to go a step beyond working out what your media and technology wants from you. If you learn what programming is and how it works, you'll be learning to speak what amounts to a basic language of the twenty-first century.

Think about the way a great gamer approaches a new videogame. Sure, he may play the game as it's supposed to be played for a few dozen or hundred hours. But when he gets stuck, what does he do? He goes online to find the 'cheat codes' for the game.

Now, with infinite ammunition or extra-strength armour, he can get through the entire game. He's still playing the game, but from outside the confines of the original rules.

After that, if he really likes the game, the gamer goes back online to find its modification kit – a simple set of tools that lets a more advanced user 'mod' (change) the way the game looks and feels. Instead of running around in a dungeon fighting monsters, a kid might make a version of the game where players run around in a school fighting their teachers – much to the chagrin of parents and educators everywhere. He might upload his version of the game to the internet, watching with pride as other kids download his game and comment about it in gamers' forums. Some day that gamer might even start building original videogames – making the progression all the way from player to cheater to modder to programmer.

When humans first acquired language, we didn't just learn to listen, we learned to speak. When we got written language, we didn't just learn how to read, we learned how to write. And now that we have computers and the internet, we can't just settle for being users – especially when we can't trust the people programming these media and technologies to do so on our behalf.

Learning to program lets you see through the veil of reality as it is currently constructed, and beyond to the strings and wires through which the illusion is perpetuated. It's like going behind the scenes at Disneyland, where the real mechanics happen.

What's more, learning to program makes *everything* look different. You begin to see the other kinds of program running our world, from the marking system used to maintain the values of your school curriculum, to the economic operating system keeping the wealthy rich.

They're all just programs, and they're all accessible to anyone who cares to learn the code. It's a program-or-be-programmed world.

FIRST DAY OF
SCHOOL

AN EXCERPT FROM

TOM BROWN'S SCHOOL DAYS

by Thomas Hughes

Tom Brown's School Days (1857) is set at Rugby, which has in many ways become the stereotype of the English public school. Subsequent British and American school stories directly inspired by Hughes's popular book include Louisa May Alcott's *Little Men*, James Hilton's *Goodbye, Mr Chips*, J.D. Salinger's *The Catcher in the Rye*… and particularly *Harry Potter and the Philosopher's Stone*, not to mention J.K. Rowling's other Hogwarts books. Like Rugby, Hogwarts is obsessed with sports; though they didn't play Quidditch at Rugby in Tom Brown's day, the version of football they innovated in the 1850s is today known worldwide as… rugby. More importantly, in both *Tom Brown's School Days* and the Harry Potter series, when boarding-school students require guidance and assistance, they don't turn to their teachers (whom they fear as much as they respect) but to one another.

When the 11-year-old Tom Brown first arrives at Rugby in the middle of term time, he is befriended by Harry East − who becomes the Ron to Tom's Harry. The two will go on to have many adventures together… but first, East must procure for Brown the proper headwear.

I say, you fellow, is your name Brown?'
'Yes,' said Tom, in considerable astonishment, glad, however, to have lighted on some one already who seemed to know him.

'Ah, I thought so. You know my old aunt, Miss East. She lives somewhere down your way in Berkshire. She wrote to me that you were coming to-day, and asked me to give you a lift.'

Tom was somewhat inclined to resent the patronising air of his new friend, a boy of just about his own height and age, but gifted with the most transcendent coolness and assurance, which Tom felt to be aggravating and hard to bear, but couldn't for the life of him help admiring and envying – especially when young my lord begins hectoring two or three long loafing fellows, half porter, half stableman, with a strong touch of the blackguard, and in the end arranges with one of them, nicknamed Cooey, to carry Tom's luggage up to the School-house for sixpence.

'And hark 'ee, Cooey; it must be up in ten minutes, or no more jobs from me. Come along, Brown.' And away swaggers the young potentate, with his hands in his pockets, and Tom at his side.

'All right, sir,' says Cooey, touching his hat, with a leer and a wink at his companions.

'Hullo though,' says East, pulling up, and taking another look at Tom; 'this'll never do. Haven't you got a hat? We never wear caps here. Only the louts [*town boys*] wear caps. Bless you, if you were to go into the quadrangle with that thing on, I don't know what'd happen.' The very idea was quite beyond young Master East, and he looked unutterable things.

Tom thought his cap a very knowing affair, but confessed that he had a hat in his hat-box; which was accordingly at once extracted from the hind-boot, and Tom equipped in his go-to-meeting roof [*hat worn on the way to chapel*], as his new friend called it. But this didn't quite suit his fastidious taste in another minute, being too shiny; so, as they walk up the town, they dive into Nixon's the hatter's, and Tom is arrayed, to his utter astonishment, and without paying for it, in a regulation cat-skin at seven-and-sixpence, Nixon undertaking to send the best hat up to the matron's room, School-house, in half an hour.

'You can send in a note for a tile [*a tall silk hat*] on Monday, and make it all right, you know,' said Mentor [*i.e. a guide and adviser*]; 'we're allowed two seven-and-sixers a half [*two hats for each half-year, costing seven shillings and sixpence apiece*], besides what we bring from home.'

Tom by this time began to be conscious of his new social position and dignities, and to luxuriate in the realised ambition of being a public school-boy at last, with a vested right of spoiling two seven-and-sixers in half a year.

'You see,' said his friend, as they strolled up towards the school-gates, in explanation of his conduct, 'a great deal depends on how a fellow cuts up at first. If he's got nothing odd about him, and answers straightforward, and holds his head up, he gets on. Now, you'll do very well as to rig, all but that cap. You see I'm doing the handsome thing by you, because my father knows yours; besides, I want to please the old lady. She gave me half a sov. this half, and perhaps'll double it next, if I keep in her good books.'

There's nothing for candour like a lower-school boy, and East was a genuine specimen – frank, hearty, and good-natured, well-satisfied with himself and his position, and choke-full of life and spirits, and all the Rugby prejudices and traditions which he had been able to get together in the long course of one half-year during which he had been at the School-house.

And Tom, notwithstanding his bumptiousness, felt friends with him at once, and began sucking in all his ways and prejudices, as fast as he could understand them.

East was great in the character of cicerone [*guide*]. He carried Tom through the great gates, where were only two or three boys. These satisfied themselves with the stock questions, 'You fellow, what's your name? Where do you come from? How old are you? Where do you board?' and, 'What form are you in?' […]

'And now come in and see my study – we shall have just time before dinner; and afterwards, before calling over, we'll do the close.'

Tom followed his guide through the School-house hall, which opens into the quadrangle. It is a great room, thirty feet long and eighteen high, or thereabouts, with two great tables running the whole length, and two large fireplaces at the side, with blazing fires in them, at one of which some dozen boys were standing and lounging, some of whom shouted to East to stop; but he shot through with his convoy, and landed him in the long, dark passages, with a large fire at the end of each, upon which the studies opened. Into one of these, in the bottom passage, East bolted with our hero, slamming and bolting the door behind them, in case of pursuit from the hall, and Tom was for the first time in a Rugby boy's citadel.

He hadn't been prepared for separate studies, and was not a little astonished and delighted with the palace in question.

It wasn't very large, certainly, being about six feet long by four broad. It couldn't be called light, as there were bars and a grating to the window; which little precautions were necessary in the studies on the ground-floor looking out into the close, to prevent the exit of small boys after locking up, and the entrance of contraband articles. But it was uncommonly comfortable to look at, Tom thought. The space under the window at the farther end was occupied by a square table covered with a reasonably clean and whole red and blue check tablecloth; a hard-seated sofa covered with red stuff occupied one side, running up to the end, and making a seat for one, or by sitting close, for two, at the table and a good stout wooden chair afforded a seat to another boy, so that three could sit and work together. The walls were wainscoted half-way up, the wainscot being covered with green baize, the remainder with a bright-patterned paper, on which hung three or four prints of dogs' heads; Grimaldi winning the Aylesbury steeple-chase [*a famous 1832 horse race*]; Amy Robsart [*the heroine of an 1821 Walter Scott novel*], the reigning Waverley beauty of the day; and Tom Crib [*a champion boxer*], in a posture of defence, which did no credit to the science of that hero, if truly represented. Over the door were a row of hat-pegs, and on each side bookcases with cupboards at the bottom, shelves and cupboards being filled indiscriminately with school-books, a cup or two, a mouse-trap and candlesticks, leather straps, a fustian bag, and some curious-looking articles which puzzled Tom not a little, until his friend explained that they were climbing-irons, and showed their use. A cricket-bat and small fishing-rod stood up in one corner.

This was the residence of East and another boy in the same form, and had more interest for Tom than Windsor Castle, or any other residence in the British Isles.

WHAT'S RIGHT ABOUT BEING WRONG

Q&A WITH KATHRYN SCHULZ

Kathryn Schulz is a *wrongologist*. OK, that's a made-up word. What's true is that she researches, writes and lectures on the topic of being wrong – which includes everything from why we get embarrassed when we botch a maths question to the fact that making mistakes can lead to amazing artistic, scientific and personal discoveries.

Schulz's book *Being Wrong: Adventures in the Margin of Error* is a great resource about wrongness for grownups. We asked her to help us understand what's so right about being wrong.

UNBORED: Why do people like to be right?

SCHULZ: People like to be right for a good reason – it's an experience that feels great! When you've worked hard to understand a passage in a book or solve a maths or science problem, being right shows that you've been a good listener, paid attention and practised. That's something that should make anyone feel proud.

That said, some of us also like to be right to pump up our egos. We take being right as a sign that we're really smart and responsible. And that can be a problem. For example, it might feel really good to tell someone 'I told you so.' But we can get so caught up in being right that we forget how it feels for the other person who is now being told they are wrong.

UNBORED: Can two people be right, if they have different answers to the same question?

SCHULZ: Absolutely! There are questions that have two answers, such as 'What's your favourite colour?' Everybody knows it's fine if my favourite colour is green and your favourite colour is blue. Likewise, everybody knows it's not OK if I think the sky is green and the grass is blue. Maybe you and your family are vegetarians and believe strongly that it's wrong to eat meat, but your best friend's family loves to grill steaks and burgers. Does that make them wrong? It's important to be able to listen when someone has a different version of what's right than you do. It would be great if everyone's first response when they encounter something different is to be curious about it. I'd love to see the phrase 'tell me more about that' become as popular as saying 'hello'.

UNBORED: Why do people dislike being wrong?

SCHULZ: I'm not trying to claim that all mistakes are wonderful. A patient can die if a doctor makes a serious error. If a car crashes because the brakes weren't properly installed, that's terrible.

But it doesn't help anyone if we act like mistakes are awful unacceptable things that are only made by stupid, irresponsible people. That's not true – we all make mistakes – and acting like

Illustrations by Heather Kasunick

mistakes are always a bad thing only hurts people, including ourselves. That attitude also makes it harder to talk openly about mistakes, understand why they happened, and prevent them from happening again. I don't want to suggest that there's something wrong with feeling embarrassed in the face of one's mistakes – that's pretty natural, I'd say. Unfortunately, schools often reinforce this idea that it's somehow shameful to get things wrong.

UNBORED: Why is it OK to be wrong?

SCHULZ: Getting things wrong is fundamental to how we learn. Besides, always having to be right is stressful – not to mention impossible! Accepting that you will sometimes be wrong frees you from the anxiety of having to be perfect.

UNBORED: Can being wrong lead to great discoveries?

SCHULZ: Any writer knows that you have to write a lot of bad drafts to get a good book. For scientists, proving that a theory is wrong helps them change and expand their understanding of the world. And that's true for the rest of us, too.

Scientists *try* to work out if they're wrong – but sometimes, accidental mistakes produce great results. When Scottish scientist Alexander Fleming was studying a bacteria known as Staphylococcus, he accidentally grew a mould that helped him discover penicillin, one of the most effective antibiotics available today.

UNBORED: How can kids embrace the good side of wrong?

SCHULZ: A friend of mine came up with the One 'I Told You So' Per Lifetime Rule. If you tell yourself that you only get to say that phrase once in your entire life, it makes you stop and think whether or not claiming you are right is worth it. Saying 'I told you so' can wreck relationships.

Being wrong doesn't mean we are intellectually or morally inferior. It's how we make progress.

FIVE CLASSICS
OF WRONG

One of the great themes of literature is a character's realisation that she has been wrong about the way that she sees another character, or everything. Though it usually comes with a large dose of embarrassment, in the end this perspective-altering revelation always turns out to be a good thing.

    Here are five novels in which wrongness is an important theme. In some cases, it's clear to the reader from the start that the main character is wrong. In other cases, a key part of the reading experience is seeing the character's mistakes through that character's eyes.

1813
PRIDE AND PREJUDICE
By Jane Austen
Having made a snap judgement about Mr Darcy early in the story, Elizabeth Bennet continually misinterprets his actions.

1843
A CHRISTMAS CAROL
By Charles Dickens
Ebenezer Scrooge is so heartless that it takes three ghosts to show him the error of his ways.

1960
TO KILL A MOCKINGBIRD
By Harper Lee
Jem and Scout believe that Boo Radley is a scary monster; in fact, he is protective and benevolent.

1964
HARRIET THE SPY
By Louise Fitzhugh
Harriet is judgemental about her friends. When they find out how she feels, she must change her ways.

1967
THE OUTSIDERS
By S.E. Hinton
The Greasers and the Socs think they have nothing in common. But they enjoy watching the same sunsets.

DO THE RESEARCH!

By Jessamyn West

Wondering about something? Here are a few tips on using a library and doing research online.

HOW TO USE A LIBRARY

Libraries are public institutions – funded by taxes. So if you have suggestions for how your library could be better, let them know.

Libraries are free, forever. So use them – and use them often! Each public library operates differently, but most can help you do the following.

Find information

An important part of what librarians do is help you find information, whether it's for homework or just something that you're curious about. They enjoy helping people in their communities by answering questions.

Visit the librarians at your local library, or get in touch with them over the phone.

Ask the librarians anything: 'Can you find a photograph of my house from before I lived in it?' 'Where can I find zombie-based retellings of classic stories from literature?' 'What is the oldest recording that I can listen to on the internet?' You'll be surprised how much information they can dig up.

Read

Of course, libraries have great books on those shelves. Many libraries also offer e-books and audiobooks, which you can read or listen to from your own personal device.

If the library doesn't have a book you want, don't give up. Sometimes, they'll buy it at your request. Or they might borrow it from another library through the interlibrary loan system. If someone else has checked out the book you want, you can reserve it – you'll be notified when it's back in the library. You can do most of these things online.

Larger libraries often have great collections of magazines or graphic novels – and you can ask them to let you know when new ones are available.

Get recommendations

You can ask your librarian for recommendations: 'If I liked this book, what else would I like?'

Public libraries have a commitment to privacy and intellectual freedom. This means that you can check out whatever you want, read whatever you want, or ask a librarian any question that you want and that information stays private.

Play games

Many libraries offer gaming events and provide games to play at the library – or to check out so you can play them at home. If you're new to gaming, your library may have gaming magazines and books, too.

Use computers

If you don't have a computer at home, libraries have public computers that anyone can use.

Illustrations by Heather Kasunick

HOW TO DO RESEARCH ONLINE

Doing research online involves a little bit of legwork, some good guesswork, and time to evaluate your results.

Go beyond Google

Not everything online is accessible via a Google search. Luckily, there are helpful websites that list all sorts of online research resources.

- Wikipedia (wikipedia.org) is a user-created encyclopaedia. Its longer articles include citations (references to original sources, online or offline) at the end.

  Like any encyclopaedia, Wikipedia is a good starting point for research but should be used to *find* original source materials, not as an original source itself. If you can't verify a fact that you find in Wikipedia, do not rely on it.

- Your own public library. Copies of older magazines, decades-old obituaries, and other information may be locked away in databases that your library card can unlock.

Make good choices about search terms

Search engines are mostly pattern-matching machines, so they might not know, for example, that 9/11 and September Eleventh refer to the same thing. Here are some tips on getting good search results.

- Figure out how to talk to the search engine. If your question is *What are the lyrics to Rebecca Black's popular song 'Friday'?* then you should type the following string of words into the search box: *"Rebecca Black" Friday song lyrics*.

- Each search engine creates a search term (or *query*) in slightly different ways. You can save time learning things like how to exclude terms (for example, vampires but not Twilight), and how to search for words in a particular order by using quotation marks ("to thine own self be true"). Also, search engines offer searching tips and advanced search options.

- Make sure you've spelled everything correctly!

Evaluate your results

The search engine has delivered a first set of results. Before you click on any of them, ask yourself if the results look useful.

- Did you, for example, get a lot of President Bill Clinton links when you were looking for the funky musician George Clinton? If the results aren't useful, improve your query – in this case, search for the phrase "George Clinton" in quotes.

- Keep track of what you've found, by using the bookmarking feature of your web browser, or a bookmarking website like Delicious, or an app like Evernote.

BANNED BOOKS
YOU SHOULD READ

Imagine a library that wasn't allowed to loan books by Roald Dahl or J.K. Rowling – yet novels by these authors are among the most frequently banned or challenged in recent years! Older books targeted by would–be censors include J.R.R. Tolkien's *Lord of the Rings* series, Anne Frank's *The Diary of a Young Girl*, and Mary Shelley's *Frankenstein*.

Books are challenged or banned because a person or group strongly believes that library visitors (kids in particular) need to be protected from 'inappropriate' ideas or information.

Free speech advocates argue that only parents should have the right and responsibility to restrict access to certain library books – and even then, they should only restrict their own children's access. Thanks to the efforts of librarians and others, the majority of library books challenged each year are not banned or restricted.

Here are five 'great banned books' for kids, which we picked from banned-books.org.uk, a website created by a consortium of British libraries.

ADVENTURES OF HUCKLEBERRY FINN
By Mark Twain, 1884

Huckleberry Finn is a 13-year-old runaway who floats down the Mississippi River in the company of Jim, an escaping slave. They encounter robbers, slavers, feuding families, and con artists. At first Huck worries that it's wrong to help a slave escape, but because Jim is such a good, loving person, Huck changes his mind. Though Huck and the novel are anti-racist, some object to the book's use of a racial slur common at the time.

TO KILL A MOCKINGBIRD
By Harper Lee, 1960

Jean Louise 'Scout' Finch, a tomboy, recalls growing up in a rural Alabama town during the Great Depression. When her lawyer father, Atticus, is appointed to defend a black man for a crime he didn't commit, Scout learns how important it is to obey your conscience, no matter what the consequences. Some object to the fact that the novel (and Atticus) condemns racism but not racists.

REVOLTING RHYMES
By Roald Dahl, 1982

The author of *Charlie and the Chocolate Factory* and *James and the Giant Peach* puts a macabre twist on six folk tales. Dahl's rhyming version of 'Goldilocks', for example, concludes with the title character being devoured by the three bears as well-deserved punishment for stealing their food and breaking their furniture. Note that the original folk tales on which these stories are based were intended for an audience of grownups as well as kids. Almost all of Dahl's books have appeared on a banned or challenged book list at some point, but this title more than the others – because some feel it is too gruesome.

HIS DARK MATERIALS
By Philip Pullman, 1995–2000 series

12-year-old Lyra Belacqua finds herself caught in the middle of a cosmic war, on one side of which is the Authority (who is mistaken for God by the church to which Lyra's mother belongs), and on the other side of which is her father, the scientist Lord Asriel. Witches, zeppelins and armour-wearing polar bears make an appearance. Some feel the series is disrespectful of Christianity.

HARRY POTTER AND THE PHILOSOPHER'S STONE
By J.K. Rowling, 1997

When Harry, an 11-year-old orphan, learns of his magical destiny, he enrols at the Hogwarts School of Witchcraft and Wizardry. Some feel that the novel contains occult or pagan imagery. In 2005, Cardinal Joseph Ratzinger, who became pope later that year, described the Harry Potter series as 'subtle seductions, which act unnoticed and by this deeply distort Christianity in the soul before it can grow properly'.

Illustration by Heather Kasunick

PLAYGROUND COUNTING-OUT GAMES

When you're playing Tig or Hide and Seek, how do you select who's It? Instead of arguing, the most fun way to decide is to turn the choosing process itself into a counting-out game.

Here are a few that kids have played for decades.

Spuds Up

Everyone stands in a circle and puts both fists ('spuds', an old slang word for potatoes) forward. One person (the counter) chants:

> One potato
> two potato
> three potato
> four.
>
> Five potato
> six potato
> seven potato
> more.

The counter

The counter uses her chin as a 'potato'

While naming each potato, the counter moves her fist around the circle, tapping each player's spuds in order; when she gets around to herself, she taps her own chin, then taps the fist that she's not using for counting out. Whichever spud she's tapping when the counter gets to the word 'more' is eliminated – so that player puts his spud behind his back. (If the counter's chin is out, she doesn't tap it the next time around.) Then she starts the rhyme again, beginning with the next spud.

When a player's two spuds are out, he leaves the circle. The game continues until there is only one spud left – and that player is It.

TIP: If you don't have much time to play, each player can just put one spud in – instead of two.

Illustrations by Mister Reusch

British rhymes

Ip-dip-doo
The cat's got the flu
The dog's got chicken pox
And so have you.

Ip-dip, sky blue
Who's It? Not you.
Not because you're dirty
Not because you're clean
My mother says you're on
    the football team.

Ip-dip-dip
My little ship
Sailing on the water
Like a cup and saucer
But you are not It.

Ippa-dippa-dation
My operation
How many people
Are waiting at the station?

Ip-dip-doo
Doggie did a poo
Who trod in it?
Out goes you.

American rhymes

You can make up your own
counting-out rhymes, or try
some of the ones that we've
collected.

Ink-a-dink
A bottle of ink
Cork fell out
And you stink.

Superman, Superman fly away
Superman, Superman save
    the day.

Skunk in the barnyard, pee-yew!
Somebody farted, that's you.

Pizza pizza pizza pie
If you eat it, you will die
If you die, I will cry
Pizza pizza pizza pie.

Boy Scout, Boy Scout
Please step right out.

More counting-out games

Tarzan, Tarzan, in a tree
How many gallons did he pee?

Bubblegum, bubblegum,
    in a dish
How many pieces do you wish?

*If the counter was pointing to you
when she got to 'pee' or 'wish', you
say a number between 1 and 10.
Then the counter points around
the circle while counting, and
whichever person she ends up
on is not It.*

Engine, Engine Number Nine
Going down Chicago line
If the train goes off the track
Do you want your money back?

*If the counter was pointing to
you when she got to 'back', you
say 'Yes' or 'No.' Then the counter
spells out Y-E-S or N-O around
the circle, and whichever person
'gets' the last letter is not It.*

My mother and your mother
    were hanging up clothes
My mother punched your
    mother right in the nose
What colour was the blood?

*The counter then spells out
whichever colour was chosen.
Whichever person 'gets' the last
letter of the word is not It.*

The last player with a
spud in the game is It

HISTORICAL COUNTING-OUT GAMES

Wee-Wo, Wack
In the early nineteenth
century, children in New
York used the following
counting-out rhyme:

Hannah, Man, Mona, Mike
Barcelona, Bono, Strike
Hare, Ware, Frown, Vanack
Harrico, Warico, Wee-Wo,
    Wack.

One spot, two spot
In the 1933 Marx Brothers
movie *Duck Soup*, which your
grownups should show you
straight away, the following
counting-out rhyme is used:

One spot, two spot, zig-zag,
    tear
Pop-die, pennygot,
    tennyum, tear
Harum-scarum, rip 'em,
    tear 'em
Tay, taw, toe.

BACK OF THE CLASSROOM GAMES

By Josh

Once upon a time there was no such thing as a smartphone, an iPod or even a handheld videogame.

When we were bored – on long car trips, in doctors' waiting rooms, and sometimes even in the back of the classroom – we'd play these games.

THE CIRCLE–HAND GAME

According to legend, the Circle-Hand Game (sometimes called the Hole-Tempting Game) was invented in the 1920s by students at the City College of New York. We also hear that every submarine crew plays this game – which makes sense, because they must get pretty bored.

Using your thumb and forefinger, make the 'OK' sign, otherwise known as a circle. If you can trick a friend into looking directly at your circle-hand, you score a point. But if they only look at it out of the corner of their eye and can poke their finger into the circle-hand, then they score a point. However, if you trap their finger in your circle-hand, you score 10 points.

One common rule is that you must not raise your circle-hand above your waist; a less strict variation allows you to place your circle-hand anywhere except directly in front of someone's face.

Another version of the game allows you to lightly punch someone in the shoulder when you score a point against them; this can be amusing, but your grownups will not like it. After you punch, you must wipe off the punch. If you forget to wipe off the punch, the person you punched gets to punch you 10 times.

Try these tips:

- Make a circle-hand, and don't say anything to your intended victim; even if she knows what you're doing, eventually she won't be able to help herself – she'll look.

- Make a circle-hand, then say something like, 'Oh! What's this I found in my pocket?' Or 'Hey, is this yours?' Or: 'Does this belong to you?'

- If you're playing the punching variation of the Circle-Hand Game, one good trick is to make a circle-hand on your shoulder just before someone punches you there.

Illustrations by Mister Reusch

COIN FOOTBALL

You'll need three coins of the same size, the larger the better. Sit facing your opponent across a table.

Defence

1. The defending player forms a football goal by placing her palms on the edge of the table with the tips of her stretched-out thumbs touching; or, sometimes, by placing her fists on the edge of the table, with only her little fingers extended.

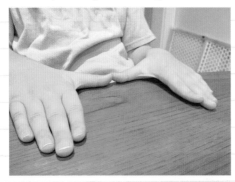

Attack

1. The attacking player forms the coins into a triangle, with one coin near the edge of the table, and the other two coins in front of that one.

2. The attacking player then taps sharply down on the first coin, sending the other two sliding across the table; flicking is also OK.

3. Next, the attacking player chooses one of the three coins and tries to tap it so that it slides between the other two coins without touching them.

4. He repeats this until he's able to tap a coin into the goal – one point! If he hits one of the coins with the tapped coin, or hits a coin off the table, or isn't able to slide a coin between the other two coins, then it's the other player's turn.

PAPER RUGBY

First, you need to make a rugby ball using an A4 sheet of paper. Tear one out of a notebook or borrow one from your grownup's printer.

Make the rugby ball

1. Fold the A4 sheet of paper twice in half, lengthwise.

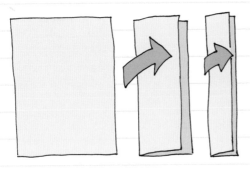

2. With the paper oriented vertically in front of you, fold the lower right corner diagonally up and to the left, forming a triangle shape. Now fold straight up, so the strip's bottom edge is straight across again.

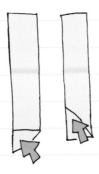

3. Next, fold the lower left corner diagonally up and to the right, forming another triangle shape. Continue until you reach the top,

4. Finally, fold the top edge's corners down (to make it more tuck-able); then tuck the top edge down into the rugby ball's final fold.

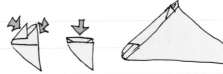

The pitch and the rules

- Now that you have a rugby ball, you'll need a pitch; any tabletop will do, though rectangular ones are the most rugby pitch-like.

- The team with the ball advances down the pitch by flicking the rugby ball, either with a thumb or finger. You only get one flick per turn; if the ball stops with any part of it sticking out over the far edge of the table, it's a try – five points!

- If the ball goes off the side of the table, it's placed back on the table at the approximate section of the 'touchline' where it went off.

- If the ball stops short of the far edge of the table, then you make a drop goal attempt: use a finger from one hand to hold the rugby ball vertically, and use a finger from your other hand to flick the ball into the air and through the goal posts. (What goal posts? The defending player forms goal posts by touching the tips of her stretched-out thumbs together, and pointing her fingers straight up in the air. Please note that you do not want to flick the rugby ball into someone's eye!) If the drop goal is successful, you score one point.

- It can also be fun to play a version of the game where you just kick drop goals back and forth.

FOOL YOUR FRIENDS INTO SAVING THE PLANET

By Sophie Meyer

If you care about the environment, you probably want to tell your friends so that they will care, too. The problem is, most kids don't like being told what to do, especially by someone their own age.

So you have to do what boring teachers *don't* do: instead of lecturing your friends, make personal choices that will subtly persuade your friends to ask *you* about environmentalism. Instead of spreading a message, spread curiosity.

Convincing a group of kids to agree on anything, even which pizza to order or which movie to see, can be a Herculean task. If you've already tried handing out pamphlets on carbon emissions, marching up and down your school hallway shouting environmental slogans, or wearing a 'Save the Whales' T-shirt, you may have noticed that your peers can be very good at ignoring you. That's why in order to really make a difference, activists need to be sneaky. Here are a few strategies.

Share your eco life

Every time I welcome a new friend into my home, their first response is puzzlement: *What's up with this family?* they wonder. From our aversion to turning on the air-conditioning – often seen as a necessity here in scorching-hot Arizona – to the chicken coop we built from salvaged materials, my family isn't what you'd call normal.

The first time my friend Alex came over, he asked of the big orange bowl in our sink, 'What's this for?' I explained that we collected our dishwater and used it to water our plants. 'Huh,' he said. However, the next time Alex visited, he brought Tim with him. 'Why is there an orange bowl in your sink?' Tim asked. Alex answered before I could: 'It's for collecting their dishwater so they can use it to water the plants.' How had Tim missed the memo?

Alex had originally been sceptical, but because I'd invited him to see the way I lived, now he was an insider – and his tone made our homegrown water-conservation method seem commonplace.

Give conversation–starting gifts

If your friends realise you're trying to get them to ask you about environmentalism, they won't ask. So get sneaky!

For example, everybody loves good food, right? Our chickens lay brown, green and even speckled eggs. Who would suspect such a colourful

Illustrations by Heather Kasunick

gift might cloak ulterior motives? When I bring a carton full of eggs to my friends' parents, kids and adults alike respond with interest and excitement: 'Oooh, why are they so colourful? What made you want chickens? Where do you keep them? What do they eat?' They've walked right into my trap! They're asking for a quick lecture on composting, sustainable chicken coop construction, and eating locally.

Homegrown fruit and vegetables also make great gifts – and conversation starters. Really, any environmentally friendly gift can do the trick.

Don't make people feel bad

Vegetarianism and other special diets make kids curious, so your mealtime decisions can be real conversation-starters. Unfortunately, a shrill announcement that you don't eat certain foods can alienate people. Instead, allow your friends and other peers to notice for themselves that you've stopped eating meat, or are otherwise making more sustainable choices. If you let them frame their own questions, it won't feel like a lecture – and they'll be more likely to listen to your answer.

My friend Cleo is a vegan. When sitting down at our lunch table, one can't help but notice that her lunch bag contains hummus and veggies, tofu dogs or edamame. She orders her burritos minus cheese, sour cream, lard tortillas and any beans cooked with meat. When asked why she makes these choices, Cleo responds with disdain: 'I just think it's really messed-up that some people think it's OK to eat animals. Not only is it cruel, it's destroying the planet.' Few people ask her any follow-up questions.

Sara is also a vegan, but she takes a different approach: 'For me, becoming a vegan just felt like the right thing to do,' she says. 'I don't like the idea of eating animals, both because of their inhumane treatment and the burden that the meat industry places on the environment.' Instead of making her friends feel stupid, Sara invites more questions. Her answer is about her own choices, not about the bad choices of others.

If you're a kid, you're probably used to being given answers to questions you didn't ask, and consequently don't care about. You're probably familiar with the routine of going to school and being told what you need to know, regardless of what you want to know. You're probably sick of it; I know I am. Maybe, if you got to ask your own questions, you'd find answers that matter to you.

Celebrate different approaches

Each of us can protect and improve the planet through her unique efforts. While I raise chickens, you might be organising an effort to pick up rubbish on your street, or riding your bike to school. It's this variety that makes environmentalism interesting and exciting.

The art of persuasion begins with having something worthwhile to talk about; and interesting conversations begin with diverse experiences and ideas. If you don't know what your cause is yet, don't worry! There's plenty of work to be done, and room enough for everyone to lend a hand.

Think about what problems bother you, what issues interest you, and what initiatives excite you. Start your search close to home: in your neighbourhood, at your school or at your church.

Remember that your choices matter

It's not just grownups whose choices affect the environment. If you can plan for your grownups to drop you off where you want to go on their way to work or the shops instead of making a special trip, you'll help them waste less petrol and cut down on their carbon emissions. If you can walk, ride your bike or use public transport to get where you're going, that's even better.

Think about every decision in terms of the planet you want to grow up on. Ask yourself: 'What am I doing well? What can I do better?'

Set goals

How many people will ask you about your choices this week? Who will you infect with enthusiasm?

What starts with you can become something greater. All it takes is a lot of creativity, enthusiasm, thoughtfulness… and a little sneakiness.

HOW TO SURVIVE
SUSTAINABLY

AN EXCERPT FROM

THE SWISS FAMILY ROBINSON

by Johann David Wyss

In **The Swiss Family Robinson** (1812), when a Swiss pastor, his wife, their four sons (Fritz, Ernest, Jack and Franz), and two dogs (Turk and Flora) are shipwrecked in the East Indies, they don't despair. Fortified not only by their religious faith but also by a commitment to what we would now call sustainability (the responsible management of natural resources), the resilient group figures out how to produce everything they need from soap to wellies, build an amazing treehouse, and feed themselves – without ever ruining the fragile ecosystem of their new home.

This excerpt is from early in the novel, when 14-year-old Fritz is going exploring with his father and Turk. Fritz's father, who is the story's narrator, proves to be a capable natural scientist – and someone deeply concerned with preserving the natural world.

We proceeded, and entering a little wood that extended to the sea, we rested in the shade, near a clear stream, and took some refreshment. We were surrounded by unknown birds, more remarkable for brilliant plumage than for the charm of their voice. Fritz thought he saw some monkeys among the leaves, and Turk began to be restless, smelling about, and barking very loud. Fritz was gazing up into the trees, when he fell over a large round substance, which he brought to me, observing that it might be a bird's nest. I thought it more likely to be a cocoa-nut. The fibrous covering had reminded him of the description he had read of the nests of certain birds; but, on breaking the shell, we found it was indeed a cocoa-nut, but quite decayed and uneatable.

Fritz was astonished; where was the sweet milk that Ernest had talked of?

I told him the milk was only in the half-ripe nuts; that it thickened and hardened as the nut ripened, becoming a kernel. This nut had perished from remaining above ground. If it had been in the earth, it would have vegetated, and burst the shell. I advised my son to try if he could not find a perfect nut.

After some search, we found one, and sat down to eat it, keeping our own provision for dinner. The nut was somewhat rancid; but we enjoyed it, and then continued our journey. We were some time before we got through the wood, being frequently obliged to clear a road for ourselves, through the entangled brushwood, with our hatchets. At last we entered the open plain again, and had a clear view before us. The forest still extended about a stone's throw to our right, and Fritz, who was always on the look-out for discoveries, observed a remarkable tree, here and there, which he approached to examine; and he soon called me to see this wonderful tree, with wens growing on the trunk.

On coming up, I was overjoyed to find this tree, of which there were a great number, was the gourd-tree, which bears fruit on the trunk. Fritz asked if these were sponges. I told him to bring me one, and I would explain the mystery.

'There is one,' said he, 'very like a pumpkin, only harder outside.'

'Of this shell,' said I, 'we can make plates, dishes, basins, and flasks. We call it the gourd-tree.'

Fritz leaped for joy. 'Now my dear mother will be able to serve her soup properly.'

I asked him if he knew why the tree bore the fruit on its trunk, or on the thick branches only. He immediately replied, that the smaller branches would not bear the weight of the fruit. He asked me if this fruit was eatable.

'Harmless, I believe,' said I; 'but by no means delicate. Its great value to savage nations consists in the shell, which they use to contain their food, and drink, and even cook in it.'

Fritz could not comprehend how they could cook in the shell without burning it. I told him the shell was not placed on the fire; but, being filled with cold water, and the fish or meat placed in it, red-hot stones are, by degrees, introduced into the water, till it attains sufficient heat to cook the food, without injuring the vessel. We then set about making our dishes and plates. I showed Fritz a better plan of dividing the gourd than with a knife. I tied a string tightly round the nut, struck it with the handle of my knife till an incision was made, then tightened it till the nut was separated into two equally-sized bowls. Fritz had spoiled his gourd by cutting it irregularly with his knife. I advised him to try and make spoons of it, as it would not do for basins now. I told him I had learnt my plan from books of travels. It is the practice of the savages, who have no knives, to use a sort of string, made from the bark of trees, for this purpose.

'But how can they make bottles,' said he.

'That requires some preparation,' replied I. 'They tie a bandage round the young gourd near the stalk, so that the part at liberty expands in a round form, and the compressed part remains narrow. They then open the top, and extract the contents by putting in pebbles and shaking it. By this means they have a complete bottle.'

We worked on. Fritz completed a dish and some plates, to his great satisfaction, but we considered, that being so frail, we could not carry them with us. We therefore filled them with sand, that the sun might not warp them, and left them to dry, till we returned.

As we went on, Fritz amused himself with cutting spoons from the rind of the gourd, and I tried to do the same with the fragments of the cocoa-nut; but I must confess my performances were inferior to those I had seen in the museum in London, the work of the South Sea islanders. We laughed at our spoons, which would have required mouths from ear to ear to eat with them. Fritz declared that the curve of the rind was the cause of that defect: if the spoons had been smaller, they would have been flat; and you might as well eat soup with an oyster-shell as with a shovel.

[...]

We proceeded towards a pleasant wood of palm-trees; but before reaching it, had to pass through an immense number of reeds, which greatly obstructed our road. We were, moreover, fearful of treading on the deadly serpents who choose such retreats. We made Turk walk before us to give notice, and I cut a long, thick cane as a weapon of defence. I was surprised to see a glutinous juice oozing from the end of the cut cane; I tasted it, and was convinced that we had met with a plantation of sugar-canes. I sucked more of it, and found myself singularly refreshed. I said nothing to Fritz, that he might have the pleasure of making the discovery himself. He was walking a few paces before me, and I called to him to cut himself a cane like mine, which he did, and soon found out the riches it contained.

He cried out in ecstasy, 'Oh, papa! papa! syrup of sugar-cane! delicious! How delighted will dear mamma, and my brothers be, when I carry some to them!' He went on, sucking pieces of cane so greedily, that I checked him, recommending moderation. He was then content to take some pieces to regale himself as he walked home, loading himself with a huge burden for his mother and brothers.

We now entered the wood of palms to eat our dinner, when suddenly a number of monkeys, alarmed by our approach, and the barking of the dog, fled like lightning to the tops of the trees; and then grinned frightfully at us, with loud cries of defiance. As I saw the trees were cocoa-palms, I hoped to obtain, by means of the monkeys, a supply of the nuts in the half-ripe state, when filled with milk. I held Fritz's arm, who was preparing to shoot at them, to his great vexation, as he was irritated against the poor monkeys for their derisive gestures; but I told him, that though no patron of monkeys myself, I could not allow it. We had no right to kill any animal except in defence, or as a means of supporting life. Besides, the monkeys would be of more use to us living than dead, as I would show him. I began to throw stones at the monkeys, not being able, of course, to reach the place of their retreat, and they, in their anger, and in the spirit of imitation, gathered the nuts and hurled them on us in such quantities, that we had some difficulty in escaping from them. We had soon a large stock of cocoa-nuts.

Fritz enjoyed the success of the stratagem, and, when the shower subsided, he collected as many as he wished. We then sat down, and tasted some of the milk through the three small holes, which we opened with our knives. We then divided some with our hatchets, and quenched our thirst with the liquor, which has not, however, a very agreeable flavour. We liked best a sort of thick cream which adheres to the shells, from which we scraped it with our spoons, and mixing it with the juice of the sugar-cane, we produced a delicious dish. Turk had the rest of the lobster, which we now despised, with some biscuit.

We then got up, I tied some nuts together by their stems, and threw them over my shoulder. Fritz took his bundle of canes, and we set out homewards.

GREEN
YOUR CLEAN

By Helen Cordes

We all know that we've got to reduce pollution. We try to walk or bike instead of riding in smog-making cars, because we want a clean planet. Ironically, though, our efforts to keep ourselves and our homes clean can create other, equally nasty types of pollution.

Many of the cleaning products we use contain chemicals that can foul the water and air, and harm us too. Detergents for dishes and laundry often have chemicals called surfactants – substances that surround the dirt, break it up, and take it down the drain. These surfactants then flow into rivers, where they can keep fish and other marine life from getting enough oxygen. Detergents may also contain phosphates, which cause an overgrowth of algae that prevents sunlight and oxygen from reaching animal and plant life in the water.

Many body products that we put on our hair and skin also have risky ingredients – which is a big problem, when you consider that people your age use an average of 15 of these chemical-laden products a day. Parabens (preservatives) and phthalates (softening and fragrance-enhancing chemicals) are commonly found in makeup and shampoo, among other body products. These chemicals can alter our hormones. And when they find their way into the water and soil, these chemicals cause animals to suffer from hormone disruption; this has led, for example, to frogs, fish, birds and other creatures becoming infertile.

Not to worry – you don't have to give up your sparkly clean status. Just use nontoxic cleaning and body product alternatives. Your body and the animal kingdom will thank you.

HOME CLEANERS

It's easy to switch to healthier household cleaning supplies, because most use the same safe, cheap ingredients: bicarbonate of soda, vinegar, salt, borax, liquid Castile soap and washing soda. You can find these ingredients in your own home or at supermarkets or chemists. Ask your grownups to stock up on a basic stash of ingredients and reusable containers, and remind them of how much money they'll save with safer cleaning ingredients. Britons spend an average of £163 on cleaning products each year!

Spray cleaner

Mix 1 teaspoon Castile soap, 2 tablespoons white vinegar and 1 teaspoon borax with 2 cupfuls hot water. You can add a natural scent with a few drops of essential oils such as eucalyptus, lavender or tea tree oil. Spray this all-purpose cleaner onto tabletops, counter tops, the floor and other surfaces and scrub with a rag. Then rinse off with a damp, clean cloth.

Laundry detergent

Mix 50g washing soda with 50g borax, and then drizzle in 30ml liquid Castile soap, and mix thoroughly. When you're ready to start the load going, heat up the mixture in a cup of hot water so it dissolves, and then add to the laundry.

Illustrations by Heather Kasunick

Window cleaner

For streak-free glass, add ½ teaspoon liquid soap and 3 tablespoons vinegar to 500ml water in a spray bottle. Shake and spray, then wipe glass with a soft cloth or crumpled newspaper.

Soft scrubber

Pour 100g bicarbonate of soda into a bowl and add enough liquid soap until it feels like icing. Scoop some onto a sponge and scrub bathtubs or sink. If you want to keep any leftover scrubber soft for another job, add a teaspoonful of glycerine.

Washing–up liquid

Combine 3 tablespoons liquid Castile soap with 2 teaspoons vegetable glycerine (helps to make bubbles, which are fun but optional) and 2 tablespoons white vinegar or lemon juice (helps clean grease) in 500ml warm water.

Oven cleaner

You don't need superstrong chemicals to clean an oven. Sprinkle water generously over the bottom of the oven, and cover with enough bicarbonate of soda to form a paste over the entire surface. Sprinkle more water, and let the paste sit overnight. The next morning, the grime should clean up with a sponge and a dab of soap.

BODY CLEANERS

No one wants to smell or look dirty. But the body products industry makes us all feel like we absolutely must use oodles of products 24/7 just to leave the house. This is good news for company profit, but it's bad news for our health (our bodies need to sweat – it's a way to make sure our internal organs don't get overheated), and for the Earth. So let's stay clean using homemade products with gentler ingredients.

Body wash

Combine 250ml liquid Castile soap, 3 tablespoons coconut or almond oil, and a few drops of your favourite essential oil (optional for those who don't like fragrance or may be allergic to scents) in a jar or dispenser. Cover and shake before using.

SAY NO
TO ANTI-BACTERIAL ANYTHING

If you think it's better to buy 'anti-bacterial' products – including liquid soaps and hand sanitisers – please reconsider, say experts at public health organisations such as the Environmental Working Group (EWG). The overabundance of anti-bacterial substances such as triclosan in many cleansers and body products has led to the evolution of germs that are highly resistant to antibiotics.

What this means is that when people really need an antibiotic medicine to fight off germs that are making them sick, the medicine may not work.

If you want to see what's in your favourite body products and cleaners, and which ingredients may be harmful, search EWG's database (ewg.org/skindeep). Greenpeace is also very active in fighting the impact of toxic chemicals on the environment.

Shampoo

Mix 60ml liquid Castile soap, 60ml water, and ½ teaspoon almond or coconut oil in a jar for a basic shampoo. If you'd like an anti-dandruff ingredient, add 2 tablespoons apple cider vinegar and a cup of tea made by steeping some sprigs of fresh rosemary in warm water. If you have dry hair or a tender scalp, add 60ml aloe vera gel, which you can find at chemists or health foods shops.

Zit zappers

Make a mask that's mostly from your fridge! Mix 1 tablespoon grated cucumber, 1 tablespoon plain yogurt, 2 teaspoons cosmetic clay (find it at the chemist or in health food shops), and a few drops of lavender essential oil. Leave on your face for 15 minutes, and remove with a warm, wet flannel. To dry up a spot, dab a few drops of tea tree essential oil and lavender oil on it. And keep your body more zit-resistant by taming stress, eating healthily and drinking lots of water.

Natural deodorant

Put 100g bicarbonate of soda, 100g corn flour, and a few drops of essential oil such as peppermint or lavender in a jar. Cover, shake and smooth on your pits with your hand. If you'd prefer a spray deodorant, pour 60ml each of witch hazel, aloe vera gel and water into a spray bottle. Add one teaspoon vegetable glycerine and a few drops of your favourite essential oil if you'd like. Shake before spraying.

Dr Emanuel Bronner

DR BRONNER'S
MAGIC SOAP

Emanuel H. Bronner (1908–1997) was born in Germany, the son of a Jewish soap maker. When he was 21, he emigrated to the United States; several years later, his parents were killed by the Nazis. He gave speeches in public places in Chicago about his eccentric world-peace philosophies, and in 1947 was committed to a mental hospital. He escaped, and in 1948 resumed speaking out in public places in Los Angeles, where he also sold his handmade peppermint soap.

When Bronner noticed that people came to buy soap but didn't always stay for the speech, he began printing his views on soap labels. These labels, along with the increasing popularity of the soaps, gained counterculture attention in the 1960s, with the tiny-print, much-hyphenated soap statements spelling out a philosophy that Bronner called All-One-God-Faith.

By the time of Bronner's death, the soap factory produced over 1.5 million litres of liquid soap and 270,000kg of bar soap a year. His best-known product is still Doctor Bronner's 18-in-1 Pure Castile Soap, which you can find at health food shops or online.

Bronner's family have expanded the business and have started many ventures to promote health and peaceful cooperation, including: using nontoxic, organic ingredients; sharing company profits among employees; buying 'fair trade' ingredients that give fair wages to suppliers, including palm oil from a mill owned by women in Ghana; and blending olive oil from farmers in Palestine and Israel who support peaceful cooperation in that region.

JUMBLE SALE

Car boot sale. Jumble sale. Flea market. Garage sale. Whatever you call the event, selling your unwanted or unneeded stuff is a great way to make a little extra cash.

A successful jumble sale involves a lot more work than plopping old dolls' clothes out in public and hoping people show up to buy them. Still, getting ready for a sale is more than half the fun. Here are some tips to make your sale a successful good time.

Sort the items you want to sell

Dust or wash any old items

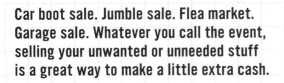

Use tape or stickers and a marker to price your items

Start sorting

At least one month before the sale, start sorting the items you want to sell into different piles (stuffed animals, action figures, sports memorabilia, plastic ponies). Dust or wash any dirty items. If you're having a hard time letting go of that Barbie car or *The Very Hungry Caterpillar* board book ask yourself if you've used them in the past year. If the answer is no, sell them!

Use masking tape or stickers and a marker pen to put prices on each item. In general, you should price a desirable item – an iPod docking station, say – at a quarter of its current market value. Less desirable items – that old *Snakes and Ladders* boardgame – will go for much less. (Though to budding game designers, it's useful!) If you're having a hard time deciding how much to ask for something, check the price for the same item on eBay.

Join forces

In the United States, neighbours often club together to sell their jumble in what's called a 'yard sale'. In the UK, we're usually more more reserved about talking to our neighbours, but maybe it's time the traditional jumble sale and the American yard sale combined forces. If there are other families who are itching to get rid of their unappreciated treasures, consider teaming up and hosting your sales on the same day. Not only will you attract more buyers, but you'll also be able to split advertising costs (more on that below).

Stay on the right side of the law

Call your city or county council to find out if you need a licence allowing you to do business in order to hold a jumble sale. Also, find out if there are regulations for your advertising posters. (In some cities, you aren't allowed to stick posters on trees or street signs, for example.) Licences may take a few weeks to process. If you don't want to start up a new jumble sale, you could join a car boot sale. The website yourbooty.co.uk has a searchable database for local ones that you can join.

Advertise

Depending on your budget, you may want to take out a classified ad in your city or local newspaper, or place a free listing online. If you are going along to a car boot sale you can put an ad in any of the new car boot sale apps. When writing an ad, be as specific as possible. 'Hundreds of Magic cards, almost-new kids' clothing and quality electronics,' for example, is much more attention-grabbing than 'Lots of stuff for sale.'

Use brightly coloured poster board (bright pink, yellow and green are attention-grabbing). Using permanent markers, write the time, address and directions (use arrows!), and mention any really cool items you're selling. The words 'free' and 'food' are also effective, but you'd better be prepared to have items and food to give away. Otherwise you'll have some disgruntled visitors.

Put up signs the night before the sale. Make sure you put them on well-trafficked streets and bike past them (or ask a grownup to drive you) to make sure you can read them from the road.

Set out your stall

Nothing makes people want to spend their money more than a well-set-up shop. Place similar items – holiday decorations, purses, skates – together. Using baskets or trays to set categories apart from one another is also very appealing. Put clothes on racks if possible.

Popular items – bicycles, TVs – should be placed at the front front to catch the eyes of casual passers-by. You can use signs to point out particularly interesting goods.

Also, consider a little entertainment. If you are holding a jumble sale in the driveway, either crank up some music (get your neighbours' permission first) or even consider live music. If you and your friends play music, you can set up a small band. Add a jar for tips and you can raise money for your school or favourite charity. Bonus!

Ask younger kids to run a drinks or cake stall. Offer them a cut of the profits.

Prepare a neat pile of newspapers and plastic bags so that your customers can safely wrap up and carry home their new treasures.

Sell!

Start your day with plenty of small change. Have one table that is solely for dealing with money (you can use a toy cash register or a lock box, but keep an eye on them; the pros like to keep their money in bum bags). Do not accept cheques. Jumble sales are cash only! Also, remember to keep an eye on your goods. Outdoor sales have been known to attract pickpockets.

A lot of your stuff will be sold by the middle of the morning. Rearrange your displays every now and then, so that they don't look sad and picked-over.

Got things you just want to get rid of? Put them in a 'Free' basket.

Arrange for a local charity to pick up anything that you don't sell.

TAKE STUFF APART
& FIX IT

By Helen Cordes

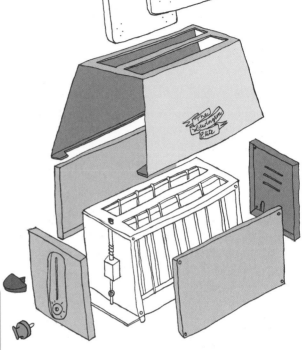

How does it work? Ever wonder this when you flick a light switch or hear music pour out from the radio?

Fixing things yourself teaches you the answer to these mysteries – and the skills you pick up can save you and your family some serious money. Besides, by doing a little 'reverse engineering' (engineer-speak for taking things apart), you could even be inspired to invent a new device.

> **IMPORTANT!** Before you fix something or take it apart, make sure it's safe to do so. Your grownup will need to check whether there are dangerous electric, glass or chemical parts. Some electronics such as mobile phones and computers may have toxic chemicals such as cadmium or mercury that you shouldn't touch. Instead of taking those electronics apart, see if they can be fixed up by experts and reused. Search online to recycle unwanted electronics or find local organisations that accept old tech stuff.

You'll need:

You can scout for cheap used tools at car boot sales. A well-stocked tool box includes:

- Claw hammer
- Screwdrivers
- Pliers with wire cutters
- Adjustable wrench
- Tape measure
- Sandpaper
- Handsaw
- Gaffer tape
- Nails and screws
- Precision craft knife (e.g. an X-acto knife). Use with grownup supervision.
- Torch

Illustrations by Heather Kasunick

TAKE STUFF APART

More and more people – such as Gever Tulley, founder of the Tinkering School programme – tell us that kids should be encouraged to take things apart, in order to see how they work.

Whether it's an old clock, radio, toaster, video or even washing machine, it's easy to find take-apart possibilities for free. Your garage or shed may already contain something that your grownups don't mind you deconstructing. Or ask your neighbours.

When you are taking things apart, you'll learn more if you check out a book or website that explains how that gadget works. Try to identify the parts that make it go.

When you've finished taking a device apart, try to use its parts to build something else. Obsolete inkjet printers, for example, contain useful pulleys and gears. An old electric toothbrush or digital camera might not do the job any more, but its motor can come in handy for a toy or kinetic sculpture.

FIXING STUFF

Leaky tap

Tap leaks are often caused by a cracked washer (a little metal ring that helps prevent leaks), which costs pennies to replace. As you unscrew each part of your tap fixture, place the parts in order on a towel so that you can replace them in the correct order when the job's done.

Clogged drains

If the water drains slowly in the sink or bathtub, try sticking your finger down the drain to see if there's hair or gunk built up. If that's not the problem, make a fizz bomb to loosen up the gunk that may be out of your finger's reach: put 2 tablespoons bicarbonate of soda in 125ml vinegar and pour the foaming mixture down the drain, followed by lots of hot water. But if you or your grownup has already poured a chemical clog remover down the drain, don't try this – the fizz bomb could shoot the chemicals out of the drain; they'll burn your skin.

Lights that won't light

Be sure to match the watt recommendation printed on the lamp or fixture with the bulb's watt number and unplug the lamp before you change the bulb. Also, look into switching to LED or CFL bulbs to save energy. If the bulb isn't the problem, check the fuse box (the 'command centre' for your house's electricity) with a grownup. While you're at it, you can help your grownup label the fuse box's switches.

Broken furniture

Chairs, doorknobs and other household items can wiggle because of a loose screw or two – make them like new with a screwdriver. Wooden garden tables or chairs might wobble because weather changes can make wood shrink or expand – grab a hammer and tap those nails back in tight.

Car repairs

Car repairs have become trickier over the years now that computers have been integrated into car engines. That doesn't leave a lot of things you and your grownup can do to fix your car. But you can still check tyre air pressure and the gauges for oil and windscreen wiper fluid, all of which are fun.

FIX A COLD RADIATOR

A radiator that won't heat up or is warm at the bottom and cold on the top probably has trapped air and needs a 'bleed' to bring it back to life.

You'll need:
- Radiator key (available at DIY shops if yours has gone missing).
- Small jar or bowl
- Kitchen rags

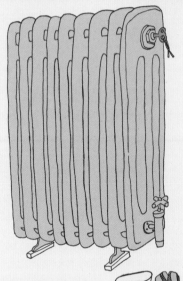

Here's what to do:

1. Start by turning off the heat and waiting for the entire radiator to be cool. Never bleed a warm radiator – you could get scalded.

2. Turn off the circulation pump (on older radiators, you'll turn a knob at the bottom of the radiator anti-clockwise).

3. Insert the radiator key into the 'bleed screw', which is a knob at the top of the radiator.

4. Put a rag underneath the bleed screw to catch any drips and then slowly turn the key anti-clockwise (keep the bowl handy in case those drips turn into a gush). You'll hear hissing – this is air being forced through the radiator pipes.

5. When water squirts through the bleed screw, quickly turn the key clockwise. Use the rag to mop up any water.

TRAIN YOUR GROWNUP
TO SAVE THE PLANET

By Colin Beavan

For an entire year, Colin Beavan and his family decided they were going to do everything they could to help the environment. They called this The No Impact Year, because they wanted to see if they could live without damaging the planet.

So they didn't drive or take the bus or fly anywhere on aeroplanes. They switched off all electricity in their entire flat and washed their clothes by stomping on them in the bathtub. What's more, this No Impact Man (that's what Beavan started to call himself) and his family didn't buy anything except food, which had to come without packaging and be grown within 250 miles of their home.

And guess what? The No Impact Year taught Beavan and his family some very important lessons. Walking and biking and scootering and saying no to takeaway food (which is served in wasteful containers) not only made them healthier, but also gave them more energy to do fun things. They also discovered that you don't need to be constantly plugged into your tech to have fun. That's not because technology is bad – in fact, Beavan blogged about his experience via his laptop. But when tech takes over your life, both the Earth and people lose.

We asked Beavan for tips families can use to help the planet.

Skate, walk or bike whenever you can!

Walk & bike
Get around by bike or by foot a few days each month. You'll use less fossil fuel, create fewer greenhouse gases, and get exercise. Plus, we'll all breathe fewer fumes. If you can stay off the road just two days a week, you'll reduce greenhouse gas emissions by an average of 720kg per year. Walk, bike or scooter to school whenever you can.

Hang out with your friends
One of the benefits of the No Impact life is that because you aren't spending time buying stuff, you have extra hours to be with people you like and want to get to know better. Play charades. Sing.

Dim the lights
Replace incandescent lightbulbs with fluorescent alternatives. If you live in a block of flats, push for hall lights that operate on motion sensors and only turn on when someone is there.

Illustrations by Mister Reusch

Ditch the burgers

If your family can swing it, stop eating beef. Worldwide, beef production contributes more to global warming than cars, buses, planes and trains combined. The carbon footprint – the measurement of the impact our activities have on the environment – of the average meat eater is about 1,350kg of carbon dioxide (CO_2) larger than that of a vegetarian. The more carbon dioxide in the Earth's atmosphere, the warmer the Earth gets. That's a problem because higher temperatures not only can melt the polar ice caps but also lead to more flooding in some parts of the world and more droughts in the places that are already hot. Cutting beef out of your family's diet will reduce your CO_2 emissions by more than 1,000kg annually per person.

If saying a permanent goodbye to steak seems too drastic, try starting with Meatless Mondays.

Throw weekly No Impact celebrations

For one day or afternoon or even an hour each week, go seriously No Impact. Don't buy anything, don't use any machines, don't switch on anything electric, don't cook, don't answer your phone, don't get in a car or bus. In other words, don't use *any* resources and in the process give yourself and the planet a break.

Every No Impact hour that you live per week cuts your carbon emissions by 0.6 per cent annually. Commit to four hours per week, that's 2.4 per cent; do it for a whole day each week and you'll cut your impact by nearly 15 per cent a year.

Freaked out by the idea of no tech time? Make sure you have plenty of No Impact activities planned. Ride bikes, play boardgames, visit a farmers' market, read, take a walk, make an obstacle course, build a snowman. Better yet, take care of your garden! You'll discover you can handle – and even enjoy – being unplugged.

Volunteer at a community garden

Drink from the tap

Did you know that bottled water costs more per gallon than petrol? Or that the average Briton consumes 34 litres of bottled water each year? You can save money and your environment by switching to tap water. If you do, you'll use up one less litre of fossil fuel (natural resources that cannot be renewed) and emit half a kilo less greenhouse gases into the atmosphere.

Give away (some of) your money

If an average British family contributes one per cent (£400) of its annual income (£40,000) to an environmental charity, they could offset 42 tons of carbon dioxide per year. Have a family meeting to decide which organisation you want to support. If you get pocket money, decide with your grownups how much you are going to save each week to contribute to your family's charitable giving.

Donate one day's TV time to eco-service

Take one day off from TV – the average UK viewer watches four hours of TV a day – and try voluntary eco-service instead. Those hours add up to more than 370kg of carbon dioxide each year.

Planting trees is one great way to help the environment because they absorb carbon dioxide, which is a greenhouse gas. You can also volunteer at a community garden or spend an afternoon picking up rubbish at a local park.

Give (& get) green gifts

A present doesn't have to be bought from a shop. Guitar lessons, art classes and all kinds of hand-me-downs are just as fun as that stockpile of plastic figurines. Encourage your grownups to give each other non-material gifts, too, like a gift certificate for a massage or a wine tasting class.

Wipe out waste

In addition to recycling and buying products made from recycled materials, be mindful of all the appliances you turn on and off all day. Look around your home for energy-hogging electronics; unplug your toaster, blender, stereos, and mobile phone and computer chargers when you're not using them. Check your family's progress every month by looking at your energy bill together.

Hang-dry your clothes

Washing your clothes with cold water can cut your laundry energy use by up to 90 per cent. Then, let your clothes hang-dry instead of using the dryer. Repair your broken DVD player or worn-out shoes instead of buying new replacements. When it's time to get out of town, consider going on half the family holidays you normally do but staying twice as long – you'll still have as much time on holiday but won't take as many plane rides.

Believe with all your heart that how you live your life makes a difference

Every step toward living a greener life inspires everyone else who is trying to do the same thing – whether you're aware of it or not. We are the masters of our destinies.

To learn more about No Impact Man and his tips for living green, check out noimpactman.com. Or get your grownups to read Beavan's book, No Impact Man.

WHERE YOUR RUBBISH GOES

50% or so of your rubbish goes into landfills

10% or less goes to incinerators or is dumped at sea

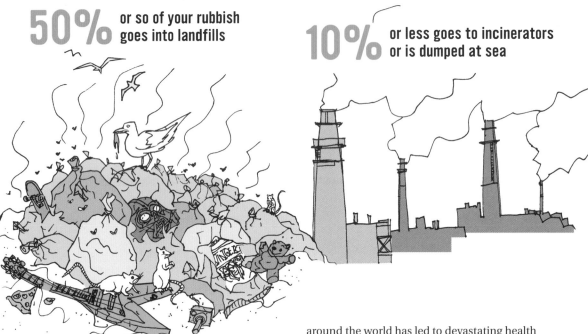

Each year, the average British citizen tosses out over 260kg of waste. But our rubbish is not something most of us are encouraged to think about.

When we unwrap a frozen pizza or decide it's time to get rid of those ratty jeans, our response is so automatic we almost don't know we are tossing something into the rubbish bin. But where does our refuse go after it's picked up on rubbish day?

Dumps

When your grownups were kids, rubbish went to tips, which were open-air pits that unintentionally served as feeding zones for rats and other animals. (The first rubbish tip was created in 500 BC in Athens; over the centuries, contaminated waste around the world has led to devastating health problems – including the bubonic plague, cholera and typhoid fever.) Not only do tips stink, but the toxic chemicals found in some rubbish seeps into the soil and groundwater.

Landfills

Today, most tips have been replaced by landfills, which are enormous pits lined with a layer of clay and protective plastic to prevent leaking. According to DEFRA, around 50 per cent of British rubbish goes into landfills.

When rubbish gets to a landfill, it is placed into a 'disposal cell' – where it is smooshed down and covered with a layer of soil. Some landfills collect methane (a gas created by all that rotting rubbish) and turn it into an energy source.

When a landfill gets, well, filled, it is 'capped'. If regular tests show that there are no toxic chemicals in the soil, that land may be turned into a park or golf course, or even a ski area.

Illustrations by Mister Reusch

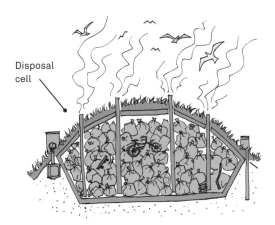

Disposal cell

Unfortunately, landfills aren't foolproof. Common household substances, including mothballs, shoe polish, and even margarine can cause the liners to crack and leak. And because there's no air or water to help rubbish disintegrate inside a sealed landfill, those 'disposable' nappies you wore when you were a toddler will still be around for decades.

Combustion facilities

Also called incinerators; less than 10 per cent of our rubbish goes here. Rubbish incinerators generate energy for the communities whose trash they burn. That's a good thing. But an improperly functioning rubbish incinerator can cause air pollution. And all burned rubbish creates ash, which then has to go to – you guessed it – a landfill.

40% or so of your rubbish is recycled

Recycling

Recycling is when you take an unwanted item, including items made of paper, glass, plastic or metal, and target it for reuse rather than discarding it as rubbish. Making wallets from old tyres, and other craft projects that make something fun out of junk, *is* recycling. Recycling lengthens the lifespan of materials – for example, plastic bottles are turned into carpets or fleece jackets – though it doesn't do so as efficiently as reusing stuff.

Upcycling

Upcycling means reusing objects for the same purpose, over and over again. In the old days, people returned milk bottles to the dairy – that's one example. So is melting aluminium cans and making more cans at a savings of 90 per cent of the energy required to make new cans from scratch; newspaper is also upcycled efficiently. Composting (turning food and garden waste into soil fertiliser) could also be thought of as a form of upcycling – if you're growing food.

In addition to recycling and upcycling, we can reduce the amount of rubbish we produce. Here are a few simple steps you can take to shrink your family's load of rubbish.

Skip the single servings

Instead of packing an individual pot of yogurt or other pudding in your lunchbox, buy a large pot and put portions in a small container that you can reuse. Avoid plastic bags, because they often get thrown out.

Borrow stuff

Next time you want something you won't use very often, consider asking a friend or neighbour if they'll loan you theirs.

HOW TO CRITICISE
EVERYTHING

By Ginia Bellafante

For a lot of years I had a really fun job: I was the television critic for the *New York Times*. Some people, maybe because they were just a teeny bit jealous, would make jokes about it: 'You watch TV for a living? Tough life!'

I would be lying if I told you that working as a television critic is as hard as running a municipal sewer system or clocking hours as a geriatric nurse, or tackling late shifts as a waitress in a chicken-wing joint. Even compared to other jobs in journalism it gets high points for cushiness. What would you rather do: watch 10 straight hours of *Doctor Who*, or spend weeks unravelling a debt crisis in some foreign country where you may not even like the food? That said, there is still a lot about the job that isn't easy.

It takes a long time to develop the skills of a critic. But keeping in mind a certain set of questions and guidelines will help you get better, I promise!

Go beyond your first reaction

First of all, being a critic involves a lot more than rendering simple one-note judgements: 'I love *iCarly*!' 'I think *iCarly* STINKS like my little sister's foot.' A good critic gets beyond how she feels while watching a television show or a film or a play, reading a book or eating a restaurant meal (yes, reviewing food is also a job) and considers the subject within a larger frame of reference.

What does that mean? Let's say someone asked you to write a review of *Brave*, or *The Twilight Saga: Breaking Dawn – Part 2*, or *Toy Story 3*. Your first reaction might be: 'This looks cool!' Or 'It's sad that Andy is going away to school and Woody and Buzz and the rest of the toys will be lonely.' Your first thought is important, because your criticism should relay an emotional response. But giving the reader more than your immediate personal impression is important, too. If you were reviewing a restaurant that specialised in unique cheeseburgers you would want to consider, for instance, how unique they are compared to other cheeseburgers you've eaten. Is the cheeseburger made at Big Billy's Special Cheeseburger cooked differently from the kind at McDonald's? How do the cooking styles compare? Is Big Billy's variety worth the higher price?

Illustrations by Mister Reusch

Establish the context

Another way of saying 'a larger frame of reference' is 'relevant context'. Though drawing comparisons to other animated movies might also be a good idea, the relevant context of *Toy Story 3* is the two other Toy Story movies. So you might begin by talking about the way the third movie advances the characters' stories. You might want to think about whether *Toy Story 3* is as funny and moving as *Toy Story 2* (assuming that you found *Toy Story 2* funny and moving).

Wrestle with the message

Next, you might want to wrestle with the movie's message, and how it differs (or doesn't) from the preceding films' messages. (A movie's message is whatever the movie has to say about life and the world we live in generally, and its central themes specifically.) In the instance of *Toy Story 3*, you'd want to ask yourself what the movie has to say about: growing up and moving on, attachments, and the camaraderie and loyalty that are forged among friends.

Always ask yourself: Does it accomplish what its creator intended?

If a TV show's intent is to depict a twenty-first-century secondary school in completely realistic terms, does the portrayal feel realistic? Do the characters talk like secondary school students you know? Or do they sound fake – like a grownup trying to manufacture the voice of a 13-year-old?

Go further

Once you've established the creator's intent, try to get beyond it, too. Look for ideas and opinions that an author or screenwriter or musician might not even realise their work is expressing. That's fun for readers. The intent of *Toy Story 3* probably wasn't to make daycare centres seem like a downer, but because the story uses a daycare centre as a lonely place for toys to end up, that message is there almost by accident.

Stay away from adjectives

At the newspaper where I work, a famous columnist and former theatre critic gave me some really good advice: 'You don't want to say, "The lead actress in the play is pretty." You want to say what precisely holds your attention about her looks.' So you'd want to try something like this: 'The lead actress in the play has the beauty of someone who looks as though she has spent the last six months surfing.' Avoiding adjectives nudges you towards greater specificity, which always pays off – because it gives the reader a clearer picture of what you're thinking.

Keep plot descriptions to an absolute minimum

You don't want to go on and on, tossing every detail of the story at the reader. You merely want to give the reader a sense of the story's essence. Plot descriptions waste space and feel lazy.

Trust yourself

You should know your facts and study up on what you're reviewing. If you are reviewing a book by an author who has written others, you'll want to read those other books to get a broad sense of the writer's interest and style, for example. But once you've done all of your homework, you should have confidence in the opinions you're putting out there. Never be afraid to say what you think.

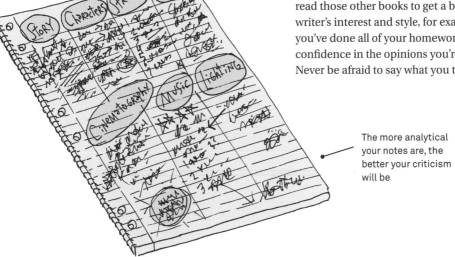

The more analytical your notes are, the better your criticism will be

SHOOT AND EDIT
A STOP-MOTION MOVIE

Stop motion (also known as stop action) is an animation technique in which you can make an object appear to move on its own. How? By shooting lots and lots of photos, moving the object slightly between each shot. Stop motion requires patience, but it's simple and fun.

Stop-motion animation has been around since the 1890s – and it's still used today, in movies from *The Empire Strikes Back* (the Tauntauns and AT-AT walkers) to *Wallace & Gromit: The Curse of the Were-Rabbit*, and in the TV series *Robot Chicken*. Thanks to digital cameras, in recent years it's become a popular hobby: YouTube is bursting with claymation movies (featuring clay figures) and 'brickfilms' (stop-motion animations featuring LEGO minifigs), many of which were made by kids.

Here's what you'll need:

- Digital camera (with the image resolution set to LOW, to save on memory); and a cord to connect the camera to your computer.
- Tripod, to stabilise the camera; or just use a pile of books, or whatever gets the job done.
- Video editing software – Apple's iMovie and Windows Movie Maker are pre-installed on new Macs and PCs; there are free video editors out there, too. Before purchasing a camera or video editing software, make sure that they are compatible!
- Figures and set materials: LEGO, clay models (for flexibility, build the models around armature wire), toys and stuffed animals, socks, cut-out drawings on paper, and so forth. Use your imagination.
- **Optional:** Lighting, i.e. a lamp. If available, a gooseneck or a clip-on lamp works really well.
- **Optional:** A sheet or towel, preferably solid-coloured, to serve as a non-distracting backdrop.

Illustrations by Mister Reusch

Shoot your movie

1. Get inspired! Watch some stop-motion movies. The 1933 version of *King Kong* is a classic; Tim Burton's *The Nightmare Before Christmas*, *James and the Giant Peach*, and *Corpse Bride* are spooky-kooky; and so is the Neil Gaiman adaptation *Coraline*. The Roald Dahl adaptation *Fantastic Mr Fox* is truly amazing. You can also search YouTube and other video sites for 'brickfilms', or check out bestbrickfilms.com

2. Brainstorm your movie. Keep it very simple! You will need to shoot at least 10 photos for every second of film (the more frames per second, the smoother the animation), so even a 30-second movie might take you a couple of hours.

3. Create a set. To minimise viewer distraction, a blank backdrop is a good idea: a white wall, perhaps; or you can hang up a solid-coloured sheet or large sheet of paper. If you're using a LEGO baseplate, try sticking it down securely with putty or double-sided tape.

4. Lights, camera, action! Turn off the flash on your camera – it will create an ugly glare. Use either natural light, or else close all the curtains and light the set with your lamps. (To reduce shadows, make sure that you're not between the light source and the set.) Put the camera onto a tripod or a pile of books, or whatever – you don't want it to move. As noted above, set your camera resolution to a LOW setting; large image sizes will eat up lots of camera and computer memory and might even crash your editing software.

5. Shoot a photo of your figure. Without moving the camera, lighting or set, adjust the figure a tiny, tiny bit. Shoot another photo. Whatever movement the figure is making should take place over several frames of the movie – and you can always remove unwanted photos while editing your movie. So go ahead and take lots and lots of photos. (Some animators suggest taking two photos of each shot; it's a good idea.) However, you should delete mistakes from your camera as you go; this will save you time later.

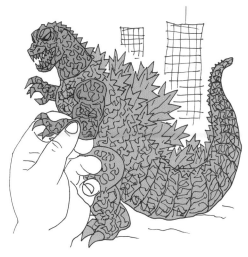

6. Repeat Step 5 until you've finished your movie. If you fill up your camera's memory, you will need to upload the photos to your computer, erase the camera's memory, and resume shooting. If you can accomplish this without moving the camera, all the better.

Edit your movie

1. Upload all photos to your computer, saving them in a clearly marked file. Now create a new project in your video editing software, and import the photos from their file. For assistance with these operations, consult your camera guide, software instructions, and grownup. If your software won't find your photos, it may mean that it's not compatible with your camera. You may need different software... or a different camera.

2. *Every video editor works differently, so consult your software's instruction manual; what follows are general instructions and tips.* Note that you're going to be creating a fast-moving slideshow, not an actual film. Decide how long you want each photo to appear before showing the next one: 10 photos per second is a good place to begin. Add effects, if any; but turn off the 'Ken Burns' auto-zooming effect. Once you're completely satisfied with the animation, add titles and credits. If you want to add a soundtrack (voiceover, sound effects, music), do so at the end; if you decide to change the movie after this, it will be tricky to re-sync the audio.

3. If you're making a longer movie, with multiple animations, you should save each individual animation as a separate movie. Once you've finished editing every animation, you can import them into the final movie and add transitions.

STOP-MOTION APPS

If you have access to an Apple iPhone, you might want to give one of these free apps – which don't require you to upload your photos to a computer before making a stop-motion movie – a try.

Stop-Motion Camera is a basic, easy-to-use app for beginners. There's no way to save your movie and make changes later, but if you're just looking to get started, this is a fun way to do so.

Frame X Frame offers more advanced functionality (for example, you can customise the time interval between frames) than Stop-Motion Camera. But it's still a good app for beginners.

Stop Motion Cafe, unlike the other apps mentioned here, allows you to save a project and continue editing it until you're fully satisfied.

BEST EVER

STOP-MOTION MOVIES

By Josh

The article on making your own stop-motion movies mentions a few classics of the genre. But there are many other terrific examples, too – including these.

1955–1989 series
THE GUMBY SHOW

Directed by Art Clokey

This wild 1950s–1960s TV show about a clay figure named Gumby, his pony Pokey, and his mischievous nemeses, the Blockheads, was revived in the late 1980s. All together, then, there are over 230 episodes of *The Gumby Show*. They are viewable on YouTube.

1955
GUMBASIA

Directed by Art Clokey

If you can find it (on YouTube, for example, or via the nonprofit digital library The Internet Archive), watch Clokey's weird and beautiful three-minute claymation movie, which inspired (and helped fund) *The Gumby Show*. It's a parody of Walt Disney's *Fantasia*, and an avant-garde masterpiece in its own right.

1974
CLOSED MONDAYS

Directed by Will Vinton and Bob Gardiner

This 11-minute film, in which the art in a gallery comes to life, stunned film festival judges and won that year's Oscar for Best Animated Film.

1977–1979 series
THE LITTLE PRINCE AND FRIENDS

Directed by Will Vinton

Vinton's trilogy of 27-minute-long TV fairy tales *Martin the Cobbler* (1977), *Rip Van Winkle* (1978) and *The Little Prince* (1979) are very influential. Vinton has publicly credited his parents for letting him play with their video camera when he was a kid.

PS: *Claymation*, a short 1978 documentary featuring the behind-the-scenes technical processes used by Vinton and his animators, made that term (copyrighted by Vinton) synonymous with clay animation.

1985
RETURN TO OZ

Claymation by Will Vinton

The claymation special effects for this dark, too-intense-for-some-kids movie were nominated for an Oscar. The movie is live action, but its villain, the Nome King, is animated – very effectively. He emerges out of rock walls in a terrifying manner.

PS: After this career high point, Vinton's studio created the lame California Raisins and M&M's characters.

1989–2008 series
WALLACE & GROMIT SHORTS

Directed by Nick Park

In *A Grand Day Out*, the eccentric inventor Wallace and his brilliant dog, Gromit, build a rocket and fly to the moon in search of cheese.

In *The Wrong Trousers*, a sinister penguin moves in with them. In *A Close Shave*, an evil dog steals the blueprints to Wallace's knit-o-matic and wash-o-matic machines. And in *A Matter of Loaf and Death*, a mock murder mystery, Gromit falls for a dog named Fluffles.

PS: Also check out the excellent 2005 feature film *Wallace & Gromit: The Curse of the Were-Rabbit*.

1992
MONA LISA DESCENDING A STAIRCASE

By Joan Gratz

Using a technique called 'clay painting', Joan Gratz's award-winning film takes us on a tour of modern art from Van Gogh to Warhol.

2000
CHICKEN RUN

By Nick Park and Peter Lord

From the *Wallace & Gromit* studio, it's a Second World War-style prison-escape movie set on a chicken farm!

2009
A TOWN CALLED PANIC

By Stéphan Aubier and Vincent Patar

Three plastic toys named Cowboy, Indian and Horse accidentally order 50 million bricks… which sends them on a journey to the centre of the Earth, not to mention to a parallel universe. This very funny movie is based on a surreal Belgian TV series.

MAKE ZINES &
MINI-COMICS

A zine (pronounced zeen) is an independent publication. It's published by you, and everything inside it is there only because you want it there – not because you're trying to sell ads, say, or appeal to a particular audience.

A zine can be one page or dozens of pages; typed or handwritten; carefully designed or slapdash. It can feature stories, drawings, photos, comics, information, activities – or a combination of these things. You can sell copies of your zine, swap it for other zines, or give it away. Yes, you can even sell ads.

Though the origins of zines can be traced back to sixteenth-century political pamphleteers (who had access to printing presses), in the 1970s cheap photocopying made self-publishing affordable for almost everyone. The 1980s saw a 'zine revolution'; but after blogging came along in the mid-1990s, the fad died down. Paper zines are still around, though – they'll never go away entirely.

If you like working with paper, making a zine is fun and easy. Self-publishing a zine is a great experience for future writers, cartoonists, journalists, graphic designers, illustrators and others.

You'll need:

- An idea: What is the focus of your zine? Why would someone read it? But don't try to please others – you should make a zine that *you'd* like to read.
- Several sheets of white A4 paper. Borrow some from your grownup.
- Pencil and pen (black ink only)
- Stapler and ruler
- **Optional:** Putty rubber, which you can find at an art supply shop.
- **Optional:** Scissors, glue stick, old magazines and newspapers (for making collages)
- A workspace. If you're using a nice tabletop, make sure you cover it up with layers of newspaper.

Here's what to do:

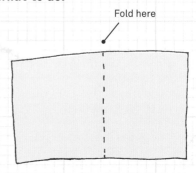

Fold here

1. Orient the paper horizontally, and fold it from left to right. (There are lots of other possible zine formats, but this is the most common.) As you can see, you immediately have a front and back cover, plus two inside pages. Want four more inside pages? Fold another piece of paper the same way. Repeat until you're satisfied.

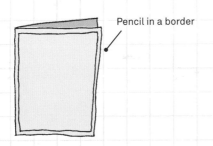

Pencil in a border

- Sometimes photocopiers can't 'see' blue ink, so you should avoid using it. Avoid red too.
- Marks from some pens will show through the page of your zine, so be careful about that.
- Cut up magazines and newspapers, then use the glue stick to make collages.

2. Using a pencil and ruler, lightly sketch borders around each page – at least 1cm along each edge. Why? Because a photocopier won't reproduce writing or drawing that's near the page's edge.

Make double-sided copies

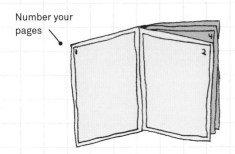

Number your pages

3. Number the pages, beginning with the inside front cover. Put each page's number in the top outside corner of that page's border.

5. Ready to go to press? First, if you don't like the way they look, erase the pencilled borders. Next, take your pages to a print shop, and (with a grownup's help, if necessary) make double-sided copies. You may need to adjust the copier's settings, so do a few test prints before you begin.

Assemble, fold and staple in the centre

Create the content

4. Now go ahead and make your zine. Anything goes, so we won't offer editorial instructions for this step. But here are a few practical tips.

- Keep writing and art inside the page borders.
- You might like to make a table of contents on the first page. Also a masthead – a list of the zine's editor(s), contributors and so forth.
- Don't make the text too small, because photocopying will make it hard to read.
- To make headlines, particularly headlines in exciting typefaces, try using a word-processing program. Print out headlines, then cut and paste them into your zine.

6. Staple twice in the middle seam, once near the top edge and once near the bottom edge. Always staple from the outside of the zine in – the loose ends of the staples go on the inside.

Illustrations by Heather Kasunick

Mini-Comics Tips

Our friend Rick is a cartoonist and illustrator; his 12-year-old son, Jonathan, wants to be one, too. We asked them for pointers on making a mini-comic, which is a particular type of zine.

• Writing out the story ahead of time can be very useful. Planning backwards from the end can be a helpful strategy. But it's also OK to just start with the first panel and figure it out as you go.

• Pacing—from one panel to the next—is important. If it's all action, all the time, your comic will be exhausting to readers. Try mixing up action scenes with panels in which nothing happens. A panel in which we see a character reacting to something that just happened can be very funny.

• Make your characters distinctive-looking, so that readers don't get confused about who's who.

• Change the perspective from which the reader is viewing the scene. Think of your comic as though it were a movie: include zoom-outs and close-ups; bird's-eye views; head shots, etc.

• Draw the word balloon after you've written the words; otherwise, you might run out of room.

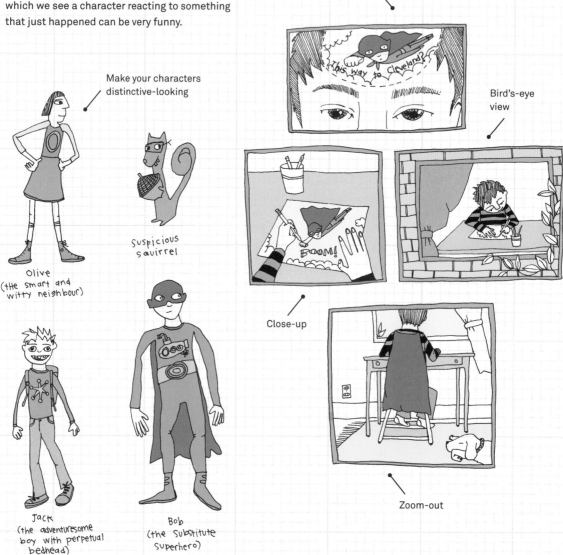

Make your characters distinctive-looking

Olive
(the smart and witty neighbour)

Suspicious squirrel

Jack
(the adventuresome boy with perpetual bedhead)

Bob
(the substitute superhero)

Head shot

Bird's-eye view

Close-up

Zoom-out

BEST EVER

CLEAN HIP HOP SONGS

By Josh

Why don't your grownups want you to listen to rap music? For the same three reasons that my grownups didn't want me to listen to rap (also known as hip hop) back when it was still a brand-new phenomenon. Because too many hip hop songs (1) celebrate sex, drugs and violence, (2) denigrate women, and (3) show off the lyricist's command of swearwords.

These days, many grownups are aware that hip hop is hardly the only musical genre whose lyrics are guilty of Crimes 1, 2 and 3. What's more, they're aware that hip hop songs are written from a perspective that may not be the writer's own. Just because a song celebrates crime doesn't mean that the songwriter is a criminal, or knows or admires any criminals. Get it?

Still, even a grownup who is a hip hop fan might not feel comfortable playing Eminem songs when her kids are listening. Alas, even most old-skool, alternative, and indie hip hop songs – politically progressive and linguistically rewarding as they most certainly are – aren't really appropriate for kids. I wanted a playlist of authentically great hip hop tunes that were clean enough to play without worrying. I spent a week listening to hip hop tunes, and reading their lyrics. Here are the results of my research, along with some conversation-starting facts. Enjoy these tracks with your grownup!

1985
THE SHOW
Artist: Doug E. Fresh & MC Ricky D
Album: *The Show / La Di Da Di*
The one-eyed, London-born rapper MC Ricky D – also known as Slick Rick – moved with his British Jamaican family to New York in 1977. Thanks to his sophisticated accent and one-of-a-kind storytelling skills, during hip hop's so-called golden age he quickly rose to stardom. In this famous collaboration with Doug E. Fresh (one of the earliest pioneers of beatboxing) and a team of DJs known as the Get Fresh Crew, Rick tells a story about meeting a girl on a subway train. When she tells him that 'My name is Maggie, but you can call me Michelle,' he sings her a few lines from a Beatles song – further evidence of his English origins.

1987
I KNOW YOU GOT SOUL
Artist: Eric B. & Rakim
Album: *Paid in Full*
Uh-oh! At one point in this song, Rakim raps 'It's a four-letter word when it's heard, it control your body to dance.' Is he about to swear? No need to dive for the volume control. The word to which Rakim is referring is 'soul'. Phew!

During the golden age of hip hop (let's call it 1984–1993), DJ Eric B. and MC Rakim were considered the single most talented duo around. More recent duos like OutKast, Black Star and Blackalicious might never have existed were it not for Eric B. & Rakim's influence.

1989
TREAD WATER
Artist: De La Soul
Album: *3 Feet High and Rising*
In this song, a crocodile, a squirrel and other animals tell the members of De La Soul to maintain a positive attitude. (Mr Fish, for example, says: 'As for me, I'm in tip-top shape today,/'Cause my water's clean and no-one's menu says "Fresh Fish Filet".') De La Soul formed when Kelvin Mercer (nicknamed Posdnuos), David Jude Jolicoeur (Trugoy), and Vincent Mason (Mase) were at school together; their debut album is one of the greatest examples of the use of snippets from other songs (known as 'samples') to form a complex collage of sound. This song, for examples, samples a hit 1970s tune by the funk band The People's Choice.

Fun Fact: Trugoy is 'yogurt' spelled backwards. 'Posdnuos', meanwhile, is backward-ese for 'soundsop'. Whatever that means.

1990
HAM'N'EGGS
Artist: A Tribe Called Quest
Album: *People's Instinctive Travels and the Paths of Rhythm*

Alternative hip hop pioneers A Tribe Called Quest (Phife Dawg, Q-Tip, Ali Shaheed Muhammad, Jarobi White) celebrate African-American soul food in this song; they also encourage the practice of vegetarianism. At one point, Q-Tip and Phife describe what their grandmothers might feed them: 'Asparagus tips look yummy, yummy, yummy!/Candied yams inside my tummy/A collage of good eats, some snacks or nice treats/Applesauce and some nice red beets.' The song's catchy chorus might just inspire your grownup to lower his cholesterol level.

1990
MONIE IN THE MIDDLE
Artist: Monie Love
Album: *Down to Earth*

In this song, which is set in a school, and which features complex rhyme schemes, a young woman proclaims her right to decide what she wants out of a romantic relationship, not to mention life. 'I made my decision, precisely, precision is a must/For me to solve another riddle/Step into a brand new rhythm, ism schisms/Nope, I'm not with 'em.'

Monie Love (Simone Wilson) was one of the first British hip hop artists ever signed by a major label.

1991
FLY GIRL
Artist: Queen Latifah
Album: *Nature of a Sista*

You probably know Queen Latifah as an actress: She played 'Motormouth' Maybelle in the musical-movie version of *Hairspray*, for example; and she has provided the voice of Ellie the mammoth in three Ice Age movies. But back in the day, Latifah was a pioneering female rapper. As such, she demanded that men treat women with the respect that they deserve.

In this song, she tells a would-be suitor, 'Easy love is something that I ain't/Besides, I don't know you from a can of paint!'

Latifah is one of only three hip hop artists who have been nominated for an Oscar in an acting category. The other two? Will Smith and Mark Wahlberg.

1991
120 SECONDS
Artist: Freestyle Fellowship
Album: *To Whom It May Concern*

'I'll say, "Foul play",/Hey, which way does Willy Wonka stay?/We came to see the chocolate sway,' raps Aceyalone in this nonsensical, ultra-inventive song whose wordplay and pop culture references are dizzying. The four members of this 'jazz rap' group – Aceyalone, Myka 9, P.E.A.C.E. and Self Jupiter – became friends when they attended the same school in Los Angeles. It's never too early to begin.

Did you know: 'Freestyling' is a form of rapping (and skateboarding, among other things) in which you make it up as you go along.

1992
TELEVISION, THE DRUG OF THE NATION
Artist: The Disposable Heroes of Hiphoprisy
Album: *Hypocrisy is the Greatest Luxury*

Is your grownup worried about the bad influence of TV on the minds of his fellow citizens? If so, then he will doubtlessly appreciate the message of this hard-driving song, in which Michael Franti raps: 'TV is the reason/Why less than 10 per cent of our nation reads books daily/Why most people think/"Central America" means Kansas, "Socialism" means un-American, and "Apartheid" is a new headache remedy.'

PS: Central America is a geographic region consisting of Belize, Costa Rica, El Salvador, Guatemala, Honduras, Nicaragua and Panama. Socialism is a political philosophy which advocates the social ownership of factories and utilities, and the cooperative management of the economy. Apartheid was a system of racial segregation in South Africa from 1948 until 1994. If you didn't know these things, then maybe you should take Franti's advice and do a little more reading.

1992
TENNESSEE
Artist: Arrested Development
Album: *3 Years, 5 Months & 2 Days in the Life of…*

At a time when 'gangsta' rap was extremely popular and lucrative, Arrested Development, an 'alternative' hip hop group founded by MC Speech and DJ Headliner, bucked the trend by writing songs about peace, love and religion. In 'Tennessee', which became a No. 1 hit, Speech explains what he has learned by visiting those parts of the South in which his ancestors were slaves: 'Now I see the importance of history/Why people be in the mess that they be.'

PS: The album's title refers to how long it took the group to get their first record contract.

2002
TURN THE PAGE
Artist: The Streets
Album: *Original Pirate Material*

When Mike Skinner – the British rapper and musician known for his 'Mockney' accent and his Birmingham City FC shirts – was working on the debut album for his project The Streets, he became obsessed with the then-recent historical movie *Gladiator*. That's why 'Turn the Page' tells an epic tale about a modern-day rapper who imagines himself as the reincarnation of a Roman soldier. In *Gladiator*, Maximus is reborn after his home burns down; the narrator of this song imagines the destruction of British 'garage' hip hop as it had been known before The Streets came along.

2002
FIRST IN FLIGHT
Artist: Blackalicious
Album: *Blazing Arrow*

Known for their tongue-twisting lyrics, Blackalicious is a duo that includes MC Gift of Gab and DJ Chief Xcel. In this song, Gift of Gab sounds like Obi-Wan Kenobi when he gives the following advice: 'No need to force the progression, just ride the wind/You'll know the answer to the Where and Why and When.'

Ask your grownups if they recognise the voice of this track's special guest. It's poet Gil Scott-Heron, whose unique spoken-word performances in the 1970s were one of the key formative influences on hip hop.

2003
REMIND MY SOUL
Artist: Akrobatik
Album: *Balance*

The underground hip hop artist Akrobatik strikes a dynamic balance, in this song, between nostalgia for the legacy of African-American resistance to oppression (he invokes Harriet Tubman, Malcolm X, Bob Marley, Nat Turner, Arthur Ashe and Martin Luther King Jr) and also for pre-gangsta rap music, on the one hand and, on the other hand, an idealistic, progressive vision of the future of both society and hip hop. Akrobatik laments what he describes as the 'We crabs in a barrel/You ain't gettin' out until I do first' mind-set, and calls instead for unified activism against social injustice.

2004
BRIDGING THE GAP
Artist: Nas
Album: *Street's Disciple*

Nas, who started writing rhymes at the age of nine, is considered by many to be one of the greatest rappers of all time. On this song, which features a guest appearance by his father, the jazz cornetist Olu Dara, he attempts to bridge the generation gap between rappers and older musicians. 'The blues came from gospel, gospel from blues/Slaves are harmonisin' them aah's and ooh's,' Nas recounts. 'Old-school, new-school, no-school rules/All these years I been voicin' my blues.'

PS: Nas is a spokesman for P'Tones Records, a free after-school music programme for kids.

2006
KICK, PUSH
Artist: Lupe Fiasco
Album: *Lupe Fiasco's Food & Liquor*

This song by Lupe Fiasco (real name: Wasalu Muhammad Jaco) is a skateboarders' love story. A skater boy tells the girl he likes that, 'I would marry you/But I'm engaged to these aerials and varials/And I don't think this board is strong enough to carry two.' The girl turns out to be an even more experienced skater, and sets the boy straight: 'Now, let me make one thing clear/I don't need to ride yours, I got mine right here.'

PS: Lupe Fiasco's debut album contains the lyrics, 'I used to hate hip hop, yep, because the women it degraded.' Here, he's making the point that boys and girls are equals.

Fun Fact: An 'aerial' is any skateboard trick performed on a half-pipe; a 'varial' is a type of aerial.

2011
NUMBERS IN ACTION
Artist: Wiley
Album: *100% Publishing*

Grime is a style of music that developed on London's pirate radio stations in the early 2000s out of British garage hip hop, jungle and electronica. Along with Dizzee Rascal, Wiley – an English rapper and music producer with Caribbean roots – was one of the first to bring grime into the mainstream. In this defiant yet optimistic song, he explains what it means to invent a brand-new style: 'They tell me, "Kick back a little," 'cause I'm too raw/… I've got the vision I can open up a new door.'

HIP HOP
HOORAY

Hip hop was invented 1974, in certain boroughs of New York by DJs who spun and scratched funky dance records on turntables, and by MCs who rapped along to these records on a microphone. In those old-school days, hip hop lyrics were mostly about bragging playfully and celebrating good times with friends.

By 1983, when the goofy movie *Flashdance* worked breakdancing into its plot, hip hop seemed tired out. It might have gone the way of other fads, but by 1984 'new-school' hip hop acts like Run-D.M.C. had reinvented hip hop – making it more ferocious-sounding while engaging with social issues. This was the start of hip hop's so-called golden age. At about the same time, 'gangsta rap', which would give hip hop a bad name with grownups, combined a ferocious sound with lyrics that seemed to celebrate crime and violence.

In the late 1980s, as a reaction to gangsta, 'alternative' hip hop came along. The creative music of A Tribe Called Quest, De La Soul, Eric B. & Rakim, and others defined the second half of hip hop's golden age, which supposedly ended circa 1993.

Alas, much of today's mainstream hip hop is boring and lame. However, alternative hip hop paved the way for today's great 'jazz', 'underground', 'indie' and 'conscious' hip hop acts. So maybe the golden age of hip hop isn't over yet.

FOOL AROUND
WITH SOUND

By Walter Schleisman

Compared to your grownups who – when they were your age – couldn't create professional-sounding music unless they had a record contract and a domineering parent, you're lucky. Today, you can use intuitive and fun digital audio programs on your computer to mess around with other people's songs... or create your own.

Make your own music

Most digital audio programs come pre-loaded with 'loops' (short samples of music) that were recorded in studios by musicians. Even if you don't know how to play a note, you can make your own songs by arranging these pre-loaded loops in whatever order you wish. Many digital audio programs allow you to layer your own voice over loops, or create your own loops.

Which program should you use? If you have access to a Mac, a program called GarageBand is probably already loaded onto the computer. If you have a PC, you will probably need to buy software – for example, Sony's ACID Music Studio. There are also free programs that can be downloaded; Audacity is a popular one.

Edit someone else's song

Do you have a favourite song that's perfect in every way… except that it repeats the chorus forever? Or maybe it's appropriate to play in the car except for one long string of swearwords? Search YouTube for tutorials on bleeping swearwords – and other fun tricks, from making ringtones to inserting sound effects.

DIGITAL AUDIO TERMS

.wav

When a computer records a sound wave (the sound of your voice, for example), it creates a digital 'wave' file. A .wav file takes up a lot of hard drive storage space, so digital audio programs often have settings that automatically convert sound files into .mp3 or .aac files.

.mp3, .wma, .aac

These are common types of compressed sound wave files – which aren't as rich and realistic as a .wav, but which require less memory. If you're recording yourself, and you want a high-quality sound, adjust the audio program's settings to record sound as a .wav file.

Karaoke–ise any song

Eliminating vocals on a song has been the dream of many a talent-show contestant. These days, it can be done fairly easily.

If the vocals are panned in the centre of a stereo track – i.e. the vocals appear on both of the track's channels – you can try removing everything that's common to both channels. Using Audacity, for example, you'd split the stereo track into left and right channels, make both mono, 'invert' one of the channels, and play back the result. Note that this technique is not perfect – for example, inverting can remove bass and rhythm parts in addition to vocals.

If you want a super-high-quality sound and can afford to purchase a piece of hardware that plugs into your computer, it's worth trying a device like the Thompson Vocal Eliminator.

Make a medley

Want to create one song out of portions of several of your favourite songs? You can upload songs into a single file, and mix up bits and pieces of them until it sounds good to you.

> **IMPORTANT!** Although you're allowed to share original songs that you've written and recorded, it's illegal to copy and share songs that belong to someone else. Also, although the loops that come pre-loaded in GarageBand are royalty-free, other loops might be protected by copyright laws. So… go ahead and use loops that you sample from songs, but don't sell or share them.

Create a soundtrack

Your videos and movies are always cooler with soundtracks, and your video editing program will allow you to add music. But don't create the music until after you finish your video. Otherwise you will find yourself remaking the soundtrack every single time you edit the video.

Pump up your practices

Whether you play the bassoon or the electric guitar, you can use loops to make practising more fun. Also, many digital audio programs have tuners you can use to make sure that you're in tune and playing the right note. Record yourself to hear how brilliant you sound.

Illustrations by Mister Reusch

RECORDING AND EDITING TIPS

If you are going to record your voice or a 'live' instrument:

- Make sure you are in a quiet room.

- Turn off phones that might ring in the middle of the perfect take.

- Don't get too close to the mic or too far away. 30–45cm is great for voice or most instruments. Loud instruments need to be farther away.

- Use headphones to listen to music while you record yourself playing along; otherwise, you'll record the music in the background.

- Before and after you record, leave a few seconds of quiet on the track. When you're editing, the quiet parts will help you blend different takes together seamlessly.

If you are going to edit music:

- **Be patient.** It's hard to find the exact spot to cut and put the song back together. You will know if you messed up, because the beat will be off – or there will be a popping sound.

- **Magnify.** Zoom in on the audio file – so you can view it in detail. This may be confusing at first, but you will start to notice things like a little extra peak where the bass drum or snare drum appear. These markers will help you figure out where you are in the song.

- **Analyse.** Music has a form – so when you're digitally editing a song, figure out which part of the track is the chorus, the verse, the guitar solo, the intro or the downbeat (the first beat of a new measure). Soon you'll be able to recognise their sound-wave forms.

GET YOUR
BLOG ON

Blog with your grownup!

Blogging didn't exist when your grownups were kids. If they wanted to write for other people, they joined school newspapers or sent letters or emails to their friends. They even talked on the phone, sometimes for hours at a time. Their private thoughts were confined to the paper pages of diaries.

The word blog is short for 'web log'. A log is a written record of what happens; ship captains and explorers use them to record daily activities. Today, thanks to the web, blogs make it possible for anyone to broadcast their political views, innermost secrets, and undying enthusiasm for anything from baking to Arsenal FC. Also, blogs can be a way to form communities with others who share your interests.

Setting up a blog is easy
Popular programs such as Tumblr (tumblr.com) WordPress (wordpress.com), and Blogger (blogger.com) walk you through each step of the start-up process; you can be ready to publish in less than 30 minutes.

You must be at least 13 to have your own blog on any of these sites. And while there are kids-only blog-making sites out there, they usually stink. Not only are they clogged with ads for everything from Happy Meals to 'Lose weight fast!' but you aren't even allowed to decide which topics you're going to blog about. They don't let you set up something like your own magazine or journal, which is the whole point of blogging.

IMPORTANT! If you are younger than 13, you and your grownup can create and maintain a blog together. Why not just pretend you are older than you really are? Two reasons: 1) you don't want to break the law; and 2) blogging with your grownup is fun.

Choose a theme
The best blogs aren't a slew of random thoughts that popped into the blogger's head. Instead, a good blog centres around a single theme and then explores it from a million different angles. Your theme should be something you are into or want to learn more about – space travel, technology, beading, horses, the environment, gymnastics, movies, sewing, parkour, hip hop, cooking, ADHD, science fiction. The possibilities are as endless as your interests.

Pick your photos
Photos are essential to a good blog. But it's best to stick to pictures or drawings or cartoons that

illustrate your theme – a beautiful chocolate brownie cake for your baking blog, or your latest woodworking project for your building blog – and not include any photos of yourself. Why? The sad truth is that if your readers know you're a kid, they might harass you or worse. So you shouldn't reveal your age.

> **IMPORTANT!** Don't just grab any image from Flickr or another website. Whether it's a photo of the Mayan ruins of Tulum from a Guatemalan tourism site or an image of a cocker spaniel from Crufts, many online images are copyrighted, which means that they are owned by someone else and you legally have to get the permission of a person or organisation to reprint them. Some copyrighted photos – especially of celebrities – require that you pay to use them.

If you want to use a photo that isn't taken by you, you must email the person who owns the copyright and ask for permission. If they say yes, there usually is an agreement that the photo will run with what's known as a photo credit (example: 'Photo courtesy of Springer Spaniel World' or 'Reprinted with permission from Shaun White'). If you use a film still, you should credit the studio.

The same goes for videos. Yes, YouTube rocks. And yes, embedding (that's the term for 'putting') videos in your blog will make it more interesting. But if you didn't create the video yourself, you have to make sure it's OK to make it a part of your blog. If the video is on YouTube, the person who created it is given the option to allow or not allow others to embed the video in their websites. If you can embed it, chances are it's perfect legal to use it. But to be on the safe side, it's best to contact the creator and get permission first.

Add links

Blogs aren't just about what you write. They're also a great way to tell your audience about things other people are writing or blogging about. See a story in the newspaper about an upcoming comics convention? Create a post that links to it. Want to point your readers to a recipe for nachos? Link to it!

Keep your reader's attention

Use descriptive headlines to draw people to your new post. While 'Crufts Comes to Birmingham' certainly gets the point across that there's a dog show coming to the Midlands, it doesn't grab you the way 'Midlands' Best Golden Retrievers and Poodles Compete for Top Prize' does. Also, resist the temptation to write a novel. Studies show online readers like their information in small chunks. Some bloggers don't write paragraphs longer than 60 words!

Carefully consider comments

One of the cool features about blogs is that you can interact with people from all over the world who also care about your theme. Unfortunately, it can also be tough to figure out if the grownup or kid on the other end of the comment is a good person or a jerk. Some families decide to not allow any comments on kids' blogs. Others set up the comments feature so that every comment or email first goes to the grownup's email to be approved. To ensure your privacy, only use your first name when you blog.

Post often

Blogs are like tropical fish. They live if you take care of them; they die if you don't. Readers will come back to blogs that have new content on a regular basis. This doesn't mean you should skip your homework to blog about the World Cup. But don't ignore your blog for weeks at a time, either.

Illustrations by Mister Reusch

SECRET HISTORY OF GETTING AROUND

By Jay Walljasper

490 BC Pheidippides, a messenger, runs 26 miles from Marathon to Athens to announce Greece's victory over an invading Persian army. We honour this feat today by calling long-distance foot races 'marathons'.

1271 Italian Marco Polo sets off from Venice, travelling by horse, boat, camel and foot to China. He is 17 and will not return home for 24 years.

1522 The *Victoria*, commanded by Portuguese captain Ferdinand Magellan, is the first ship to sail around the world. Magellan dies in the Philippines, but his crew continues the voyage.

1700s Innovations in upholstery increase the average speed of stage-coaches. It is the comfort of their passengers, not the speed of horses, that determines how fast they travel.

Early 1800s As steam engine technology advances, some doctors warn that train passengers might suffer crushed bones from travelling at speeds approaching 35 miles per hour.

1827 The first school bus, drawn by horses, carries 25 girls to school at Abney Park, near London.

1863 The Tube opens in London – it's the world's first underground transport service. Forty thousand passengers use it on the first day.

1885 Bertha Benz makes the first long-distance journey by car to visit her mother in Pforzheim, Germany. Her husband Karl had invented the first petrol-powered car three years earlier.

1903 Wilbur and Orville Wright – bicycle mechanics from Dayton, Ohio – make the first flight by aeroplane. Orville stays aloft a total of 59 seconds.

1928 The first transatlantic airline begins service between Germany and New Jersey. Passengers don't fly in aeroplanes but in Zeppelins, which are technologically advanced versions of hot-air balloons.

Early 1940s London Tube stations are used as shelters during Second World War air raids.

1953 The first street designed exclusively for walkers is opened in Rotterdam, Netherlands. Today pedestrian streets are found across Europe and other parts of the world.

1960s Jet packs – backpacks with rocket engines that propel people through the air – inspire worldwide excitement. Several experimental prototypes are demonstrated but it turns out they are only practical for use by astronauts on the moon.

1960s The 'Beeching Cuts' result in massive rail closures across the UK. Many of these unused rail lines are turned into walking and cycling trails.

1962 Satish Kumar and Prabhakar Menon depart Bangalore, India, on foot, walking 8,000 miles to Moscow, Paris, London and Washington DC to bring a message of peace to world leaders.

1963 The last streetcar runs on the streets of Los Angeles, one of hundreds of US cities to convert their transit fleet to buses. The demise of many rail transit systems was linked in court cases to an illegal conspiracy by General Motors and other automobile-based companies. (See the movie *Who Framed Roger Rabbit*.) Only 18 years later, the nearby city of San Diego builds America's first modern streetcar system called light rail. 25 US cities now offer light rail, including Los Angeles.

1964 The first Japanese Bullet Train zooms between Tokyo and Osaka reaching speeds of 130 miles an hour. Some Chinese passenger trains now regularly run at 215 miles an hour.

1970s Kids in Marin County, California, invent mountain biking by modifying their street bikes to ride on the steep local hills.

1973 The Arab-Israeli war prompts an oil embargo that leads to a petrol shortage across the UK and the US. Both countries will end up imposing strict (lower) speed limits to encourage people to use petrol more efficiently.

1974 The city of Curitiba, Brazil, pioneers a faster form of public transit (called Bus Rapid Transit) where buses travel in their own special lanes. Today 85 per cent of the city's population takes these buses, and BRT lines are being created in the United States.

1976 Bogota, Colombia, closes several streets on a Sunday morning so people can bike and walk. Today, as many as 2 million people fill the streets every week in Bogota, and the idea has spread to many other cities around the world.

1982 Mark Luther perfects the 'ollie' – a skateboarding move in which both the skater and the board bound into the air. Kids had been skateboarding since at least the 1950s, but the emergence of tricks boosts the sport to new levels of popularity.

1984 Richard Branson founds Virgin Atlantic Airways, initially flying between London's Gatwick Airport and Newark Liberty International Airport just outside New York City.

1997 The first Toyota Prius, a hybrid electric/petrol car that emits less pollution, is sold in Japan. In 2010, Chevrolet introduces the all-electric Volt car.

1999 Bertrand Piccard and Brian Jones fly around the globe in a hot-air balloon. They leave Switzerland on 1 March and travel 26,600 miles before landing at Mauritania, Africa, on 21 March.

2010 The Barclays Cycle Hire programme opens in London. Cyclists log 10,000,000 kilometres, the equivalent of cycling to the moon and back 13 times, in the first six months of operation.

Illustrations by Mister Reusch

RIDE
THE WIND

AN EXCERPT FROM

AROUND THE WORLD IN 80 DAYS

by Jules Verne

Two of the French novelist Jules Verne's most famous tales – *Journey to the Centre of the Earth* (1864) and *Twenty Thousand Leagues Under the Sea* (1869) – are voyages into unknown worlds. *Around the World in 80 Days* (1873) follows the eccentric Englishman Phileas Fogg as he travels around the known world, in record time, by steamship and railway. He races from London to Suez; from Suez to Bombay; from Bombay to Calcutta; from Calcutta to Hong Kong; from Hong Kong to Yokohama; from Yokohama to San Francisco; from San Francisco to New York; and from New York to London. When the train to New York is attacked by Sioux warriors near Nebraska's Fort Kearny, Fogg rescues his manservant, Passepartout... but the train to Omaha leaves them behind. Fix, a Scotland Yard detective who has been trailing Fogg and causing trouble, steps in to save the day.

Phileas Fogg found himself twenty hours behind time. Passepartout, the involuntary cause of this delay, was desperate. He had ruined his master!

At this moment the detective approached Mr Fogg, and, looking him intently in the face, said: 'Seriously, sir, are you in great haste?'

'Quite seriously.'

'I have a purpose in asking,' resumed Fix. 'Is it absolutely necessary that you should be in New York on the 11th, before nine o'clock in the evening, the time that the steamer leaves for Liverpool?'

'It is absolutely necessary.'

'And, if your journey had not been interrupted by these Indians, you would have reached New York on the morning of the eleventh?'

'Yes; with eleven hours to spare before the steamer left.'

'Good! you are therefore twenty hours behind. Twelve from twenty leaves eight. You must regain eight hours. Do you wish to try to do so?'

'On foot?' asked Mr Fogg.

'No; on a sledge,' replied Fix. 'On a sledge with sails. A man has proposed such a method to me.'

It was the man who had spoken to Fix during the night, and whose offer he had refused.

Phileas Fogg did not reply at once; but Fix, having pointed out the man, who was walking up and down in front of the station, Mr Fogg went up to him. An instant after, Mr Fogg and the American, whose name was Mudge, entered a hut built just below the fort.

There Mr Fogg examined a curious vehicle, a kind of frame on two long beams, a little raised in front like the runners of a sledge, and upon which there was room for five or six persons. A high mast was fixed on the frame, held firmly by metallic lashings, to which was attached a large brigantine sail. This mast held an iron stay upon which to hoist a jib-sail. Behind, a sort of rudder served to guide the vehicle. It was, in short, a sledge rigged like a sloop.

During the winter, when the trains are blocked up by the snow, these sledges make extremely rapid journeys across the frozen plains from one station to another. Provided with more sails than a cutter, and with the wind behind them, they slip over the surface of the prairies with a speed equal if not superior to that of the express trains.

Mr Fogg readily made a bargain with the owner of this land-craft. The wind was favourable, being fresh, and blowing from the west. The snow had hardened, and Mudge was very confident of being able to transport Mr Fogg in a few hours to Omaha. Thence the trains eastward run frequently to Chicago and New York. It was not impossible that the lost time might yet be recovered; and such an opportunity was not to be rejected.

[…]

At eight o'clock the sledge was ready to start. The passengers took their places on it, and wrapped themselves up closely in their travelling-cloaks. The two great sails were hoisted, and under the pressure of the wind the sledge slid over the hardened snow with a velocity of forty miles an hour.

The distance between Fort Kearny and Omaha, as the birds fly, is at most two hundred miles. If the wind held good, the distance might be traversed in five hours; if no accident happened the sledge might reach Omaha by one o'clock.

What a journey! The travellers, huddled close together, could not speak for the cold, intensified by the rapidity at which they were going. The sledge sped on as lightly as a boat over the waves. When the breeze came skimming the earth the sledge seemed to be lifted off the ground by its sails. Mudge, who was at the rudder, kept in a straight line, and by a turn of his hand checked the lurches which the vehicle had a tendency to make. All the sails were up, and the jib was so arranged as not to screen the brigantine. A top-mast was hoisted, and another jib, held out to the wind, added its force to the other sails. Although the speed could not be exactly estimated, the sledge could not be going at less than forty miles an hour.

'If nothing breaks,' said Mudge, 'we shall get there!'

Mr Fogg had made it for Mudge's interest to reach Omaha within the time agreed on, by the offer of a handsome reward.

The prairie, across which the sledge was moving in a straight line, was as flat as a sea. It seemed like a vast frozen lake. The railroad which ran through this section ascended from the south-west to the north-west by Great Island, Columbus, an important Nebraska town, Schuyler, and Fremont, to Omaha. It followed throughout the right bank of the Platte River. The sledge, shortening this route, took a chord of the arc described by the railway. Mudge was not afraid of being stopped by the Platte River, because it was frozen. The road, then, was quite clear of obstacles, and Phileas Fogg had but two things to fear – an accident to the sledge, and a change or calm in the wind.

But the breeze, far from lessening its force, blew as if to bend the mast, which, however, the metallic lashings held firmly. These lashings, like the chords of a stringed instrument, resounded as if vibrated by a violin bow. The sledge slid along in the midst of a plaintively intense melody.

'Those chords give the fifth and the octave,' said Mr Fogg.

These were the only words he uttered during the journey.

[…]

While each of the party was absorbed in reflections so different, the sledge flew past over the vast carpet of snow. The creeks it passed over were not perceived. Fields and streams disappeared under the uniform whiteness. The plain was absolutely deserted. Between the Union Pacific road and the branch which unites Kearny with Saint Joseph it formed a great uninhabited island. Neither village, station, nor fort appeared. From time to time they sped by some phantom-like tree, whose white skeleton twisted and rattled in the wind. Sometimes flocks of wild birds rose, or bands of gaunt, famished, ferocious prairie-wolves ran howling after the sledge. Passepartout, revolver in hand, held himself ready to fire on those which came too near. Had an accident then happened to the sledge, the travellers, attacked by these beasts, would have been in the most terrible danger; but it held on its even course, soon gained on the wolves, and ere long left the howling band at a safe distance behind.

About noon Mudge perceived by certain landmarks that he was crossing the Platte River. He said nothing, but he felt certain that he was now within twenty miles of Omaha. In less than an hour he left the rudder and furled his sails, whilst the sledge, carried forward by the great impetus the wind had given it, went on half a mile further with its sails unspread.

It stopped at last, and Mudge, pointing to a mass of roofs white with snow, said: 'We have got there!'

POLAR FLEECE
SNOWBOARD HAT

Polar fleece, which was invented in 1979, is made from a synthetic material that's also used to make plastic fizzy drink bottles. Fleece rocks for crafts! Why? It is available at almost every fabric shop and comes in tons of colours and patterns, from camouflage to peace signs to the logos of your favourite teams. Here are instructions on sewing a groovy hat.

Before you start: if you don't know how to use a sewing machine, make sure that you or your grownup has it set up and ready to go before you begin this activity. It's easy to sew this hat, but the fun factor takes a serious nosedive if neither of you can work the machine.

You'll need:

- 45cm-long piece of polar fleece fabric, about 150cm wide
- Thread to match
- Basic sewing kit (needle, tape measure, pins, scissors)
- Metre rule
- Pattern paper
- Pen or fabric pencil
- Sewing machine. Fleece is thick and stretchy so use a sewing machine needle for knits (a ballpoint, stretch or universal needle is a good choice). Use the longest stitch your machine allows, generally 4mm, when you are sewing fleece.
- Grownup supervision

Determine your hat size

Use a tape measure to find your head circumference – that's the distance around your head. Measure just above your eyebrows. Write this number down so you remember it.

Draw your pattern

Carefully measure out the hat and tassel patterns on pattern paper, then cut round the outside.

1. Make the bottom on the triangle half the width of your head circumference. Cut off the tip of the triangle at the point where it measures 3cm. This is where you will attach the tassel.

2. For the tassel pattern, draw a 10cm x 20cm rectangle on the pattern paper. Draw a horizontal line 2.5cm from the bottom and seven vertical lines spaced 1.25cm apart.

pattern

fabric

wrong side of fabric

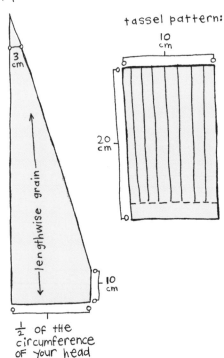

Hat pattern:

3 cm

lengthwise grain

10 cm

½ of the circumference of your head

tassel pattern:

10 cm

20 cm

Illustrations by Heather Kasunick

Cut the fabric

1. Fleece is usually 150cm wide. Fold the fabric so that it measures half the width of the hat from the fold to the lengthwise edge as shown in the illustration opposite (Figure A).

   TIP: The selvedge edge is the finished outside edge of the fabric when it is on the bolt. Because it doesn't fray, making the bottom edge of the hat on the selvedge edge means you don't have to do a hem on it.

2. Pin the hat pattern on the fabric along the fold (Figure B). Because fleece is thick, use long pins with large heads. Cut out the pattern.

3. Open the fabric up as shown below (Figure C). Pin the tassel pattern on a single layer of fabric.

4. Make your tassel by cutting along the seven cutting lines. Cut from the top down to the 2.5cm stitching line as illustrated (Figure D).

   TIP: To prevent cutting through the stitching line, place masking tape along the line.

5. Fold the strips on top of one another (like an accordion) along the 2.5cm side (Figure E).

Sew your hat

1. Cut the hat and remove the pattern.

2. With the right side of the hat fabric facing up, attach the tassel by laying the folded tassel along the fold line as shown. Place the uncut end of the tassel even with the cut edge of the tip of the hat (Figure F).

3. Refold the hat long the fold line. Pin the outside edge (Figure G).

4. Start sewing! Keep your stitches 5mm from the edges. Pivot and sew across the tip to secure tassels in the seam as shown here. Remember not to sew the bottom edge or you'll end up with a goofy-shaped pillowcase instead of a hat.

   TIP: If you want to get fancy, although we like using the selvage for the bottom edge, you can also make a real brim by folding the bottom edge of the hat up 8cm to the wrong side of the hat. Pin, press the seam open with your finger, and then sew 5mm from raw edge.

5. Turn the hat right side out. Instant snowboarding coolness.

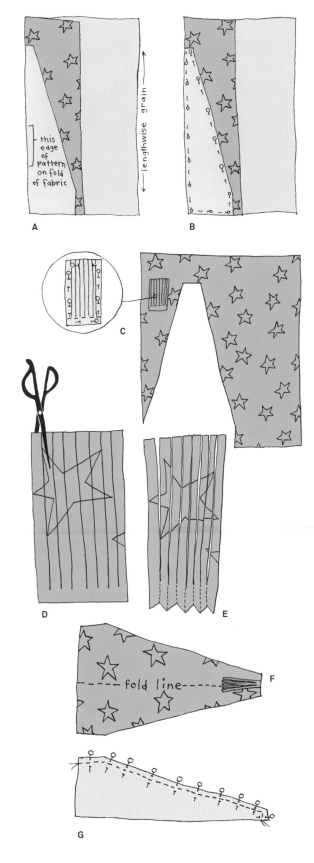

BEST EVER
CAR-FREE MOVIES

By Josh

Some social critics (most famously Jane Jacobs and Lewis Mumford) have argued that the car is a menace to civilisation.

Our reliance on cars, they remind us, has contributed not only to air pollution and climate change, but to the rise in obesity and accidental deaths. It has also isolated us from one other, because cars make it convenient for us to drive long distances (to work, school and elsewhere) instead of walking or taking public transport.

Here are some favourite movies in which people travel by means other than cars.

1924
THE THIEF OF BAGDAD
Directed by Raoul Walsh
The swashbuckling Douglas Fairbanks – who'd previously portrayed a musketeer and Robin Hood – plays an athletic thief who falls in love with a caliph's daughter. He travels via flying carpet… and flying horse.

1926
THE GENERAL
Directed by Buster Keaton and Clyde Bruckman
Considered one of the greatest films ever, *The General* is set in the American Civil War. Buster Keaton is a train engineer whose locomotive gets stolen; many dangerous and hilarious stunts later, he gets it back.

1935
CAPTAIN BLOOD
Directed by Michael Curtiz
In Errol Flynn's first starring role, the dashing actor plays a man sentenced to slavery in the English colony of Port Royal. He escapes and turns pirate, then defends the colony against French warships in a thrilling sea battle.

1937
CAPTAINS COURAGEOUS
Directed by Victor Fleming
When spoiled rich kid Harvey (Freddie Bartholomew) falls off a steamship, he's rescued by a fishing schooner. Tough but kindly fisherman Manuel (Spencer Tracy) teaches him the ways of the sea. It's a tear-jerker.

1943
FLIGHT FOR FREEDOM
Directed by Lothar Mendes
In this movie made during the Second World War, Rosalind Russell portrays a well-known aviatrix – loosely based on real-life flyer Amelia Earhart – who fights against male prejudice. On a top-secret government mission, she vanishes.

1949
TWELVE O'CLOCK HIGH
Directed by Henry King
Gregory Peck stars as a stern officer in an epic about the US Army's Eighth Air Force, which flew dangerous bombing missions over Germany during the Second World War. The movie uses actual combat footage during the battle scenes.

1954
20,000 LEAGUES UNDER THE SEA
Directed by Richard Fleischer
This action-packed adaptation of Jules Verne's classic science-fiction novel is set aboard the *Nautilus*, a high-tech submarine invented by the mysterious, cruel Captain Nemo (James Mason). Cryptid fans will be excited to hear that the movie features a giant squid battle.

1956
AROUND THE WORLD IN 80 DAYS
Directed by Michael Anderson
Another Jules Verne adaptation: a detective trails Phileas Fogg (David Niven) and Passepartout (the Mexican comedian Cantinflas) as they hopscotch around the globe via boat, train and hot-air balloon.

1956
EARTH VS. THE FLYING SAUCERS
Directed by Fred F. Sears
After Earthlings fire upon a flying saucer, an alien armada attacks Moscow, Washington, London and Paris. The special effects by Ray Harryhausen might look silly now, but they were brilliant at the time.

1961
THE ABSENT-MINDED PROFESSOR
Directed by Robert Stevenson

Nerdy Professor Brainard (Fred MacMurray) discovers a bouncy substance called Flubber which, when bombarded with radiation, allows his junky old Model T car to sail through the air.

1965
THOSE MAGNIFICENT MEN IN THEIR FLYING MACHINES
Directed by Ken Annakin

A madcap romp set in the first decade of flight. Biplane pilots from America, England, Germany, France and Italy compete in a race – full of aerial stunts and crashes – from London to Paris.

1971
BEDKNOBS AND BROOMSTICKS
Directed by Robert Stevenson

During the Second World War, Miss Price (Angela Lansbury), an apprentice witch, wants to help the British war effort. So she and three children fly – on a brass bed – into a cartoon world, in search of a magical medallion.

1981
TIME BANDITS
Directed by Terry Gilliam

Kevin, an 11-year-old history buff, joins up with a bumbling gang of dwarves who transport themselves across time and space. In search of riches, they rob Napoleon, Robin Hood, King Agamemnon… and then confront an evil sorcerer.

1984
NAUSICAÄ OF THE VALLEY OF THE WIND
Directed by Hayao Miyazaki

A peace-loving warrior princess, who travels by 'windriding' on a jet glider, tries to prevent two warring nations from destroying their planet, whose ecosystem is in jeopardy.

1985
PEE-WEE'S BIG ADVENTURE
Directed by Tim Burton

When the bow-tie-wearing man-child Pee-Wee Herman (Paul Reubens) loses his beloved bicycle, he voyages across a wacky version of America – via boxcar and motorcycle – to get it back. Very strange and funny.

1985
THE GOONIES
Directed by Richard Donner

Hoping to save their homes in the 'Goon Docks' from demolition, a gang of tween friends led by Mikey (Sean Astin, who later played Sam in the Lord of the Rings movies) ride their one-speed bicycles in search of pirate treasure.

1986
THRASHIN'
Directed by David Winters

Rival skateboard gangs battle for supremacy in this *Romeo and Juliet*-inspired movie full of crazy stunts and chases – and a joust too! Famous skaters Tony Alva, Tony Hawk, Christian Hosoi and Steve Caballero make appearances.

1988
WHO FRAMED ROGER RABBIT
Directed by Roger Zemeckis

Though you may be distracted by the ground-breaking interaction between real and cartoon characters in this fun mystery, its plot concerns the demise of Los Angeles streetcars and the rise of the automobile.

1989
KIKI'S DELIVERY SERVICE
Directed by Hayao Miyazaki

Kiki, a 13-year-old witch, moves to the city with her talking cat, Jiji. In order to perfect her broom-riding skills, she starts a delivery service – and, later, uses her ability to rescue a friend from a runaway dirigible.

1996
JAMES AND THE GIANT PEACH
Directed by Henry Selick

In this half-real and half-animated adaptation of Roald Dahl's novel, a seven-year-old boy escapes from his wicked aunts inside a giant peach borne aloft by seagulls – and accompanied by huge insects.

2001
HARRY POTTER AND THE PHILOSOPHER'S STONE
Directed by Chris Columbus

In the first instalment in the Harry Potter film series, Harry learns to fly a broom – and play Quidditch. He also travels via steam engine. In fact, nobody but a Muggle drives a car.

2003
BELLEVILLE RENDEZ-VOUS
Directed by Sylvain Chomet

After her bicycle racer grandson is kidnapped by car-driving gangsters, Madame Souza teams up with an elderly trio of improvisational musicians to rescue him. A pedal-powered contraption comes in handy.

2006
WHO KILLED THE ELECTRIC CAR?
Directed by Chris Paine

In the 1990s, big auto manufacturers like GM briefly produced cars with engines powered by rechargeable battery packs instead of petrol… and then they destroyed them. This documentary asks why.

2007
THE GOLDEN COMPASS
Directed by Chris Weitz

Perhaps the coolest customer in this film, which is based on the first novel in Philip Pullman's His Dark Materials trilogy, is Lee Scoresby (Sam Elliott). He's a skilled Texan 'aeronaut' who saves the day in his hot-air balloon.

FIX YOUR
WHEELS

By Josh

When I was 15, I worked in a local bicycle shop. Though I never became a talented mechanic, I did learn how to maintain and adjust my bike, and fix flat tyres. For a kid, a bicycle is freedom; taking good care of your wheels is not only a way to save money on repairs, but very satisfying.

You don't have to be mechanically inclined or good with your hands in order to take good care of your bicycle, skateboard or scooter. Paying attention to the condition of your equipment and taking the time to maintain it properly are more important.

> **IMPORTANT!** An improperly repaired bicycle or skateboard can be hazardous. Grownup supervision is a must. When in doubt, consult a trusted bike or skate shop.

BICYCLE MAINTENANCE

You'll need:

- A good pump with built-in pressure gauge. The longer the pump is, the easier it is to inflate your tyres.
- A light lubricant (e.g. Triflow)
- Water spray
- Sponge or toothbrush
- Detergent and warm water
- Protective paint (e.g. Rust-Oleum)
- 3 tyre levers
- Chalk for marking punctures
- Patch kit (sandpaper, glue, patches)
- Spare tubes
- Adjustable wrench
- Clean rags and old newspapers

Keep tyres properly inflated

Bicycle tyres get soft within a week after you've pumped them up. You need a good pump with a pressure guage. (At home an electric air compressor is handy.) If you ride with soft tyres, not only does it take more effort to get anywhere, but if you hit a pothole or go off a curb, you can bend the wheel rim and/or puncture the tube. Look on the tyre sidewall for the recommended pressure (PSI means pounds-per-square-inch), and never over-inflate.

Keep parts lubed

Lube is what keeps the metal parts moving against each other easily. Note that liquid lubricants work longer but attract dirt; 'dry' lubricants (which are sprayed on) stay cleaner.

1. Spray the chain with water before you lube, otherwise the lube might wash gritty stuff inside the rollers.

2. Place some newspapers underneath the bike, to catch drips, and don't go crazy with the lubricant – just a quick spray on the chain, and the pivot points (i.e. where things move) on the brakes and derailleur gears. If you over-spray, these parts will get greasy and dirty.

3. When you've finished, wipe off excess lube with clean rags.

Illustrations by Heather Kasunick

Keep it clean

If you've been off-roading, scrub the bike with a sponge or toothbrush (or special brushes), warm water and a little detergent. Then rinse off the soap with clean water, re-lube the chain and pivot points, and dry with rags.

Prevent rust

Whenever the bike gets wet, dry it off with rags and then apply lube to the chain and brake and derailleur pivots. Store the bike indoors – keeping it on the porch or in the garage will lead to rusting. If you chip or scratch the paint on your bicycle, that area will get rusty unless you touch it up – either with a protective paint like Rust-Oleum, or else with nail polish.

Check the brake pads

Bits of sand and other stuff get embedded in the brake pads. Pick them out every so often, or else the pads will turn into scouring pads and scratch up the rims. When the grooves in the brake pad disappear, replace the pads – it's easy, and you'll improve your braking.

Get a tuneup

About once a year, it's sensible to take the bike to a bike shop mechanic, who has the proper tools and know-how to dismantle and lube up the wheels, bottom bracket, and headset. A tuneup isn't cheap, but it will save you money – and your bike – in the long run.

Fixing a flat tyre

Although there are a lot of steps listed here, once you've had a little practice, you can usually fix a flat tyre in just a few minutes. Not counting the time it takes for the patch-kit glue to dry, of course.

1. Open your brake quick-release or, if you have v-brakes and cantilevers, unhook the cable. This makes wheel removal a lot easier; also, you can damage your brake pads if you don't do this first.

2. Then open the wheel quick-release (or unscrew axle nuts if you don't have a quick-release) and remove the wheel by pulling up on the bike with one hand while pushing down on the wheel with the other. Don't handle the chain – your hand will get very greasy.

3. Release any air still in the tyre by taking the cap off the tube and pressing down on the valve (with a finger or tool) and squeezing the tyre with your other hand.

4. Insert a tyre lever under the tyre's edge opposite the valve stem. Pull down on the top of the lever to prise a section of the tyre over the rim.

5. Hold the lever in place against the spokes (that's why there's a hooked end on most tyre levers), insert a second lever about 10cm away, and do the same thing. Continue doing this until the tyre's edge is off the rim. If you're having trouble getting the tyre off, don't force it; you might need to let more air out of the tube.

6. Pull out the tube, being careful of the valve stem.

7. Next, find out why you got the flat. Run your eye over the outside of the tyre. Slide a rag around inside the tyre, in both directions, and see if it snags on a nail or piece of glass or wire. Remove the offending item carefully – don't poke or cut yourself.

8. Check the rim strip – a piece of rubber around the inside of the rim that protects the tube from the rim's sharp edges – to see if it has shifted.

9. If there's a huge hole in the tube or the valve is broken, the tube is ruined. If you can't find the puncture in the tube, inflate the tube and listen for a whistle or feel for leaking air. Sometimes it's necessary to submerge the tube in water and look for bubbles.

10. Mark the puncture with a piece of chalk. Scuff the spot with sandpaper from the patch kit, brush off the dust, and apply a thin layer of glue about the same size as the patch you'll use. (Roll the glue tube from the bottom, otherwise next time you need glue it will be dried out.)

11. Let the glue dry for five minutes, then peel the foil off the patch and apply. Roll the end of your pump over the repair to tighten the bond.

12. Inflate the repaired tube (or spare) just enough so it smooths out. Place it inside the tyre, starting with the valve stem. Stand up, lean the wheel against your legs with the valve hole on top.

13. Hold the tyre and tube with both hands, place a portion of the tyre edge on the rim and insert the valve stem into the rim hole. Work the edge back onto the rim by moving your hands apart, away from the valve stem.

14. When you reach the bottom of the wheel, don't force the last section onto the rim. Try letting air out of the tube. Pop a couple of centimetres of tyre edge onto the rim, then another, until the whole thing pops on.

15. Make sure the thick base of the valve isn't pinched under the tyre edge by pushing the valve into the tyre. Inflate the tube halfway, remove the pump and spin the wheel to make sure the tyre is sitting correctly on the rim. If a section of tyre edge pops above the rim as you're inflating, let some air out and gently push the tube into place.

16. When you reinstall the wheel, make sure it's aligned properly in the frame (rear wheel) or fork (front). Tighten the quick-release or axle nuts, give it a few spins to make sure it's on straight, then make sure you get the brakes working.

SKATEBOARD MAINTENANCE

Know your stick

- The **trucks** are the T-shaped contraptions that hold the wheels.
- The **truck bolts** fasten the trucks to the **deck**.
- The part of the trucks attached to the deck is the **baseplate**; the piece with the axle is the **hanger**.
- **Axle nuts** hold the wheels on.
- In the centre of each truck is a bolt called the **kingpin**; tightening or loosening the kingpin adjusts the amount of resistance the trucks give when you shift your weight to turn.
- Rubber **bushings** surround the kingpin and make the trucks flexible.
- Inside the wheels are ring-shaped **casings**, which are sealed sets of bearings.
- For more height, insert a plastic platform between the baseplate and the deck; it's called a **riser**.

You'll need:

- Unit Skateboard Tool, which is several tools in one.
- Lube – whatever you use for your bicycle.
- Vinegar – to use as a degreaser.

Tighten your trucks

If you're having trouble balancing, tighten the kingpins. Check to see if the rubber bushings are worn down; if they are, replace them (see below). If the trucks are wobbling, tighten the truck bolts that have become loose.

Loosen your trucks

If the skateboard won't turn as easily as you'd like it to, loosen the kingpins. Are your bushings brand new? If so, then they just need to be broken in.

Replace the bushings

1. Loosen the kingpin until the nut comes off. Remove the metal washer beneath the nut.

2. Pull the hanger off the base. Remove the two rubber bushings on each truck.

3. Install new bushings – make sure they're the same size as the old ones. Place the lower one on the kingpin, the hanger on top of it, then the upper bushing. Then the washer and the nut.

4. Tighten the nut until the steering is perfect.

Adjust the wheels

If your wheel keeps getting wobbly, get a new axle nut. Unscrew the old axle nut, remove the wheel, pour vinegar on a rag and clean grease off the axle. Replace the wheel and tighten the new nut until the wheel is snug.

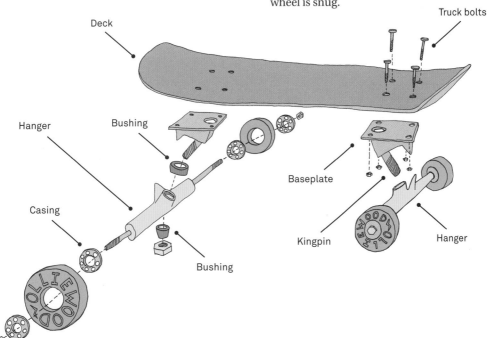

Deck

Truck bolts

Hanger

Bushing

Baseplate

Casing

Kingpin

Hanger

Bushing

TAKE THE
TRAIN OR BUS

By Josh

When Elizabeth and I – not to mention all of our friends – were growing up, we were encouraged to take public transport.

Sometimes the bus or train was a little scary: smelly drunks, loud teenagers, creepy-looking people. But getting to a friend's house, a comic-book shop or a pizza place when we wanted to get there (as opposed to when it was convenient for our grownups to drive us, which was never) made the trip worthwhile. Besides, unsupervised travel is an adventure.

Today, many grownups believe that the world is an unsafe place. Which explains why most of today's kids' books and movies are about orphans; kids with protective families don't have adventures worth telling. *Harry Potter's Father Drives Him to School...* boring!

If your grownups worry about you taking public transport, ask them why. Is it because they're afraid you might be hurt? Point out that violent crime rates across the UK have dropped more than 50 per cent since they peaked in 1995. Also, the most dangerous place is *in the family car*. That's right: over a thousand kids are injured every year while travelling inside cars.

You might also encourage your grownups to read *Free-Range Kids*, by Lenore Skenazy. In 2008, Skenazy caused a fuss when she wrote a newspaper story about her decision to allow her nine-year-old son to take the New York subway home alone from the shopping centre; in response to all the fussers, Skenazy says that 'Worst First' thinking (the idea that we should make decisions based on the worst possible scenario) is a big mistake. 'Free-Rangers believe in helmets, car seats, seat belts – safety!' her blog's homepage explains. 'We just do NOT believe that every time school-age kids go outside, they need a security detail.'

If your grownup thinks it's OK for you to take the train or bus, but worries that you might get lost, take a trial run. Ask them to meet you somewhere – and carry a phone in case anything goes wrong. That's exactly what my son Sam did, one Saturday afternoon. And things did go wrong! But it all worked out OK, and we both learned from the experience. Here's Sam's story.

A KID'S FIRST SOLO BUS RIDE
By Sam

I decided to ride the No. 39 bus from a stop near our house to the Soldier's Monument bus stop three-and-a-half miles away. I felt nervous, but

Illustrations by Mister Reusch

I had my mother's mobile phone (which I was embarrassed to use because it was so old that it actually had an antenna) and I knew that my father would meet me at the other end for lunch.

My father's advice:

- Stand slightly to one side to let people exiting the bus or train get off before you try to board.

- Never try to get onto the train or bus once the doors begin to close.

- Stay away from the edge of railway platforms, and out of the street.

- Take an aisle seat, not a window seat, because some people take a long time to get up once they've sat down and you don't want to get stuck.

- If you're in the aisle seat and someone wants you to slide over to the window so they can sit down, jump up and invite them to slide in.

- He also told me I should 'buzz' the driver for my stop, but I didn't know what he meant – so I didn't end up doing it.

I boarded the bus, paid the fare and told the driver I wanted to get off at the Monument stop. He said OK. I sat down in one of the front seats. After a few stops, some elderly passengers boarded, so I gave up my seat and moved farther back into the bus.

The bus ride went a lot quicker than I expected, so I didn't notice that we'd arrived at the Monument stop until we'd driven past it! I couldn't figure out how to 'buzz' the driver, so I made my way to the front and told him, 'Next stop, please.' By then we were at the end of the line, about half-a-mile away from my stop. I got off the bus and called my father. He was at the restaurant where we were planning to have lunch, so he told me to walk there.

What a disaster.

I had started to trudge back to the Monument when the No. 39 passed me on its return trip. Suddenly, it came to a halt. The driver opened the door and yelled, 'Get on!' I told him I couldn't, because I had no more bus fare. He said that I didn't need to pay, because he had forgotten to drop me off at the Monument. He gave me a lift, and my father and I had our lunch.

After that, bus rides didn't seem too scary.

Learn from our mistakes

1. Before your first solo bus or train ride, your grownup should go over a map of the route with you, pointing out landmarks (shops, parks or other places you know), so you'll have some idea of how close you are to your stop. Your grownup might even mark those landmarks on a map. If you're taking the train, study the schedule; local and express trains make different stops. If you or your grownup is super-nervous about this excursion, do it together beforehand.

2. When boarding a bus, not only should you always have your fare ready – exact change, if possible, so you don't hold up the queue behind you (or show everybody else how much you're carrying) – you should always carry some emergency fare money with you too.

3. Stay alert! Make sure you know which stop is coming up next, and how many stops are left before your destination. If you're above ground, watch for landmarks. Move to the front of the bus or train shortly before you arrive at your stop. On a bus, work out how to signal the driver (there's usually a button to ring a bell) then go ahead and do so when it's time.

Comic by Joe Alterio

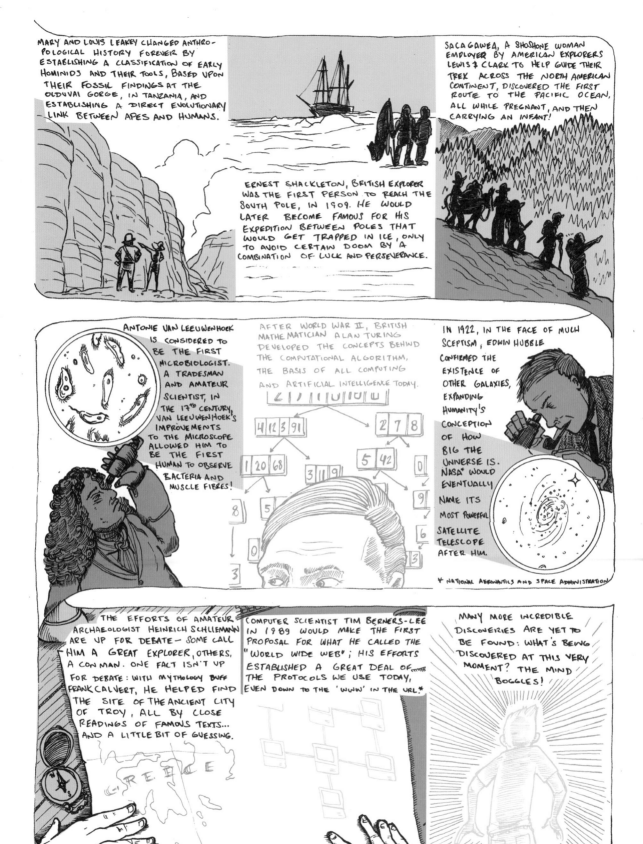

MARY AND LOUIS LEAKEY CHANGED ANTHROPOLOGICAL HISTORY FOREVER BY ESTABLISHING A CLASSIFICATION OF EARLY HOMINIDS AND THEIR TOOLS, BASED UPON THEIR FOSSIL FINDINGS AT THE OLDUVAI GORGE, IN TANZANIA, AND ESTABLISHING A DIRECT EVOLUTIONARY LINK BETWEEN APES AND HUMANS.

ERNEST SHACKLETON, BRITISH EXPLORER WAS THE FIRST PERSON TO REACH THE SOUTH POLE, IN 1909. HE WOULD LATER BECOME FAMOUS FOR HIS EXPEDITION BETWEEN POLES THAT WOULD GET TRAPPED IN ICE, ONLY TO AVOID CERTAIN DOOM BY A COMBINATION OF LUCK AND PERSEVERANCE.

SACAGAWEA, A SHOSHONE WOMAN EMPLOYED BY AMERICAN EXPLORERS LEWIS & CLARK TO HELP GUIDE THEIR TREK ACROSS THE NORTH AMERICAN CONTINENT, DISCOVERED THE FIRST ROUTE TO THE PACIFIC OCEAN, ALL WHILE PREGNANT, AND THEN CARRYING AN INFANT!

ANTONIE VAN LEEUWENHOEK IS CONSIDERED TO BE THE FIRST MICROBIOLOGIST. A TRADESMAN AND AMATEUR SCIENTIST, IN THE 17th CENTURY, VAN LEEUWENHOEK'S IMPROVEMENTS TO THE MICROSCOPE ALLOWED HIM TO BE THE FIRST HUMAN TO OBSERVE BACTERIA AND MUSCLE FIBRES!

AFTER WORLD WAR II, BRITISH MATHEMATICIAN ALAN TURING DEVELOPED THE CONCEPTS BEHIND THE COMPUTATIONAL ALGORITHM, THE BASIS OF ALL COMPUTING AND ARTIFICIAL INTELLIGENCE TODAY.

IN 1922, IN THE FACE OF MUCH SCEPTISM, EDWIN HUBBLE CONFIRMED THE EXISTENCE OF OTHER GALAXIES, EXPANDING HUMANITY'S CONCEPTION OF HOW BIG THE UNIVERSE IS. NASA* WOULD EVENTUALLY NAME ITS MOST POWERFUL SATELLITE TELESCOPE AFTER HIM.

* NATIONAL AERONAUTICS AND SPACE ADMINISTRATION

THE EFFORTS OF AMATEUR ARCHAEOLOGIST HEINRICH SCHLIEMANN ARE UP FOR DEBATE — SOME CALL HIM A GREAT EXPLORER, OTHERS, A CON MAN. ONE FACT ISN'T UP FOR DEBATE: WITH MYTHOLOGY BUFF FRANK CALVERT, HE HELPED FIND THE SITE OF THE ANCIENT CITY OF TROY, ALL BY CLOSE READINGS OF FAMOUS TEXTS... AND A LITTLE BIT OF GUESSING.

COMPUTER SCIENTIST TIM BERNERS-LEE IN 1989 WOULD MAKE THE FIRST PROPOSAL FOR WHAT HE CALLED THE "WORLD WIDE WEB"; HIS EFFORTS ESTABLISHED A GREAT DEAL OF THE PROTOCOLS WE USE TODAY, EVEN DOWN TO THE 'WWW' IN THE URL.*

* UNIFORM RESOURCE LOCATOR

MANY MORE INCREDIBLE DISCOVERIES ARE YET TO BE FOUND: WHAT'S BEING DISCOVERED AT THIS VERY MOMENT? THE MIND BOGGLES!

SOCIETY: RESOURCES

Visit our website: Unbored.net

GET SOCIAL

Book Crush (2007), by Nancy Pearl. Recommendations of great fiction and nonfiction for kids about social issues – among lots of other topics.

Channel 4 FactCheck (blogs.channel4.com/factcheck). This blog 'goes behind the spin to dig out the truth and separate political fact from fiction', which is particularly useful during an election. When the planning minister claims that 91 per cent of land in rural England is undeveloped, or when the PM claims he's given tax collectors an extra £900million, FactCheck digs in.

E-Petitions (epetitions.direct.gov.uk). A website set up by the government which makes it easy to create and sign petitions online – and thus influence government and Parliament in the UK. Any petition that gets at least 100,000 signatures will be considered for debate in the House of Commons.

Landshare (landshare.net). Whether you want to grown your own veg but don't have anywhere to do it, or have a bit of spare land, or just want to lend gardening tools or help out on a plot, of you have a passion for homegrown food, this thriving online community – of more than 55,000 growers, sharers and helpers – is the place to begin.

Mixed: Portraits of Multiracial Kids (2010), by Kip Fulbeck. A collection of photographs with a forward by Barack Obama's half-sister, Maya Soetoro-Ng.

New Moon Girls (newmoon.com). An online community and magazine created by and for girls, and edited by Helen Cordes; it often looks at current events and social issues.

Number 10 Downing Street (number10.gov.uk) is the official site of the Prime Minister. It's useful not merely for news about the PM's latest speeches and Questions, but for learning more about how the government works (who does what in Whitehall, how tax money is spent, etc.) and also about past prime ministers and the building (built by Sir George Downing in the seventeenth century) itself.

Pay It Forward Movement (payitforwardmovement.org). Do a favour for another person. What's expected is that the recipient of the favour will do the same for others. This website is full of ideas for ways you can be helpful.

TheyWorkForYou (theyworkforyou.com). This website lets you find out what your MP, MSP or MLA is doing in your name, read debates, and see what's coming up in Parliament. Interested in a particular issue? You can sign up for email alerts here. Don't know who represents you? Just enter your UK postcode.

YOUR SCHOOL

Centre for Ecoliteracy (ecoliteracy.org). An organisation devoted to the green school movement – which includes school gardens, healthy lunches and teaching about the environment.

Horrible Histories (1993–present series). Kids love these illustrated history books, which present the unusual, gory or unpleasant aspects of history in a tongue-in-cheek manner. Series author Terry Deary, who tops the list of most-borrowed nonfiction children's authors every year, explains: 'Everything I learned [at school] after 11 was a waste of time… it was boring, badly taught and not related to the real world.'

ipl2 (ipl.org). An online learning and teaching environment that gives links to trusted resources on every topic. It also offers an 'Ask a Librarian' feature.

Ker-Punch! (via iTunes). A brainteaser app – produced by one of this book's editors – based on a back-of-the-classroom game that he used to play.

Khan Academy (khanacademy.org). Learn what you want, at your own pace – thanks to nearly 3,000 videos teaching lessons on everything from arithmetic to physics and history.

Life Skills for Kids: Equipping Your Child for the Real World (2000), by Christine M. Field. A homeschooler offers lessons on everything from using a cheque book to boiling an egg, to doing the laundry and reading a map.

Program or Be Programmed: Ten Commands for a Digital Age (2010), by Douglas Rushkoff. Rushkoff, who is one of this book's contributors, argues that it's critical to make media, of all sorts – instead of just consuming it.

RefDesk (refdesk.com). A site that indexes and reviews trusted online sources. A great resource for any research projects you're doing.

Stop Bullying (stopbullying.gov). Extensive anti-bullying resources, including what to do if bullying is violating your civil rights.

Zotero (zotero.com). A free online tool that allows you to store, cite and organise all of your research in one place.

SAVE THE PLANET

50 Simple Things Kids Can Do To Save The Earth (50simplekids.com). A website by the authors of the bestselling book *The New 50 Simple Things Kids Can Do to Save the Earth* (2009). Encourages kids to make a difference by providing them, their friends and their families the tools to take action.

Environmental Working Group (ewg.org). A great site filled with information about toxins and chemicals in food and popular products – as well as health tips and news on energy, farming, environmental and health issues.

Family Apothecary (action-pack.com/shop). A collection of natural remedies from the international kids' digital magazine *Action Pack*.

Fix It, Make It, Grow It, Bake It: The DIY Guide to the Good Life (2010), by Billee Sharp. For tips on greening your home, see the chapter 'Homely Habitats'.

Freecycle (freecycle.org/group/uk) is a network of British 'gifting' groups, which aims to divert reusable goods from landfills. From mobile phones to mobile homes, people worldwide are choosing to freecycle rather than discard. Doing so cuts down on the need to manufacture new goods.

Freegle (ilovefreegle.org) is another organisation that aims to increase reuse and reduce landfill by offering an online forum where people can give away, and ask for, things that would otherwise be thrown away.

Green Living: A Practical Guide to Eating, Gardening, Energy Saving and Housekeeping for a Healthy Planet (2002), by Sarah Callard and Diane Mills. The title says it all.

Home Energy Diet, The: How to Save Money by Making Your House Energy-Smart (2005), by Paul Scheckel. Tips on energy efficiency, cost-effective improvements and indoor air quality.

It's Easy Being Green: A Handbook for Earth-Friendly Living (2006), by Crissy Trask. Practical day-to-day information for those looking to adopt greener living (and shopping) habits.

Make Stuff (make-stuff.com). Become less wasteful! Along with other DIY projects, the site features dozens of recycling and upcycling projects.

Re-Creative: 50 Projects for Turning Found Items into Contemporary Design (2006), by Steve Dodds. Tips on design, potential material resources and safe and ethical scrounging guidelines.

Reuseit (reuseit.com). Info on how to recycle and reduce household waste – as well as useful facts about materials such as plastic bags and bottles.

Save Britain's Forests (@Savebritforests). This Twitter feed aims to protect national treasures like the Forest of Dean, Alice Holt, Kielder, Thetford, Grizedale, Bedgebury, Sherwood Forest and the New Forest from being auctioned and fenced off, run down, logged or turned into golf courses.

Sneaky Green Uses For Everyday Things (2009), by Cy Tymony. For upcycling ideas, see the chapter 'Sneaky Product Reuse Projects'.

ULS Report, The (use-less-stuff.com). A newsletter offering tips on reducing waste and conserving resources. The editor is co-author of the still-helpful book *Use Less Stuff: Environmental Solutions for Who We Really Are* (1998).

MAKE YOUR OWN MEDIA

Adventures in Cartooning (2009), by James Sturm, Andrew Arnold and Alexis Frederick-Frost. A fun graphic novel that teaches you... how to make your own graphic novels!

Best Old Movies For Families (2007), by Ty Burr. Before you start directing your own movies, you might want to study the classics. This is an excellent guide.

Brickfilms (brickfilms.com). This is a community for the popular hobby of 'brickfilming', the creation of stop-motion films using plastic toys, such as LEGO. You need to become a member to access the site.

Cartooning: Philosophy and Practice (2011), by Ivan Brunetti. A noted cartoonist provides a simple yet sophisticated guide to improving your craft as a cartoonist. Lots of helpful exercises – all you need is a pencil.

Free Pixels (freepixels.com). Stock photos and images that you can use for your blog or website.

Kids Learn to Blog (kidslearntoblog.com). Tips and ideas for kids under 13 about making and maintaining a blog that is both brilliant and safe.

Magic Books & Paper Toys (2008), by Esther K. Smith. Learn how to make books that are more than just books. The chapters 'Pop!,' 'Flip!' and 'Fold!' are particularly fun.

Make a Zine! (2008), by Bill Brent and Joe Biel. Helpful tips on making a zine.

What It Is (2008), by Lynda Barry. One of our favourite cartoonists challenges and encourages young and old would-be artists and writers with questions like 'What is an image?' and 'Can we remember something we can't imagine?'

Whatcha Mean, What's a Zine? The Art of Making Zines and Mini-Comics (2006), by Mark Todd and Esther Watson. Practical tips on all aspects of making and distributing zines.

YouTube (youtube.com). Get inspiration for your own stop-motion movies by searching YouTube for 'brickfilm' and 'stop motion'. Also see the website Best Brick Films (bestbrickfilms.com).

GETTING AROUND

Airliners (airliners.net). An extensive resource about aeroplanes. Not only does it include photographs of all planes currently flying, you can enter the tail number of a plane you've flown on and see where else it has travelled.

Ask the Pilot (askthepilot.com). Airline pilot and world traveller Patrick Smith is extraordinarily knowledgeable. His website and 2004 book of the same title offer answers to every possible question you might have about flying.

Bicycling Guide to Complete Bicycle Maintenance & Repair, The (sixth edition, 2010), by Todd Downs. Learn how to take care of your bike – and, if you're mechanically inclined, how to take it apart and put it together again.

BusItLondon (busitlondon.co.uk) is a website and mobile phone app that uses London Bus data from Transport for London to plan your multi-leg bus journey in the capital.

Cycling Embassy of Great Britain (cycling-embassy.org.uk). An activist organisation whose goal is to make biking safer and more convenient.

Lazy Environmentalist, The: Your Guide to Stylish, Green Living (2007), by Josh Dorfman. Not ready to give up your car? See the chapter 'Vehicular Inspiration: Cars – To Own, To Rent, To Drive'.

Railway Maps of the World (2011), by Mark Ovenden. A compendium of historical and contemporary railway maps and posters from every corner of the world. Trainspotters will dig it.

Transition Network (transitionnetwork.org) Trains communities to rebuild ecological resilience. Initiatives so far have included creating community gardens to grow food; business waste exchange, which matches the waste of one industry with another industry that uses that waste material; and repairing old items rather than throwing them away.

World Carfree Network (worldcarfree.net). A global movement seeking to revitalise towns and cities, and create a sustainable future. Every 22 September, this group organises World Carfree Day.

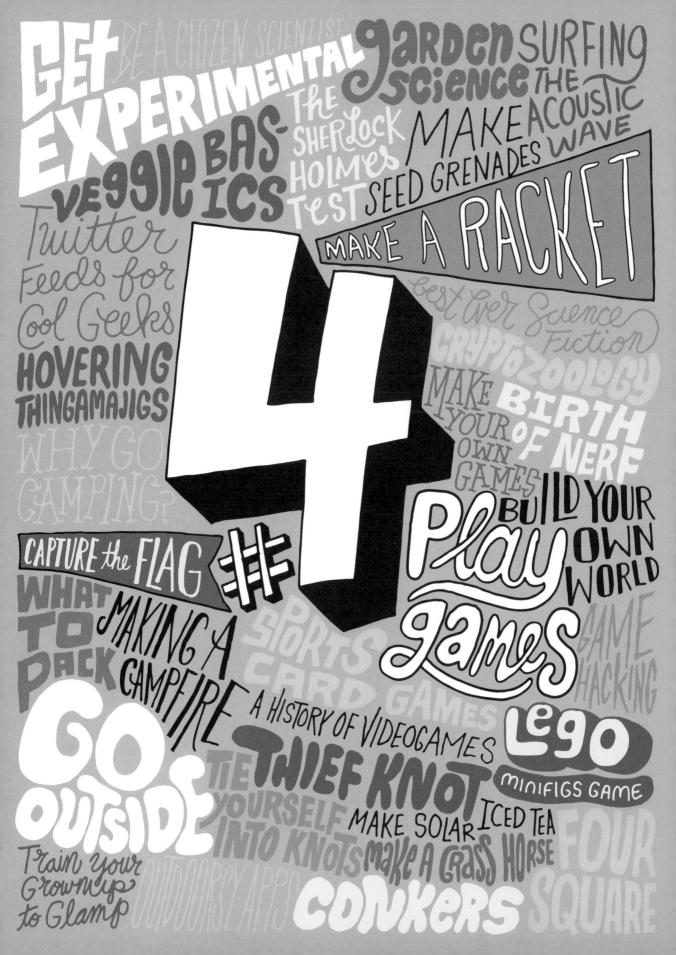

EXPLORE

MAKE AN ORIENTEERING COURSE

WRITE WITH INVISIBLE INK

PIONEERING

POLAR EXPLORER

DRACULA'S VOYAGE

Best ever grownup-free Adventures

MAPPING AND NAVIGATING

TRAIN YOUR

MORE HIDING AND SEEKING TIPS

Disguise yourself

ADVENTURE

GROWNUP TO GEOCACHE

RUN AWAY FROM HOME

DIGITAL TRAVEL

BEST EVER

QUIZ: WORLD SAVVY

LEARN MORE ABOUT THE WORLD

BEST CAR GAMES

MOVIES FROM AROUND THE WORLD

WAY, WAY OUT

EXPAND YOUR HORIZONS

Plan a car Journey

SET SAIL FOR ADVENTURE

TRAIN YOUR GROWNUP TO LET YOU GO SOLO

A TERM IN BUDAPEST

BE A CITIZEN SCIENTIST

By Deb Chachra

What does someone who does science look like? It's a grownup in a white lab coat (and maybe with white hair too), standing in front of a blackboard covered with equations, or in a lab filled with chemicals, or beside a complicated-looking piece of equipment, right? Wrong. Someone who does science might look like, well, you!

You don't have to be a scientist to do science. You can work with scientists and with other volunteers on important research-related tasks that involve careful observation, measurement or computation while playing a videogame, counting frogs in your neighbourhood or identifying galaxies – to name just a few examples. These sorts of projects are known as *citizen science*.

When you go to university to become a scientist, which is what I did, you learn two major things. The first is *how* to do science, which means learning a set of skills: how to design experiments; how to actually do the experiments, which might involve a whole set of techniques; how to analyse data; and also how to present your work so it's clear and understandable to others interested in repeating or building on your research. When you do experiments that can be repeated by other scientists, and carefully go through all the possible answers to the questions you are asking, you're using what's called the *scientific method*.

Using the scientific method, a scientist does experiments or collects information to answer a question that no one has answered before. In doing so, she is adding to what we know about the world around us.

Which brings us to the second major thing that scientists-in-training learn: *what* science to do. In order to make decisions about what questions to ask, or experiments to run, scientists normally spend years studying, because they need to know what questions have already been answered and they need to make sure that they understand the answers.

Once scientists understand how to use the scientific method, and decide what questions they want to ask, they sometimes ask non-scientists to get involved, which is where you come in. Becoming part of scientists' projects allows you to contribute to the world's knowledge, while learning something fascinating, exploring your neighbourhood and developing new skills.

Want to be a citizen scientist? Read on.

Frogs and hail and whale sharks, oh my!

Scientists need volunteers to collect data from a much bigger geographical area than they could do on their own.

OPAL (opalexplorenature.org/explore-nature), the Open Air Laboratories network, runs a wide range of programmes that let you help scientists while exploring nature. The UK has a long history of citizen science in the service of the natural environment, and you can get involved by doing one of OPAL's surveys, like finding all the creatures

Illustrations by Heather Kasunick

in your local pond or in a nearby hedge, or taking up the challenge to count as many bugs as you can in a set time.

Cell Slider (clicktocure.net) enlists you to help find a cure for cancer! A common research technique is to take a small sample of tissue from patients, and treat it so different cells can be distinguished. But someone has to look at the cells – which is where you come in, as you help analyse the images. A tutorial will help you learn the difference between normal and cancerous cells. Some of the cancerous cells will be yellow – this means they're responsive to a known therapy, and identifying them helps the scientists learn what treatments work and why.

The Ecocean Whale Shark Photo-identification Library (whaleshark.org), which helps with the global conservation of this threatened species, asks volunteers to submit photos of whale sharks, along with sighting information. Each whale shark has a unique pattern of dots that, like a fingerprint, can be used to identify it. Using pattern recognition and photo management tools, scientists will track that particular shark; they'll even send you a photo when someone else spots it!

Stars on your screen like grains of sand

You can also volunteer on a project whose scope is enormous – so the more people involved, the better!

Galaxy Zoo (galaxyzoo.org) asks you to help scientists learn about galaxies by looking at photos – on your computer screen – that were taken by the Hubble Space Telescope. With a million or so galaxies to look at, this project can use lots of eyeballs. By answering questions about what they see in the photos, volunteers have helped scientists learn about all the different colours and shapes of galaxies – and understand how these galaxies, and our own, formed.

TWITTER FEEDS FOR
COOL GEEKS

@sciencemuseum: London's Science Museum has a Twitter feed that's full of great links about science and engineering, Scientist of the Week and Lunchtime Reading features, and photographs from the museum and elsewhere.

@NASAVoyager2: How far away (in terms of light-travel time) is the spacecraft Voyager 2, right now? And what is it discovering? Ask, and you'll get an answer!

@ProfBrianCox: The jetsetting British physicist and science presenter tweets about science, his work, and his adventures around the world.

@lowflyingrocks: If an asteroid or comet passes dangerously close to the Earth, you'll be one of the first to learn about it. Your friends will be very impressed.

@MarsCuriosity: The Mars Science Laboratory and its rover, Curiosity, blasted off from Earth in November 2011. You can follow the mission's adventure here.

The Encyclopedia of Life (eol.org) initiative aims to collect information about every one of the 1.9 million species with whom we share our planet. You can get involved in a myriad of ways, from leaving comments to creating a collection of related species to uploading photo or video of that weird-looking bug you spotted in your garden.

Use your brain for science

There are some things that scientists want to do that humans are a lot better at than computers.

Explore The Valley of the Khans (exploration. nationalgeographic.com/mongolia). Join a National Geographic expedition from your computer! Help archaeologists find places in Mongolia to investigate more closely by tagging likely-looking objects (structures, roads, rivers) on satellite images.

Foldit (fold.it/portal) is an online game that challenges you to fold colourful structures – which are actually proteins, the building blocks of all living things – into new shapes. Computers have a tough time figuring out what possible shapes proteins can fold into, but humans are good at seeing the possibilities. By playing a fun, competitive game, you can help scientists understand the structure of proteins, which is key to understanding how they work – in fact, game players found a new configuration for an enzyme associated with the AIDS virus, which scientists are now investigating further, as a target for a vaccine.

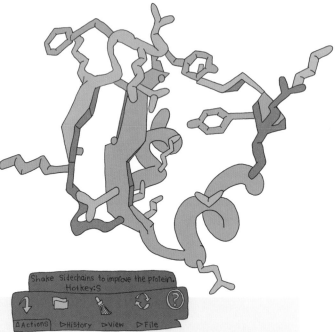

BECOME A
SCIENTIST

Has citizen science piqued your interest? Try:

- Talking to scientists, at nearby universities and labs, about doing research with them. PS: We scientists love talking about what we do. If you meet a scientist or learn about someone doing interesting research, you should always feel free to ask them for more information.

- Participating in the UK-wide National Science and Engineering Week (britishscienceassociation. org/national-science-engineering-week), held in March every year.

- Attending local and regional science fairs, like The Big Bang (thebigbangfair.co.uk) and others.

- Signing up for the CREST Award programme (britishscienceassociation.org/crest) and doing your own science, technology or maths project.

- Competing in the National Science and Engineering Competition (thebigbangfair.co.uk/nsec.cfm) with your own project.

- Checking your local science museum's website for citizen science activities.

- Putting extra effort into maths and science classes at school.

THE SHERLOCK HOLMES
TEST

AN EXCERPT FROM

A STUDY IN SCARLET

by Arthur Conan Doyle

Arthur Conan Doyle based his detective character Sherlock Holmes, who was introduced in this 1887 story, on his former professor, Dr Joseph Bell, who pioneered using science to aid criminal investigations.

After making detailed observations of crime scenes, Holmes compares what he's found against his previous knowledge and then 'reasons backwards' both logically and imaginatively – in order to come up with possible explanations for any details that don't add up. Instead of looking first for answers, Holmes formulates questions that may lead to answers. Which is an excellent illustration of the scientific method.

Broad, low tables were scattered about, which bristled with retorts, test-tubes, and little Bunsen lamps with their blue flickering flames. There was only one student in the room, who was bending over a distant table absorbed in his work. At the sound of our steps he glanced round and sprang to his feet with a cry of pleasure. 'I've found it! I've found it,' he shouted to my companion, running towards us with a test-tube in his hand. 'I have found a re-agent which is precipitated by haemoglobin, and by nothing else.' Had he discovered a gold mine, greater delight could not have shone upon his features.

'Dr Watson, Mr Sherlock Holmes,' said Stamford, introducing us.

'How are you?' he said cordially, gripping my hand with a strength for which I should hardly have given him credit. 'You have been in Afghanistan, I perceive.'

'How on earth did you know that?' I asked in astonishment.

'Never mind,' said he, chuckling to himself. 'The question now is about haemoglobin. No doubt you see the significance of this discovery of mine?'

'It is interesting, chemically, no doubt,' I answered, 'but practically—'

'Why, man, it is the most practical medico-legal discovery for years. Don't you see that it gives us an infallible test for blood stains. Come over here now!' He seized me by the coat-sleeve in his eagerness, and drew me over to the table at which he had been working. 'Let us have some fresh blood,' he said, digging a long bodkin into his finger, and drawing off the resulting drop of blood in a chemical pipette. 'Now, I add this small quantity of blood to a litre of water. You perceive that the resulting mixture has the appearance of pure water. The proportion of blood cannot be more than one in a million. I have no doubt, however, that we shall be able to obtain the characteristic reaction.' As he spoke, he threw into the vessel a few white crystals, and then added some drops of a transparent fluid. In an instant the contents assumed a dull mahogany colour, and a brownish dust was precipitated to the bottom of the glass jar. [...]

'Beautiful! beautiful! The old Guaiacum test was very clumsy and uncertain. So is the microscopic examination for blood corpuscles. The latter is valueless if the stains are a few hours old. Now, this appears to act as well whether the blood is old or new. Had this test been invented, there are hundreds of men now walking the earth who would long ago have paid the penalty of their crimes.'

'Indeed!' I murmured.

'Criminal cases are continually hinging upon that one point. A man is suspected of a crime months perhaps after it has been committed. His linen or clothes are examined, and brownish stains discovered upon them. Are they blood stains, or mud stains, or rust stains, or fruit stains, or what are they? That is a question which has puzzled many an expert, and why? Because there was no reliable test. Now we have the Sherlock Holmes test, and there will no longer be any difficulty.'

GARDEN SCIENCE

By Helen Cordes

Planting a vegetable garden not only helps your family save money on food and gives you easy access to vitamin-packed, fresh-picked produce, but also is a way to experiment and solve problems the way scientists do.

You'll need to do some scientific field work to discover the best and easiest ways to garden in your climate and your particular garden. So get out your notebook and start working out how to give your veggies the ample sun and rich soil they need to grow strong.

Experiment with seeds and seedlings

Now it's time to determine how best to grow the seeds and baby plants available in your local plant shop. You'll find all the info you need on seed packets and on the little markers that come in plant pots. But the best tool you've got is scientific observation. Once you see what 'works' in your soil in specific locations, you'll be ready to make your second season even more spectacular.

That's why garden diaries are so important. Just jot down what you did and what worked best. Follow the instructions on the seed packet, particularly about how deep to plant the seed. Gardening experts say most people bury seeds too deep for them to 'germinate' – the time it takes for the sprout to poke up out of the soil. Observe how many days germination takes (the packet tells you the average number of days from planting to sprouting) as well as how many days it takes from sprouting to harvesting your veggies (packets also show this average). How do your plants compare with the seed or seedling info? Faster or slower?

You can include anything you want in your garden diary, from recipes to drawings of your garden during certain times of the growing season. Draw or write down who visits your garden – do you see bees or certain birds or insects?

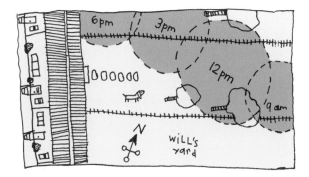

6pm 3pm

oooooo 12pm

9am

N

WiLL's yard

Track your sun

Most veggies – including green beans, peas, tomatoes and carrots – love sun, and need at least six hours a day to thrive. Here's how to decide where to put a sun-wise garden. When it's planting time in your area (it's earlier in the year for warm climates and later in colder climates), take a weekend day to track the sun. Starting in the morning, go outside every three hours and see where the sun shines brightest in your garden. Make a simple sketch of your garden, and chart your data showing which areas are sunniest each time you check.

At the end of the day, you've found your garden spot – the place where the sun shines longest. Just be sure to check with your grownups before digging to make sure you're not digging up a much-loved flower garden.

If your garden or patio is small or shady, garden in containers instead of a plot. Veggies grow well in large pots. You can move the pots around to your garden's sunny spots, which you'll notice change a bit over the growing season as the sun rises higher in the sky.

Plants aren't picky – you can use any type of container you can find, including metal or plastic buckets. Or try hammering together a simple box from wood scraps. Get a grownup to help you poke or drill holes in the bottom for water drainage. Size-wise, just make sure the container gives your veggie's root system plenty of space to grow. Container gardens need to be watered more than plot gardens.

Illustrations by Heather Kasunick

Layer on some worm poo

Actually, the polite word is worm 'castings', and you can create these nutrient-rich turds in your own home. The best worm poopers are red wigglers, and you'll need to buy them from a worm supplier, locally or by mail order. (The worms you might find in your garden aren't nearly as good.) Red wigglers grow like lightning and have their own babies once they're three months old, which is why you can even share your potty-happy worms with friends once your worm population grows.

Your worm supplier will give you specific instructions on how to keep the worms happy, but the gist is that your worms live in a covered plastic tub lined with wet, torn newspaper and munch your veggie scraps. Every few weeks, you'll scoop out some poo (which are dry-ish little pebbles that don't stink) and feed your plants.

The best worm poo-ers are red wigglers

Dig in

Do you think you'd grow very well if all you ever ate was bread and you never moved around? That's why your garden soil needs to be nutritious and loose enough to let the plant roots grow deep and strong. If you want to see how healthy your garden dirt is, put some in a pot and plant a few green bean seeds. Then plant a few bean seeds in another pot filled with garden soil mix from a shop, and put them next to each other in the sun. Make sure you water them equally. Write down which pot sprouts quicker, and measure the bean growth over the next few weeks. Which soil is better?

If you're just starting a garden in typical garden soil, you'll probably need to mix in some purchased garden soil that's fortified with compost, the rich organic matter made from decomposed (rotted) plant material. That way, you'll have the best chance of growing healthy plants.

You can make your own compost by throwing all the household vegetable scraps, coffee grounds, and fallen leaves into a garden container that's large enough for you to mix up with a pitch fork. In the autumn, ask your friends to bring over their bags of leaves to make a giant pile to jump in – the more smashed your leaves, the quicker they'll turn into compost. Water the compost pile and mix it around occasionally. Over the next several months, the pile will break down into lovely compost to add to your garden soil the next season.

Don't stop at plants

Gardening not only provides food that reduces pollution because it doesn't need to be shipped across the country (or world), but also is part of a whole new system of living interactions called 'permaculture'. Permaculture principles are based on mutual benefit. For example, the chickens and ducks on a farm give the farmers eggs and also eat insects and scraps. The fish and frogs living in the duck ponds eat mosquito larvae and other garden pests.

VEGGIE BASICS

These veggies grow easily.

Peas

Snow peas are wonderful because you can plant the seeds in chilly spring or early autumn and eat them right off the vines when they're ripe. Peas in the pod are fun to shell and it takes only a few minutes to cook in a little water, then serve with butter and a shake of salt.

Carrots

Carrot seeds are so teeny that all you need to do is sprinkle them on top of the soil and gently rake them in. Within a week, you'll see ferny tops appear. Thin them so the carrots down below have room to grow nice and fat.

Beans

Bean seeds can sprout in just a few days, and yield tender green beans in just over a month. Choose dwarf beans because they're compact and easy to harvest. Or consider climbing beans, which make long vines: get a grownup to help you put a tall pole in the garden and tie strands of sturdy twine from the top of the pole to several small wooden stakes placed evenly in a circle around it. Plant bean seeds next to each stake, and they'll grow up the twine and create a leafy tipi that you can hang out in.

Salad greens

Sow seeds from a pack of colourful mixed varieties in a pot right next to the back door, and simply snip off the baby greens with a scissors for the salad bowl – more leaves will grow from the plant. Grow them before it gets too hot otherwise your salad greens will start to taste bitter.

Cherry tomatoes

Get cherry tomatoes or other dwarf tomato varieties for a container or plot garden. Give them plenty of sun, water and periodic fertiliser. Like most veggies, if you grow too many to eat, just put the excess in plastic bags and freeze for a soup or casserole later.

Your family can also keep bees in your garden to harvest honey and help boost the bee population that is struggling now because of pollution and population growth. Lots of kids keep bees – there are even kid-sized beekeeper clothes with netted areas to protect your face. The bees live in wooden boxes that are easy to fit in a garden. Just about every region has a beekeeping organisation that includes a programme to teach kids the craft.

In fact, gardening and other activities such as beekeeping have become so popular that you're certain to find helpful advice from grownup experts wherever you live. Ask your grownup or local librarian to help you find organisations or shops that will provide whatever expertise you need. Or just notice in your neighbourhood if there's someone who's a super gardener or keeps chickens. People who love doing clever and healthy things to grow their own food love to share advice – and seeds and seedlings and produce.

Harvest honey, keep bees!

You don't have to live in the country to be a 'permie'. Plenty of city families now keep a few chickens to not only enjoy the eggs but also have insect-free gardens. You can find plenty of info about keeping chickens in books or through an online search. Kids who keep chickens say they're wonderful, affectionate pets.

Flowers

Don't forget flowers to feed the bees and birds! Flower nectar is nirvana for bees, who help us out by pollinating our food crops. Likewise, sunflowers are a great snack to share with birds. You can toss nasturtium flowers and leaves in a salad – they taste like pepper.

Cucumbers

You can get lots of cucumbers from one plant. Pick them, peel them, slice them into a saucer of salted water to keep in the fridge for a refreshing, healthy and instant snack.

Pumpkins

When a young pumpkin first forms, 'brand' it with your name and watch it grow. Sketch your name or initials on the pumpkin and carefully carve with a knife, just breaking the skin, or poke shallow holes close to each other over your sketch. When the pumpkins are ripe, there's plenty to do: make jack-o'-lanterns, roast the seeds (toss them with olive oil and salt before baking till crispy) or give the fresh seeds away to friends so they can grow their own next year.

Herbs

Herbs are among the easiest plants to grow, plus they smell great when you water them and they can be used as medicine that actually tastes good. Fresh peppermint makes a refreshing tea that also calms a queasy stomach. You can also dry peppermint leaves (just put the leaves in a bowl or hang in a net bag until they are dry) to brew a sinus-clearing hot tea in the winter. If you're stressed out, munch on a fresh lemon balm leaf topped with a drop of honey – lemon balm can calm you when you're tense. Basil is a cinch to grow and makes delicious pesto for pasta.

MAKE A RACKET

Drink Bottle Bike Exhaust

By John Edgar Park

A

Bikes are fun. LOUD bikes are brilliant! Upcycle an old drink bottle into a (non–polluting) 'exhaust pipe' that will make your bike sound like a motorcycle.

Your ride will sound like you've got a revving engine, but what you're really building is a resonator for the old playing-card-in-the-spokes trick. It'll make a terrific racket, and get people to move out of your way – no more need to ring your bike bell.

You'll need:

- A 400ml drink bottle with cap (aluminium bottles are louder, but plastic will work, too)
- A used-up plastic gift card
- A pop rivet gun and some 25mm short aluminium pop rivets (or small screws, nuts and some LocTite or other thread locker to prevent loosening). Use with grownup supervision.
- A screw with 2 nuts and 1 washer for attaching the hose clamps
- A rotary tool with cut-off wheel, abrasive buffs, grinding stone and 32mm drill bit (or substitute a hacksaw, precision craft knife, sandpaper and drill with 32mm bit). Use with grownup supervision.
- A vice that can hold the bottle firmly in place
- Masking tape
- Permanent marker
- 2 hose clamps that fit the bottle neck and bike chain stay
- Screwdriver
- Small adjustable wrench
- Dust mask and safety goggles

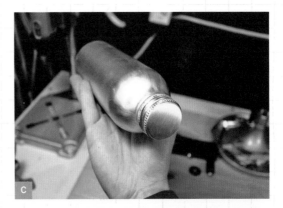

> **WARNING!** It's always important to use safety glasses or goggles when operating power tools. Work in a well-ventilated place and wear a dust mask to avoid breathing in particles. Grownup supervision is a must.

Try this:

1. Instead of advertising whatever brand of liquid came in the bottle, the first thing to do is go for a stylish brushed aluminium look by sanding the paint off the bottle. To avoid denting it, make sure the bottle is full of liquid, with the cap screwed on tightly, before sanding. (If using a plastic bottle, simply remove the label.)

   Put the bottle in a vice, then don your dust mask and goggles. Use the 180-grit abrasive buff on the rotary tool to remove the paint (Figure A). (If you don't have a rotary tool, use the sandpaper.) The abrasive buffs work well in curved areas like the bottle's neck (Figure B), and they have some give, so they don't gouge the metal. Set the tool to about 15,000 RPM and use light pressure, moving vertically to create a consistent 'grain' in the aluminium.

   If you want your Drink Bottle Bike Exhaust to have an ultra-smooth finish (Figure C), once all the paint is off, you can switch to the 280-grit buff to add finishing touches.

2. You've got to remove the bottom of the bottle so the sound isn't muffled, but is instead amplified. Empty the bottle, then recap it. Wrap masking tape around the bottom to indicate your cut line. Clamp the bottle in your vice gently, switch the rotary tool to the cutoff wheel, and use a speed of about 20,000 RPM to carefully cut off the bottom (Figure D). Remember to let the tool's speed do the work; don't apply much pressure. (Alternately, use a hacksaw to remove the bottom.)

3. To smooth the sharp edge where the bottle's bottom used to be, affix the grinding wheel to your rotary tool and de-burr the metal (Figure E), or else use a small metal file. Keep the bottle in the vice for this, and wear your goggles and dust mask. As always, a grownup should supervise.

4. Use the permanent marker to measure and mark the slot for the card, then use the rotary tool's cutoff wheel to cut the slot (Figures F and G), or else carefully use the craft knife – with grownup supervision. Keep the bottle in the vice for this, and wear your goggles and dust mask.

5. Next, we'll drill holes in both the card and bottle, in order to attach the card securely to the bottle. Measure for two aligned holes on both the card and bottle where they will be attached. Make two marks, each 10mm in and over from the top and bottom edge at one end of the card, then drill two 32mm holes in the card (Figure H) and use it as a template to mark the bottle holes. Drill out the 32mm holes in the bottle (Figure I). Your grownup should supervise.

6. The card needs a good, tight connection to the bottle to transmit as much vibration into sound as possible. Insert the card into the slot, put on your goggles, then use the rivet gun to pop the rivets into place (Figures J and K). If you don't have a rivet gun, it's OK, just thread in your small screws, tightening the nuts with a small

adjustable wrench, and then paint on the thread locker to prevent things from loosening. Either way, a grownup should supervise this step, too.

7. Wrap one hose clamp around the bottle cap (Figure L). Wrap the other around the bike's chain stay. Then thread the screw, washer and nuts (Figure M). Position everything so that the card will come into contact with the spokes, but make sure that nothing else (such as a pedal) will hit the bottle (Figure N). Tighten it all up with

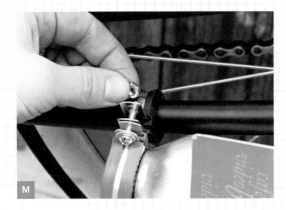

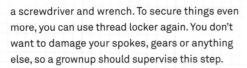

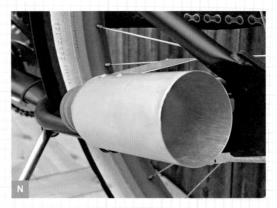

a screwdriver and wrench. To secure things even more, you can use thread locker again. You don't want to damage your spokes, gears or anything else, so a grownup should supervise this step.

8. Ride your sweet cruiser (loudly) into the sunset.

A version of this project originally appeared online on Make (blog.makezine.com). See the Drink Bottle Bike Exhaust in action at youtu.be/ni-mXPfiHHg

SURFING
THE ACOUSTIC WAVE

This Drink Bottle Bike Exhaust is an example – a particularly fun example – of what physicists and engineers call an *acoustic cavity resonator*.

When an acoustic wave enters a resonator's chamber (in this case, the wave enters the bottle via the gift card, which is being repeatedly vibrated by the bicycle wheel's spokes), instead of dispersing, the wave is reflected off the chamber's interior surfaces. Waves with the same frequency, wavelength and amplitude travelling in opposite directions combine to create a 'standing wave', i.e. a wave that remains in near-constant position. (If you've ever canoed down fast-flowing river rapids, then you've probably noticed a watery version of the standing wave phenomenon. Glider pilots seek out windy versions in the lee of mountain ranges.) Because the acoustic wave energy from the gift card is bouncing around inside the bottle instead of dispersing, and because with each crank of the bike's pedals you're adding more acoustic wave energy, the intensity of the standing wave is increased until the sound is super-noisy.

The manufacturers of car and motorcycle exhaust pipes take acoustic resonance very seriously; so do musical instrument builders. Some avant-garde musicians – like Pauline Oliveros, who founded the Deep Listening Institute, and who has

performed her compositions in reverberant spaces like caves, cathedrals and huge underground water cisterns – have even made resonance the subject of their compositions. Organ pipes, the sound boxes of stringed instruments, and the bodies of woodwind instruments are all examples of acoustic cavity resonators. Two flutes that are identical except for the length and shape of their tubes will sound different; the same thing is true of guitar bodies. So think of your Drink Bottle Bike Exhaust as a musical instrument, and employ the scientific method.

Experiment! And enjoy your noisy ride.

- Collect a few different drink bottles and tap them with a pencil while listening for the sound; take notes. Cut the bottoms off all the bottles, and tap them again; take notes. Which acoustic cavity resonator makes the sound that you like most?
- The gift card shape is another factor. It's like a finger hitting the spokes, but if it were cut into the shape of two fingers, or three, what would be the effect on the acoustics?
- If your Drink Bottle Bike Exhaust is too noisy, will cutting a bit off the bottom make it quieter, or noisier? Or will it have no effect at all?
- Can you create a muffler for your Drink Bottle Bike Exhaust, perhaps by placing gaffer tape over some portion of the open end, or by stuffing a sock inside? How else might you influence the sound?

HOVERING THINGAMAJIGS

Did you know? If atoms have more electrons than protons, then they are negatively charged; and if they have more protons than electrons, then they are positively charged.

This popular science experiment takes advantage of the fact that negatively charged objects are attracted to positively charged ones, while objects with similar charges repel away from each other.

You'll need:

- Three 30cm-long PVC pipes of varying diameters
- Thin Mylar tinsel 'icicles'; 1mm wide works best.
- Sharp scissors

Try this:

1. Create a thingamajig by tying together three strands of tinsel with two knots, spaced 15cm apart. (The knots can be tricky to tie. Try winding the loose ends of the tinsel around your index finger, then rolling them off with your thumb. This should form a loose knot; pull it tight.) Snip off any extra tinsel from the two knotted ends of your thingamajig.

2. Now make a few more thingamajigs, each one with a different number of tinsel strands (e.g. four, five, six).

3. Rub one of the PVC pipes through your hair (or someone else's) for 10 seconds; doing so will give the pipe a negative static charge.

4. Holding one of your tinsel thingamajigs by a knot, let it drop onto the pipe; as soon as it touches the pipe, it will pick up a negative static charge and leap into the air. Why? Because similar static charges repel away from each other. Try to keep the thingamajig hovering in the air.

5. Your experiment has begun! Take notes on how well the thingamajig floats; you might also want to document your experiment by taking photos. Video is even better, because floating tinsel is hard to capture in a photograph.

6. Recharge the PVC pipe and drop a different thingamajig on it. PS: When a negatively charged and a positively charged object get together, the result is 'static cling'; so a thingamajig may attach itself to something positively charged – like your dog, or a TV screen, or even you.

7. Repeat the process with each thingamajig. Which thingamajig floats the best?

8. Try the same experiment with the other PVC pipes. Which diameter of pipe works the best?

9. Try giving a negative charge to the PVC pipes with something besides hair that is positively charged. For example: your skin (not your hands, which may be moist), fake fur, a woolly jumper, a silk scarf, leather gloves, a fleece jacket, cat or dog fur. Record how much of a charge each substance gives to the pipes.

10. Try doing the same experiment on a dry day and a humid day. Notice any differences?

Illustration by Mister Reusch

MAKE SEED GRENADES

Illustration by Mister Reusch

Seed grenades (also known as seed balls, *bolitas de arcillas*, *tsuchi-dango* and *saatbomben*) were first used centuries ago. By packing seeds into a just-sturdy-enough vessel, which might also contain some fertiliser, then scattering these balls on the ground, farmers ensured that their precious seeds were protected from birds, insects, sun and wind until rainfall caused them to germinate. Ingenious!

In the 1970s, seed balls were rediscovered and popularised by Japanese 'Do-Nothing Farming' pioneer Masanobu Fukuoka. Around the same time, guerrilla gardening pioneer Liz Christy began throwing wildflower 'seed grenades' into fenced-off vacant lots around her New York neighbourhood. What Fukuoka and Christy had in common was a determination to make inhospitable soil bloom.

If you're too impatient to tend a garden or you don't have a patch of dirt to call your own, this springtime experiment provides a perfect excuse for you get in on the guerrilla gardening act.

You'll need:
- Seeds of three distinct species of wildflowers native to your area, one species per grenade type.
- Air-dry clay (e.g. the kind sold by Crayola).
- About 450g organic compost
- Small balloons
- 400g flour
- Newspaper torn into 5cm-wide strips
- A dozen eggs
- Mixing bowls
- A long nail
- A small straw
- Masking tape
- Towels you can get dirty

Clay Seed Grenades

1. Mix a little bit of clay with compost and just enough water to form a mix that holds together without crumbling.

2. Pinch off a small amount of the mixture, stick a few of the first variety of wildflower seeds into it, and roll it into a ball. Roll the ball in more compost.

3. Make a dozen or so of these clay seed grenades, then leave them to dry on a windowsill or counter.

Papier-mâché Seed Grenades

1. Blow up a dozen or so balloons – until they're no bigger than your fist.

2. Mix the flour with 750ml water, until the mixture reaches pancake batter consistency.

3. Dip the newspaper into the mixture, then squeegee off the excess gunk by pulling the newspaper between two closed fingers.

4. Wrap each inflated balloon with papier-mâché (that's what you've made), leaving an empty space about as big as a coin around the balloon's knot. Once the shells have dried, pop and remove the balloons.

5. Fill each shell with compost mixed with a tiny bit of water, and a few of the second variety of seeds. Put a piece of tape over the papier-mâché seed grenade's hole.

Eggshell Seed Grenades

1. Using the nail, poke a small hole at the centre of an egg's smaller end, and a larger hole at the other end; then use the nail to break the yolk.

2. Using the straw, blow the contents of the egg out of the larger hole into a bowl. Repeat with the other eggs. Because you're not using these eggshells for a craft, you don't need to clean them out perfectly.

3. Tape the small hole closed, then fill the eggshell with compost, a little water and a few of the third variety of seeds. Put a piece of tape over the eggshell seed grenade's hole.

Once you've made three types of seed grenade (these are just suggestions; feel free to come up with your own grenade forms – just don't use glass or anything toxic), you're ready.

With grownup supervision, toss the grenades into untended public spots. The idea is that they'll break on impact. Keep visiting these spots and take notes – which species of flower grows best?

⌶⊠▣ ⊞▢⏀▣ Å✪✳ ▣✳▢⌶ ▪✪▢⌶

BEST EVER

SCIENCE FICTION

By Josh

Science fiction frees our imagination from the spell cast on it by everyday life. In doing so, it reminds us that another world is possible. Here are a few favourites.

1952
ISLANDS IN THE SKY

By Arthur C. Clarke

In this early novel – about a teenage space enthusiast who wins a trip to an orbiting space station – the British author of *2001: A Space Odyssey* offers plausible details of life in outer space… years before humankind actually voyaged there!

1963
PODKAYNE OF MARS

By Robert Heinlein

Podkayne, a teenager who grew up on Mars, and her brilliant little brother, Clark, are travelling to Earth when they're kidnapped by terrorists. When a nuclear bomb is set to go off, Podkayne must rescue a 'fairy' (alien) baby from Venus.

1967–1968 series
THE TRIPODS

By John Christopher

Earth has been conquered by aliens, who control the minds of everyone over 14. In *The White Mountains* (1967), 13-year-olds Will, Henry and Beanpole join the anti-alien resistance. In *The City of Gold and Lead* (1968), Will infiltrates an alien city; and in *The Pool of Fire* (1968), the resistance forces go on the attack.

1971–1972 series
SWORD OF THE SPIRITS

By John Christopher

In the post-apocalyptic *The Prince in Waiting* (1970), 13-year-old Luke is named the future 'Prince of Princes'. In *Beyond the Burning Lands* (1971), Luke becomes a hero when he slays a giant amoeba; and in *The Sword of the Spirits* (1972), he leads an army against his own home city.

1978
A SWIFTLY TILTING PLANET

By Madeleine L'Engle

In this sequel to *A Wrinkle in Time* (1962) and *A Wind in the Door* (1973), Charles Wallace Murry, a brilliant and perceptive boy, travels back through time in order to prevent a globally destructive nuclear war.

1979
THE HITCHHIKER'S GUIDE TO THE GALAXY

By Douglas Adams

Hapless Englishman Arthur Dent, humanoid alien Ford Prefect and others escape Earth's destruction and discover that the 'Answer to the Ultimate Question of Life, the Universe and Everything' is… 42.

1980–1982 series
ISIS

By Monica Hughes

In *The Keeper of the Isis Light* (1980), Olwen, a teenage girl, lives alone on the planet Isis, where she awaits colonists from Earth – who can't accept her as one of them.

In *The Guardian of Isis* (1981), a settler named Jody N'Kumo is banished from the Earthling colony. In *The Isis Pedlar* (1982), Jody's great-grandson tries to save the colony.

1985
ENDER'S GAME

By Orson Scott Card

'Ender' Wiggin is a brilliant child who is recruited by Earth's outer-space Battle School as a potential leader of the planet's military forces against an insectoid alien enemy. The book is extremely popular, though too violent for many kids.

1995
THE EAR, THE EYE, AND THE ARM

By Nancy Farmer

In Zimbabwe in the year 2194, the ruler's 13-year-old son and his siblings are kidnapped by gangsters, forced to slave in a plastic mine, and accused of witchcraft. Mutant detectives – known as The Ear, The Eye and The Arm – seek them out.

2007
THE H-BOMB GIRL

By Stephen Baxter

Laura, a 13-year-old girl who moves to Liverpool in 1962, discovers that her teacher and others are time travellers from a dystopian future… and they each want to steal a key that Laura's father gave her. Only the Beatles, it turns out, can save the world from nuclear holocaust.

CRYPTOZOOLOGY

By Max Glenn

In the field of natural history, a creature whose existence has been reported by local legends or by eyewitness accounts, but not yet proven, is known as a 'cryptid'. The study of cryptids is known as 'cryptozoology'.

Here is a list showing similarities and differences between some of my favourite cryptids and their characteristics.

WALKING CRYPTIDS

Dangerous, Two-Legged

The **Dover Demon**, a small creature with a watermelon-shaped head and glowing eyes, was spotted crawling along a stone wall in the town of Dover, Massachusetts, in 1977.

The **Lake Worth Monster**, described as being half-man, half-animal (goat or ape), lives in Lake Worth, Texas, where it 'threatens' couples who park near the lake.

Dangerous, Four-Legged

The **Buffalo Lion** is a buffalo-sized maneless lion that lives in Africa. It is said to be deadly.

El Chupacabra is a hairless dog-like creature, with a row of spikes along its back. It has been sighted in Puerto Rico and Mexico, where it is said to drink the blood of sheep and goats.

Harmless, Two-Legged

Bigfoot, also known as Sasquatch, is a large, hairy 'wild man' or ape-like creature that lives in the United States. It walks on two legs, and supposedly smells very bad.

The **Loveland Frog** is a humanoid creature with green, leathery skin and the face of a frog. It has only been spotted near Loveland, Ohio.

The **Yeti**, also known as the Abominable Snowman, is a bear- or ape-like creature that inhabits the snowy Himalayan region of Nepal, India and Tibet.

Harmless, Four-Legged

The **Giant Sloth** of South America can weigh up to three tons. Although supposedly extinct, it has been spotted in contemporary times.

The **Mokele-Mbembe**, which has been described as half-elephant, half-dragon, lives in the remotest part of the Democratic Republic of Congo. It is strictly vegetarian.

SWIMMING CRYPTIDS

Dangerous, Freshwater

The **Ahuizotl**, which looks like an oversized otter with four human hands – plus an extra hand on the end of its tail – tips people who are fishing in Mexico out of their boats.

The **Kappa** is a small humanoid with scaly, reptilian skin; it looks like a Ninja Turtle. It lurks in rivers and ponds on Kyushu, Japan, and plays pranks on people – sometimes drowning them.

Illustrations by Mister Reusch

The **Vodyanoy**, also known as the Vodnik, looks like an old man with webbed hands and a greenish beard. It lingers next to ponds in Russia and Eastern Europe, trying to drown people.

Harmless, Freshwater

The **Loch Ness Monster**, known affectionately as 'Nessie', lives in Scotland's Loch Ness. It has a large body and a long narrow neck; it resembles a plesiosaur, an extinct aquatic reptile.

Ogopogo, or Naitaka, is a sea serpent that lives in Okanagan Lake, Canada.

Dangerous, Seawater

The **Kraken** is a sea monster that resembles a colossal squid or octopus; it attacks and sinks ships sailing near Greenland.

Mermaids are fish-tailed creatures with female human heads, arms and torsos. They sing to sailors, sometimes distracting them and causing them to fall into the water and drown.

Umibozu are monstrous, humanoid creatures who terrorise sailors and fishermen off the coast of Japan. Their shaved heads ('bozu' in Japanese) make them look like Zen monks.

Harmless, Seawater

The **Auvekoejak** is a furry fish-man, resembling a polar bear, who swims the frigid waters near Greenland and in the Arctic regions of Canada.

Chessie is a serpent-like sea monster that lives in Chesapeake Bay, the largest estuary in the US.

The **'U28' sea monster** was a 20 metre-long, crocodile-shaped creature which was spotted (and accidentally killed) by the commander of a German U28 submarine during the First World War.

FLYING CRYPTIDS

Dangerous

The **Jersey Devil**, a winged devil-like creature, mostly inhabits the Pine Barrens – a heavily forested area in southern New Jersey. In 1909 it went on a spree, attacking dozens of people.

The **Orang-Bati**, which inhabits the Indonesian island of Seram, resembles an orangutan with bat wings. It raids villages, abducts children and carries them away to be eaten.

The **Kongamato**, whose name means 'breaker of boats', is a pterodactyl-like creature that has attacked people in the swamps of Zambia, Angola and the Democratic Republic of Congo.

Harmless

The **Ahool** is a giant bat or flying ape (possibly related to the Orang-Bati), which lives in the western Javanese rainforests of Indonesia. It is named after its distinctive cry.

The **Mothman** is a large white humanoid with a wide wingspan, spotted in the Point Pleasant area of West Virginia. Its first appearance, in 1966, may have predicted a bridge collapse.

The **Devil Bird** is a Sri Lankan jungle creature which shrieks in a terrifyingly human voice whenever someone is about to die.

MAKE YOUR OWN GAMES

By Chris Dahlen

Listen to your
playtesters

Prototype and test
your game

At least once in your life, you should design a game – whether it's a videogame, a boardgame or a game you can play in a park or on the street. Making a game will challenge both halves of your brain and exercise every skill you possess.

But what's most valuable about designing games is that doing so forces you to collaborate – not only with the creative types who may join your game-making team, but with the players who test it. You'll enjoy setting up a situation and seeing what players make of it; they'll enjoy finding ingenious solutions to every challenge you devise. Here are a few tips.

Choose which type of game to make

If you want to create a videogame, try one of the game-making tools available for free or cheap online, like YoYo Games' GameMaker. Some commercial games, like *Portal 2* or *Little Big Planet*, give users the tools to design their own levels. Using software like Inform7 or Choicescript, you can even make a game with nothing but text.

Ready for a bigger challenge? Learning how to program in a language like Java, C++, Python or ActionScript will give you more control over what you build.

Or you can skip the computer altogether and make a boardgame. Just grab your paper and pencil, some dice and maybe some poker chips to stand in for game pieces.

Illustrations by Mister Reusch

Start prototyping an idea

'Prototyping' means building a model for testing and learning purposes. If your prototype game idea doesn't work – if it's too hard or easy, or confuses everybody, or just doesn't feel fun – fix it or ditch it. Game designer and instructor Marc LeBlanc tells his students to 'fail fast', and that's good advice for anything you try in life.

A dramatic 'mechanic' is crucial

The boardgames and videogames we buy look really polished and professional – but they didn't start that way. As you prototype, instead of focusing on how the game looks, focus on what people who make games for a living call 'gameplay' (the overall experience) and 'mechanics' (the rules).

If you've ever played the boardgame *Snakes and Ladders*, you may remember there's a ladder that stretches almost to the top of the board, and next to it, a snake dropping all the way back down. If you hit the snake, you'll tumble from a near-win to almost certain defeat – but three spaces later you might hit the ladder again, and you're right back at the top! All that drama was made possible by a simple decision: that some snakes and ladders should be longer than others.

Don't get distracted by unimportant stuff

When you prototype, you should make sure you're working on the right things. If you're prototyping a boardgame, you don't need to cut every game token into a perfectly round circle. If you're prototyping a videogame, don't spend all your time coding your own physics engine and rewriting it until it's 'perfect'.

Derek Yu, creator of the videogame *Spelunky*, has published a whole set of tips on how to finish your game – from knowing your limits to borrowing tools instead of making your own. His second tip is the best: *Actually start the game.*

No matter what kind of creative work you end up doing in your life, you'll learn that although talent matters, it's also really important to learn how to start a project, crank away at it until it's good enough, then smile and move on. I'd argue that learning how to finish fun projects is your true life's work – all those games, songs, paintings and whatever else you produce along the way are just the byproducts.

Provoke emotion in your audience

Think about how you want players to feel

Like any creative person, you want to provoke emotion in your audience – but not bad emotions. If you make a game difficult and unforgiving, the players will feel challenged, maybe too challenged to enjoy themselves; lower the pressure a bit and give them more freedom, and the players will relax and start exploring.

In every game you make, try exploring the things that matter to you – a place you've lived, a relationship (with a friend, relative, teacher, for example) that nags at you, a problem that causes you stress, or a piece of technology you really want to master. Even lighthearted zombie-fighting games should come from the heart!

Anna Anthropy's quick-draw computer game, *Calamity Annie*, is merciless; unless you have a lightning-fast mouse hand, you'll die thousands of times before you make it through. But the game isn't impossible – keep at it and you will get better. As Anthropy puts it, 'Persevering, and following danger, will get you to the happy ending.' That's something she's learned in her own life, and it's the emotional point of her game.

Find a game-making community

Whether you choose to design a videogame or boardgame, look for a big, active community in your town – or online at sites like ludumdare.com or tigsource.com. There, you can ask for (and offer) tips, tutorials and playtesters.

Sure, there are plenty of solo game inventors out there, but most of them still recruit someone here or there to do the art or the music, or to playtest their games. Community is crucial.

Listen to your playtesters

Your game isn't just about you and your ideas. Until your playtesters start playing, there is no game. And once they jump in, you don't really know what they'll do. Will they play by the rules? Will they find a mistake they can take advantage of? If your game has resources, will the players hoard them? When you playtest your game, you'll spot the problems with your design, and with any luck you'll also be surprised by the amazing things people think to do in your games, and the hilarious situations they land in.

You may have noticed that our top game designers – even Will Wright (*The Sims*, *Spore*) and Shigeru Miyamoto (*Super Mario Bros.*, *The Legend*

Q&A WITH REYN GUYER

Inventor, creator and musician Reyn Guyer led the teams that gave the world the game *Twister* and toys made of Nerf. Here, he tells you how to foster ideas, 'kill your darlings' and deal with the unexpected twists and turns that your projects can take.

UNBORED: Is it easier to work alone or with a team?

GUYER: I've rarely seen an idea come to fruition without having a team involved. When you put two or three people together, my experience is that the ideas multiply exponentially. If you sit and try to come up with ideas by yourself, your chances of coming up with something useful are very minimal.

In my experience, your ideas multiply with the addition of up to five people on a team. After that it becomes a committee and you get too rational about the process.

UNBORED: I understand that Nerf balls came from a brainstorming session?

GUYER: One of the gentlemen on the team was trying to develop a caveman game with foam rocks. You were allowed to throw and hit somebody with a foam rock if they were trying to steal the money under your rock. Or if it wasn't money, it was marbles, or other rocks. Anyway, the game never really had merit, but one of the other inventors began bouncing one of the rocks over a net, and we all looked at each other and said, 'OK, time out!' We went to our desks and began cutting out little balls – out of the foam that we had. And of course you know what happened to those foam balls.

UNBORED: You've said that *Twister* was just one of eight similar game ideas that you pitched to Milton Bradley. How did the game come about?

GUYER: I was working at my desk alone trying to develop an inexpensive child's game: 'Send in a buck and get this little game where the kids would walk around on a mat and have coloured pieces of cardboard around their ankles.' And I all of a sudden said, 'Uh oh, this is bigger than that!' I went out in the bullpen (a large open work area in an office) and drew on a 2m x 1m piece of corrugated *of Zelda*) – aren't exactly household names. There are many reasons for this, from the industry's reluctance to put a spotlight on its talent, to the geeky and introverted natures of some (but only some!) of our best designers. Game creators probably deserve more attention than they get. At the same time, it's important to remember that a game's players – not its creators – are the stars.

Players love the game itself, and they love to remember what they made of it: their experiences, their successes, their clever ideas and their persistence. When you design games, you're not just entertaining people – you're helping them teach themselves a lesson, see a side of themselves of which they weren't aware, and overcome challenges they thought were beyond their reach.

Creating and playing games is a learning experience – full of lessons for life. This isn't the only way to learn these lessons, but it's one of the most fun!

board, and drew 24 squares on it, and had eight people standing around with colours around their neck, in teams of two, and I said, 'Let's go.'

I had artists and secretaries and accountants, and it was obvious as soon as we got on the mat that it didn't make much difference what we were doing on the mat, it was just plain old FUN. And that's what sparked me to hire a team.

UNBORED: Was *Twister* an instant success?

GUYER: Good luck is such a large part of it. In fact, *Twister* was turned down by Sears, the retailer.

I got a call from Mel Taft at Milton Bradley saying, 'We're really, really sorry. We have all the spot commercials made, we've even bought some space and everything's ready to rock, and Sears turned it down and our management thinks we simply can't do it.' He apologised, we cried and that was it.

UNBORED: How did the game end up succeeding?

GUYER: Since he had already spent the money with the Public Relations people, Mel Taft and the PR person went to *The Tonight Show Starring Johnny Carson* (a popular TV show), wherein they had arranged to have Carson play the game on

the show. And by good fortune, the show's guest, (glamorous actress) Eva Gabor enticed him onto the mat and that was it, it changed the whole thing around.

UNBORED: It sounds like the playtesting was also crucial.

GUYER: There's always a gap between the manner in which you presume a toy or a game will be used, and the way the consumer ultimately uses it. Because people become creative. I don't think anyone, for example, plays the game *Monopoly* the same way. So yes, you do need to learn from playtesting, what responses are.

A lot of the ideas that have some success, if you go back to the root, they broke some sort of norm or rule. In the case of *Twister* for example, putting people together that intimately in the social setting wasn't the norm, and still is unusual. And the same would be true of Nerf – 'no throwing balls in the house.'

People tell me, 'Well, I have got this great idea,' and I say, 'Well, where is it?' And they say, 'Well, I've just got this great idea.' The first rule of invention of any sort is 'make one'. Until you've made one, you don't have something that you can talk to somebody else about, really.

ADVENTURE | **287**
Play Games

BUILD YOUR OWN
WORLD

AN EXCERPT FROM

── FLOOR GAMES ──

by H.G. Wells

The science-fiction author H.G. Wells, who wrote *The Invisible Man* and *The War of the Worlds*, among other immortal classics, was also a father who enjoyed playing imaginative games with his kids.

In 1911 and 1913, Wells published two booklets describing several of his family's favourite floor games – military battles, island adventures, city planning – in meticulous detail. The books were illustrated with photos of the author and his two sons stretched out on the playroom floor, having fun.

The home that has no floor upon which games may be played falls so far short of happiness. [...] Upon such a floor may be made an infinitude of imaginative games, not only keeping boys and girls happy for days together, but building up a framework of spacious and inspiring ideas in them for after life. [...]

Now, the toys we play with time after time, and in a thousand permutations and combinations, belong to four main groups. We have (1) SOLDIERS, and with these I class sailors, railway porters, civilians, and the lower animals generally, such as I will presently describe in greater detail; (2) BRICKS; (3) BOARDS and PLANKS; and (4) a lot of CLOCKWORK RAILWAY ROLLING-STOCK [i.e. railway vehicles] AND RAILS. [...]

Lots of boys and girls seem to be quite without planks and boards at all, and there is no regular trade in them. The toyshops, we found, did not keep anything of the kind we wanted, and our boards, which we had to get made by a carpenter, are the basis of half the games we play. [...] The best thickness, we think, is an inch for the larger sizes and three-quarters and a half inch for the smaller; and the best sizes are a yard square, thirty inches square, two feet, and eighteen inches square – one or two of each, and a greater number of smaller ones, 18 x 9, 9 x 9, and 9 x 4½. [...]

[Our box of wooden bricks] came to us by gift from two generous friends, unhappily growing up and very tall at that; and they had it from parents who were one of several families who shared in the benefit of a Good Uncle. [...]

How utterly we despise the silly little bricks of the toyshops! They are too small to make a decent home for even the poorest lead soldiers [i.e. action figures], even if there were hundreds of them, and there are never enough, never nearly enough; even if you take one at a time and lay it down and say, 'This is a house,' even then there are not enough. [...]

Let me now say a little about toy soldiers and the world to which they belong. Toy soldiers used to be flat, small creatures in my own boyhood, in comparison with the magnificent beings one can buy to-day. [...] I wish, indeed, that we could buy boxes of tradesmen: a blue butcher, a white baker with a loaf of standard bread, a merchant or so; boxes of servants, boxes of street traffic, smart sets [*fashionable intellectuals*], and so forth. We could do with a judge and lawyers, or a box of vestrymen. It is true that we can buy Salvation Army lasses and football players, but we are cold to both of these. We have, of course, boy scouts. With such boxes of civilians we could have much more fun than with the running, marching, swashbuckling soldiery that pervades us. They drive us to reviews [*military parades*]; and it is only emperors, kings, and very silly small boys who can take an undying interest in uniforms and reviews.

And lastly, of our railways, let me merely remark here that we have always insisted upon one uniform gauge [*track size*] and everything we buy fits into and develops our existing railway system. Nothing is more indicative of the wambling sort of parent and a coterie of witless, worthless uncles than a heap of railway toys of different gauges and natures in the children's playroom.

GAME HACKING

Q&A WITH STONE LIBRANDE

Interview by Courtney Stanton

From dreaming up new ways to play with familiar boardgames to developing one-of-a-kind videogame experiences like *Spore* and *Diablo III*, Stone Librande has broken every rule in the world of game design.

Librande is the creative director at Electronic Arts (publisher of some of the most notable and popular videogames of all time), and he teaches classes in which the next generation of game designers learn how to find a vision and a voice. He's also a dad who has invented and 'modded' (modified, hacked) games of all sorts with the help of his two sons.

    Our friend Courtney Stanton, an online game producer, asked Librande what advice he'd offer to kids interested in designing games of any kind.

UNBORED: What's the easiest way to start designing a game?

LIBRANDE: The easiest thing is to just grab some toys from your room – LEGOs, little knights, soldiers, dragons, robots, Barbie dolls – and use those as the game pieces. And then you can build a framework around those pieces with some turns. You need to define the two ends of the game experience – the setup and the victory condition. Then you start moving through the game, trying to get from 'How do we start?' to 'How do we end?' and see what kinds of problems occur, what kinds of conflict arise. You sort out the conflicts with rules, and fix the problems by taking out frustrating, hard to calculate or boring things – and replacing them with fast things.

UNBORED: Can you give an example of how to replace a boring game element with a 'fast' one?

SPORTS CARD GAMES
By Sam Glenn

Since I was nine, I've enjoyed *Match Attax*, the English Premier League-based trading card game. But I started to get fed up with how simplistic the rules are – you're not really playing a realistic football game. What you're playing is 'War'.

    Now, I'm also a fan of the *Strat-O-Matic* tabletop sports simulation games – which use statistical research and complex rules, involving probability tables and dice-rolling, to replicate athletes' abilities very accurately. *Strat-O-Matic* makes the gamer feel like an actual sports team manager. So I decided to hack *Match Attax* and make it more realistic, like a *Strat-O-Matic* game... though not nearly so complex.

    I have rules for shooting and saving, passing, slide tackling, and dribbling, all of which add more depth and realism. For example, Stoke City striker Peter Crouch's *Match Attax* card has a 77 attack rating so, according to the table I've created, a roll of 1 to 4 (on a 6-sided die) would mean that his shot is on target. Chelsea goalkeeper Petr Cech's *Match Attax* defence score is an 87, so in order to save Crouch's shot he'll need to roll a number between 1 and 5.

    Crouch rolls a 3, so his shot is headed into the goal. Cech rolls a... 6. GO-O-O-O-AL!

LIBRANDE: When I was around 10 or 12, we took our *Candy Land* game (which we had outgrown) and modded it. We renamed it *Candy Landmine*. We drew grids over the *Candy Land* board so instead of just sticking to the main path, players could now move faster by going off-road – moving along the squares of the grid. We also changed the game's victory condition, so instead of being the first to reach Home Sweet Home, the goal was now to be the first to blow up Home Sweet Home... with peppermint-stick bazookas and gumdrop grenades. We liked converting a little kid's game into something where we were blowing up things – it was kind of rebellious and subversive and it made us feel really cool. For the game design class that I teach, I buy kids' boardgames that are on sale, remove the playing cards, give my students markers and blank index cards, and say, 'Just start making up your own games with this stuff.'

UNBORED: When you're designing your first game, is it better to come up with a new angle on a game you already know and like - or should you start from scratch?

LIBRANDE: I think it's always easier to start with something you know and then modify it. People already do that with their favourite boardgames – like *Monopoly*, where many people play according to the rule that 'All money paid in penalties goes to the player who lands on the Free Parking space.' What's so interesting is that almost everybody knows this rule, which has been around since long before there was an internet... and yet it's not in the *Monopoly* rulebook! You'd play *Monopoly* with someone who taught you this rule, and then when you grew up you'd teach it to your kids, and later they'd teach it to their kids. It's a powerful thing, modifying a game's rules.

UNBORED: What is the most common mistake that a first-time game designer usually makes?

LIBRANDE: Somewhere in the back of their mind, (grownup first-time game designers) are thinking, 'I'm going to sell this game. I'm going to take it to a bigger audience.' But instead of designing game rules that will work perfectly for a mass audience, grownups should pay attention to how kids on a playground make up games. No kid ever breaks out the rules for Tag and says, 'Hey, you're playing by the wrong rules of Tag according to my rulebook.' Kids constantly modify the rules of playground games – they say, 'From now on, you can't go out of the sand pit,' or 'No climbing on the slide.' Grownups should open up their minds, and learn from kids about game design.

LEGO MINIFIGS **GAME**
By Max Glenn

My friend Jon and I can spend hours building armies of LEGO minifigs. Each army is a mishmash of figures from different sets, like Star Wars characters, superheroes, medieval knights, aliens and pirates. Then we'll play that one of the armies is barricaded inside a castle, while the other storms the castle. The army inside the castle wins if they survive all attacks.

It is fun, but we get into a lot of arguments during the battles: 'Chewbacca shoots Spider-Man.' 'He missed!' 'No, he didn't!' 'Yes he did, Spider-Man is too fast.'

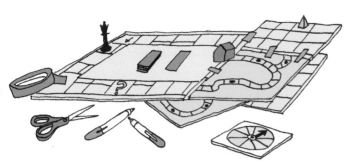

UNBORED: If you're a kid designing games for other kids, what are the most important principles?

LIBRANDE: It doesn't matter how brilliant you think your game is – you can't force a player to have fun, they're either going to have fun or they're not.

The point is to keep players entertained, to design a game in which the players get really involved. If kids are playtesting your game and they start throwing the pieces at each other, you know that you're moving in the wrong direction.

UNBORED: What can kids learn from the game design theory that you teach?

LIBRANDE: It depends on how old your game's players are. Younger kids don't care much about game rule systems – so the rules of their games need to be flexible. Older kids can understand rule systems, and in fact they get really picky about

game rules and want to enforce them. When my sons reached a certain age, they didn't like it when I'd try to play a game that combined LEGO with some other toy. They said, 'You can't put those toys together! One's LEGO and the other one's Matchbox and they just don't go together!' At any age, though, every game player wants to get really involved in the experience – if something is boring or broken, they'll lose interest.

UNBORED: What motivates kids to sit down and design a game, instead of just playing around?

LIBRANDE: For any game, you need some starting condition, you need some obstacle to get over, and then you need a goal – a way of determining who has won. You can apply those three things to almost any toy or activity. If you have little race cars, and you say, 'Here's where you start, here's the racecourse, and here's how you determine the winner,' then you've designed a game. If you've got two little wrestler figures, you can just smash them into each other… or you can make up rules about 'You have to keep the figures' feet on the ground,' and 'When you get pinned you can only do these certain moves.' Free play comes naturally to kids, but when you just have pure chaos, no one has much fun for very long.

We also really like the boardgame *Heroscape*, whose figures are drawn from different eras (Old West, Roman Empire, Second World War) and also from fantasy or myth (Greek mythology, superheroes) and science fiction (robots, aliens). We don't argue too often when we play *Heroscape*, because the players take turns, instead of all shouting at once, and because each figure has a card with its attack and defence scores listed. You roll dice to decide each battle.

Jon and my Dad and I invented a version of our minifig war using the *Heroscape* rules as a guide. We agreed that each piece of armour added a point to a minifig's defence score, and that each weapon added a point to its attack score. You could add

attack points if your figure was in a vehicle, or if they could fly. You could add defence points if you were up on the castle's wall, defending against invaders on the ground. The castle's walls had their own defence score. Each turn, we'd roll a die to see how many of your minifigs could attack during that turn.

Although we still argue about some of the minifig's attack or defence points ('Yoda can fly!' 'No he can't!'), the rules and the dice-rolling made the game much more fair and fun. The 'rules' version of our game does take longer than the 'no rules' version, so sometimes we still like to play the 'no rules' version. But if we don't want to get angry, we'll play the 'rules' version.

Illustration by Heather Kasunick

A HISTORY OF

Comic by Joe Alterio

VIDEOGAMES

BY JOE ALTERIO

THE SILVER AGE 1984-1999
ALL YOUR BASE ARE BELONG TO US

WHILE AMERICAN PRODUCERS FOCUSED ON ARCADE CABINETS, THERE WAS SOME ATTEMPT AT PRODUCING HOME SYSTEMS, THOUGH THEY MET WITH ONLY LIMITED SUCCESS...

AT THE SAME TIME, THE GROWING HOME COMPUTING CULTURE WAS HELPING TO REVIVE AN INDUSTRY BY PROVIDING A PLATFORM FOR SMALL DEVELOPERS AND UNIQUE, EVEN WEIRD, STORIES.

BUT A MAN IN JAPAN WOULD PROVIDE THE BIGGEST BOOST TO AN ART FORM IN A RUT.

SHIGERU MIYAMOTO USED HIS MEMORY OF GROWING UP IN A SMALL RURAL TOWN TO INFLUENCE THE GAMES HE WOULD DEVELOP FOR NINTENDO - MARIO BROS, LEGEND OF ZELDA, DONKEY KONG, AND SCORES OF OTHERS...

HE WANTED GAMES TO TELL A STORY - WITH THAT SIMPLE IDEA, HE REINVENTED THE INDUSTRY.

THE ARRIVAL OF CD-ROM MEDIA ALSO MEANT GAMES COULD BE BIGGER, MEANING MORE COMPLEXITY, BETTER GRAPHICS, AND MOVIE-LIKE CUT SCENES AND SCORES.

MYST (1990)

DOOM (1991)

SIMCITY (1992)

THE BRONZE AGE
ALL TOGETHER NOW
1999-2011

ALTHOUGH THE FIRST NETWORKED MULTIPLAYER GAME WAS SPECTRE (1991), IT WAS THE SEGA DREAMCAST IN 2000 THAT ANNOUNCED THE NETWORKED GAME ERA.

OVER THE PAST TEN YEARS, GAMING HAS MOVED EVER CLOSER TO BECOMING A COMPLETE SOCIAL EXPERIENCE. STARTING WITH LAN* COLLEGE PARTIES, FOR FPSS* LIKE QUAKE, NETWORK PLAY HAS BECOME A LYNCHPIN FOR GAMING.

*LOCAL AREA NETWORK *FIRST PERSON SHOOTER

THE RISE OF MASSIVELY MULTIPLAYER ONLINE ROLEPLAYING GAMES LIKE WORLD OF WARCRAFT HAVE FORCED GAMERS OUT OF THEIR ISOLATION AND CLOSER TOGETHER.

AS SOCIAL NETWORK GAMING STEPS UP THE TREND, THE WII AND THE XBOX'S KINECT ARE TAKING THE IDEA A STEP FURTHER, ASKING US TO INTERACT IN PERSON TO PLAY.

SO WHAT HAPPENS NEXT?

FULLY INTERGRATED, IMMERSIVE GAMING, WHERE PLAYERS UPLOAD THEMSELVES INTO AN AVATAR?

GREAT! +5 +10 +15

BRUSH BRUSH BRUSH

GAMING THEORY, APPLIED TO EVERYDAY LIFE?

OR, MAYBE SOMETHING... A BIT SIMPLER?

FOUR SQUARE
THE PLAYGROUND GAME

Four Square is played by four or more kids with a basketball, volleyball or football on a court divided into – you guessed it – four numbered squares.

Rules of the game:

- Draw a court with chalk in a playground or on the street; you can also make one with tape in a gym. Each side of the court should be about 2.5m long, but if you want to experiment with the size, go right ahead. Divide the court into four smaller squares of equal size, and number the squares anti-clockwise, 1 to 4.

- The first four players each claim a square, while everyone else waits in a line.

- The highest ranking square is the 4; the player in that square is the King or Queen. The ball is always served from the back corner (the 'mailbox') of the 4-square, into the 1-square – that is, from the highest- to the lowest-ranked player.

- The server first calls any special rules (e.g. Aerials, Catching, Double-Taps) before dropping the ball and serving from the bounce. There's 'no blood on serves', which means: if the 1-square player can't hit the ball on the serve, then the player in the 4-square serves again. Special rules last only for that round.

- You may move freely around and outside the court, but when the ball is bounced into your square, you must hit it to another square without letting it bounce twice.

- You can hit the ball with one or both hands, your forearms or elbows.

- Note that the court's inside lines are 'out'; so if a ball hits an inside line, it's out of bounds. It's OK for the ball to hit one of the court's outside lines. If you let the ball bounce twice, catch or miss the ball, hit the ball out of bounds or back into your own square, or if you break a custom rule, then you're out – go immediately to the back of the line. The first player in line then steps into the 1-square, while everyone on the court advances to a higher square – unless the next higher square is occupied.

- The object of the game is to eliminate players so that you can make it to the 4-square and be the King or Queen... for a little while, anyway.

Other rules:

- If the ball lands in your square, other players are not allowed to touch it until you've hit it. If they do, it's called 'poaching' and they're out.

- Players waiting in line may not touch the ball.

Illustration by Mister Reusch

THE COURT

King (or Queen)

2.5m square court

The Mailbox

A ball may bounce only once within a square

A player who hits the ball out of bounds is out

The ball is always served from the back corner (the 'mailbox') of the 4-square, into the 1-square

Illustration by Heather Kasunick

SPECIAL RULES

Aerials
This allows balls to be hit in the air without bouncing first.

Annihilator
If you catch the ball before it lands in your square – between your legs, or knees – then whoever hit it is out.

Catching
If you catch the ball before it lands in your square – sometimes you have to yell a code word (invented by the King or Queen) as you catch it – then whoever hit it to you is out.

Double-taps
You can hit the ball twice in the air – once to set yourself up for a spike, and once to spike it – after it has bounced in your square.

Juggling
Also known as Bobbles or Popcorn. You can bounce the ball lightly between your hands before hitting it to another square.

Pegman
Any player can catch the ball, yell 'Pegman', then attempt to hit another player with the ball (below the neck). If the ball hits that player, they are out. If it misses that player, or hits that player above the neck, then the player who threw the ball is out.

Rolling
You're allowed to hit the ball so low that the ball rolls instead of bounces; normally, you'd be out.

Football rules
You can only use your head or foot to hit the ball.

Style points
Everyone must try to exhibit an excellent or unusual move on each play; if you don't, you're out.

Two and up
If the ball bounces in your square twice before you hit the ball, you can tap the ball upward into another player's square while shouting 'Two and up!' and not be eliminated.

Underhand-only
All hits must be made with your hands open, palms up.

WHY GO CAMPING?

By Matthew De Abaitua

People have camped throughout human history – but it is only in the last hundred years or so that people have done it for fun. Before then, camping was part of a nomadic way of life or it was confined to soldiers, missionaries and explorers.

As more people moved out of the countryside to live in the cities, they began to wonder what they had lost by leaving the wild, and what could be gained by returning to it – if only for a weekend. Grownups worried that their children would not be strong enough to cope with the world – not just strong in the arm, but in the heart and mind too. The ability to bounce back and cope with things when they don't always go your way is called 'character' – and camping has always been seen as 'character building'. Character means: courage, patience and tolerance.

In America, the first organised summer camp was founded in Connecticut, in 1861. After the American Civil War, the tradition of the summer camp continued as a way of giving boys something to do in July and August, as there was concern that they were spending too much time at home in these months – and so were losing, yes, their character.

In 1902, writer and artist Ernest Thompson Seton invited boys who had been vandalising his estate near Greenwich, Connecticut, to camp there, in his homemade 'Indian village'. Seton's methods were studied by Robert Baden-Powell, who in 1907 founded England's Scout movement. Seton and

D.C. Beard (author of *The American Boy's Handy Book*) later founded the Boy Scouts of America, and Seton would write the first *Boy Scout Handbook*. At the same time, the Girl Guides were founded in England, while in America the Camp Fire Girls were formed by Grace Gallatin Seton and D.C. Beard's sisters, Lina and Adelia (who wrote *The American Girl's Handy Book*). In addition to camping out by Maine's Sebago Lake, the Camp Fire Girls' character was built through learning handicrafts like jewellery-making – a sign of the times.

Why go camping? Camping can be a nightmare. Rough weather, broken gear and a bad attitude can all make camp life unbearable. But as the founders of Scouting knew, the very fact that it can go wrong is what makes camping so rewarding. A good camping trip is not something you can pick up off the shelf and plug in. It needs your effort and positive spirit to make it work.

Illustrations by Mister Reusch

Videogames started in the woods

In the 1930s, the Forest School was established in the woods of the New Forest in southern England. At the Forest School's camps, trials – for example, swimming across a river while holding a lighted candle or climbing a difficult tree – were designed to test courage and skill. We all want to prove ourselves. The big difference between the trials of videogames and the trial of outdoors is that, in the real world, there is no 'respawning'. Every risk you take has real consequences – and that's why being outdoors can make you feel so alive.

Fragging your friends in *Call of Duty* is a digital version of the war games played since ancient times. Though first-person shooter videogames offer a Capture the Flag multiplayer option, if you really want your nerves to tingle with the primal sensation of stalking, hunting and sneaking around in the dark, then play Capture the Flag at dusk or at nighttime while camping.

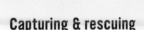

CAPTURE
THE FLAG

Equipment
A flag – for which you can use anything, including someone's jacket.

The playing field
Each team has its own agreed-upon territory, and they each designate an object within their territory (usually a tree or rock) as the 'jail'. The teams assemble at a starting point near the boundary line between the territories; each team remains on its own side of the boundary. At a signal, the teams set their flags within 200 steps of the starting point – the flag must be visible. However, it's OK to put it somewhere difficult to reach – for example, up a tree.

Strategy
At another signal, the game begins. The object is to enter the enemy's territory, capture the flag, and carry it across the line into home territory without being caught. Guards may be posted near the flag – but they cannot get nearer than 15 metres to it, unless an enemy raider penetrates within that 15-metre circle. They may then follow her and attempt to capture her.

Capturing & rescuing
A raider in enemy territory may be captured by tagging him; when a raider is captured he must go with his captor to the jail. A prisoner may only be released by a teammate touching him; but the prisoner must be touching the jail with a hand or a foot at the time. The prisoner and rescuer then walk to their own territory before rejoining the game; usually they get 'free walk-backs' (they can't be captured while going home). A rescuer can rescue only one prisoner at a time – and if she is tagged before rescuing someone, she goes to jail, too!

Winning
If the flag is captured, it must be carried across the boundary line, at which point the game ends. If the raider is caught before he reaches home, the flag remains at the point where it was rescued and the game continues.

Camping makes you stronger

Camping strips away home comforts and conveniences. Not only do you have to do everything for yourself, you also have to think ahead and plan before you do it. That is why the Scout motto since 1907 has been 'Be Prepared'. The ability to anticipate what you might need, and to adapt to a situation if it does not turn out the way you expected, is what makes good character.

WHAT TO PACK
FOR CAMPING

Presuming the grownups are in charge of the tent, bedding, food, soap and toilet paper, rubbish bags, and other essentials, what should you pack? Packing is like a game: you can't pack more than you're able to carry.

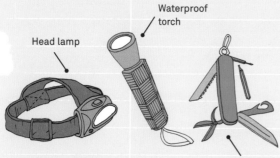

Head lamp

Waterproof torch

Swiss Army knife

Camping necessities

- Your clothes should be suitable for sunny mornings, rainy afternoons and cold nights. Count out underwear and socks (including thick socks for hiking) for each day you'll be away – then throw in a couple of spares. Count on it being muddy, so make sure that whatever you put on your feet is waterproof; walking boots are great because their soles are tough. Pack a waterproof coat and a trusty battered hat that can protect you both from the sun and rain.

- If you plan on hiking around with all your clothes in a pack, it might be worth stuffing them into compression sacs; this will keep them dry and leave more room for other items. If there is going to be swimming at camp, pack swimwear and a thin light towel.

- You'll need a waterproof torch. You might also like a light that straps around your forehead and keeps your hands free for reading at night.

- From the bathroom, you will need a toothbrush, lip balm if you use it, and some anti-bacterial gel to clean your hands.

- It's not a bad idea to have a few energy-giving cereal bars in your bag.

- You might also take a knife – they come in handy for all sorts of things, from cutting food to cutting ropes. Discuss this with the grownups first. Any knife has to fold back into its handle.

- Make room to pack a book or two, some playing cards (I play a lot of *Magic: The Gathering* with my daughter when we camp), and a map of the area in which you are camping.

- Pack some thick string – useful for playing conkers, hanging up a tarp to protect you from the rain, or making into a washing-line in case you need to dry your clothes.

Everyone should know how to manage a campfire

In Victorian times, many people went camping because they believed fresh air and outdoor fires cured the 'diseases of the city', such as tuberculosis. Today, our diseases of the city are stress, anxiety and mental exhaustion. Combined with the light physical exercise of camp life and the relaxing effect of birdsong (we are hardwired to find this calming, because if the birds are singing, no predators are nearby), staring into a campfire relaxes the mind.

The campfire also brings people together. We sit in a circle and talk and share the food cooked over the fire: this is the beginning of civilisation. Archaeologists suggest that our ancestors were using fire between 700,000 and 1.5 million years ago.

Fires are very dangerous, particularly in and around the home. But rather than forbid campfires altogether, it is better to learn the responsible way to set and extinguish a campfire.

MAKING A
CAMPFIRE

A campfire is created by fuel, ignition and air. Fuel is composed of tinder, kindling and dry logs. Tinder is material that burns quickly and easily, such as dried pieces of bark, balls of paper and very thin twigs. The tinder lights the slightly larger pieces of fuel called the kindling: these are dead sticks a couple of centimetres in diameter.

Try this:

1. To set a campfire, establish a fire ring of stones. These stones will protect the base of the fire from the wind, reflect heat back, and act as a fire-proof border preventing the fire from spreading.

2. I put a dry log in the middle of the fire and then balance my tinder upon the flat edge of the log.

3. Around the tinder, make a tipi of kindling. Around the kindling, lay one or two small dry logs. Light the tinder with a match.

The most effective way to bring a low fire to life is to add more oxygen by blowing on it or wafting the fire with a large piece of cardboard; this will turn smouldering embers into leaping flames. Add larger pieces of fuel carefully. Too little fuel and your fire will burn itself out; too much fuel and it will be smothered.

Wood that is damp or green – which means it still has sap – will not burn well, because the fire will expend too much energy heating up the water in the wood. Never cut a branch straight off a living tree. I make my campfires out of a combination of dead wood foraged from the forest floor (don't take too much of this, as rotting wood is a vital part of the forest ecosystem) combined with dried logs, often bought from the campsite owner.

CAMPFIRE SAFETY BASICS

- Grownup supervision is a must.
- Never put anything man-made into a fire – the fumes from burning plastic are noxious. And never set a campfire near a tent: modern tents are made of highly flammable material.
- The campfires of the early European settlers of America and the American Indians were different from one another: the Indian fires were small and efficient, whereas the fires of the settlers were large and extravagant. A campfire used for cooking should be small and controlled, more Indian than settler.
- A fire should never be left to burn itself out. Always extinguish it at the end of the evening by dousing it thoroughly with water. Keep plenty of water nearby when you are making a fire.

You can build your own bedroom

Our ancestors made tents out of animal bones and fur to shelter from the rain. Nomadic people – that is, cultures that move from place to place rather than settling in one town or city – have developed tents into amazing engines for living. The ability to make shelter in the middle of nowhere reminds me of how resourceful we really are – I find it exciting every time.

Tent design has undergone a revolution in the last 40 years, becoming easier to put up, lighter to carry, more rainproof and larger on the inside. The invention of the dome tent in the late 1960s meant that backpackers, for the first time, had a tent in which they could comfortably sit and that was easy to put up. Its rounded shape meant that it was more stable and that the wind flowed around it.

Look after your tent, and it will look after you. That means making sure it is put away dry and assembled with care.

Life is about being and doing

Camping puts you in places you would never normally be, at times you would never normally be there – such as in a forest at night, or a field at dawn. Our normal lives keep to a strict routine of school, work, meals, TV, games and bedtime. Camping is way of throwing the whole routine out, and getting rid of the things you think you need, so that you can learn what is really important.

Camping is temporary. You will go home again. You will enjoy that big comfy bed once more. But that break from the everyday helps us realise that things are the way they are because that is how we have made them and chose them, and that there are alternatives available to us if they are ever required.

Finally, camping is about actually *doing* things. Not passively watching or playing at them, but being in the world and acting. Camping is where we can learn by living and doing and not by listening and reading alone. Education is not all about the mind: the hand needs to be taught how to make things, and the heart needs to be educated into feeling compassion towards and understanding of other people. Because camping combines social, physical and intellectual challenges, it is a significant step towards being a free-range person.

A good camping trip needs your positive spirit

Camping is temporary

Be prepared!

TRAIN YOUR GROWNUP
TO GLAMP

'Glamping' (glamorous camping) often means staying in an outfitted yurt, fishing in a stocked lake, and frying breakfast over a fire pit – but we're using the term to refer to a less rugged style of camping that everyone can enjoy.

If the idea of waking up in the woods appeals to you, but you aren't excited about hiking with a heavy pack and eating freeze-dried soup out of the packet, then glamping might be the answer.

CAR CAMPING

Families with young children – and/or a grownup who absolutely must take a shower every single morning – don't often go on camping trips. That's too bad, because camping is a fun, inexpensive and memorable way to spend time together. Perhaps it's time to open your mind to another kind of camping: car camping. True, you're not deep in the woods, you're surrounded by other campers, and you're not exactly pitting your wits against the elements. But you're sleeping in a tent that you pitched (one complete with pillows, inflatable mats and reading lamp), you're cooking outdoors (on a grill, or a camping stove, if the campsite doesn't allow open fires), and if you want to, you can take day hikes from there.

Photography by Matthew De Abaitua

Bring bicycles
Campsites are safe places to bike, and a bike makes every trip away from the campsite – to take a shower or fetch kindling – quicker and more fun.

Go geocaching
Geocachers around the planet have hidden over a million caches (containers, often filled with prizes) and uploaded their latitude and longitude to the official Geocaching website (geocaching.com). Download a geocaching app to your grownup's smartphone and map your campsite's location; you'll almost surely find some treasure hunts.

Make yourself comfortable
When you car camp, you're not carrying everything on your backs, so bring along a few luxuries that will ensure a good time. Your grownup, for example, might want a real coffee cup from home.

Don't forget coins
Showers, laundry and other campsite amenities require coins, so stockpile 'em in the weeks before you leave home.

CAMPING

Even if your family does decide to hike to a more or less secluded campsite, there are plenty of ways to 'glam' the trip without overloading your packs – or spoiling the outdoorsy experience.

Hike smarter, not harder

You know what makes you feel tired when you're hiking? Being last! Being first makes you feel excited and energetic. So shake things up every now and then. If someone is slower than the rest of the group, give them a head start after each rest break. Also: If a grownup tells a ghost story, that will take your mind off the hike. Marching songs work, too; so do the rhymes from clapping games (see elsewhere in this book).

Cook and charge

Planning to use a camping stove, in addition to (or instead of) campfires? The new BioLite camping stove – which was originally designed for use in developing countries where firewood and fuel is scarce – is pretty neat. It's lightweight and folds easily, boils a litre of water in 4½ minutes by burning twigs and pine cones, and charges mobile phones and LED lights!

Include a fireproof glove

A fireproof leather glove – which you can buy from places that sell wood-burning stoves – is helpful for moving logs around within a fire. It's also useful when you want to snap dead branches and twigs off trees without injuring your hand.

Pack raincoats – even if there's no rain

Why? Because it might rain anyway; and even if it doesn't, raincoats are an excellent protection against mosquitoes in the evening. Also: pack a warm hat, even in the summertime; it will keep you warm while you sleep.

Plan your fun in advance

When packing for a camping trip, we often focus on our hiking, eating, sleeping and toilet needs. But on a mellow, low-effort camping trip, you'll spend most of your time sitting around the campsite. You might want to bring a deck of cards, multiple sheets of song lyrics (from old-time campfire songs to Beatles and ABBA tunes) for sing-alongs, and an exciting novel to read aloud. Kids with a snarky sense of humour might prefer a lame novel, to mock.

OUTDOORSY APPS

Sometimes smartphones can enhance your enjoyment of nature, instead of just detracting from it. And you can get reception in some pretty remote locations, these days. Here are a few favourite outdoorsy apps.

Star Walk

Features a 360-degree star map that allows you to identify constellations, stars, planets, galaxies and satellites currently overhead – even if they're invisible to the naked eye.

iBird UK & Ireland Guide

Teaches you to identify birds, and offers habitat and ecology information, photos and hand-drawn illustrations, and range maps. Plus tips on protecting each species and its habitat.

OutDoors Great Britain

A mapping and GPS app for Britain's walkers and hikers, runners and cyclists. Includes national parks Ordnance Survey maps, and walking routes throughout the UK. You can download other users' homemade maps from the EveryTrail website (everytrail.com).

Alan Rogers Camping

After the Second World War, Alan Rogers helped create Europe's camping, caravanning and motor caravan industry. He published his first guide to campsites and camping holidays in 1968. This app is the twenty-first-century version of his famous series of guides.

Many apps require you to log in before using them – so do that before you leave home. Also, because using these apps drains your phone's battery it's wise to bring along a solar charger or another power source.

Illustrations by Heather Kasunick

TIE YOURSELF
IN KNOTS

Sailors, mountain climbers, firefighters, hunters and others who handle rope ('line') on a daily basis will tell you that there are not only many types of knots (binding knots for keeping loose objects together, slip knots for attaching a line to an object, friction hitch knots for attaching one line to another in a way that is easily adjusted, and so forth) but a huge variety within these types.

So how to decide which few knots we'd squeeze into these pages? We asked two tall-ship sailors of our acquaintance – Captain Matt and his mate, Megan – to demonstrate the most useful knots they know. Plus, just for kicks, we'll demonstrate one knot that you'll probably never need to use.

Reef (or square) knot

A reef knot is used to tie the two ends of a short line together in order to secure something – a bundle of sticks, for example. Here's how to tie it:

1. 'Right over left, left over right, makes a (square) knot both tidy and tight.' Easy! If you've tied this knot correctly, both 'working' ends of the line will end up on the same side of the knot.

    PS: If you accidentally form a right-over-left + right-over-left knot, though it may look like a reef knot, it's actually a 'false', 'lubber's', or 'granny' knot – which can slip or release unpredictably, or else it can jam.

THIEF KNOT

Imagine that you're a sailor whose worldly possessions are stored in a ditty bag, one whose opening is cinched up tightly with a piece of line. You suspect that another sailor is rummaging through your bag when you're not around – but how do you find out if you're right? As you can see from the photo here, the thief knot (yellow line) looks exactly like a reef knot (blue line), except for one subtle difference – the line's working ends are on opposite sides of the knot, not the same side.

The idea is that the thief will untie your thief knot, rummage around in your bag, then use a reef knot when he re-ties the line. Busted!

Illustrations by Mister Reusch

Bowline

Used to make a fixed loop at the end of a line, the bowline (pronounced BOE-lin) is easy to tie and untie rapidly – which is handy on boats, and also in rescue situations. Here's how to tie a bowline:

1. Imagine the working end of the line as a rabbit, and the place on the line where the knot will begin as a tree. Make a loop near the end of the line; this is the rabbit's hole.

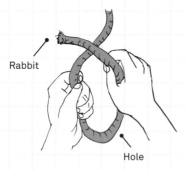

2. Then the rabbit (the line's working end) comes up the hole, runs around the tree from right to left, then jumps back down the hole.

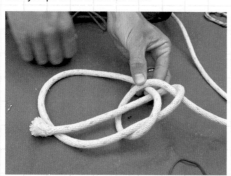

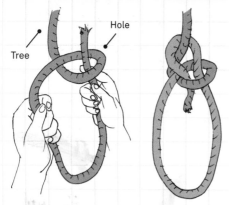

3. Pull the knot tight. Sailors practise tying a bowline with their eyes closed or behind their back – you should too.

Clove hitch

Sailors use the clove hitch, which is easy to tie and adjust, for fastening a line to a mast; or if you're camping in the woods or your garden, you can use it to fasten a line to a tree or pole. Here's how to tie it:

1. Make a turn around a post with the line's working end running underneath the standing part.

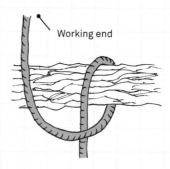

2. Take a second turn around the pole in the same direction, and feed the line's working end through the 'eye' of the second turn. Pull tight.

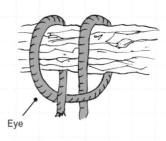

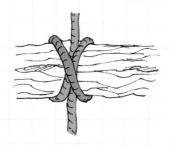

Captain Matt's clove hitch

If you want to tie your line to a standing post – as opposed to, for example, a tree – here's a quick and easy method.

1. Form two loops in the line, as shown below. The loops should be large enough to fit around the end of the post.

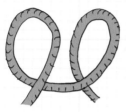

2. Stack the loops on top of each other, as shown below.

3. Drop both loops together around the end of the post. Pull tight.

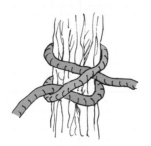

Shear lashing

If you build a lean-to or tipi, you'll want to secure your poles (two for a lean-to, three for a tipi) together by lashing. All lashings start with wrapping the line around the poles. To make the lashing more secure, you then wrap the line around the wrapping itself; doing so is called 'frapping'.

To build a tipi, you'll need three poles, and you'll use what's called tripod lashing. Here's how to build the entrance to a lean-to, using shear lashing:

1. Lay two poles alongside each other. Begin with a clove hitch near the end of one of the poles. Then, loosely but neatly wrap the line around both poles seven or eight times.

2. Make two loose 'fraps' between the poles.

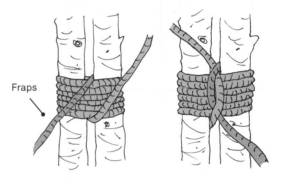

Fraps

3. Finish with a clove hitch. Spread the poles apart. If your lashing is too loose or tight, you may need to start again.

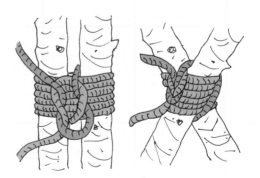

Tomfool knot

Firefighters use it to pull each other out of narrow spaces, and hunters use it to haul dead animals by the legs... but you probably don't need to know how to tie a tomfool knot. Still, it's fun to learn, because it has two slippery loops which can be tightened (gently, and temporarily) around, say, your sibling's or friend's hands. Never, ever the neck! Here's how to tie it:

1. Create two opposing loops (one overhand, one underhand).

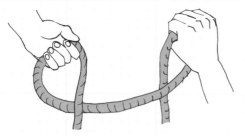

2. Stack the right loop on top of the left.

3. Reach through the top loop and grab the right side of the lower loop. Reach through the lower loop and grab the left side of the upper loop.

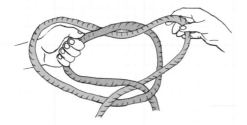

4. Pull the loops with both hands until you have something that looks like a pair of handcuffs.

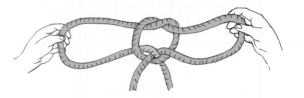

5. To tighten the two loops, pull on the working ends of the line.

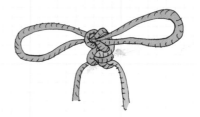

MAKE
SOLAR
ICED TEA

It's fun to make, there's no risk of spilling boiling water, and the brewing process doesn't use any gas or electricity.

If your grownups don't want you drinking caffeinated tea, try a herbal tea – peppermint, lemon, camomile. And even if you don't enjoy *any* sort of iced tea, you might want to make some for grownups on a hot summer day – they'll be very grateful.

You'll need:

- 2 tea bags
- Something sweet; instead of refined sugar, try honey or brown sugar
- Ice
- A large, clean, clear glass jar with a lid

Try this:

- Make sure your jar is clean. Fill jar with water. Add tea bags – leave tags hanging outside the jar. Put the lid on tightly. Place jar in a sunny spot. Come back in half an hour.

- Pour over ice, add something sweet to taste (solar tea is less bitter than tea brewed in boiling water, so it doesn't need much sweetening), and enjoy. Note that if you don't want to muck up the brewing jar, then you can add sweetener to the tea in the glass.

- To make Malaysian-style *teh*, add some condensed or evaporated milk to your solar iced tea; if you want a more authentic flavour, sweeten your *teh* with gula melaka (palm sugar).

> **IMPORTANT!** We don't recommend using loose leaf tea, which might have bacteria growing on it. The water won't get hot enough to kill any bacteria on the tea.

MAKE A GRASS HORSE

By Josh

When I was 11 or so, I met a boy my age from Laos at a picnic. We couldn't speak each other's language, but he taught me how to transform five stalks of timothy-grass into an horse-shaped figure. This project is tricky at first! But be patient, and you'll get the hang of it.

IMPORTANT! If you're allergic to grass, it might be wisest to avoid this project!

Timothy-grass, which is often harvested and turned into hay for animals, grows in virtually every part of the United Kingdom. You'll most often find it in meadows, where it can be recognised by its long, stiff stalks and spiky green flower-heads. (Meadow foxtail, a grass that looks like timothy-grass, but which has a much softer flower-head, won't work as well.)

1. Pick 10 stalks of timothy-grass (Figure A). (You'll only need five to make the creature, but I usually ruin a few stalks when I'm getting warmed up, so it's good to have extras.) Select several stalks with long flower-heads, and then add a few others with short heads. Both lengths are useful.

   TIP: You don't want to pull the entire plant up by its roots, nor do you want to snap the head off the stalk, so here's how to harvest timothy-grass: firmly grip the stalk just above where it enters the plant's sheath, then pull upward – like you're drawing a sword from its scabbard – until the stalk pops free.

A

2. Select two timothy-grass stalks with longer flower-heads. Aim them in opposite directions, then arrange them so that their heads are five centimetres apart.

    Using the thumb and index finger of your left hand, pinch the two stalks between the heads. Using your right hand, coil the flower-head on the right tightly around the stalks (Figure B). Then tuck the tip of the flower-head between the two stalks, and tighten them up again – so the head won't come uncoiled (Figure C).

3. Now pinch the stalks with your right hand, and coil the flower-head on the left tightly around the stalks, tuck its tip between them tightly. Pull on the two stalks sticking out to either side, which will draw the two flower-heads together tightly (Figure D). Now you've got a timothy-grass bundle (Figure E).

    If you've made it this far without wrecking a couple of timothy-grass stalks, then you're already better at this than I am.

    Now make a second timothy-grass bundle.

4. One of these bundles will become the horse's head. Choose a bundle, and hold it vertically – so that one stalk is in your hand and the other is pointing up into the air. Take the end of the top stalk and insert it into the bottom loop of the timothy-grass bundle (Figure F).

   Pull the stalk through the loop, and keep on pulling until the bundle bends (Figure G). Does it look a little bit like a horse's head? If not, call it a dog.

5. Now insert the two stalks attached to the horse's head into the last loop on either end of the other timothy-grass bundle, and pull the two bundles together – making sure the 'head' bundle remains bent. You've just given the horse a body! And the stalks are its legs. True, the horse has three front legs and only one hind leg, but we'll fix that problem in the next step (Figure H).

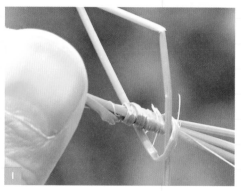

6. Choose a piece of timothy-grass with a very short flower-head. Insert its stalk through the last loop in the horse's body – where its rear end would be. Pull it through, and you've got a tail (and a second hind leg, too).

7. Wind the tail's stalk around the other stalks tightly, a few times, then tie it off in a knot (Figure I). This will prevent your timothy-grass horse from falling apart. Now take it inside and put it in a vase with water.

CONKERS

Every autumn, horse chestnut trees drop spiky greenish-brown pods onto the ground. Crack one of these pods open, and inside you'll find a chestnut. If there's such a tree in your neighbourhood, then you're in luck.

Brits call horse chestnuts 'conkers', and since at least the mid-nineteenth century we've used them to play an excellent game of the same name.

> **WARNING!** Grownup supervision is a must when drilling your conker. Exercise caution when playing conkers.

Make a conker

1. Choose a large, hard conker, and carefully drill a hole through it. You and your grownup can use a long nail, screwdriver or even a drill to make the hole.

2. Thread a piece of string or a shoelace through the hole, and tie a large knot at one end to prevent the conker from slipping off the string.

3. Repeats Steps 1 and 2 until each player has a conker.

How to play conkers

One player dangles his conker at the end of the full length of its string; the other player strikes it with his own conker. Take turns striking each other's conker until one of them breaks.

TIP: Hold the end of the string with one hand, and with the other hand lift the conker over your head. Pretend the string is an axe handle and the conker is the blade; now strike!

More rules

- A widely accepted rule holds that each player gets to take three swings at the opponent's conker in a row.

- If the two strings get tangled, whichever player yells 'tanglies' first takes the next turn.

Scoring

A conker that breaks another conker gains a point – whether it was attacking or being attacked at the time. Not only that, the winning conker steals any points belonging to the conker that broke.

A new conker is called a *none-er*; a conker that has broken a none-er becomes a *one-er*; a conker that has broken two none-ers (or one one-er) becomes a *two-er*; and so forth.

Illustrations by Mister Reusch

PIONEERING POLAR EXPLORER

Q&A WITH ANN BANCROFT

One of the world's best-known polar explorers, Ann Bancroft was the first woman to reach the North Pole by dog sled and the first American woman to ski across Greenland. She also led the first group of women to the South Pole.

Bancroft has dyslexia and was, in her words, a 'lousy' pupil. She wants kids to know you can succeed in anything you want in life – even if you aren't great at school. That's why this former gym teacher and her expedition teams use the latest technologies to communicate what they learn in the planet's outer reaches with students across the globe. She hopes that you'll feel inspired to go and create your own adventures.

UNBORED: **What did you like to do when you were a kid?**

BANCROFT: I grew up in a rural area on the outskirts of St Paul, Minnneapolis. I grew up in a family that loved being in the out-of-doors, which was great because I was a shy kid who loved being outside. That's where I felt best about myself and where I thought the adventure was.

We always had animals, from a pig to a lamb to horses and even a burro. I felt like the animals understood me better than anyone else.

I wasn't a good student. I have a learning disability – dyslexia – and it wasn't known for a long time, so school was very painful for me. So I think that enhanced how the animals and the acres around our house were a refuge for me.

UNBORED: **How did you get the idea that you could be an explorer?**

BANCROFT: My mum is an avid reader, but I was a slow reader and my retention was bad. So she'd put books in front of me that would entice me because of their subject matter. She was always finding books about nature and the outdoors, from *Black Beauty* to *Rascal* to *A Light in the Forest*.

Endurance (a book about the legendary Ernest Shackleton expedition to Antarctica) was on my parents' bookshelf. I would leaf through the book and the pictures were these extraordinary black-and-white photos of the time. I saw those pictures of the dog teams and I could sense the adventure. I saw them playing soccer on the ice and I immediately put myself in there and thought *that's for me*.

Later, when I was crossing Antarctica in 1992–1993 and pulling a 110kg sled, a thought came back to me. I remembered pretending to drag a sled heroically across some Arctic or Antarctic landscape in the alfalfa fields behind our house when the snow drifts were high. In my head, I told my mother *I'm doing what I was meant to do!*

Illustrations by Mister Reusch

UNBORED: How did you get a spot on the 1986 North Pole expedition?

BANCROFT: I interviewed, just like you would for a job. It helped that I was from Minnesota and the leaders (including polar explorer Will Steger) were, too. I was really into climbing and winter camping and was working after hours from my teaching job at a mountaineering store. There were six women trying for it and they chose me.

UNBORED: What's the coolest technology you use on your expeditions?

BANCROFT: The thing about technology is that people tend to focus on the gizmos, but *food* is also a technology. We only have two true meals each day and have to get at least 6,000 calories. When we went to the North Pole, I ate a stick of butter every day because your body needs that fat to stay warm. I imagined it was a Snickers bar to get it down. It's hard for a body to eat foods that are so rich, so the technology is about getting all those calories and fat into a meal that is light and can be heated up with hot water and doesn't taste like cardboard.

We work really hard with a dietitian and nutritionist. In my work I'm using maths, science, geometry, history, geography – all of it. When you're a kid you think you'll never need some of those things. But on an expedition you use every topic under the sun. And I *love* it because even if you are a crummy student, you still have a hunger to learn.

UNBORED: What's your favourite expedition food?

BANCROFT: I get a half-metre-long chocolate bar every day and it's nearly a centimetre thick. It's quick energy during the day – we don't stop for a hot meal because we are moving for 14–18 hours each day. We also snack on nuts, jerky and other stuff you can crumple in your pocket to keep it from freezing.

UNBORED: Beyond food, what other tech do you use?

BANCROFT: When we went to the North Pole in 1986 there was no GPS. We travelled by sextant (an instrument used to measure the angle between the sun, or a star, and the horizon) and used maths,

Photography courtesy of Ann Bancroft

In 1992–1993, when Ann Bancroft crossed Antarctica, she pulled a 100kg sled!

prisms, compasses, wind direction, and looking at the angle of the sun to navigate. In 1992–1993 in Antarctica we had GPS, but back then the devices were the size of a page of paper and fat and heavy. Now they are just the size of a tiny digital recorder.

We also relied on the compass and wind direction. Because the sun was up 24 hours in Antarctica, we couldn't really use the night sky to navigate.

On our 2000–2001 trip across Antarctica, we had satellite phones and talked twice a week to CNN to communicate with students. But nobody could call us. Batteries don't last in that kind of cold so you have to turn the phones off right after you use them.

UNBORED: Do you get used to the cold?

BANCROFT: I hate being cold! But your body adapts to the environment eventually. You have to get in all those calories to stay warm. If you eat some of that chocolate bar in that environment, you can feel your body's furnace heating up.

UNBORED: What's working with dogs like?

BANCROFT: The dogs we end up taking on expeditions are like us. They have to make the team. They have to be in shape. And they have to want to go. They have to have that adventurous spirit.

Based on my experience as an elementary school teacher, working with the dogs is a lot like being with students. You have to sort out who can sit next to whom. You need to tell them to keep their hands to themselves sometimes, 'cause they goof off. Dogs pout, have best friends and not-such-best friends. You have to break up fights, motivate them when they are tired. They are so much like us and so they require the same things: a good diet and rest so they don't get burned out by the work.

I always like dogs because I can share my secrets and they don't give them up to the human team members. There's nothing better than a fluffy furry coat to bury your frostbitten face into and have a cry.

UNBORED: Do you take sentimental objects on your journeys?

BANCROFT: I always bring a picture of home in greener times and I never leave home without my diary. I also bring a collection of poems chosen by my friends and family. My mother came up with the idea of poetry because you can chew on those poems during the day when you're pulling. Also, I always have my nieces and nephews paint my skis (sled dogs were banned from Antarctica in 1990, in order to protect native species, so Bancroft and her team now pull their own sleds). You spend a lot of time looking down, labouring. Seeing those painted skis always tells me I'm not alone.

UNBORED: Any advice for kids?

BANCROFT: I want you to feel comfortable taking a risk. That might be moving away from the wall and trying a new activity in gym, or dabbling in art even if you don't think of yourself as an artist. Life is full of so many wonderful opportunities. But we won't find what we love unless we continue to explore the world around us.

I want you to dream of faraway places and keep the real world alive. So step away from your wonderful gizmos and use your *brain* as a wonderful gizmo to transport yourself to other places.

DRACULA'S
VOYAGE

AN EXCERPT FROM

— DRACULA —

by Bram Stoker

In Bram Stoker's novel *Dracula* (1897), the vampire Count Dracula travels from Transylvania to England by shipping himself inside a crate. In Varna, a port on the Black Sea, the crate is loaded aboard the *Demeter*, a Russian schooner. As the *Demeter*'s log (a journal kept by the captain) indicates, sinister things begin to happen during the month-long voyage; by the time the ship arrives in the northern England town of Whitby, the crew has vanished and the captain has died.

LOG OF THE 'DEMETER'
Varna to Whitby

Written 18 July, things so strange happening, that I shall keep accurate note henceforth till we land.

On 6 July we finished taking in cargo, silver sand and boxes of earth. At noon set sail. East wind, fresh. Crew, five hands… two mates, cook, and myself, (captain). […]

On 13 July passed Cape Matapan. Crew dissatisfied about something. Seemed scared, but would not speak out.

On 14 July was somewhat anxious about crew. Men all steady fellows, who sailed with me before. Mate could not make out what was wrong. They only told him there was *something*, and crossed themselves. Mate lost temper with one of them that day and struck him. Expected fierce quarrel, but all was quiet.

On 16 July mate reported in the morning that one of the crew, Petrofsky, was missing. Could not account for it. Took larboard [*port or left side of ship*] watch eight bells [*for four hours*] last night, was relieved by Amramoff, but did not go to bunk. Men more downcast than ever. All said they expected something of the kind, but would not say more than there was *something* aboard. Mate getting very impatient with them. Feared some trouble ahead.

On 17 July, yesterday, one of the men, Olgaren, came to my cabin, and in an awestruck way confided to me that he thought there was a strange man aboard the ship. He said that in his watch he had been sheltering behind the deckhouse, as there was a rain storm, when he saw a tall, thin man, who was not like any of the crew, come up the companionway, and go along the deck forward and disappear. He followed cautiously, but when he got to bows found no one, and the hatchways were all closed. He was in a panic of superstitious fear, and I am afraid the panic may spread. To allay it, I shall today search the entire ship carefully from stem to stern.

Later in the day I got together the whole crew, and told them, as they evidently thought there was some one in the ship, we would search from stem to stern. First mate angry, said it was folly, and to yield to such foolish ideas would demoralise the men, said he would engage to keep them out of trouble with the handspike [*a metal bar*]. I let him take the helm, while the rest began a thorough search, all keeping abreast, with lanterns. We left no corner unsearched. As there were only the big wooden boxes, there were no odd corners where a man could hide. Men much relieved when search over, and went back to work cheerfully. First mate scowled, but said nothing.

22 July.—Rough weather last three days, and all hands busy with sails, no time to be frightened. Men seem to have forgotten their dread. Mate cheerful again, and all on good terms. Praised men for work in bad weather. Passed Gibraltar and out through Straits. All well.

24 July.—There seems some doom over this ship. Already a hand short, and entering the Bay of Biscay with wild weather ahead, and yet last night another man lost, disappeared. Like the first, he came off his watch and was not seen again. Men all in a panic of fear, sent a round robin [*a petition on which the signatures form a circle, so none of the signers seem like the ringleader*], asking to have double watch, as they fear to be alone. Mate angry. Fear there will be some trouble, as either he or the men will do some violence.

28 July.—Four days in hell, knocking about in a sort of maelstrom, and the wind a tempest. No sleep for any one. Men all worn out. Hardly know how to set a watch, since no one fit to go on. Second mate volunteered to steer and watch, and let men snatch a few hours sleep. Wind abating, seas still terrific, but feel them less, as ship is steadier.

29 July.—Another tragedy. Had single watch tonight, as crew too tired to double. When morning watch came on deck could find no one except steersman. Raised outcry, and all came on deck. Thorough search, but no one found. Are now without second mate, and crew in a panic. Mate and I agreed to go armed henceforth and wait for any sign of cause.

30 July.—Last night. Rejoiced we are nearing England. Weather fine, all sails set. Retired worn out, slept soundly, awakened by mate telling me that both man of watch and steersman missing. Only self and mate and two hands left to work ship.

1 August.—Two days of fog, and not a sail sighted. Had hoped when in the English Channel to be able to signal for help or get in somewhere. […] We seem to be drifting to some terrible doom. […]

2 August, midnight.—Woke up from few minutes sleep by hearing a cry, seemingly outside my port. Could see nothing in fog. Rushed on deck, and ran against mate. Tells me he heard cry and ran, but no sign of man on watch. One more gone. Lord, help us! Mate says we must be past Straits of Dover, as in a moment of fog lifting he saw North Foreland, just as he heard the man cry out. If so we are now off in the North Sea, and only God can guide us in the fog, which seems to move with us, and God seems to have deserted us.

3 August.—At midnight I went to relieve the man at the wheel and when I got to it found no one there. The wind was steady, and as we ran before it there was no yawing. I dared not leave it, so shouted for the mate. After a few seconds, he rushed up on deck in his flannels. He looked wild-eyed and haggard, and I greatly fear his reason has given way. He came close to me and whispered hoarsely, with his mouth to my ear, as though fearing the very air might hear. '*It* is here. I know it now. On the watch last night I saw It, like a man, tall and thin, and ghastly pale. It was in the bows, and looking out. I crept behind It, and gave it my knife, but the knife went through It, empty as the air.' And as he spoke he took the knife and drove it savagely into space. Then he went on, 'But It is here, and I'll find It. It is in the hold, perhaps in one of those boxes. I'll unscrew them one by one and see. You work the helm.' And with a warning look and his finger on his lip, he went below. There was springing up a choppy wind, and I could not leave the helm. I saw him come out on deck again with a tool chest and lantern, and go down the forward hatchway. He is mad, stark, raving mad, and it's no use my trying to stop him. He can't hurt those big boxes, they are invoiced as clay, and to pull them about is as harmless a thing as he can do. So here I stay and mind the helm, and write these notes. I can only trust in God and wait till the fog clears. Then, if I can't steer to any harbour with the wind that is, I shall cut down sails, and lie by, and signal for help…

It is nearly all over now. Just as I was beginning to hope that the mate would come out calmer, for I heard him knocking away at something in the hold, and work is good for him, there came up the hatchway a sudden, startled scream, which made my blood run cold, and up on the deck he came as if shot from a gun, a raging madman, with his eyes rolling and his face convulsed with fear. 'Save me! Save me!' he cried, and then looked round on the blanket of fog. His horror turned to despair, and in a steady voice he said, 'You had better come too, captain, before it is too late. He is there! I know the secret now. The sea will save me from Him, and it is all that is left!' Before I could say a word, or move forward to seize him, he sprang on the bulwark and deliberately threw himself into the sea. I suppose I know the secret too, now. It was this madman who had got rid of the men one by one, and now he has followed them himself. God help me! How am I to account for all these horrors when I get to port? *When* I get to port! Will that ever be?

Illustration by Mister Reusch

MAPPING AND NAVIGATING

By Chris Spurgeon

Aidan's ever expanding Land of... BRILLIANTNESS!

A map is a picture of a place that can be used for navigation. Just like with any other picture you make, it's up to you to decide what it looks like, what you put in and what you leave out.

Although many maps are very accurate and highly detailed, there's no law saying they *have* to look a certain way.

Personal maps

Here are some ideas for personal, silly, crazy and otherwise less than perfectly realistic maps.

• Get a road map of your county that your grownups don't need. Using it as your canvas, draw in places you've visited – or want to visit.

• See if you can draw a map of the inside of your home... from memory. When you're done, travel from room to room and see how accurate your map is.

• Draw a map that shows your favourite places in your town, city or country (or in the world), and also your least favourite places.

Illustrations by Heather Kasunick

Try orienteering

Enjoy maps and mapmaking – plus a bit of competition with your friends? Then orienteering may be for you.

Orienteering is a sport that combines running (or walking, skateboarding, cycling and so forth) with map navigation. At the beginning of a race, each orienteer is given a map marked with checkpoints (called 'controls') and a compass. As quickly as they can, the orienteers visit each control in order, then race to the finish line.

There's no set route from control to control, so how you navigate the course is up to you. Say the next checkpoint is on the other side of a hill… is it faster to run right up the hill and down the other side, or race along a longer but flatter path around the hill? Is it faster to run a bit out of your way along a trail, or just bash through the forest? Faster to find a bridge across that stream, or just splash through? In orienteering these types of on-the-fly decisions make the difference between winning and losing.

So that each orienteer doesn't just follow others around the course, orienteering races start each competitor separately, a minute or two apart. And to make sure that the orienteer actually visits every control point, there is usually a way to check in at each one. Some races place a uniquely shaped paper punch at the controls, and the orienteer punches a card they carry with them to check in.

MAKE AN
ORIENTEERING COURSE

Pick a location

Orienteering races are usually held in forest areas like country parks. But city parks, urban neighbourhoods, and even school gardens can work.

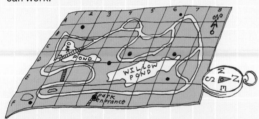

Work out where to place the controls

Orienteering isn't a treasure hunt – when you're at the correct spot you should have no trouble spotting a control. But that doesn't mean you can't be a little sneaky. If you decide that a big tree that everyone will approach from the south is a great spot for a control, there's no reason you can't put the control on the north side of the tree. Also, instead of putting a control at a bend on a trail, you can put it several yards off the trail. (Just make sure the map shows that it's off the trail!) You can arrange the controls however you like, but usually it's best if they form some sort of loop, so racers end up finishing at the spot from which they started.

Draw the map

For places like country parks, you can often make copies of the official park map. (It's a good idea to make enlarged copies, so you have more room to show the exact spot of the controls.) On the map, mark the location of each control as precisely as you can. It's OK to provide clues, like 'all the way down on the ground' or 'between the boulders'.

Place the controls

Just before it's time to run the race, the organiser will have to go around the course setting up the controls. You can use anything for control markers – ribbons, flags, old bottles painted orange, you name it. Place something at each control point so people can prove they found it. For example you can mark each control with a secret number or symbol that the orienteer must record on a piece of paper they carry. Make sure your friends who will be running the race don't see where you're putting the controls.

Start the race!

Give each of your friends a map and a way to confirm that they found each control (such as a piece of paper and a pencil). Start the orienteers on the course one after another, a minute or two apart – and record what time everyone started. When they finish, you'll need this info to figure out who was quickest.

Clean up

After the race, make sure you go back and retrieve your controls. Leave the course the same way you found it!

Map an imaginary world

Drawing flat maps on pieces of paper is fun, but if you want to map an entire (imaginary) planet you'll need to use something round. Any round object will do, but if you have an outdated world globe with a stand, that's even better.

Remove the globe from its stand (there may be a screw holding the globe in place) and give it a few coats of flat white paint. Once the paint is dry, grab some magic markers or paint and go crazy! Make up your own continents and countries. Fill the oceans with sea serpents and the land with mountains, deserts and rivers. Then make up stories and histories about your imaginary world.

Locate confluence points

The entire world is covered with imaginary lines – plotted by mapmakers. Called lines of longitude and latitude, they split the Earth into small divisions, the same way that lines on a piece of graph paper split the paper into little squares. If you look at a globe or map, the major lines of longitude are the ones that run north and south (and meet at the north and south poles), and the major lines of latitude are the ones that run east and west.

Places where lines of longitude and latitude cross are called *degree confluence points*, and there

are thousands of them on our planet (64,442 of them to be exact). You are probably no more than 40 miles away from a confluence point right now. Why not organise a trip to find it? Here's how:

- A fairly detailed map of your county will usually show the latitude and longitude lines. Once you've figured out which confluence point is closest to you, your grownups can help decide the best way to reach it.

- Whether you're driving, cycling or hiking there, it's helpful to have a GPS unit, or a GPS-equipped mobile phone, with you.

- When you get to the confluence point, snap a photo and compare it with ones other visitors to the same spot have uploaded to the Degree Confluence Project site (confluence.org).

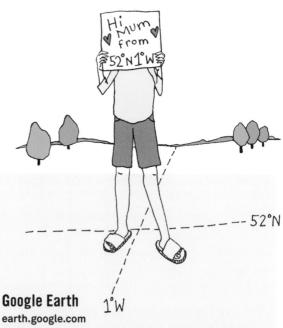

DIGITAL TRAVEL

Here are a few of our favourite ways to see the world via your computer.

Google Street View

google.com/streetview

Millions and millions of images from streets all over the globe. Though some countries, especially in Europe, have banned the publication of images from Google Street View, saying that they invade ordinary citizens' privacy, there is still a whole lot to take in.

Robot Flâneur

robotflaneur.com

'Flâneur' is French for a person who strolls idly around a city – with nowhere in particular to be. This website uses shots from Google Street View to bring you street-level photos of major world cities, from Berlin to Johannesburg to Tokyo.

Google Earth

earth.google.com

'Fly' anywhere in the world and see 3D images of buildings, volcanoes, mountains, rivers, icecaps.

Museums

All the world's great museums have websites, some with extensive online collections. For example, the Smithsonian in Washington DC (si.edu) is the world's largest museum. Its website is a great way to explore anything from archaeology to modern art to the history of planes and spaceships. Likewise, the excellent website of the British Museum (britishmuseum.org) can introduce you to armour fittings, mummy cases and more.

TRAIN YOUR GROWNUP
TO GEOCACHE

By Chris Spurgeon

Illustrations by Mister Reusch

All around the world there are hidden treasures – more than a million of them, at last count – just waiting to be found. Some of these treasures are hidden right in your neighbourhood. Welcome to geocaching, the world's biggest game of hide-and-seek.

What is a geocache?

Geocaches ('caches' for short) are containers of various sizes (often quite small) that are hidden from sight. They can be anywhere… under a park bench, behind a loose brick in a wall, inside a tree stump – hidden by someone like you.

How to get started

Your first step is to visit the official Geocaching website (geocaching.com), which lists the description and exact location of over a million caches around the world. Enter your postcode (where you live, or somewhere you're visiting), and you'll be given the descriptions of nearby caches… along with their longitude and latitude.

Note that using the Geocaching website is free, though with a paid membership you get some extra features – like automatic notification whenever new caches are created in your area. Also, except for the cost of a GPS unit or maybe a smartphone app, geocaching is free. There's no need to buy 'official' geocaching gear.

Avoid disappointment

Look at the geocache's webpage to see how recently it has been found – if the last date is from a year or more ago, or if other geocachers have left notes saying they couldn't find this one, then the hunt might not be worth the effort. That said, if you arrive at a location where a cache is supposed to be hidden, don't give up quickly. In addition to being cleverly hidden, caches come in many different sizes – from 'micro' (match holders, film canisters, and other containers just large enough for a tiny log sheet) to airtight food containers and buckets – and some of them are covered with camouflage tape, or shaped like bolts, logs or rocks.

On the trail of a cache

Next, using a GPS-enabled device – e.g. a handheld GPS unit or a GPS-equipped mobile phone, with or without a geocaching app installed – you and your grownup can start searching for caches. You may need to drive to a location near the cache, then get out and start walking. Many caches are hidden in city parks, near but not right on the beaten trail.

Once your GPS device says you're within a metre or so of a cache, you'll need to rely on your eyes – you might be steps away from a cleverly hidden geocache and not see it. Don't give up! If you still can't find it, you can sometimes get additional clues from the Geocaching site.

What to do with a cache

When you find the cache, it usually contains a logbook in which you can record the date and your name, and leave comments; you can also leave comments at the website.

If the cache contains trinkets, you can take one; it's customary to bring trinkets with you to leave in those caches which contain them.

Bottom line: you should always put the cache back exactly where you found it, so someone else can enjoy the search.

Beware of muggles

In the geocaching world, people who happen to be walking around in parks near where you're searching for a cache, and who aren't also searching, are 'muggles'. It's bad form to let muggles see you find a cache; wait for them to leave.

Muggles are non-geocachers

Don't let muggles see you find a cache!

MORE
HIDING AND SEEKING TIPS

Use an app

Though you don't need to add a geocaching app to your smartphone, using one does make it convenient to go geocaching on the spur of the moment – when you're already walking or biking in a park, say, or whenever you have some time to kill. Otherwise, you might need to plan your trip in advance from your computer at home. There are geocaching apps (both free and for sale) available for all major brands of smartphones.

Be prepared

Although you can hunt for a geocache on the spur of the moment, it's a good idea to prepare for the adventure as though you're going on a long day-hike. Insect repellent, a bottle of water, sturdy shoes, and a fully charged mobile phone are important. If you're worried about ticks, wear long trousers tucked into your socks. Avoid nettles, bring a raincoat if it's cloudy, and don't forget a pen or pencil for writing your name on the cache's log sheet.

Hide a geocache

Hiding a cache is as fun as searching for one – it's like designing a boardgame or videogame. It's very important to read the 'Listing Requirements' at geocaching.com; this explains what sorts of locations are OK and what sorts aren't. (Don't hide a cache on private property without permission for example, and don't disturb wild animals' nests or historical sites.) Then, choose a cache container that is waterproof and write 'GEOCACHE' on it. Include a logbook, cheap toys for kids, and other goodies. Finally, hide the cache where muggles won't find it accidentally, log the location's GPS coordinates, and submit your cache at the Geocaching website.

Learn the lingo

- **Geoswag** is stuff left in caches for swapping.

- **BYOP** means 'bring your own pencil' to record your name on the log sheet.

- **TFTC** is a note you can write on a log sheet or a cache's webpage; it means 'Thanks for the cache.'

- A **UFO** is an 'unnatural formation of objects' (e.g. a pile of sticks or stones) concealing a cache.

- A **muggle** is a non-geocacher.

Cache in trash out

Many geocachers like to clean up the area around the cache. There is an official International Cache In Trash Out weekend every year, but why not bring a rubbish bag along on every hunt? It's a really nice thing to do.

DISGUISE
YOURSELF

Sometimes explorers must camouflage themselves – become undetectable, if not actually invisible. Animals' spots, stripes and colouration allow them to blend in with their surroundings; green–and–brown camo garb does the same for soldiers sneaking through forests. But what if you're exploring in an urban area?

Spies who want to move around cities undetected disguise themselves; so do famous restaurant critics who don't want to be recognised when dining. You can hide in plain sight too.

Disguise your voice

Talk in an accent – try anything from talking like the Queen to a twangy Texas drawl. You can find dialect recordings online (do a web search for 'English dialects'); study them, then record and listen to yourself speaking that way until you're an expert.

It's a good idea to learn the slang words that go with your accent. For example, the Australian phrase 'fair dinkum' (pronounced *fay-uh ding-kum*) means 'true' or 'real'. And in the American Midwest, people ask 'Do you want to come with?' instead of 'Do you want to join us?'

Disguise your style

If you favour a beach kid look (think flip flops and sun-bleached T-shirts) switch to hoodies and tracksuit bottoms. Or dress up in more formal clothes. Whatever you do, don't wear any of your usual clothes.

You can also add padding to your stomach or your bum, by wearing several layers of clothes or using a small pillow. Don't go overboard, otherwise it will look fake.

You can stuff cotton balls in your mouth to make your face wider, but you'll talk like Marlon Brando in *The Godfather* – in fact, that's exactly why he sounded that way. Don't know what this means? Ask your grownup to 'Talk like Marlon Brando in *The Godfather*'. Then you'll get the idea.

Disguise your walk

Spies know that every person has a distinctive way of walking, so study your own walk. Get someone to record you walking, then analyse the video: Do your toes point out? Do you stomp heavily? Are your shoulders hunched over? Do you take

Illustrations by Mister Reusch

short and quick steps that make you look like you're in a hurry, or is your pace relaxed? Write down 5–10 words to describe how you walk. Then walk in a way that is the opposite of at least four of those descriptions. If one word is 'slow', step it up! If you look at the ground, keep your head up.

You can change the way you sit too. If you slouch, sit ramrod straight. Or vice versa.

Disguise your hair

The easiest and most realistic way to disguise your hair is by wearing a wig. The cheap wigs you get with Halloween costumes aren't very lifelike, but good wigs can be really expensive.

If you want to change your hair colour quickly and temporarily, you can use spray-on hair colour – just note that it's not convincing from up close, because real human hair is full of different shades. You can also use a curling iron to add wave to straight hair, or a flat iron to straighten wavy or kinky locks; irons are hot and dangerous, so only do this with grownup supervision.

If all else fails, you can always wear a hat – if you've got long hair, pin it up beneath the hat.

Disguise your handwriting

Practise writing with your non-writing hand; the more you practise, the more legible your handwriting will be – but it won't look like your own.

Practise copying someone else's handwriting – you never know when doing so will come in handy. Not that we're suggesting you forge notes from your grownup to your teacher!

Alter key elements of your own handwriting. If you write lightly, try pressing down more heavily when you write – or the other way around. If your cursive slopes left, try sloping it to the right. Make your letters larger or smaller. Dot your i's and cross your t's differently.

WRITE WITH
INVISIBLE INK

In 2011, the Central Intelligence Agency (CIA) declassified the United States government's six oldest classified documents, dating from 1917 and 1918. The documents describe the techniques used by First World War-era spies for writing invisible messages. A few of these techniques only require stuff you can find in your own kitchen. For example:

- Dip a toothpick or cotton bud in an acidic fluid – lemon juice, onion juice, apple or orange juice, and vinegar will all do the trick – and write a message with it. (One of the CIA's 1918 documents notes that prisoners sometimes write secret messages using ink made by mixing table salt with urine! Yuck.) When you run a hot iron over the paper, or hold it to a hot radiator, the ink will turn brown and become legible.

- To make the ink even more invisible, dilute it by adding equal parts bicarbonate of soda and water to the acidic fluid.

If you have an ultraviolet ('black light') lightbulb, you can write a secret message using a special property marking pen. The page will look blank until you view it under the black light. Other inks fluoresce (glow faintly) under ultraviolet light too: you can make your own ink by mixing a teaspoon of laundry detergent with one cup of water.

BEST EVER
GROWNUP-FREE ADVENTURES

By Josh

Exploring the world – whether in the city or in the woods – without grownup supervision is an important part of growing up. You've already heard of Alice in Wonderland, Huckleberry Finn and the Baudelaire family, so here are a few other fictional adventurers who'll inspire you. I have my dad to thank for introducing me to all of them.

1906
THE RAILWAY CHILDREN
By E. Nesbit

When their father, who works for the Foreign Office, is falsely accused of selling state secrets to Russia, 12-year-old Bobbie and her brother and sister (Peter and Phyllis) move from London with their mother to a house in a small village, near a railway. With the help of an elderly gentleman, a regular passenger on the train to whom Bobbie, who wishes to be an engine-driver (and who, like Nesbit, is a rebellious tomboy) waves every day, the three children succeed in procuring their father's release from prison.

Nesbit previously wrote the funny and fantastical Psammead series (including 1899's *The Story of the Treasure Seekers*, 1901's *The Wouldbegoods*, 1902's *Five Children and It* and 1904's *The Phoenix and the Carpet*. If you enjoy Nesbit's grownup-free adventures, you will no doubt also like the writings of her contemporary, Frances Hodgson Burnett. These include such classic children's novels as *A Little Princess* (1905), *The Secret Garden* (1911) and *The Lost Prince* (1915).

1929
EMIL AND THE DETECTIVES
By Erich Kästner

While alone en route to Berlin by train, young Emil Tischbein is robbed by a sinister stranger. Instead of turning to grownups for assistance, he crowd-sources a solution. He enlists the help of his cousin, a bicycle-riding girl whose name is Pony, a streetwise boy called Gustav and 24 other kids. Together, Emil and 'the detectives' set a trap for the thief.

Kästner's Emil books paved the way for later kids' detective novels, from Enid Blyton's Famous Five series and Hergé's Tintin comics, to Donald J. Sobol's Encyclopedia Brown and Eoin Colfer's Artemis Fowl series. *Emil and the Three Twins* (1933) is this book's sequel.

1930–1947 series
SWALLOWS AND AMAZONS
Written and illustrated by Arthur Ransome

During holidays in northwestern England, nine friends aged seven to 13 – the Walker siblings (called the Swallows), tomboys Nancy and Peggy Blackett (called the Amazons), and Dick and Dorothea Callum – camp out on an island, sail around in dinghies, prospect for gold, and explore lakes, rivers and forests… all the while gloriously free from grownup supervision. A version of the author appears in the form of Uncle Jim ('Captain Flint'), who participates in – but never directs – their imaginative adventures, which take place between the two World Wars, and which are influenced by the characters' love of Robert Louis Stevenson's *Treasure Island*.

In 1990, The Arthur Ransome Society was formed in England in order to 'encourage children and others to engage, with due regard to safety, in adventurous pursuits'.

1942–1963 series
FAMOUS FIVE
By Enid Blyton

This series of 21 books, which was hugely popular, stars four school-age kids and a dog named Timmy.

Each school holiday, the siblings Julian, Dick and Anne visit their cousin Georgina, a tomboy who only answers to the name George. Tramping around the English and Welsh countryside, the five go adventuring, run away, get into trouble and various fixes, solve mysteries, and otherwise have a wonderful time.

PS: The original editions of the books featured characters whose non-English ethnicity was supposed to make them villainous; these passages were later altered.

1943
ADAM OF THE ROAD
By Elizabeth Janet Gray

Adam, the 11-year-old son of a famous minstrel, pursues the scoundrel who stole his dog across medieval England. Along the way, he becomes self-reliant, and he learns to think for himself about his society: Why are all the members of Parliament wealthy, while the people they rule are poor? Why don't women have the same rights as men? Good questions in the medieval era, the 1940s, and today.

If you like historical fiction, Marguerite De Angeli's *The Door in the Wall* (1949) is a great read about a medieval boy's adventures; and Rosemary Sutcliff's *The Eagle of the Ninth* (1954) and *The Lantern Bearers* (1959) are set in Roman-occupied Britain in the second century AD.

1943–1966 series
DONALD DUCK COMICS
Written and illustrated
by Carl Barks

In the mid-1950s, Walt Disney's Comics and Stories was the best-selling comic book in the United States. The most popular issues featured Carl Barks' 10-page stories about Donald Duck and his nephews, Huey, Dewey and Louie – not to mention Uncle Scrooge and the thieving Beagle Boys. The triplets are members of the Junior Woodchucks, a Boy Scouts-like

organisation whose guidebook contains valuable information on every possible topic. Though brave, Donald is a foolhardy and accident-prone grownup; his intrepid nephews keep saving the day.

In the 1980s–1990s, Carl Barks' duck stories were reissued by several different publishers. They're being reissued again now – in beautiful archival editions – by Fantagraphics.

1949
THE FABULOUS FLIGHT
Written and illustrated
by Robert Lawson

At the age of seven, Peter P. Pepperell III, whose father works in the US State Department and designs model railways as a hobby, begins to shrink – until he's pocket-sized. By the age of 12, Peter has learned to communicate with animals; he rides around on a rabbit and befriends a slang-talking seagull named Gus. When a reclusive middle-European scientist invents a tiny but super-powerful explosive, Peter and Gus volunteer to steal it away from him. Peter's father designs a nifty compartment in which Peter can ride while on Gus's back, and away they go!

Lawson is best remembered for his illustrations for other authors' classics, such as *The Story of Ferdinand*, *Mr Popper's Penguins* and *Adam of the Road*. But he wrote several great kids' books – including *Ben and Me* (1939), *Rabbit Hill* (1944) and *Mr Revere and I* (1953).

1959
MY SIDE OF THE MOUNTAIN
By Jean Craighead George

With his understanding family's permission, 13-year-old Sam Gribley runs away from New York City to the Catskill Mountains, where he lives off the land using nothing but a penknife, a ball of cord, and some flint and steel. He learns to catch fish with hooks made from twigs, builds a shelter, makes his own clothing, forages for edible plants and trains a falcon. You'll want to run away, too.

This novel's sequel, *On the Far Side of the Mountain* (1990), is also an exciting read. So is *Julie of the Wolves* (1972), George's prize-winning novel about an Alaskan Indian girl who runs away and lives with a wolf pack. Also: check out the author's 1995 cookbook, *Acorn Pancakes, Dandelion Salad, and 38 Other Wild Recipes*.

1961
THE PHANTOM TOLLBOOTH
By Norton Juster

Milo is given a miniature tollbooth and a map of 'The Lands Beyond'; he drives through the tollbooth in his toy car and is transported to the Kingdom of Wisdom – where King Azaz the Unabridged (who insists that letters and words are more important than mathematics and science) is at war with his brother, the Mathemagician (who champions maths and science). Accompanied by the 'watchdog' Tock, Milo sets out to rescue Princesses Rhyme and Reason – a quest that will demand both logic and imagination.

In 1970, *The Phantom Tollbooth* was adapted by Chuck Jones into a very smart, stylish animated film.

1963
THE WOLVES OF WILLOUGHBY CHASE
By Joan Aiken

After her parents are lost in a shipwreck, Bonnie Green escapes from the orphanage where she was sent by Miss Slighcarp, a sinister con artist masquerading as her governess, and embarks on a long journey by foot to London. Accompanied by her orphaned cousin Sylvie, and aided by Simon, a young goose-herder and beekeeper, Bonnie eventually triumphs.

The novel is the first in Aiken's 12-part Wolves Chronicles series, which is set in an alternative nineteenth-century England that's plagued by hungry wolves and dangerous political plots. The first four sequels to *Willoughby Chase* are the most fun: *Black Hearts in Battersea* (1964), *Nightbirds on Nantucket* (1966), *The Whispering Mountain* (1968), and *The Cuckoo Tree* (1971). Also well worth your time: Aiken's novel *Midnight is a Place* (1974), and her many short stories.

1963
BY THE GREAT HORN SPOON!
By Sid Fleischman

During the California Gold Rush of 1848–1855, 12-year-old Jack runs away to seek his fortune, because his once-wealthy family has fallen on hard times; his butler, Praiseworthy, tags along. Together, the partners stow away aboard a steam packet, foil the plots of con artists and highwaymen, prove their worthiness to the grizzled miners of California, and prospect for gold.

Among Fleischman's many other books for kids, we strongly recommend these: *Mr Mysterious & Company* (1962), *The Ghost in the Noonday Sun* (1965), *Chancy and the Grand Rascal* (1966) and *Jingo Django* (1971). Fleischman also wrote about magic and magicians.

1965–1977 series
THE DARK IS RISING
By Susan Cooper

Simon, Jane and Barney Drew are ordinary kids who get caught up in a battle between the Light, a magical force which seeks to set humankind free, and the Dark, which brings chaos to human affairs. While helping the Light search for its lost Things of Power (including a grail, a harp and a sword) which will be crucial in winning the final battle, they befriend Will, an 11-year-old boy who learns that he is an Old One – a magical being who serves the Light.

The Light's greatest champions are the legendary King Arthur and his wizard Merlin. Forget the Avalon High series – if you enjoy contemporary Arthurian fantasy,

try Mark Twain's *A Connecticut Yankee in King Arthur's Court* (1889); Rosemary Sutcliff's *Sword at Sunset* (1963), and her King Arthur trio *The Light Beyond the Forest* (1979), *The Sword and the Circle* (1979) and *The Road to Camlann* (1981). Also: T.A. Barron's *Lost Years of Merlin* series (1996–2006).

1967
FROM THE MIXED-UP FILES OF MRS. BASIL E. FRANKWEILER
By E. L. Konigsburg

Claudia, an 11-year-old geek, takes her nine-year-old brother along when she runs away to live at New York's Metropolitan Museum of Art. It's impossible to read about how Claudia and Jamie survive by their wits without feeling a little jealous.

Konigsburg is the only author to win a prestigious Newbery Medal (for *Mixed-Up Files*) and a runner-up Newbery Honour in the same year. She won the Honour for *Jennifer, Hecate, Macbeth, William McKinley, and Me, Elizabeth*, a novel about 10-year-old goth girls – which was written before the phrase 'goth girls' existed.

1967
THE GREAT BRAIN
By John D. Fitzgerald

Half the stories told here – by the Great Brain's younger brother, J.D. – concern the Great Brain's brilliant schemes to swindle J.D. and other kids living in a small Utah town in the early twentieth century – out of their prized possessions. The other stories recount how the Great Brain uses his keen mind to help unfortunate kids (including those facing discrimination) out of a jam.

The characters in Fitzgerald's Great Brain series (1967–1976) are based on his own family (he's J.D.). The first three sequels after *The Great Brain* are the best: *More Adventures of the Great Brain* (1969), *Me and My Little Brain* (1971) and *The Great Brain at the Academy* (1972).

1968–1970 series
THE CHANGES
By Peter Dickinson

Set in an England which has mysteriously reverted to a medieval way of life, this exciting fantasy trilogy was written and published in reverse order. In *The Weathermonger* (1968), a boy who can control the weather and his sister are sent on a mission to discover why England has fallen under the 'Changes' enchantment – which causes people to fear modern technology, among other things. In *Heartsease* (1969), a gang of kids gets an old tugboat running and – pursued by machinery-smashing adults – attempts to flee England, rescuing a 'witch' in the process. And in *The Devil's Children* (1970), a young English girl survives the beginning of the Changes by joining a nomadic, resourceful band of Sikh immigrants who have not been affected by the enchantment.

Dickinson's YA novels *Emma Tupper's Diary* (1970), *The Dancing Bear* (1972), *The Blue Hawk* (1975) and *AK* (1990) are also thrilling, and mostly grownup-free, adventures.

1975
THE MACHINE GUNNERS
By Robert Westall

During the Battle of Britain (1940), six children – Chas, Cyril, Clogger, Carrot Juice, Audrey and Nicky – living in the northeast English town of Garmouth, which is regularly bombed by the Luftwaffe, find a crashed German aircraft complete with a working machine gun. They conceal the gun in their fort; later, Nicky hides out in the fortress after his house is bombed… and so does a German gunner whom the children have captured. When a bomber heads for Garmouth, the six machine gunners attempt to shoot it down.

When the Library Association's Carnegie Medal for Literature asked the general public to vote on their all-time favourite Medal-winning novel, *The Machine Gunners* was voted onto the Top Ten list.

RUN AWAY
FROM HOME

By Elizabeth

Jigokudani Monkey
Park, Japan

Illustrations by Mister Reusch

At least since the days of ancient Rome, Greece and Egypt, people have travelled to other parts of the world in order to see new sights, taste new foods and learn about other cultures.

Travelling around Europe (taking the 'Grand Tour') was once considered a necessary part of a wealthy young man or woman's education. Today's practice of taking a 'gap year' between school and university, in order to travel and perhaps do some volunteer work, is a version of the same idea. Even cheaper, thanks to world-flattening technologies that allow us to talk, instant-message or video-conference in real time with friends anywhere in the world, is the practice of not going anywhere at all.

But what fun would that be? Here are several reasons that you should leave home.

Experiences make you happy

Research suggests that experiences make people much happier than things. That's because visiting a new city with friends or family, or just spending an afternoon at a nearby farm, is fun and memorable.

When I was 14, my family went on a trip to San Francisco. Our dad stopped at every food stand in Chinatown before tucking into long French and Italian dinners. One afternoon he flopped onto the sofa in our hotel room and dropped the A-bomb of all farts. This thing was so toxic that one of my sisters cried because of the stench. More than 30 years later, we still laugh about the legendary San Francisco Fart.

I bought a very hip striped T-shirt on the same trip, but I never think fondly about it. Scientists would suggest that one reason for this is because once my brain adapted to the experience of having

No matter how short the trip,
the memories will last forever

a fancy T-shirt, it stopped firing T-shirt-related pleasure neurons. Happiness researchers say the other reason things aren't as satisfying as experiences is because every thing can be compared to a better thing, which means we'll never be satisfied. Even if you have the coolest snowboard, phone, jacket or pair of jeans in the world, in six months' time someone out there will have newer, cooler versions of them.

PS: You just learned why consumer societies like ours are so prosperous and wasteful.

Travelling is good for family bonding

Believe it or not, being with your family is fun. Once, my son Henrik and I went on a biplane tour over the lake region that separates Minnesota from Canada. The teen next to me missed out on the experience, including a (planned) nosedive toward the water, because he was busy texting. So try to resist the temptation, when on a family holiday, to keep in constant contact with your friends. They'll be there when you get home.

New perspectives make you wiser

Getting away from home opens your eyes to the fact that there is more than one perspective on just about any topic. Until you've taken in a variety of viewpoints, how can you decide for yourself which one makes the most sense?

Recently, a friend from Pakistan told me how shocked she was to learn that most Americans don't turn off the shower while they shampoo their hair. Because of water and energy shortages, Pakistanis are forced to plan their meals and bathing schedules carefully; they try not to waste a drop of water. Being from Minnesota, which boasts over 10,000 lakes, it's often tough for me to think of water being a precious resource. Talking with this friend from a different culture helped me realise how important it is to take steps to reduce my family's water consumption. I was very grateful to her for that.

Perhaps you don't know anyone who has immigrated from another country. And maybe your family isn't going to travel to another country any time soon. That doesn't mean you can't learn to see your own everyday habits and way of life through someone else's eyes. Fiction and nonfiction books and movies are one place to start. Also, you can communicate with kids your age from around the world via email and online social networking – ask your grownup and teachers to help you make a connection. But remember – if you ever get the opportunity to travel, take it. There's no substitute!

One day, you might save the world

When you are a grownup, your generation will face some serious stuff – from challenges to the environment to famines to wars. Each of these issues will be worldwide; solving them will be impossible unless lots of people from different countries work on them together. These people will need to be able to see the issues from multiple perspectives. Getting away from home, or at least (for now) from your own limited worldview early and often will help you develop the skills necessary to be one such person.

The last time my family went to Guatemala, where my daughter Luisa was born, Henrik visited a school in a village near Lake Atitlán. When he saw that the lunchroom and kitchen consisted of nothing but a bench, a hot plate, and some rice and onions, his eyes nearly popped out of his head. But then the students stood up to sing a welcome song, and it became clear that – just like Henrik – they were very proud of their school. Kids are the same everywhere, even if on the surface they seem different.

A TERM IN
BUDAPEST
By Norah Mortenson

Though I have lived in the United States most of my life, I have been lucky enough to visit South Africa, Tanzania, England, Kenya and Poland. For the first semester of eighth grade (the equivalent to the UK's Year 9), I lived and went to school in Budapest, Hungary. The United States is very different from other cultures! Here are a few things I've noticed.

• Walking around in a European city, you realise that the architecture in the United States is very new. There are fewer fast-food and chain restaurants in Europe. Also, in European cities there are parks, squares and open markets every few streets.

• In part because the petrol prices are so high in other parts of the world, people tend to use less expensive, cleaner forms of travel – including underground trains, trams, buses and even bikes.

• In Hungary, people tend to eat three meals with nothing in between. Snacking is an American habit. Also, only Americans eat Cheez-its.

• Shops in the United States stay open later and open earlier than shops in Europe. Sometimes shops on the Continent close for a few hours in the middle of the day.

• It is much easier to find your way around in America, where streets tend to be organised alphabetically or numerically, or at least on a grid of some kind. In Europe the roads are much more difficult to follow.

LEARN MORE ABOUT
THE WORLD

You don't have to travel to learn how people in other countries live. Here are fun ways to expand your global smarts without getting on a plane.

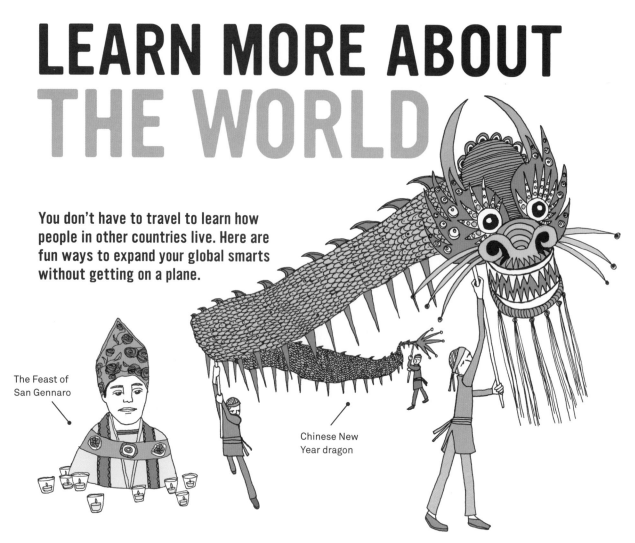

The Feast of San Gennaro

Chinese New Year dragon

Check out festivals

From Chinese New Year to Eid al-Fitr to Diwali, many cities and towns across the United Kingdom have ethnic celebrations to which the general public is welcome. You can try new kinds of food, take in arts and crafts demonstrations, listen to folktales, watch dances and listen to music.

Share a meal

If you know a kid whose grownups were born in a different country, invite the family over for dinner. Not only will you make a new friend, but you'll also learn about their customs and how they see the world. Also, choose different ethnic restaurants where you can sample the specialties, from sushi (Japan) to schnitzel (Germany) to bibimbap (North and South Korea).

Go for geography

Place an up-to-date world map on a wall near the kitchen table or other area in your home where you spend a lot of time. (If you travel a lot, mount the map on cork board and put coloured pins in the countries where your family has visited.) Globes and atlases are also great references to have around your home. *National Geographic*'s kids' website (kids.nationalgeographic.com)offers quizzes and activities to boost your geography IQ.

Make it personal

Find out more about your personal story and learn about the countries where your ancestors (or you) once lived. Does your family listen to music from that country? Do you have food or holiday traditions that have been handed down from your family's countries of origin?

Illustrations by Heather Kasunick

Rock out to world music

Update your playlists to include music from around the world. If you play an instrument, find out how different countries use that instrument. Does a Spanish guitar solo sound different from an Indonesian one? Some artists to get you started include: Mulatu Astatke (Ethiopia); Tom Zé (Brazil); Youssou N'Dour (Senegal), DJ Rhekha (New York, but she mixes hip hop with the traditional Bhangra music of South Asia). You can also watch international pop music on YouTube.

Throw a global birthday bash

Star Wars and pony parties are so Year 3! A great book titled *Growing Up Global* suggests you make your celebration include special themes from other countries, including Bastille Day (France), Cinco de Mayo (Mexico) or Chinese New Year.

Encourage your school to go global

A programme called ePals (epals.com) provides opportunities for students to be digital pen pals with kids from across the world. If you're studying water pollution in the North Sea, for example, you can connect with kids across the globe who are studying the same issue and how it impacts their own communities. Of you can just learn more about what kids in a different country eat and what they like to do with their friends.

Follow a sports team

Pick an international sports team to follow. Football is particularly great because it's played in almost every country in the world. You can choose your team based on your heritage, a friend's heritage, your family's favourite type of food, or the language that you are studying at school. The Federation Internationale de Football Association website (fifa.com) has tons of information to help you learn about all the teams and member countries.

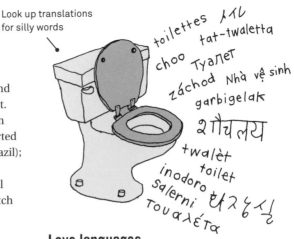

Look up translations for silly words

Love languages

Yes, memorising whether the French word for 'pavement' is masculine or feminine can get boring. But learning a foreign language is the single best way to truly understand and enjoy a culture beyond your country's borders. If your school doesn't offer a foreign language, consider taking after-school or weekend classes or even going to a summer language camp. Some overnight camps immerse you in every aspect of a culture, from food to music to sports and games. Downloading language lessons on your MP3 player and listening to them during car rides will help your ear get used to new sounds. Looking up the translations for silly words – *toilet*, *burp*, *hamster* – online or with an app is also fun.

Enjoy dinner and a movie

Another cool idea from *Growing Up Global*: combine ethnic takeaway with a movie from the same culture as your meal. For example, you might combine watching the Mongolian film *The Cave of the Yellow Dog* with Mongolian barbecue. Or chow down on tempura or sushi while watching the Japanese anime movie *My Neighbour Totoro*. Corned beef and cabbage is the perfect compliment to the soulful *The Secret of Roan Inish* from Ireland.

PS: Choose subtitles over dubbed versions whenever possible, so that you can hear the original language.

Be a host family

Many schools offer exchange student programmes with schools in other parts of the world, which give kids the opportunity to live with 'host families' while they go to school for anywhere from two weeks to an entire school year. If your school doesn't have a programme like this, talk to your head teacher about setting one up. If they do, volunteer to host a student to live with your family.

QUIZ: WORLD SAVVY

How much do you know about the world? Take this quiz and find out.

1. On what continent is Egypt?

   Ⓐ Asia
   Ⓑ Africa
   Ⓒ Europe
   Ⓓ South America

2. What is the largest single reason children across the world die?

   Ⓐ Car accidents
   Ⓑ Poor nutrition
   Ⓒ Malaria
   Ⓓ Cholera

3. What is the longest river in the world?

   Ⓐ Yangtze
   Ⓑ Amazon
   Ⓒ Mississippi
   Ⓓ Nile

4. Which country has the world's largest Muslim population?

   Ⓐ Indonesia
   Ⓑ Mexico
   Ⓒ Iraq
   Ⓓ The United States

5. Chicago is an American city on which Great Lake?

   Ⓐ Michigan
   Ⓑ Superior
   Ⓒ Huron
   Ⓓ Erie

6. To visit Persepolis, the ruins of an ancient ceremonial capital of Persia, you would have to travel to which present-day country?

   Ⓐ Turkey
   Ⓑ Japan
   Ⓒ Iran
   Ⓓ Spain

7. Which continent includes both the Atlas Mountains and the Kalahari Desert?

   Ⓐ North America
   Ⓑ Africa
   Ⓒ Australia
   Ⓓ Asia

8. What is the main reason that a country may have difficulty feeding their people?

   Ⓐ Poor soil quality
   Ⓑ Civil war or international conflicts
   Ⓒ Unstable governments
   Ⓓ All of the above

9. Ecuador is on this continent:

   Ⓐ North America
   Ⓑ Asia
   Ⓒ Europe
   Ⓓ South America

10. The Alps is a mountain range in which continent?

    Ⓐ Europe
    Ⓑ North America
    Ⓒ Australia
    Ⓓ Africa

The following questions are discussion starters, which means that we're asking them to get you thinking about your relationship to the world. Discuss your answers with your friends and grownups. Just be honest – and then think about if there are answers you'd like to change. If you'd like to be more world savvy, you can begin by trying some of the globally minded activities listed elsewhere in this chapter.

11. It's not my problem if people don't have enough drinking water in Africa.

    ○ Strongly disagree
    ○ Disagree
    ○ Don't know
    ○ Agree
    ○ Strongly agree
    ○ Very strongly agree

12. I talk with other people (family, friends, classmates, teachers) about things going on in the world.

    ○ Never
    ○ Almost never
    ○ Not too often
    ○ Don't know
    ○ Quite often
    ○ Almost always
    ○ Always

13. When I'm with people who are very different from me, I ask them questions to find out how they think.

    ○ Never
    ○ Almost never
    ○ Not too often
    ○ Don't know
    ○ Quite often
    ○ Almost always
    ○ Always

Thanks to Dana Mortenson at World Savvy for her help.

Answers to questions 1-10: 1=B; 2=B; 3=D 4=A; 5=A; 6=C; 7=B; 8=D; 9=D; 10=A

BEST EVER

MOVIES FROM AROUND THE WORLD

By Josh

Films about kids bunking off are inspirational – because they encourage kids and grownups alike to live less scheduled and cautious lives. Movies from foreign countries are educational – because they give us some valuable perspective on our home culture. The films on this list are inspirational and educational at the same time.

CHINA

2009
NOT ONE LESS
Directed by Zhang Yimou
Wei is a 13-year-old girl called in to be a substitute teacher for one month at a rural village's school. If all the students are there when the teacher returns, Wei will receive a bonus payment. When the class troublemaker runs away to the city, Wei's students help her raise money to follow and fetch him back.

FRANCE

1956
THE RED BALLOON
Directed by Albert Lamorisse
On his way to school, lonely Pascal discovers a helium-filled balloon in his Paris neighbourhood. The balloon is a prankster with a mind of its own. When a gang of bullies comes along, Pascal must defend his new friend.

1958
MON ONCLE
Directed by Jacques Tati
Nine-year-old Gérard lives in an ultramodern house, which his wealthy parents never stop showing off. He much prefers to spend time with his sweet, bumbling uncle Hulot, who rides around town on an old bicycle. In one of the movie's many funny scenes, Gérard and his friends hide in an overgrown field and play pranks on people walking past.

1962
WAR OF THE BUTTONS
Directed by Yves Robert
A class of schoolboys divides into two gangs, who meet regularly to do battle; whoever wins gets to take buttons off the clothes of the losing side. Some of the boys come up with the brilliant idea of running into battle naked, leaving the victors with nothing to capture. An anti-war comedy.

1976
SMALL CHANGE
Directed by François Truffaut
An earlier Truffaut film, *The 400 Blows*, is about a boy from an abusive family who skips school. This movie, which features a cast of 200 kids of all ages, is much more cheerful. Still, there are hijinks: a girl stages a protest against her parents, and causes confusion with a loudhailer; brothers give a friend a bad haircut; and pupils disobey teachers.

INDIA

1955
PATHER PANCHALI
Directed by Satyajit Ray
In this realistic movie set in rural Bengal of the 1920s, an impoverished boy, Apu, and his sister share the simple joys of life: hanging out, dressing up, running around. The ending is sad, but Ravi Shankar's soundtrack makes the movie joyous.

IRAN

1987
WHERE IS THE FRIEND'S HOME?
Directed by Abbas Kiarostami
Feeling terrible that he's accidentally taken a homework notebook from a fellow pupil, Ahmed, an eight-year-old living in rural Iran, sets out to take the notebook to his friend's home – which involves wandering through a fascinating mountain village, full of distractions.

1995
THE WHITE BALLOON
Directed by Jafar Panahi
In Tehran, Razieh, who's aged seven, loses her money down a sewer – and only a young Afghan boy selling balloons will help her out. Afghan refugees are a mistreated minority in Iran, so the film is subtly criticising the effects of racism on children.

JAPAN

1959
GOOD MORNING
Directed by Yasujiro Ozu
In suburban Tokyo, when young Minoru and Isamu Hayashi are forbidden to watch sumo wrestling on the neighbours' TV set, they throw a tantrum and demand that their parents buy one of these new gizmos. Their father tells them to keep quiet, so the brothers go on a silence strike.

SINGAPORE

2002
I NOT STUPID
Directed by Jack Neo
Three kids are placed in a remedial class for different reasons: one is spoiled and lazy; one is exhausted from working at his family's business; and the other is a born artist whose parents force him to concentrate on maths and science. Together, they tackle each kid's problems.

SPAIN

1973
THE SPIRIT OF THE BEEHIVE
Directed by Victor Ericen
Six-year-old Ana lives in Spain, just after the 1936–1939 Civil War. The new government encourages everyone to see the movie *Frankenstein*; the monster supposedly represents the defeated Republican forces. Ana sympathises with the monster – and also with a fugitive soldier who is hiding out in her family's sheepfold.

TAIWAN

1984
A SUMMER AT GRANDPA'S
Directed by Hou Hsiao-Hsien
Dong-Dong and his sister spend the summer in the countryside, where they climb trees, make new friends, and slowly come to grips with the realities of grownup life.

UNITED KINGDOM

1948
OLIVER TWIST
Directed by David Lean
In this adaptation of Charles Dickens's novel, a runaway orphan is taken in by an old scoundrel, Fagin (played by Alec Guinness, who'd play Obi-Wan Kenobi in *Star Wars: A New Hope*). Nine-year-old Oliver enjoys the company of the Artful Dodger and Fagin's other rapscallions. The scene in which the boys demonstrate to Oliver how to pick Fagin's pockets is terrific. All too soon, Oliver lands in the custody of a nice, respectable gentleman – too bad!

1965
A HIGH WIND IN JAMAICA
Directed by Alexander Mackendrick
Anthony Quinn and James Coburn, two of the toughest- and scariest-looking actors of their time, play salty pirates who capture a group of three English siblings and hold them for ransom. What the poor pirates don't realise is that nothing is more dangerous and disruptive aboard a ship than innocent kids.

2000
BILLY ELLIOT
Directed by Stephen Daldry
The son of a coal miner preoccupied by the 1984–1985 miners' strike, 11-year-old Billy wants to be a dancer. Defying his father's orders to study boxing, Billy secretly does ballet. Brilliant soundtrack.

2007
SON OF RAMBOW
Directed by Garth Jennings
Will Proudfoot's family belongs to a strict religious sect; he's never watched TV or movies. He's bullied by Lee Carter, who accidentally shows Will the violent action movie *First Blood*. This inspires Will to write his own action movie, and when Lee films it with his video camera, the two unhappy boys become friends.

UNITED STATES

1953
LITTLE FUGITIVE
Directed by Morris Engel, Ray Ashley, Ruth Orkin
Seven-year-old Joey wrongly believes he's killed his older brother. Freaked out, Joey runs away from their Brooklyn apartment and spends a couple of days at Coney Island, a local amusement park. He sleeps on the beach, makes friends with grownup strangers, and safely engages in all sorts of other activities the mere thought of which is enough to give today's grownup a conniption fit.

1962
TO KILL A MOCKINGBIRD
Directed by Robert Mulligan
During the summer of 1932, six-year-old Jean Louise 'Scout' Finch and her 10-year-old brother Jem learn responsibility and compassion from their stand-offish but loving father, Atticus, who heroically confronts racism in their community… and who scolds his children for teasing their elusive neighbour Boo Radley.

PS: Mary Badham was nominated for a Best Supporting Actress Academy Award, thanks to her portrayal of the disobedient and noisy, but affectionate and brave Scout.

1982
E.T.
Directed by Steven Spielberg
Watch *E.T.* less for the lovable alien than for the scene in which 10-year-old Elliott, his older brother and their friends elude the authorities on their BMX bikes, almost as though they'd been practising for such a moment.

PS: You should also watch *The Goonies*, which Spielberg co-wrote, for the same reason: unsupervised kids, creepy grownups and BMX bikes. You'll recognise one of the Goonies from the Lord of the Rings movies.

TRAIN YOUR GROWNUP
TO LET YOU GO SOLO

Do the adults in your life usher you to and from the bus stop, even though you've walked that route 10 times a week for at least four years? Do they fret when you ask to bike to the corner shop? Do you call and text each other all the time?

Grownups these days worry about their kids' safety. But while it's important to be able to tell a safe part of town from a dangerous one and distinguish a creepy stranger from a well-intentioned and helpful neighbour, it's also good for you to be able to explore your neighbourhood or town on your own.

The statistics show that you won't be putting yourself in much danger. Crime rates across England and Wales have fallen by more than 50 per cent since they peaked in the mid-1990s. So the chances of becoming a victim of crime are at their lowest since the early 1980s, when kids were allowed – and *encouraged* – to ride bikes all over town and hop on the city bus to get to friends' houses.

If you want to strike out on your own but your grownups aren't sure it's a good idea, here are a few steps that your family can take together in order to support your independence.

Start with the facts
Don't base your family's decisions about where you can and can't go simply on feelings. Talk to neighbours and call your community police to find out exactly what hazards there are in your neighbourhood. Then stay away from them.

Practise
Instead of heading out on the bus by yourself, get an adult to go with you until you get the hang of it and feel comfortable going on you own.

Power down
If you call your grownups constantly to get their advice, try asking them to turn off their mobile phones for a day, or at least an hour. That way you'll get a chance to make independent decisions and your grownups will learn that you are OK even if you can't be reached within a nanosecond's notice.

Take turns
If your bus stop or sports practices have as many adults as kids, ask your grownups to arrange to have only one adult supervising a group of kids. Not being together 24/7 is good for everyone's self-confidence.

Dial down fear
People who watch more news and violent dramas on TV tend to see the world as more dangerous than it is. Skip *CSI* and its crime show cousins in favour of less frightening options.

Take a break
Normal kids' play – especially older boys' playfighting – feels too chaotic for many adults. If your grownups are always urging you to take it easy, try urging them to go inside. They can pop their heads out every once in a while, but otherwise they should let you play.

Illustrations by Mister Reusch

PLAN A CAR JOURNEY
(THAT'S ACTUALLY FUN)

Many grownups see car travel as merely a way to blast from Point A to Point B. That's too bad! A car journey, when done right, is the best way to travel.

Want to make your family car journeys something you actually enjoy? Read on.

> **IMPORTANT!** If you are stopping somewhere you read about in a guidebook or online, call before you veer off the motorway. Restaurants, museums and other attractions change their hours and even go out of business – so it's always best to confirm they are open.

Plan together

Some kids don't like car travel because their grownups don't let them in on the plan – other than to say, 'We're driving from Penzance to Peterhead!' Not knowing what to expect can be stressful. To prevent travel anxiety, get your entire family to sit down together with a map (digital or paper) and plot out your route. Then do some research about where you'll be driving... and get each person to decide on at least one thing they'd like to do.

Stop. Stop. Stop. Stop.

Nothing ruins car journey fun like grownups who drive like they're training for the Rally GB. So schedule in plenty of time to take breaks and see the sights. A good rule of thumb is to split drive time and doing stuff 50/50. So if your GPS says it will take four hours to get to the seaside town you're visiting, plan an extra four hours for stops. (Keep in mind that your GPS won't factor in time-sucks like Friday afternoon rush hour.)

Say YES to history

Britain is an ancient country and when you are driving across it you are rarely more than a few miles from a relic of deep history. So go with it! From ruined castles to stone circles to ancient burial mounds and giant figures carved in the hillside, there's always a place to stop and marvel at what came before us. Visit stone-circles.org.uk for a map of prehistoric sites across the UK.

Tour factories

Factory tours of companies that make anything from chocolate to china are often free; some tours include museums dedicated to the history of the company or industry. A word of advice: some 'factory' tours are nothing more than a boring spin around a warehouse. So call ahead to ask whether you'll truly be allowed to peek behind the scenes. (Most UK car factories don't allow children younger than 14 on tours.) If not, give that factory a miss.

Illustrations by Heather Kasunick

Eat beyond the motorway

Yes, Little Chef, Burger King and Costa are all conveniently located along the sides of the road. But driving even a few miles into the centre of a town will introduce you not only to a place you've never seen (and one which might have other attractions) but also to regional foods. Better yet, keep an eye out for the farm shops that are springing up all over the UK, which provide delicious food in a rustic and rural setting.

Check out regional foods!

Chappy's Seaside Café Specials:
- cornish pasty
- saffron bread
- scones & clotted cream
- mussel soup
- tea

Take nature breaks

Even if it's just a game of frisbee in a local park, make sure that at least one of your stops each day gives you time to run around outside. Check out natural attractions, from country and national parks to scenic overlooks. And if you have a little extra time, try geocaching to discover hidden treasures.

> **IMPORTANT!** Be Prepared. If you leave the country, your smartphone – including GPS, weather, web features and web-based apps – may not work unless you set up a roaming plan before you leave. (Watch out, this can be pricey.) If you're crossing any non-European Union borders, even if only for a few hours, every member of your family needs a passport. Don't get turned back at the border!

BEST CAR GAMES

During even the most well-planned road trips, you're going to have to cover some distance at times. Break up the most boring stretches by playing the parlour games described elsewhere in this book, and also these car games.

20 Questions

Choose one person to be the Answerer, whose job it is to think of a person, place or thing. Then the other people (the Questioners) take turns asking questions to figure it out. The Answerer is only allowed to say 'yes' or 'no' to each question. If 20 questions are asked without a correct guess, then the Answerer wins. The Questioner who guesses correctly becomes the next Answerer.

Trivia

Bring the cards from a trivia boardgame – or get a trivia app for your smartphone.

Mundane Game

See what mundane (everyday) details others can remember about things you've done recently. Example: 'When we stopped at the cafe, what colour shirt was the waiter wearing? What was his name? What was the Special of the Day?'

Ghost

Take turns saying letters. The object is to avoid spelling a word of three letters or longer; if you do, you get a 'G'. But don't just say random letters – if the person whose turn is after yours challenges your letter, then you must be able to name a word that could be spelled that way. If you can't, you get a 'G'. After you get a 'G', you get an 'H', and so forth until you're a GHOST... and out of the game.

Registration Plate Game

Give every person in the car a piece of paper and pencil. Write down each new type of registration plate you spot – for example, plates from different countries. If you spot a type of plate that no one else has seen, yell it out – then enter it onto your list. If you call out a type of plate that has already been spotted, or if you yell the wrong country name, you have to pull out a hair from your head. The person with the most countries wins.

SET SAIL FOR
ADVENTURE

AN EXCERPT FROM

— SOUTH —

by Ernest Shackleton

On the eve of the First World War, the Anglo-Irish explorer Ernest Shackleton set out with a crew of adventurers and a pack of sled dogs with the goal of crossing the Antarctic continent from sea to sea, via the South Pole. Unfortunately his ship, *Endurance*, was trapped and crushed by pack ice (drifting ice floes that break apart and then press together again). So Shackleton abandoned his mission and led his crew through one daring exploit after another until they arrived home safely! Today his name is synonymous with leadership – and he has inspired such adventurers as polar explorers Will Steger and Ann Bancroft.

This excerpt from *South*, Shackleton's 1919 chronicle of his ill-fated voyage, focuses not on the misadventures that would befall the *Endurance* expedition, but on the excitement of departing from the known world – in this case, South Georgia and the South Sandwich Islands, a British overseas territory in the southern Atlantic – and sailing boldly into the unknown.

We had worked out details of distances, courses, stores required, and so forth. Our sledging ration, the result of experience as well as close study, was perfect. The dogs gave promise, after training, of being able to cover fifteen to twenty miles a day with loaded sledges. The transcontinental journey, at this rate, should be completed in 120 days unless some unforeseen obstacle intervened. We longed keenly for the day when we could begin this march, the last great adventure in the history of South Polar exploration, but a knowledge of the obstacles that lay between us and our starting-point served as a curb on impatience. Everything depended upon the landing. If we could land at Filchner's base there was no reason why a band of experienced men should not winter there in safety. But the Weddell Sea was notoriously inhospitable and already we knew that its sternest face was turned toward us. All the conditions in the Weddell Sea are unfavourable from the navigator's point of view. The winds are comparatively light, and consequently new ice can form even in the summer-time. The absence of strong winds has the additional effect of allowing the ice to accumulate in masses, undisturbed. Then great quantities of ice sweep along the coast from the east under the influence of the prevailing current, and fill up the bight of the Weddell Sea as they move north in a great semicircle. Some of this ice doubtless describes almost a complete circle, and is held up eventually, in bad seasons, against the South Sandwich Islands. The strong currents, pressing the ice masses against the coasts, create heavier pressure than is found in any other part of the Antarctic. This pressure must be at least as severe as the pressure experienced in the congested North Polar basin, and I am inclined to think that a comparison would be to the advantage of the Arctic. All these considerations naturally had a bearing upon our immediate problem, the penetration of the pack and the finding of a safe harbour on the continental coast.

The day of departure arrived. I gave the order to heave anchor at 8.45 a.m. on December 5, 1914, and the clanking of the windlass broke for us the last link with civilisation. The morning was dull and overcast, with occasional gusts of snow and sleet, but hearts were light aboard the *Endurance*. The long days of preparation were over and the adventure lay ahead.

We had hoped that some steamer from the north would bring news of war and perhaps letters from home before our departure. A ship did arrive on the evening of the 4th, but she carried no letters, and nothing useful in the way of information could be gleaned from her. The captain and crew were all stoutly pro-German, and the 'news' they had to give took the unsatisfying form of accounts of British and French reverses. We would have been glad to have had the latest tidings from a friendlier source. A year and a half later we were to learn that the *Harpoon*, the steamer which tends the Grytviken station, had arrived with mail for us not more than two hours after the *Endurance* had proceeded down the coast.

The bows of the *Endurance* were turned to the south, and the good ship dipped to the south-westerly swell. Misty rain fell during the forenoon, but the weather cleared later in the day, and we had a good view of the coast of South Georgia as we moved under steam and sail to the south-east. The course was laid to carry us clear of the island and then south of South Thule, Sandwich Group. The wind freshened during the day, and all square sail was set, with the foresail reefed in order to give the look-out a clear view ahead; for we did not wish to risk contact with a 'growler', one of those treacherous fragments of ice that float with surface awash. The ship was very steady in the quarterly sea, but certainly did not look as neat and trim as she had done when leaving the shores of England four months earlier. We had filled up with coal at Grytviken, and this extra fuel was stored on deck, where it impeded movement considerably. The carpenter had built a false deck, extending from the poop-deck to the chart-room. We had also taken aboard a ton of whale-meat for the dogs. The big chunks of meat were hung up in the rigging, out of reach but not out of sight of the dogs, and as the *Endurance* rolled and pitched, they watched with wolfish eyes for a windfall.

I was greatly pleased with the dogs, which were tethered about the ship in the most comfortable positions we could find for them. They were in excellent condition, and I felt that the Expedition had the right tractive-power. They were big, sturdy animals, chosen for endurance and strength, and if they were as keen to pull our sledges as they were now to fight one another all would be well. The men in charge of the dogs were doing their work enthusiastically, and the eagerness they showed to study the natures and habits of their charges gave promise of efficient handling and good work later on.

During December 6 the *Endurance* made good progress on a southeasterly course. The northerly breeze had freshened during the night and had brought up a high following sea. The weather was hazy, and we passed two bergs, several growlers, and numerous lumps of ice. Staff and crew were settling down to the routine. Bird life was plentiful, and we noticed Cape pigeons, whale-birds, terns, mollymauks, nellies, sooty, and wandering albatrosses in the neighbourhood of the ship. The course was laid for the passage between Sanders Island and Candlemas Volcano. December 7 brought the first check. At six o'clock that morning the sea, which had been green in colour all the previous day, changed suddenly to a deep indigo. The ship was behaving well in a rough sea, and some members of the scientific staff were transferring to the bunkers the coal we had stowed on deck. Sanders Island and Candlemas were sighted early in the afternoon, and the *Endurance* passed between them at 6 p.m. Worsley's observations indicated that Sanders Island was, roughly, three miles east and five miles north of the charted position. Large numbers of bergs, mostly tabular in form, lay to the west of the islands, and we noticed that many of them were yellow with *diatoms*. One berg had large patches of red-brown soil down its sides. The presence of so many bergs was ominous, and immediately after passing between the islands we encountered stream-ice. All sail was taken in and we proceeded slowly under steam. Two hours later, fifteen miles north-east of Sanders Island, the *Endurance* was confronted by a belt of heavy pack-ice, half a mile broad and extending north and south. There was clear water beyond, but the heavy south-westerly swell made the pack impenetrable in our neighbourhood. This was disconcerting. The noon latitude had been 57° 26' S., and I had not expected to find pack-ice nearly so far north, though the whalers had reported pack-ice right up to South Thule.

The situation became dangerous that night. We pushed into the pack in the hope of reaching open water beyond, and found ourselves after dark in a pool which was growing smaller and smaller. The ice was grinding around the ship in the heavy swell, and I watched with some anxiety for any indication of a change of wind to the east, since a breeze from that quarter would have driven us towards the land. Worsley and I were on deck all night, dodging the pack. At 3 a.m. we ran south, taking advantage of some openings that had appeared, but met heavy rafted pack-ice, evidently old; some of it had been subjected to severe pressure. Then we steamed north-west and saw open water to the north-east. I put the *Endurance*'s head for the opening, and, steaming at full speed, we got clear. Then we went east in the hope of getting better ice, and five hours later, after some dodging, we rounded the pack and were able to set sail once more.

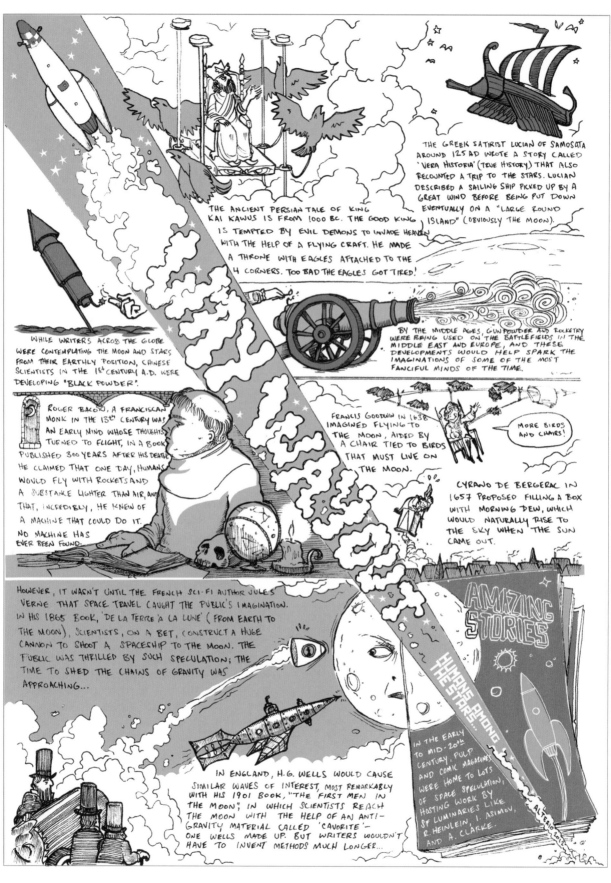

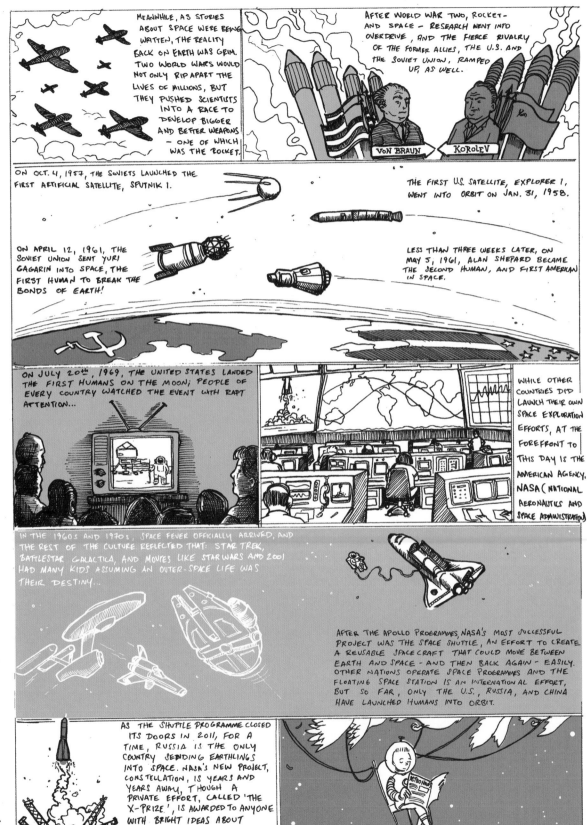

MEANWHILE, AS STORIES ABOUT SPACE WERE BEING WRITTEN, THE REALITY BACK ON EARTH WAS GRIM. TWO WORLD WARS WOULD NOT ONLY RIP APART THE LIVES OF MILLIONS, BUT THEY PUSHED SCIENTISTS INTO A RACE TO DEVELOP BIGGER AND BETTER WEAPONS — ONE OF WHICH WAS THE ROCKET.

AFTER WORLD WAR TWO, ROCKET- AND SPACE- RESEARCH WENT INTO OVERDRIVE, AND THE FIERCE RIVALRY OF THE FORMER ALLIES, THE U.S. AND THE SOVIET UNION, RAMPED UP, AS WELL.

VON BRAUN

KOROLEV

ON OCT. 4, 1957, THE SOVIETS LAUNCHED THE FIRST ARTIFICIAL SATELLITE, SPUTNIK 1.

THE FIRST U.S. SATELLITE, EXPLORER 1, WENT INTO ORBIT ON JAN. 31, 1958.

ON APRIL 12, 1961, THE SOVIET UNION SENT YURI GAGARIN INTO SPACE, THE FIRST HUMAN TO BREAK THE BONDS OF EARTH!

LESS THAN THREE WEEKS LATER, ON MAY 5, 1961, ALAN SHEPARD BECAME THE SECOND HUMAN, AND FIRST AMERICAN IN SPACE.

ON JULY 20th, 1969, THE UNITED STATES LANDED THE FIRST HUMANS ON THE MOON; PEOPLE OF EVERY COUNTRY WATCHED THE EVENT WITH RAPT ATTENTION...

WHILE OTHER COUNTRIES DID LAUNCH THEIR OWN SPACE EXPLORATION EFFORTS, AT THE FOREFRONT TO THIS DAY IS THE AMERICAN AGENCY, NASA (NATIONAL AERONAUTICS AND SPACE ADMINISTRATION)

IN THE 1960s AND 1970s, SPACE FEVER OFFICIALLY ARRIVED, AND THE REST OF THE CULTURE REFLECTED THAT: STAR TREK, BATTLESTAR GALACTICA, AND MOVIES LIKE STAR WARS AND 2001 HAD MANY KIDS ASSUMING AN OUTER-SPACE LIFE WAS THEIR DESTINY...

AFTER THE APOLLO PROGRAMMES, NASA'S MOST SUCCESSFUL PROJECT WAS THE SPACE SHUTTLE, AN EFFORT TO CREATE A REUSABLE SPACECRAFT THAT COULD MOVE BETWEEN EARTH AND SPACE - AND THEN BACK AGAIN - EASILY. OTHER NATIONS OPERATE SPACE PROGRAMMES AND THE FLOATING SPACE STATION IS AN INTERNATIONAL EFFORT, BUT SO FAR, ONLY THE U.S., RUSSIA, AND CHINA HAVE LAUNCHED HUMANS INTO ORBIT.

AS THE SHUTTLE PROGRAMME CLOSED ITS DOORS IN 2011, FOR A TIME, RUSSIA IS THE ONLY COUNTRY SENDING EARTHLINGS INTO SPACE. NASA'S NEW PROJECT, CONSTELLATION, IS YEARS AND YEARS AWAY, THOUGH A PRIVATE EFFORT, CALLED 'THE X-PRIZE', IS AWARDED TO ANYONE WITH BRIGHT IDEAS ABOUT SPACE TRAVEL...

MAYBE IT'S A BETTER TIME THAN EVER TO DREAM BIG.

Comic by Joe Alterio

ADVENTURE: RESOURCES

GET EXPERIMENTAL

AdvancedSpuds (advancedspuds.com). Info on spudzooka ammo, ignition, barrels, fuel and so forth. **Important**: These models may be unsafe!

Book of Experiments, The (1959), by Leonard De Vries and translated by Eric G. Breeze. Classic science experiments from the mid-twentieth century.

Book of Totally Irresponsible Science: 64 Daring Experiments for Young Scientists, The (2008), by Sean Connolly. This book is just what it sounds like.

Cloudspotter's Guide, The (2006), by Gavin Pretor-Pinney. A humorous and educational guide to the clouds above.

Edmund Scientifics (scientificsonline. com). Science experiment materials, components and tools.

eHow (ehow.com). More than 1 million articles and nearly 200,000 videos offering step-by-step instructions for experiments and projects.

Galaxy Zoo (galaxyzoo.org). Anyone can participate in a large-scale project of galaxy research.

GeekDad (wired.com/geekdad). A blog by the tech magazine *Wired* featuring geeky projects. Not just for fathers.

Great Backyard Bird Count (birdsource. org/gbbc). Help biologists understand bird migration patterns and the health of various bird species.

Greenwich Observatory's Solar Stormwatch (solarstormwatch.com). Spot explosions on the sun!

Grow It, Eat It (2008). The experts at the Royal Horticultural Society (Britain's gardening charity) offer kids tips on both cultivating and cooking healthy and delicious food. Everything from photosynthesis to pumpkin pie.

Home School Mom, The (thehome schoolmom.com). Links to resources related to science, maths, nature and technology. Not just for mums.

How Stuff Works (howstuffworks. com). Global warming, crime scene investigation, computer hacking – explained.

Howtoons (howtoons.com). If you prefer learning about biology, energy, technology and other topics via comic strips, then this is the website for you.

How to Smile (howtosmile.org). High-quality science, technology, engineering and maths activities and experiments from children's museums.

Instructables (instructables.com). A site crammed with user-created and uploaded do-it-yourself projects – including science projects.

Mad Professor: Concoct Extremely Weird Science Projects (2002), by Mark Frauenfelder. Great science projects, spiral-bound and printed on laminated paper – so you can use it anywhere!

Mad Science: Experiments You Can Do At Home – But Probably Shouldn't (2009), by Theodore Gray. Good stuff.

Maker Shed (makershed.com). Everything you can imagine for young and old DIY makers, crafters and scientists.

National Biodiversity Network (nbn.org. uk). A collaborative network of 60,000 volunteers gathering information about biodiversity – a measure of the health of ecosystems – in the UK. You are encouraged to submit wildlife sightings.

Otherlab (otherlab.com). A cutting-edge engineering, applied mathematics, and design company whose website is crammed with cool projects.

Royal Society Young People's Book Prize (royalsociety.org/awards/young-people). An annual prize awarded to the book that best communicates science to readers aged up to 14. The 2012 winner, for example, was *Science Experiments* by Robert Winston and Ian Graham.

Sneaky Green Uses For Everyday Things (2009), by Cy Tymony. For experiments, see the chapter 'Sneaky Energy Projects and Simulations'.

Spacehack (spacehack.org) is a directory of ways for citizen scientists to participate in space exploration.

Think Geek (thinkgeek.com). Components and electronics for your science experiments.

Wavewatcher's Companion, The (2010), by Gavin Pretor-Pinney. A lighthearted intro to ocean waves, light waves and even stadium waves.

Wired UK's Geek Dad (wired.co.uk/ news/geek-dad). A website targeting fathers who categorise themselves as 'geeks'. Popular categories include LEGO, Star Wars and Star Trek, videogames, books and field trips.

World Water Monitoring Day (world watermonitoringday.org). Choose any body of water near you, monitor it, and submit your findings to this website.

Young Rewired State (youngrewired state.org) is a network of young software developers and designers. The network's mission is to find and foster the young children and teenagers 'who are driven to teaching themselves how to code, how to program the world around them'.

Zooniverse (zooniverse.org) hosts many citizen science projects, including Galaxy Zoo Hubble, Old Weather, Ice Hunters and Ancient Lives.

PLAY GAMES

Apps for Kids (via iTunes). A podcast by Mark Frauenfelder, one of this book's contributors, and his daughter Jane.

D.I.Y. Kids (2007), by Ellen Lupton and Julia Lupton. For info on making toys, see the chapter 'Primitive Toys'.

Foxfire Book of Appalachian Toys and Games, The (1993), edited by Linda Garland Page and Hilton Smith. Old-fashioned, homemade toys and games.

Ker-Punch! (via iTunes). A brainteaser app, produced by one of this book's editors, based on a game that he used to play in the back of the classroom.

Multicultural Game Book, The: More than 70 Traditional Games from 30 Countries (1999) by Louise Orlando. Not only fun but educational.

Parlour Games for Modern Families (2010), by Myfanwy Jones and Spiri Tsintziras. Old-fashioned parlour games.

Pocket Guide to Games, The (2008), by Bart King. Old-fashioned and new-fangled games in a handy package.

Scratch (scratch.mit.edu). Scratch is a programming language allowing you to easily create your own videogames – and modify other people's games.

GO OUTSIDE

Acorn Pancakes, Dandelion Salad, and 38 Other Wild Recipes (1995), by Jean Craighead George. Recipes for foragers from the author of *Julie of the Wolves* and *My Side of the Mountain*.

Art of Camping, The (2011). This book by *UNBORED* contributor Matthew De Abaitua tells you everything you'll ever need to know not only about the practice of sleeping under the stars – from packing to pitching camp, and from building a fire to campsite games – but also its history.

Big Book of Boy Stuff, The (2004), by Bart King. See the 'Fun in the Outdoors!' chapter. Not just for boys.

Boy's Book of Backyard Camping, The (1968), by Allan A. Macfarlan. Ignore the 'boy' part of the title.

Camping Made Easy: A Manual for Beginners with Tips for the Experienced (1997), by Michael Rutter. If your grownup doesn't camp, this may help.

Camp Out!: The Ultimate Kids' Guide (2007), by Lynn Brunelle. Everything from woodcraft to campfire songs.

Lazy Environmentalist, The: Your Guide to Stylish, Green Living (2007) by Josh Dorfman. See the chapter 'The Great Outdoors: Outdoor Gear'.

Make it Wild! 101 Things to Make and Do Outdoors (2010), by Fiona Danks and Jo Schofield. Danks, an ecologist from South Oxfordshire, and Jo Schofield, another Oxfordshire mother, make a playground out of wide open spaces.

SAS Survival Handbook: How to Survive in the Wild, in Any Climate, on Land or at Sea (2004), by John 'Lofty' Wiseman. Hopefully you'll never actually need this book, but it's fun to read.

Sneaky Book for Boys, The (2008), by Cy Tymony. For survival tips, see the chapter 'Sneaky Resourcefulness'. And ignore the 'boy' part of the title.

EXPLORE

Ann and Liv Cross Antarctica: A Dream Come True! (2001) by Zoë Alderfer Rayn, illustrated by Nicholas Reti. Follow Ann Bancroft and Liv Arnesen on their 100-day journey.

Be An Expert With: Map and Compass, The 'Orienteering' Handbook (1994), by Bjorn Kjellstrom. Learn to navigate.

Camp Out!: The Ultimate Kids' Guide (2007) by Lynn Brunelle. For mapping and navigating info, see the chapter 'Getting Around and Staying Found'.

Elements of Cartographic Style (gsd.harvard.edu/gis/manual/style). Info on how to make your own maps.

Go Outside!: Over 130 Activities for Outdoor Adventures (2002), by Nancy Blakely. For navigating info, see the chapter 'Make Your Own Compass'.

Mapmakers, The (2001), by John Noble Wilford. A great history of mapmaking.

Tom Brown's Field Guide: Nature and Survival for Children (1989), by Tom Brown. A bit paranoid, perhaps, but a terrific introduction to these topics.

Your Expedition (yourexpedition.com). Follow Ann Bancroft and Liv Arnesen's 2012 trek across the South Pole to raise awareness of fresh water issues.

EXPAND YOUR HORIZONS

Babies (2010, directed by Thomas Balmés). A documentary about one year in the life of babies from Mongolia, Namibia, San Francisco and Tokyo.

Concordia Language Villages (concordia languagevillages.com). Explore different languages... and learn one.

Cool Drink of Water, A (2006) by Barbara Kerley. A photographic essay exploring how cultures around the world gather and drink water.

Coolgorilla Talking Phrasebook (coolgorilla.com). A fun translation app.

Family of Man, The (1955) by Edward Steichen. A classic book of photographs from all over the world.

Growing Up Global (growingupglobal. net). A valuable website by the author of *Growing Up Global: Raising Children to Be At Home in the World* (2009).

How Soccer Explains the World: An Unlikely Theory of Globalisation (2005), by Franklin Foer. Fans will find it eye-opening... and educational.

Idle Traveller, The: The Art of Slow Travel (2012). Travel writer Dan Kieran, who has also written a book about his slow travel adventure round Britain on a milk float, encourages travellers to slow down – connect with the landscape, travel by train rather than plane, and walk rather than drive.

International Dialects of English Archive (web.ku.edu/~idea). An archive of dialect and accent recordings.

Lazy Environmentalist, The: Your Guide to Stylish, Green Living (2007), by Josh Dorfman. See the chapter 'Travel: The World is Your Oyster.'

Life Like Mine, A: How Children Around the World Live (2002) by UNICEF. An excellent way for kids and grownups alike to gain a little perspective.

Moon Travel Guides (moon.com). Info about different travel destinations and outdoor adventure activities.

Random Obsessions (2009), by Nick Belardes. See the chapter 'Mysterious Places: Exploring Some of the World's Most Mysterious Nooks and Crannies'.

Worst-Case Scenario Survival Handbook: Life, The (2006), by Joshua Piven and David Borgenicht. See the amusing chapter 'Travel'.

Young Human Rights Reporter Competition (amnesty.org.uk/ youngreporter) is an annual contest that aims to inspire young people to become human rights reporters. In 2012, pupils in over 130 schools across the UK took part, writing compelling news stories on human rights issues ranging from child labour in India to LGBT rights in Uganda and corporate accountability in Bolivia.

INDEX

BIOS

THE UNBORED TEAM

Joshua Glenn is co-founder of the websites HiLobrow, Significant Objects and Semionaut; and co-author and co-editor of several books. In 2011, he produced Ker-Punch!, a brainteaser iPhone app. He has worked as a newspaper, magazine and website editor; and he was a columnist for the *Boston Globe*. During the 1990s he published the zine/journal *Hermenaut*. He lives in Boston with his wife and sons.

Heather Kasunick teaches visual arts at a public high school. She has exhibited at the Fitchburg Museum of Art, the Brattleboro Museum and Art Centre and The MPG Contemporary Gallery (Boston), among other venues. She lives in Massachusetts, with her husband and their dog. More info: wondercupboard.blogspot.com

Elizabeth Foy Larsen is a writer and editor whose stories on children and families have appeared in the *Los Angeles Times*, *Mother Jones*, *Parents* and elsewhere, including anthologies. She has worked as a newspaper, magazine and website editor. In the 1990s, she was a member of the team that launched *Sassy*, a magazine for teen girls. She lives in Minneapolis with her husband, daughter and two sons.

Tony Leone is principal of Leone Design, a graphic design studio and consultancy in Boston. His work has been honoured by the American Institute of Graphic Arts and the Brand Design Association, and has been featured in *Communication Arts*, *Print*, *Graphis* and elsewhere. In the 1990s, he was design director of the zine/journal *Hermenaut*. He lives in Boston with his wife, son and daughter.

Mister Reusch has made illustrations for Burton Snowboards, Harmonix Rock Band, StrideRite and others; his work has featured in books about rock poster art and tattoo designs. He teaches illustration at Massachusetts College of Art & Design in Boston. He lives in Massachusetts, with his girlfriend and their dogs and hamster. More info: misterreusch.com

CONTRIBUTORS

Joe Alterio makes art, illustrations, videogames and comics. His work has appeared in the *New York Times*, the *Boston Globe*, the *Atlantic*, *Rolling Stone*, Boing Boing, and elsewhere. He founded Robots + Monsters, a charitable fundraising site pairing artists with robot and monster fans. He lives in New York with his wife and son. More info: joealterio.com

Colin Beavan is the executive director of the No Impact Project, the author of the book and subject of the documentary *No Impact Man*, a 350.org 'Messenger', and a dharma teacher in the Kwan Um School of Zen. He was named one of MSN's 10 Most Influential Men and one of *Elle* magazine's Eco-Illuminators; his blog noimpactman.com was named one of the world's top 15 environmental websites by *Time* magazine. He lives in Brooklyn with his daughter.

Ginia Bellafante has been a staff writer at the *New York Times* for over a decade. She began as the paper's fashion critic, served for five years as a television critic and has contributed regularly to the *New York Times Magazine* and the *Book Review*. In 2011 she became the paper's Big City columnist. She lives in New York with her husband and son.

Deb Chachra, PhD, is a professor at the Franklin W. Olin College of Engineering, where she teaches and does research in materials science, bioengineering and engineering education. She also helps faculty at other institutions rethink their teaching and programmes. Originally from Toronto, she now lives in Massachusetts. More info: twitter.com/debcha

Helen Cordes writes about many topics for national and regional magazines, websites and books, but her particular passion is parenting essays. She is the editor of *New Moon Girls* magazine and the author of two Girl Power (Lerner) books. She and her husband live near Austin, Texas, where their two daughters grew up.

Chris Dahlen is the co-founder of videogames and culture magazine *Kill Screen*. He has covered music, games and tech for *Pitchfork*, *Variety* and the *Onion AV Club*, and has written for games including *Carmen Sandiego* for Facebook and *PixelVixen707*. He lives in New Hampshire with his wife and seven-year-old son.

Matthew De Abaitua's debut novel *The Red Men* was nominated for the Arthur C. Clarke Award. His book *The Art of Camping: The History and Practice of Sleeping Under the Stars* was published in 2011. He takes his three children camping a dozen times a year with his wife Cathy, and together they run the blog cathandmathcamping.com

Mark Frauenfelder is the editor-in-chief of *Make* magazine, and the founder of the popular Boing Boing blog. He was an editor at *Wired* from 1993–1998, and is the author of six books. His latest book is *Made By Hand: My Adventures in the World of Do-It-Yourself* (bit.ly/madebyhands). He is the father of two daughters who like to make things; he and his nine-year-old daughter, Jane, co-host the podcast 'Apps for Kids'.

Max Glenn wants to be a cryptozoologist, poet and mathematician. He enjoys reading and writing comics. He likes H.P. Lovecraft, *Dungeons & Dragons*, and he misses *LEGO Universe*. He is in sixth grade (Year 7).

Sam Glenn enjoys football, baseball, frisbee and canoeing. He plays the electric bass, and is learning to play the upright bass. His favourite videogame is *FIFA Soccer 12*. He is in ninth grade (Year 10).

Chelsey Johnson writes short stories and essays and is working on a novel. Since 2003 she has been involved with the Rock'n'Roll Camp for Girls in Portland, Oregon, as a volunteer and board member. She works as a teacher of writing at the College of William & Mary, and previously at Oberlin College, Stanford University and public high schools.

Flourish Klink is the Chief Participation Officer of the Alchemists Transmedia Storytelling Co. She also lectures in the department of Comparative Media Studies at the Massachusetts Institute of Technology. She is the author of innumerable works of fan fiction.

Geoff Manaugh is the creator of BLDGBLOG (bldgblog.blogspot.com), a website launched in 2004 to explore architecture, spatial fiction, planetary science, cities and myth. He is the author of *The BLDGBLOG Book*. He is a former senior editor of *Dwell* and a contributing editor at *Wired* magazine. In 2011, he became co-director of Studio-X NYC, an urban futures think tank run by the architecture department at Columbia University.

Sophie Meyer is from Phoenix, Arizona. She now attends Stanford University, where she is focusing on the natural sciences and mathematics. Sophie's interest in environmental issues is largely inherited from her parents.

Norah Mortensen loves playing football, tennis, basketball and the piano. She is very interested in the cultures of other countries and learning about biology. She is in ninth grade (Year 10).

Tom Nealon owns and operates the used and rare bookshop Pazzo Books in Boston. He is an adventurous chef who writes about the strange history of food at the HiLobrow and Cruditas websites. He and his wife have a daughter, who is nursery-school-aged.

John Edgar Park is a CG supervisor at DisneyToon Studios, the host of *Make: television*, a contributing writer for *Make* magazine, and the author of *Understanding 3D Animation Using Maya*. He lives in Los Angeles with his wife and two kids. More info: jpixl.net

Bre Pettis is a former Seattle public school teacher who taught kids how to make things. Since then he's created hundreds of video tutorials teaching all sorts of things from how to make a hovercraft to how to make your own secret compartment book. With Kio Stark, he wrote the 'Cult of Done Manifesto', which has helped millions of people get things done. He's democratising manufacturing as CEO and co-founder of MakerBot Industries and is also a co-founder of Brooklyn's hacker space, NYCResistor.

Chris Piascik is a freelance designer and illustrator from Connecticut who recently held his sixth solo exhibition. For the past four years, he has been posting daily drawings to his website; in 2012, he self-published a book of the first thousand drawings. More info: chrispiascik.com

Jeff Potter is the author of *Cooking for Geeks: Real Science, Great Hacks, and Good Food*, which the *Washington Post* called 'one of the most useful books on understanding cooking'. He has appeared on NPR, *The Today Show*, CNN International, Food Network and the Cooking Channel, and he is a trustee and spokesperson for Awesome Food, part of the Awesome Foundation. More info: jeffpotter.org

Jean Railla founded GetCrafty.com in 1997; the *New York Times* credited it with sparking the hip crafting trend. The author of the *Get Crafty* book, she has consulted on the creation of the online handicraft market Etsy.com, penned a column for *Craft* magazine, and founded the food blog Meal By Meal. She lives in New York City with her boys, Sydney (nine) and Sebastien (seven), and husband Stephen Duncombe.

Douglas Rushkoff is a media theorist, and the author of 14 books including *Media Virus*, *Life Inc* and *Program or Be Programmed*. He is the originator of such terms as 'viral media' and 'social currency', and made the Frontline documentaries *Merchants of Cool*, *The Persuaders* and *Digital Nation*. He published *A.D.D.*, a graphic novel about kids raised from birth to be videogame players, in 2012. He has a seven-year-old daughter named Mamie. More info: rushkoff.com

Henrik Schleisman wants to be a pilot when he grows up and enjoys learning about aeroplanes throughout history. He plays the trumpet and loves all Star Wars Wii and computer games. He is in fifth grade (Year 6).

Peter Schleisman plays hockey and tennis and is learning to play drums, baritone, and trombone. He likes to make movies and play the online game Cities XL. He is in eighth grade (Year 9).

Walter Schleisman drummed in his first rock band when he was in eighth grade (Year 9). His love of music led to a 10-year stint as a middle-school band and general music teacher. He is now an assistant principal and lives in Minneapolis with his wife, daughter and two sons.

Zoe Cordes Selbin is a music, arts, events and media consultant in Austin, Texas. She has worked with companies and events such as Lollapalooza, Transmission Entertainment, *The Austin Chronicle* and Austin City Limits Music Festival. Zoe was homeschooled and is now studying communication studies at Southwestern University.

Anindita Basu Sempere is a writer, educator, geek and dog rescuer. A graduate of the Vermont College of Fine Arts' programme in Writing for Children and Young Adults and the MIT Media Lab's Future of Learning Group, she's interested in the intersection between storytelling, education and technology. She is the Executive Director of The Writing Faculty (thewritingfaculty.com), an online tutoring company.

Chris Spurgeon has a life-long interest in the histories of science, geography, cartography and navigation. He's lectured on everything from map design to how the ancient Polynesians found their way at sea. He makes electronic gadgets and high-powered rockets, and there is often smoke coming out of his garage. More info: twitter.com/chrisspurgeon

Courtney Stanton is a project manager based in Boston, where she produces interactive media and games. She was the co-founder of an experimental cabaret troupe and was the producer for Erin Robinson's latest game, *Gravity Ghost*. She blogs at kirbybits.wordpress.com and tweets via @kirbybits

Kio Stark is the author of the novel *Follow Me Down*. In addition to fiction, she writes about the way humans relate to technology – and to each other, mediated by technology – and teaches at New York University's graduate Interactive Telecommunications Programme (ITP). Her previous collaboration with Bre Pettis was the renowned 'Cult of Done Manifesto'. They have a daughter named Nika.

Jay Walljasper lives in Minneapolis and gets around primarily by bike. He writes about how to make our towns and cities better places to live, and is the author of *The Great Neighbourhood Book and All That We Share: A Field Guide to the Commons*. More info: jaywalljasper.com.

Jessamyn West is the author of *Without a Net: Librarians Bridging the Digital Divide* and co-editor of *Revolting Librarians Redux*. Her day job is running the massive group blog MetaFilter. She's the editor of the long-running website librarian.net and lives in Central Vermont where she teaches people to use computers and works in a public library.

CODE KEY

Every now and then, throughout this book, you will find strings of symbols that look like this: ⅄❈✳ ◼❈▢⊥ ⊥⊠⊡ ⊞▢⊕⊡! These collections of symbols are coded messages. You can decode the messages using the code key shown here.

Can grownups use the code key to read these secret messages? Of course. However, it's unlikely that they will actually spend time doing so. Too bad for them. They'll never know what they missed.

Enjoy decoding these kids-only messages – and, once you've read them, keep *shtum*. That's slang meaning: Shh! Don't spill the beans!

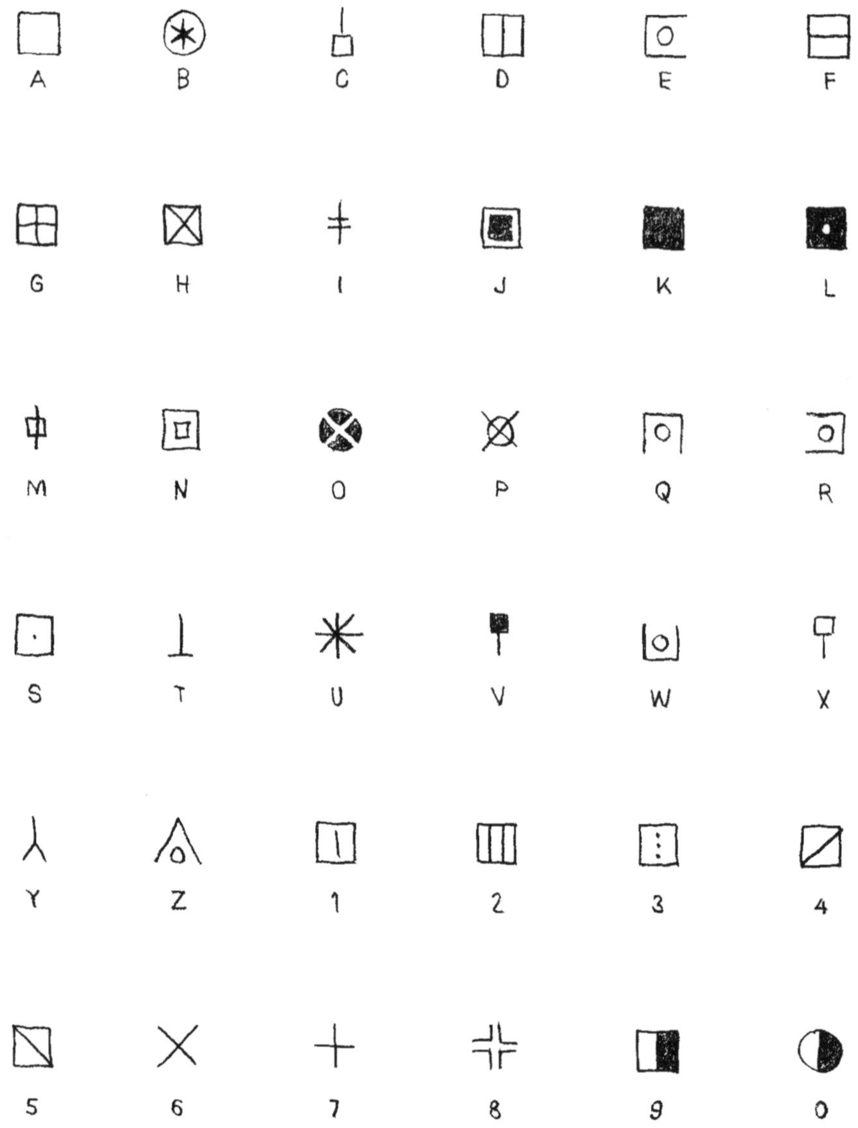

A B C D E F

G H I J K L

M N O P Q R

S T U V W X

Y Z 1 2 3 4

5 6 7 8 9 0